PRENTICE HALL

SCIENCE EXPLORER

Animals
Teaching Resources with Color Transparencies

Prentice
Hall

Needham, Massachusetts
Upper Saddle River, New Jersey
Glenview, Illinois

Teaching Support

Lesson Plan
(1 per section)
Streamline your path through every section with a core set of activities and teaching suggestions.

Color Transparencies
(avg. 4 per chapter)
Visualize key concepts dynamically with engaging art from every chapter.

Complete Answer Keys
Find all the answers in one section at the back of the book.

Reading & Review

Section Summaries
(1 per section)
Encourage all readers and English language learners with readable summaries that match the *Guided Reading Audio CDs* and *Guided Reading Audiotapes* (English or Spanish).

Review & Reinforce Worksheets
(1 per section)
Motivate students to build vocabulary, review main ideas, and interpret diagrams, charts, and graphs.

Enrichment

Enrich Worksheets
(1 per section)
Encourage all students to read, write, and visualize as they apply core concepts in a new context.

Labs & Projects

Skills Labs and Real-World Labs
(2 per chapter)
Help students get organized with blackline masters of Student Edition Labs—each in an easy-to-grade format.

Chapter Projects
(1 per chapter)
Guide students through the Chapter Projects in the student text with extensive teacher notes, scoring rubrics, and student worksheets with project rules and checklists.

Assessment

Performance Assessments
(1 per chapter)
Assess student problem-solving and process skills using scoring rubrics and suggested outcomes.

Chapter and Book Tests
(1 per chapter and 1 per book)
Prepare students for local and state exams with a variety of questions—all different from the Computer Test Bank.

Interdisciplinary Exploration

Science, Math, Social Studies, and Language Arts (1 per book)
Support the Interdisciplinary Exploration in the student text with activities you can teach on your own or use for team teaching.

RESOURCE·PRO®

The Resource Pro® CD-ROM with Planning Express® is the ultimate scheduling and lesson planning tool. Resource Pro® allows you to preview all the resources in the *Science Explorer* program, organize your chosen materials, and print out any teaching resource. With Planning Express® you can follow the suggested lessons or create your own, using resources from the program.

Prentice Hall

ISBN 0-13-054063-3
1 2 3 4 5 6 7 8 9 10   05 04 03 02 01

Chapter 1
Sponges, Cnidarians, and Worms

Chapter 2
Mollusks, Arthropods, and Echinoderms

TABLE OF CONTENTS *(continued)*

TABLE OF CONTENTS *(continued)*

Transparencies

TEACHER NOTES

TEACHER NOTES

TEACHER NOTES

TEACHER NOTES

CHAPTER 1

Alive and Well

The following steps will walk you through the Chapter 1 Project. Use the hints as you guide your students through planning, animal observations, and presentations.

◆ Chapter Project Overview

◆ Before introducing the project, bring an animal, such as an earthworm, into the classroom to show to the students. Talk about where the animal lives, what it eats, and how to take care of it.

◆ Have students read the Chapter 1 Project Overview, pages 12–13. Review the project's rules and hand out the Chapter 1 Scoring Rubric, page 16, that you will use for scoring students' work. Discuss with students what will be expected of them.

◆ Set a deadline for the project presentation and interim dates for the Check Your Progress at the end of Section 1, Section 3, and Section 4. Encourage students to copy the dates in the Project Time Line.

◆ Group students. Have them brainstorm a list of animals they would like to keep and care for. Go over their suggestions and discuss the advantages and drawbacks of those suggestions. Review each students' choice of animal. Once students have your approval, they are ready to research their animals.

◆ Explain whether or not students will be allowed to keep their animals in the classroom.

◆ Distribute copies of Chapter 1 Project Worksheet 1, page 14. Have them read over the questions they will need to answer in the planning stage of this project. Chapter 1 Project Worksheet 2, page 15, will help students through collecting data and preparing for the presentation. Distribute this worksheet once you have given students approval to acquire their animal. Remind students to refer to the hints in the Chapter 1 Project Overview as they plan and carry out the project.

◆ If some students' animals die, you will need to alter the assignment for them. In a private conference, reassure students. Tell them they can still do well on the project even though their animals died. On occasions when other students observe the animals, have these students observe a classmate's animal, preferably one of the same kind. For their presentation, ask them to give a report about the animal that died, including how they took care of it, what they learned, and what they might have done differently.

◆ Materials and Preparation

◆ Pill bugs, spiders, millipedes, crickets, fruit flies, earthworms, slugs, snails, guppies, and anole lizards are feasible options. Suggest that students observe a group or colony if the animals have a short life span. Avoid birds and mammals for health and safety reasons. Students may decide to buy fish from a pet store or fruit flies from a biological supply.

◆ Before collecting any animals from the wild, be aware of regulations in your area. Most federal, state, and local regulations prohibit collecting vertebrates such as reptiles, birds, and mammals from the wild. Some animals are endangered and protected by law. Laws protecting these animals are often strict.

◆ Check Your Progress— Section 1 Review

◆ Before students obtain their animals, make sure they anticipate weekend and holiday care. Also, have them decide what to do with their animals when the project is finished.

◆ Review students' research before allowing them to create a habitat or obtain the animal.

◆ Having the set-up day on either a Monday or a Tuesday works well because students can prepare their habitats over the weekend.

◆ Check Your Progress— Section 3 Review

◆ Give students time in class each day to feed and care for their animals. During this time, have them record their observations.

◆ Check students' observation records on a regular basis. Be sure students include details about any changes in the health and behavior of their animals.

◆ Periodically check the animals' health. Some students may not notice the declining health of their animals. If you think an animal is in poor condition, immediately discuss the situation with the student.

◆ If an animal is in poor health, decide with the student how to handle the problem. Taking an animal to a veterinarian may be advisable under certain conditions. If you decide to release the animal, offer an alternative to the student so he or she can successfully complete the project. Emphasize that it may not be the student's fault that the animal is in poor health. The animal may have been ill at the beginning of the project. All animals do not thrive in captivity.

◆ Check Your Progress— Section 4 Review

◆ Tell students that analyzing their data means looking at their observations, summarizing them, finding patterns, and deciding what these patterns tell about the animal.

◆ Remind students they will be introducing their animals to the class. Let them decide how they want to make their presentations. Encourage students to be creative.

◆ Chapter Project Wrap-Up

◆ As students give their reports, ask their classmates to take brief notes, writing down the major characteristics of each animal.

◆ After all the presentations have been made, have students evaluate their projects. Have them decide which animals were best for the project and what were the best methods for taking care of the animals. Have them write down advice to give to another student who wants to study the same kind of animal.

◆ Have students turn in any written work you require. Students may then relocate their animals to new homes.

◆ Extensions/Options

◆ If it is impractical to keep animals in the classroom, you could have students observe them outdoors. Students will need to adapt the investigation slightly. Be sure you review all necessary safety precautions with students in advance. Also, as they would for an indoor project, students should keep a precise scientific journal, recording the date, time, weather, and animal behavior each day.

◆ Consider organizing the class in groups to do the project. If space and time are limited, you may want to keep one animal for the entire class. You may also group compatible animals in the same habitat to save space.

◆ If your school is near a zoo, take students on a field trip. Ask them to compare and contrast the habitats and behaviors of the animals in the zoo with those of the animals they observed in their projects.

◆ At the end of the project, take your students to a local wildlife center to learn more about the animals they observed in class. The nature center may also be able to provide more information on difficult-to-observe animals, such as those that are nocturnal or live underground.

CHAPTER 1 PROJECT   **OVERVIEW**

Alive and Well

For this project, you will choose an animal to keep and care for. You must research the animal's needs, and design and build a secure habitat for it. Your teacher will review your research and choice of animal. After you have your teacher's approval, you will build the habitat, obtain the animal, and place it in its new home.

You may be allowed to bring your animal to class. Be sure you know what kind of habitat your animal needs, what temperatures it prefers, what it needs to eat, and how it obtains moisture (some animals do not drink water but absorb it from their surroundings or from their food). At the end of the project, you will analyze your observations, summarize what you have learned about the animal, and perhaps introduce your animal to the class in a brief presentation.

◆ Project Rules

◆ Have your teacher approve your research and plans before you obtain your animal.

◆ Your teacher will tell you if your choice of animal is protected by federal, state, or local laws. Obey any and all laws applying to your project.

◆ Always treat your animal well. If it is not moving during your time to observe, do not poke or prod it. The object of the project is to observe natural behavior. You are responsible for the well-being of your animal and should care for it in every possible way.

◆ Follow the safety guidelines for handling animals in Appendix A of your textbook.

◆ Suggested Materials

◆ You will need an animal. Pill bugs, spiders, earthworms, millipedes, crickets, fruit flies, slugs, snails, guppies, and anole lizards are all good choices.

◆ You will need food for your animal, but the kind of food will depend on the kind of animal you choose. Leaves, vegetable trimmings, and insects are some possibilities. All animals should have water or moisture.

◆ You will build a suitable habitat for your animal. A 2-liter soda bottle could serve as a terrarium for an insect. Carefully cut off the top of the bottle, fill it with soil, dead leaves, twigs, and plants. Cover the bottle with plastic wrap, and poke small holes in the plastic wrap for air.

CHAPTER 1 PROJECT OVERVIEW *(continued)*

◆ Project Hints

◆ Brainstorm a list of animals that interest you. Avoid choosing birds and mammals for health and safety reasons. Some animals are active only at certain times of the day. You may want to consider this fact when choosing your animal.

◆ Libraries, the Internet, veterinary clinics, and pet stores are good places to find information about the animal you choose.

◆ A habitat can be many things—a plastic jar filled with sand and grass; a 2-liter soda bottle filled with dirt, pebbles, and twigs; or a bowl filled with water. Make sure the animal cannot escape. Consider working with other classmates to build a habitat for several animals that will not eat or harm each other. This strategy will require extra research, but working together can make building a habitat easier.

◆ When you observe your animal, describe what the animal looks like, how much it is eating, what it does, and anything else you think is important. Also list things that may affect your animal's behavior, such as the time of day, the temperature, and the weather.

◆ There are many ways to present what you have learned. You can write a report, give a speech, draw illustrations with captions, or record a summary on videotape.

◆ Before you begin, you should know what you are going to do with your animal after the project is finished. You may be able to put the animal back where you found it. Other alternatives are keeping it as a pet, giving it to a friend, or giving it to your teacher to keep in the classroom. You must get approval from your teacher for your plans.

◆ Project Time Line

Task	Due Date	Teacher's Initials
1. Animal selected and choice approved	_____	_____
2. Animal's needs researched and habitat plan completed	_____	_____
3. Research and habitat plan approved	_____	_____
4. Habitat completed	_____	_____
5. Animal acquired and placed in habitat	_____	_____
6. Animal observations completed	_____	_____
7. Presentation of project report	_____	_____

CHAPTER 1 PROJECT   **WORKSHEET 1**

Preparing for Your Animal

Complete the following tasks using a separate sheet of paper. When the tasks have been completed, you are ready to get your teacher's approval and begin the Chapter Project.

1. Choose an animal you would like to care for during this project. Write a few sentences describing this animal, and explain why you chose it.

2. Research your animal using the library, the Internet, veterinary clinics, or pet stores. Take notes on these topics: What kind of care does your animal need? What kind of environment does it need?

3. To complete this project, you need to create a healthy, safe environment for your animal. Describe how you will create that environment. Include a drawing of the habitat you will create.

4. Every animal needs to have water and food to survive. Answer the following questions: How does your animal obtain the water it needs? What will you feed your animal? How will you get the food? How will you provide food and water for your animal on weekends or school holidays?

5. While you keep your animal, you must observe and record its behavior. Using your research as a guide, write predictions about the kind of behaviors you expect to observe.

6. At the end of the project, what will you do with your animal? If you intend to keep it, give it away, or release it into the wild, do you need permission from anyone? Do you have permission?

Recording and Analyzing Data

Record your observations in a data table organized like the one below. Include a description of the animal, what it does, how healthy it appears, and anything else you think is important.

Date	Time	Observation

◆ Analyzing and Presenting

Complete the following tasks on a separate sheet of paper. When they have been completed, you are ready to put together your presentation.

1. Write several sentences summarizing your research.

2. Write several sentences summarizing your observations from the data table.

3. Decide how you want to communicate what you have learned to your class-mates. Make a list of the things you will need to make this presentation.

CHAPTER 1

1

Alive and Well

In evaluating how well you complete the Chapter 1 Project, your teacher will judge your work in four categories. In each, a score of 4 is the best rating.

	4	3	2	1
Planning the Animal's Care	Thoroughly researches the animal's needs, and plans how to provide a healthy habitat for it. Constructs a habitat fully suited to all the animal's needs.	Adequately researches the animal's needs. Plans a healthy habitat for the animal. Constructs a habitat that is suited to most of the animal's needs.	Researches only a few of the animal's needs. Does not make complete plans for a healthy habitat for the animal. Constructs a habitat that meets only the most basic needs of the animal.	Does little or no research about the animal's needs. Plans for the habitat are inadequate for the animal selected. Makes little effort to construct a habitat.
Observing the Animal	Checks on, cares for, and observes the animal daily. Makes 15 or more complete observation entries on the animal's health and behavior.	Checks on, cares for, and observes the animal most days. Makes at least 10 complete observation entries on the animal's health and behavior.	Checks on or observes the animal only a few times. Makes at least 5 observation entries. Some entries are unorganized or incomplete.	Rarely checks on or observes the animal. Makes fewer than 5 observation entries. Most entries are unorganized or incomplete.
Presenting the Animal	Makes a thorough, well-organized presentation. Presents a complete description of the animal. Displays well-designed visual aids.	Makes an adequate presentation. Describes the animal's most important traits. Displays helpful visual aids.	Makes a presentation, but it is hard to follow. Describes only a few animal traits. Uses few or no visuals.	Gives only a brief presentation, or none at all. Describes few or no animal traits.
Working Cooperatively	Participates in all aspects of group planning, animal care, observations, and presentation of results.	Participates in most aspects of group planning, animal care, and presentation of results.	Participates in some group work, but often lets others do the planning and animal care.	Does not take part in the planning or presentation. Seldom cares for or observes the animal.

What Is an Animal? (pp. 16–22)

Objectives

After completing the lesson, students will be able to

- list and describe four major characteristics that all animals share;
- explain how biologists classify animals into groups;
- describe an animal's adaptations for getting food and escaping predators.

1 Engage/Explore

- **Activating Prior Knowledge** Engage students' interest by leading them to classify certain organisms as animals. Guide them to realize that many organisms that may not appear to be animals actually belong in that classification.

- **Discover** Prepare students for learning the characteristics of animals by having them observe different organisms and decide whether the organisms are animals.

2 Facilitate

- **Using The Visuals: Figure 1** Encourage students to list reasons for thinking the jellyfish is an animal. Describe how it obtains its food.

- **Including All Students** Guide students to recognize the levels of organization in an animal by having them examine beef bones. Direct students to draw the bone, label its parts, and record their observations.

- **Try This** Direct students to explore animal movement by designing and modeling an animal with a new way of moving.

- **Cultural Diversity** Discuss with students the animals people from different cultures use for transport and the characteristics these animals have that help them survive in their environments.

- **Including All Students** Contrast the meanings, spellings, and pronunciations of *predator* and *prey*. Point out their Latin root.

- **Building Inquiry Skills: Problem Solving** To teach students about the feeding adaptations of animals, give them a limited number of tools and a narrow container of birdseed and challenge them to find the best way to get the birdseed out of the container.

- **Sharpen Your Skills** Students learn how to identify an animal as an herbivore, a carnivore, or an omnivore based on the animal's teeth.

- **Building Inquiry Skills: Classifying** Distribute paired illustrations of predators and their prey. Ask students to list the animals' feeding adaptations.

- **Using the Visuals: Figure 6** Use the diagram to give students a brief overview of the animal groups discussed in the chapter.

- **Inquiry Challenge** Challenge students to classify animals from photographs and to construct a classification system that will distinguish each animal from all other animals.

3 Assess

- **Section 1 Review** Check students' understanding of section content by having them answer the section review questions.

- **Performance Assessment** Assess students' understanding of the characteristics that define an animal by having them choose a photograph of an animal and describe two characteristics a scientist would use to classify it as an animal. Then ask students to explain why a plant is not an animal.

What Is an Animal?

1

Guide for Reading

◆ What characteristics do all animals have in common?

◆ How are animals classified into groups?

Animals are many-celled organisms that must obtain their food by eating other organisms. In addition, most animals reproduce sexually and can move.

The bodies of animals are made up of many cells, tiny working units that make up all living things. Cells are grouped together into tissues. A **tissue** is a group of cells that perform a specific job. Tissues may combine to form an **organ.** An organ is a group of tissues that work together to do a specific job that is more complicated than the job the tissues do on their own. In most animals, organs combine to form organ systems.

Scientists classify animals into species. A **species** is a group of organisms that can mate with each other and produce offspring. Animals are heterotrophs. **Heterotrophs** are organisms that obtain food by eating other organisms. In contrast, most plants are autotrophs. **Autotrophs** are organisms that make their own food.

Most animals produce offspring by **sexual reproduction,** the joining of two sex cells. Some animals reproduce by **asexual reproduction** in which an organism produces an identical copy of itself.

A characteristic that helps an organism survive in its environment and reproduce is called an **adaptation.** Animals differ in their adaptations for getting food. Animals that eat only plants are **herbivores.** Animals that eat meat are **carnivores.** Carnivores capture **prey,** the animals they feed upon. Animals that can eat both plants and animals are **omnivores.**

Scientists have classified animals into about 35 main groups. Each main group is called a **phylum. When biologists classify an animal, they look at the structure of its body and the way it develops as an embryo at the very beginning of its life. Biologists also examine the animal's DNA, a chemical in cells that controls an organism's inherited characteristics.**

One important structural characteristic used to classify animals is whether or not the animal has a backbone. Animals without backbones make up most of the animal species on Earth. These animals are called **invertebrates.** Jellyfish, worms, snails, crabs, spiders, and insects are all invertebrates.

Animals with backbones are called **vertebrates.** Fishes, amphibians, reptiles, birds, and mammals are all vertebrates.

Name _____ Date _____ Class _____

What Is an Animal?

◆ Understanding Main Ideas

Fill in the blank ovals to complete this concept map.

1–7

◆ Building Vocabulary

From the list below, choose the term that best completes each sentence.

species	adaptation	phyla
predator	herbivore	prey
asexual reproduction	autotroph	omnivore
invertebrate		

8. An organism that makes its own food is called a(n) _____.

9. Scientists classify animals into major groups called _____.

10. A group of organisms that can mate with each other and produce offspring is a(n) _____.

11. A(n) _____ is an animal that eats both plants and animals.

12. If a coyote catches and eats a rabbit, the coyote is the _____, and the rabbit is the _____.

13. A characteristic that helps an organism survive is a(n) _____.

14. An animal without a backbone is called a(n) _____.

15. _____ is the process by which a single organism produces a new organism identical to itself.

16. An animal that eats only plants is a(n) _____.

SECTION 1-1 **ENRICH**

Rushing to Eat

Movement and feeding are characteristics of animals and animals have different methods of getting food. The amount of time an animal spends moving around, and the speed with which it moves, depends on its method for obtaining food. The graphs below show the kind of data you might get if we were to record the speed at which an animal moves throughout the day. The x-axis shows the hours of the day and the y-axis shows the speed at which the animal is moving.

Answer the following questions on a separate sheet of paper.

1. At what speed was animal 1 moving most of the time? What seems to be its top speed? Did it move at this speed for very long?

2. About how fast did animal 2 move when it was active? Was it most active during the day or during the night? How often did it stop to rest?

3. Is animal 3 active during the day or night? Was it usually moving at high speed? What was its top speed? For approximately how long did it move at this speed? How far would it have traveled during this time?

4. Which of the four animals was mostly active at night? Which one remained active through the heat of the afternoon?

5. Match the four animals with the feeding method that they most likely use.

    a. Animal 1 _____

    b. Animal 2 _____

    c. Animal 3 _____

    d. Animal 4 _____

    1. sit-and-wait predator

    2. predator that pursues its prey long distances

    3. herbivore or omnivore

Integrating Math
Symmetry (pp. 23–27)

Objectives

After completing the lesson, students will be able to

◆ recognize bilateral and radial symmetry in animals.

1 Engage/Explore

◆ **Activating Prior Knowledge** Sort a selection of objects into two groups: bilaterally symmetrical and asymmetrical. Lead students to understand that the objects were sorted based on their symmetry or lack thereof.

◆ **Discover** Direct students to find lines of symmetry in an isosceles triangle and a circle.

2 Facilitate

◆ **Building Inquiry Skills: Applying Concepts** Collect pictures of symmetrical objects, cut them in half, and give each student one half of a picture. Direct students to use what they know about symmetry to draw the missing half. They can then classify the object as radially or bilaterally symmetrical.

◆ **Including All Students** Explain the meaning of the prefix *bi-*. Have students suggest other words with the same prefix.

◆ **Using the Visuals: Figures 8 and 9** Explore the concept of a line of symmetry by having students observe the reflection in a mirror placed on the figures.

3 Assess

◆ **Section 2 Review** Check students' understanding of bilateral and radial symmetry by having them answer the section review questions.

◆ **Performance Assessment** Assess students' understanding of bilateral and radial symmetry by having them draw two objects or animals—one bilaterally symmetrical, the other radially symmetrical.

Lab

◆ **Real-World Lab: You Solve the Mystery** Show students how to observe animal tracks and apply their observations to draw inferences about the animals that made the tracks. Demonstrate that the size of the animal, the direction and speed it was going, and its actions can often be inferred by interpreting the tracks it made.

SECTION 1-2   **SECTION SUMMARY**

Symmetry

Guide for Reading

♦ What types of symmetry do complex animals exhibit?

Bodies of complex animals all have either radial or bilateral symmetry. An animal with **bilateral symmetry** has a line of symmetry that divides it into halves that are mirror images. Butterflies, fish, and humans have bilateral symmetry. (See Figure 8 in your textbook.) Animals with **radial symmetry** have many lines of symmetry that all go through a central point. Animals with radial symmetry include jellyfishes, sea anemones, and sea urchins. (See Figure 9 in your textbook.)

A few animals, including most sponges, have no symmetry. Such animals have no head and have very simple body plans.

All radially symmetrical animals live in water. Their body parts are arranged in a circular pattern around a central point, much like spokes on a bicycle wheel. Radially symmetrical animals learn about their environment mainly by using their senses of touch and taste. They can sense their environment in all directions. Therefore, they can grab prey coming from any direction.

Bilaterally symmetrical animals are often larger than those with radial symmetry. They have more complex and streamlined bodies. These streamlined bodies allow the animals to move more quickly than animals with radial symmetry. The sense organs of bilaterally symmetrical animals are located at the front end of their bodies. This helps them pick up information about what is in front of them.

SECTION 1-2   **REVIEW AND REINFORCE**

Symmetry

◆ Understanding Main Ideas

Classify the following animals as asymmetrical, bilaterally symmetrical, or radially symmetrical. If the animal has only one line of symmetry, draw the line. Write your responses on the lines below the animals.

1.

Sea Urchin

_____

2.

Sponge

_____

3.

Beaver

_____

4.

Frog

_____

5.

Sea Star

_____

6.

Ant

_____

◆ Building Vocabulary

From the list below, choose the term that best completes each sentence.

   many   bilateral symmetry
   radial symmetry   one

7. If an animal has a head end and a tail end, it has _____ .

8. All animals with _____ live in water.

9. Animals with radial symmetry have _____ line(s) of symmetry that go(es) through a central point.

10. Animals with bilateral symmetry have _____ line(s) of symmetry that divide(s) them into two parts. Each part is a mirror image of the other.

SECTION 1-2   **ENRICH**

Radial versus Bilateral

1

◆ Materials

scissors
tape or glue

◆ Procedure

Cut out the fish below. Tape the two halves together. Fold the fish fins along the
dotted lines. Attach the fins to the fish with tape or glue. The letters on the fins
should match the letters on the fish. Cut out the jellyfish. Then cut along the
dotted line. Twist the jellyfish so that the two edges overlap to form a cone-like
figure. Tape the edges together.

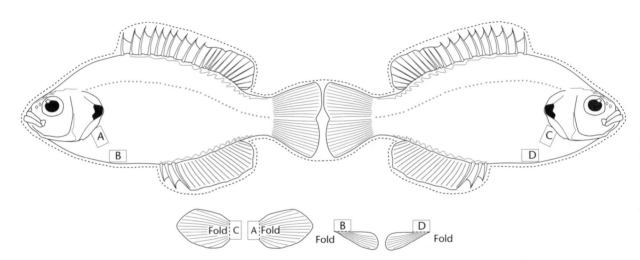

◆ Inquiry

Answer the following questions on a separate sheet of paper.

1. What type of symmetry does the fish display? How many lines of
   symmetry are there?

2. What type of symmetry does the jellyfish display? How many lines
   of symmetry are there?

3. Which animal do you think is the faster swimmer? Why?

4. This fish has one of some body parts, such as the mouth and the
   tail fin. Other of its body parts, such as eyes and the small side fins
   come in pairs. Make a generalization about where the single body
   parts occur on a fish's body and where paired body parts occur in
   relation to the line of symmetry.

Jellyfish

Cut along line

Sponges and Cnidarians (pp. 28–34)

Objectives

After completing the lesson, students will be able to

- describe the organization of a sponge's body;
- identify the main characteristics of cnidarians;
- describe life on a coral reef.

1 Engage/Explore

- **Activating Prior Knowledge** To lead students into the topic of live sponges, ask them about the ways they use sponges.

- **Discover** Direct students to observe and compare and contrast synthetic and natural sponges.

2 Facilitate

- **Exploring a Sponge** After students have examined the illustration, ask them questions about pore cells, collar cells, and the osculum.

- **Language Arts Connection** Help students write several similes about familiar animals. Direct students to share their similes in a group, making sure each group member receives a positive comment. Ask each group to share several similes with the class.

- **Integrating Chemistry** Have students investigate how materials diffuse in water.

- **Including All Students** Remind students that the *c* in cnidarians is silent by having them find three other English words that begin with a silent consonant.

- **Try This** To further students' understanding of cnidarians, provide students with live hydras to observe.

- **Including All Students** Let students model a coral reef using balloons to represent live corals and papier mâché to represent the skeletons the corals produce and leave behind.

3 Assess

- **Section 3 Review** Check students' understanding of sponges and cnidarians by having them answer the section review questions.

- **Performance Assessment** Assess students' understanding of sponges and cnidarians by having students write two diary entries, one from each animal's point of view.

Science and Society

- Describe the danger some coral reefs face through the actions of divers who ignore laws intended to protect them. Explore with students the solutions offered to protect the reefs. Then examine the issue further through a debate. After the debate, have students write newspaper editorials stating their positions.

1

Sponges and Cnidarians

Guide for Reading

1

◆ How is the body of a sponge organized?

◆ What are the main characteristics of cnidarians?

Sponges and cnidarians are animals that live in water. Sponges stay in one place, attached to hard surfaces. **The body of a sponge is something like a bag that is pierced all over with openings called pores.** Water enters these pores and carries food and oxygen into the sponge. Water also carries the sponge's waste products away.

Sponges reproduce both asexually and sexually. Budding is one form of asexual reproduction. In budding, small new sponges grow on the sides of an adult sponge. These young sponges eventually break off to live on their own. In sexual reproduction, water currents carry sperm from one sponge into the pores of another sponge. These sperm fertilize the sponge's egg cells. After fertilization, a larva develops. A **larva** is the immature form of an animal that looks very different from the adult.

Jellyfishes, sea anemones, and corals are **cnidarians.** Cnidarians are water animals that have stinging cells and take their food into a hollow central cavity. **Members of the cnidarian phylum are carnivores that use their stinging cells to capture their prey and defend themselves.** The stinging cells are on long, wavy structures called tentacles.

There are two cnidarian body plans, **polyp** and **medusa.** A polyp, such as a hydra, sea anemone, or coral, is shaped something like a vase, with the mouth opening at the top. Most polyps are adapted for life attached to an underwater surface. In contrast, a medusa, such as a jellyfish, is shaped like a bowl, with a mouth that opens downward. Medusas are adapted for a free-swimming life. Some cnidarians are polyps at one point in their lives and medusas at another point. Other cnidarians are either a polyp or medusa for all their lives. Both body plans are shown in Figure 12.

A cnidarian captures its food by using its stinging cells to inject venom, a poisonous substance, into fish and other prey. Cnidarians reproduce both asexually and sexually. Budding is the most common form of asexual reproduction.

Corals are cnidarians. At the beginning of its life, a free-swimming coral larva attaches to a solid surface. Then the coral polyp reproduces asexually, and its offspring reproduce too. The polyps produce hard skeletons around their soft bodies. Over time, the animals die but their hard skeletons remain. Eventually, these mounds of skeletons form a coral reef. Coral reefs are home to more species of fishes and invertebrates than any other environment on Earth.

Name _____ Date _____ Class _____

Sponges and Cnidarians

◆ Understanding Main Ideas

Answer the following questions on the back of this sheet or on a separate sheet of paper.

1. What function does water perform for sponges?

2. How does a sponge defend itself?

3. Describe two methods of sponge reproduction.

4. Describe how a coral reef is formed.

5. How do cnidarians reproduce?

6. In the diagram, identify the two different body plans of cnidarians. Label the mouth on each. Which animal is probably free swimming? Explain your answer.

A.

B.

Body Plan: _____   Body Plan: _____

◆ Building Vocabulary

Write an answer for each of the following questions in the spaces provided.

7. Explain what cnidarians are by describing how they feed, what kind of environments they live in, and by giving three examples.

_____

_____

_____

_____

8. What is a larva?

_____

Cnidarians and Nematocysts

1 Cnidarians have specialized cells in their tentacles called cnidoblasts. Within the cnidoblasts are tiny stinging capsules called nematocysts. Inside the nematocyst capsule is a coiled thread. This thread injects venom into anything that brushes against the capsule's trigger. The capsule's trigger is called a cnidocil. The diagram below will help you understand how this occurs.

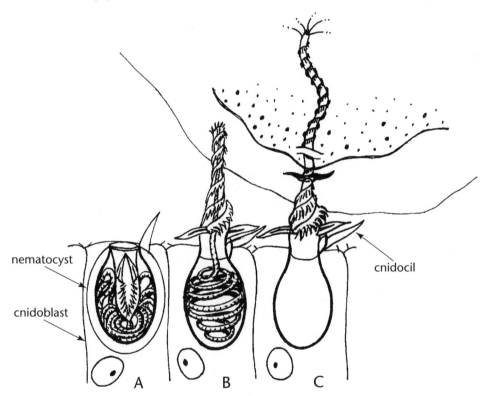

Answer the following questions on a separate sheet of paper.

1. Using information in the text and diagram above, list and describe the steps that occur in A, B, and C when a cnidarian captures food. You will need to include a step D as well. [*Hint:* What does the cnidarian do with its food after it stings it?]

2. People may be stung if they step on a dead jellyfish washed up on the beach. Why do you think this is so?

3. What functions do the stinging cells of a cnidarian serve?

Worms (pp. 35–42)

Objectives

After completing the lesson, students will be able to

◆ identify the three main groups of worms;

◆ identify the characteristics of each group of worms.

1 Engage/Explore

◆ **Activating Prior Knowledge** Ask students about situations in which they have encountered worms and what they have observed about them.

◆ **Discover** Let students observe a live planarian as an introduction to flatworms.

2 Facilitate

◆ **Using the Visuals: Figure 15** Invite students to use their knowledge of animals to test whether the worm in the figure is an animal.

◆ **Including All Students** Inform students that the three main worm groups are named after easily visible characteristics.

◆ **Inquiry Challenge** Challenge students to predict a planarian's response when a flashlight is shined on it.

◆ **Exploring the Life Cycle of a Dog Tapeworm** Review parasite/host relationships with students. After they examine the diagram, lead students through the life cycle of the tapeworm.

◆ **Building Inquiry Skills: Predicting** Challenge students to predict what happens to an animal infected with tapeworms.

◆ **Real-Life Learning** Invite a local veterinarian to class to tell students about tapeworm infections in pets and how to prevent them.

◆ **Inquiry Challenge** In a simple experiment, allow students to observe a planarian's food preferences and feeding habits.

◆ **Including All Students** Use a simple demonstration to show students the difference between digestive systems with one opening and with two openings.

◆ **Using the Visuals: Figures 16, 17, and 18** Direct students to compare and contrast flatworms, roundworms, and segmented worms after studying the photographs.

◆ **Sharpen Your Skills** Give students containers of earthworms to examine over a series of days. Students use their observations to learn about earthworm behavior.

◆ **Integrating Earth Science** Guide students in a simulation of the way earthworms loosen and mix up soil.

3 Assess

◆ **Section 4 Review** Check students' understanding of flatworms, roundworms, and segmented worms by having them answer the section review questions.

◆ **Performance Assessment** Assess students' understanding of worms by having them draw a flatworm, a roundworm, and a segmented worm. Direct them to label the special characteristics of each.

Lab

◆ **Skills Lab: Developing Hypotheses** Allow students to practice forming, writing, and testing hypotheses while learning what conditions—dry or moist, light or dark—earthworms prefer.

SECTION 1-4

Worms

1

Guide for Reading

◆ **What are the three main groups of worms?**

◆ **What are the characteristics of each group of worms?**

There are many species of worms in the world. **Biologists classify worms into several phyla—the three major ones are flatworms, roundworms, and segmented worms.** Worms reproduce both sexually and asexually. They are also the simplest animals to have a brain. Many worms can regrow a body part such as a tail end. This ability to regrow body parts is called **regeneration.**

The bodies of flatworms are flat. Planarians, flukes, and tapeworms are flatworms. Flatworms range in size from microscopic up to 10 to 12 meters.

Most flatworms are parasites that obtain their food from their hosts. A **parasite** is an organism that cannot live on its own. It needs a host from which to get its food. A **host** is the organism in or on which the parasite lives. A tapeworm is a kind of parasitic flatworm. Its body is adapted to absorbing food from its host's digestive system. A planarian is a nonparasitic, or free-living, flatworm. Planarians are scavengers and predators.

Roundworms have a body shaped like a cylinder that is pointed at each end. They are very tiny—millions can live in a square meter of damp soil. **Unlike cnidarians or flatworms, roundworms have a digestive system like a tube that is open at both ends.** Food enters through the mouth. Wastes leave the digestive system through the **anus,** an opening at the other end of the tube.

Earthworms and other segmented worms have bodies made up of many linked sections called segments. Some organs are repeated in each section. The reproductive organs occur only once.

Segmented worms have a closed circulatory system. In a closed system, such as your own, the blood flows only through connected tubes called blood vessels. In an open system, such as that of an insect, the blood leaves the blood vessels and sloshes around inside the body. A closed system moves the blood around an animal's body more quickly.

Worms

◆ Understanding Main Ideas

If the statement is true, write true. If it is false, change the underlined word or words to make the statement true.

1

_____ **1.** Three major phyla of worms are flatworms, roundworms, and <u>tube worms</u>.

_____ **2.** Worms reproduce <u>only through sexual reproduction</u>.

_____ **3.** Worms are the simplest organism with a <u>brain</u>.

_____ **4.** Planarians are nonparasitic <u>flatworms</u>.

_____ **5.** Tapeworms are parasitic <u>segmented worms</u>.

_____ **6.** Planarians have <u>one</u> opening in their digestive system.

_____ **7.** Roundworms have a <u>two-way</u> digestive system.

_____ **8.** Worms are <u>bilaterally</u> symmetrical.

_____ **9.** Earthworms are <u>segmented</u> worms.

_____ **10.** Earthworms have an <u>open</u> circulatory system.

_____ **11.** <u>Eyespots</u> help an earthworm move around.

◆ Building Vocabulary

Match each term to its definition by writing the letter of the correct definition in the right column on the line beside the term in the left column.

_____ **12.** regeneration

_____ **13.** anus

_____ **14.** parasite

_____ **15.** segment

_____ **16.** host

a. Organism that gets its food from living in or on another organism

b. Ability to regrow body parts

c. Organism in or on which another organism lives and gets its food from

d. One of the linked sections that make up the bodies of earthworms

e. Opening through which wastes exit in a one-way digestive system

The Mighty Earthworm

As a young man, Charles Darwin noticed that over the space of several years, all the rocks in a field near his house in England seemed to be sinking into the ground. Eventually he inferred that earthworms were causing this. Earthworms tunnel through the top meter or so of soil. They feed by taking in dirt and dead plant matter through their mouths. The dirt passes through the earthworms' bodies and is deposited in their tunnels and on the surface of the soil. The little piles of deposited dirt are called castings. As the worms remove soil from beneath the rocks, the rocks sink. Eventually, the rocks become buried in castings.

The diagram below represents the beginning of a simple experiment that Darwin performed. He spread a layer of small, white rocks on the surface of a field. Twenty-nine years later, the rocks could not be seen. Darwin dug a trench in the field to see what had happened to the white rocks. From their location, Darwin calculated that the earthworms in his field were depositing about 5.5 mm of castings on the surface each year.

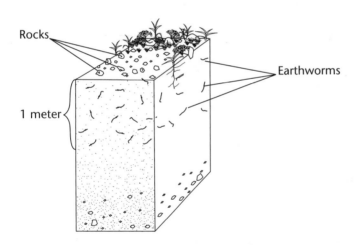

Answer the following questions on a separate sheet of paper.

1. After 29 years, about how far below the surface were the bottoms of the rocks?

2. Next to the diagram above, draw a diagram showing a cross section of the soil representing what Darwin would have seen in his trench.

3. Assuming that the rate of burial stayed the same, how long would it take for the rocks to be buried 50 cm deep?

4. Scientists speculate that the rocks would never be buried more than a meter deep. Explain why this might be so.

CHAPTER 1   **REAL-WORLD LAB**
You Solve the Mystery

A Tale Told by Tracks

Suppose that, on a chilly winter day, you
hike through a park. You suspect that many
animals live there, but you don't actually
see any of them. Instead, you see signs that
the animals have left behind, such as mys-
terious tracks in the snow. These tracks are
evidence you can use to draw inferences
about the animals, such as what size they
are and what they were doing. Inferences
are interpretations of observations that
help you to explain what may have happened in a given situation.

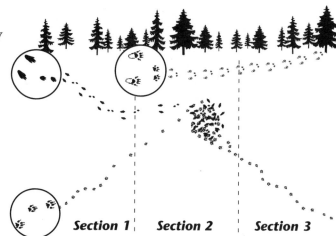

Section 1   Section 2   Section 3

◆ **Problem**   What can be learned about animals by studying their tracks?

◆ **Skills Focus**   observing, inferring

◆ **Procedure**

1. Record your data in the table on the next page.

2. The illustration shows the tracks, or footprints, left in the snow by animals living in a park. The illustration has been divided into three sections. Focus in on
   the tracks in Section 1.

3. Make two or more observations about the tracks and record them in your data
   table.

4. For each observation you listed, write one or more inferences that could be
   drawn from that observation.

5. Now look at the tracks in Section 2. Write two or more observations in the
   data table. For each observation, write one or more inferences.

6. Study the tracks in Section 3. Write two or more observations in the data table.
   Write at least one inference for each observation.

REAL-WORLD LAB *(continued)*

◆ Data Table

Section	Observations	Inferences
Section 1		
Section 2		
Section 3		

◆ Analyze and Conclude

Answer the following questions on a separate sheet of paper.

1. How many types of animals made the tracks shown in the illustration? Explain.

2. What inferences, if any, can you make about the relative sizes of the animals based on their tracks? Explain.

3. What can you infer about the speed of the animals' movements? Are they walking? Running? How can you tell?

4. In a paragraph, explain what you think happened to the animals and the order in which the events happened.

5. What inference do you feel most confident about and why? Which inference do you feel least confident about and why?

6. Apply How might making inferences be important in the work of a real detective? Explain.

◆ More to Explore

Take a walk around your community looking for indirect evidence of animal life such as tracks, feathers, empty nests, and holes in the ground or in dead trees. For each discovery, record its location, at least two observations, and one or more inferences to explain each observation.

CHAPTER 1   **SKILLS LAB**

Developing Hypotheses

Earthworm Responses

In this lab, you will practice the skill of making hypotheses to learn more about earthworms.

◆ Problem

Do earthworms prefer dry or moist environments? Light or dark conditions?

◆ Materials

2 live earthworms in a storage container
plastic dropper
water
tray
clock or watch
paper towels
cardboard
flashlight

Earthworms — Dry paper towel

Wet paper towel — Tray

◆ Procedure   *Review the safety guidelines in Appendix A.*

1. Which environment do you think earthworms prefer—dry or moist? Record your hypothesis in the space below.

_____

_____

_____

2. Use the dropper to sprinkle water on the worms. Keep the worms moist at all times.

3. Fold a dry paper towel and place it on the bottom of one side of your tray. Fold a moistened paper towel and place it on the other side.

4. Moisten your hands. Then place the earthworms in the center of the tray. Make sure that half of each earthworm's body rests on the moist paper towel and half rests on the dry towel. Handle the worms gently.

SKILLS LAB *(continued)*

1

5. Cover the tray with the piece of cardboard. After five minutes, remove the cardboard and observe whether the worms are on the moist or dry surface. Record your observations in the space below.

_____

_____

_____

6. Repeat Steps 4 and 5.

_____

_____

_____

7. Return the earthworms to their storage container. Moisten the earthworms with water.

8. Which do you think earthworms prefer—strong light or darkness? Record your hypothesis in the space below.

_____

_____

_____

9. Cover the whole surface of the tray with a moistened paper towel.

10. Place the earthworms in the center of the tray. Cover half of the tray with cardboard. Shine a flashlight onto the other half.

11. After five minutes, note the locations of the worms. Record your observations in the space below.

_____

_____

_____

SKILLS LAB *(continued)*

12. Repeat Steps 10 and 11. Record your observations in the space below.

_____

_____

_____

13. Moisten the earthworms and put them in the location designated by your
teacher. Wash your hands after handling the worms.

◆ Analyze and Conclude

Write your answers on the back of this sheet or on a separate sheet of paper.

  1. Which environment did the worms prefer—moist or dry? Bright or dark? Did
  the worms' behavior support your hypotheses?

  2. Use what you know about earthworms to explain how their responses to
  moisture and light help them survive.

  3. Think About It What knowledge or experiences helped you make your
  hypotheses at the start of the experiments?

◆ More to Explore

Do earthworms prefer a smooth or rough surface? Write your hypothesis. Then
design an experiment to answer the question. Check with your teacher before
carrying out your experiment.

Going Through Changes

The following steps will walk you through the Chapter 2 Project. Use the hints as you guide your students through choice of conditions, experiment design, data collection, interpretation of results, and presentation.

◆ Chapter Project Overview

◆ Before introducing the project, show pictures of moths and butterflies to students. Discuss how these animals changed from caterpillars to adults. Tell students they will be learning more about insect metamorphosis during this project.

◆ Have students read the project description in the text. Then distribute the Chapter 2 Project Overview, pages 40–41, and Worksheet 1, page 42. Review and discuss the project rules to make sure students understand what is expected of them. Encourage students to ask questions. At this time, you may also want to hand out the Chapter 2 Project Scoring Rubric, page 44, that you will use in evaluating students' work.

◆ Instruct students to count their mealworms daily.

◆ Materials and Preparation

◆ Mealworms can be purchased from pet stores that sell reptile and amphibian food. Such mealworms will probably be partly through the larval period. Larger larvae are generally older than smaller ones. When you purchase the mealworms, ask for their approximate age and whether they have been stored in a refrigerator. You can use that information for scheduling purposes.

◆ You can partly control the project schedule by the way you store the mealworms before distributing them to students. In nature, the larval stage usually lasts ten weeks. Adult forms can be expected two to three weeks after pupation. The onset of pupation is affected by temperature, so you can shorten the project by storing the mealworms at a warm temperature or delay pupation by keeping them cool.

◆ Mealworms should be kept in nonabsorbent containers. A standard bread pan is a good size. Also, beetles cannot crawl up the smooth sides, so no cover is necessary. Ventilation helps prevent mold. The best food is wheat bran. Make a layer of food 2 inches deep in each container. Slices of apple, carrot, or potato used as water sources should be no more than 1/4 inch thick to prevent mold. Replace the slices when they become dry, usually in a week or two.

◆ Establish a completion date for the project display and interim dates for other tasks in the project. Have students record these dates in the Project Time Line on page 41.

◆ Demonstrate how to identify larvae, pupae, and adult beetles and how to use the data table students have made in their notebooks.

◆ Distribute Chapter 2 Project Worksheet 1, page 42, which guides students in describing the chosen conditions and recording data.

◆ Check Your Progress— Section 2 Review

◆ Check each student's experiment to ensure the survival of the larvae. The moisture source should be replaced when it becomes dry. The temperature should be consistent unless temperature is the chosen condition. Placing all containers in the same general location will help control this factor.

◆ Review students' data recorded in their notebooks. Identify and respond to any misunderstandings concerning data collection or metamorphosis.

CHAPTER 2 PROJECT *(continued)*

◆ Check Your Progress— Section 3 Review

◆ Check the containers for pupae. If the larvae were a few weeks old when students began the project, at least some of the larvae should have pupated.

◆ Review each student's data. Many students may find it more helpful to review their data in small groups rather than individually.

◆ Ask students to sketch the stages of development they have observed.

◆ Review the stages of metamorphosis and instruct students to make a flowchart of these stages. Have them include their drawings of a larva, pupa, and adult mealworm in the flowchart.

◆ Check Your Progress— Section 5 Review

◆ Hand out Project 2 Worksheet 2, page 43, and have students complete the tasks. Help students relate their data to the chosen condition.

◆ Illustrate how to make graphs from sample data.

◆ Challenge students to use their data to determine what effect the conditions they chose had on mealworm metamorphosis. Remind students of the changes that occur during metamorphosis. Encourage them to consider how the conditions they studied might affect these changes. Be sure the conclusions made by students are based on their data.

◆ Chapter Project Wrap-Up

◆ Have students review the requirements you have established for their display. Tell them to make sure they include all the elements.

◆ Guide students in making diagrams of their experiments and flowcharts of the changes they observed.

◆ Extensions/Options

◆ This project can also be done with tobacco or tomato horn worms, which metamorphose into moths in a comparable amount of time. However, students will need covered containers large enough for the newly emerged adult moths to fully spread their wings.

◆ Consider grouping students according to the conditions they tested. Direct groups to discuss their results. Have them combine their data, create a new graph, and summarize their results. Instruct each group to present its findings to the rest of the class.

2

CHAPTER 2 PROJECT   **OVERVIEW**

Going Through Changes

In this project, you will raise darkling beetles. Darkling beetles start life as fertilized eggs. They develop into wormlike larvae called mealworms, then eventually change into adults. This process is called metamorphosis. To raise your beetles, you will have to care for the mealworms until they eventually turn into adults.

There are two basic types of metamorphosis, gradual and complete. Complete metamorphosis has four distinct stages: egg, larva, pupa, and adult. Adult beetles lay eggs which hatch into larvae called mealworms. You will start with mealworms. They feed and grow and eventually change into pupae. After a week or two, each pupa splits open and a beetle crawls out.

In this project, you will investigate conditions that may affect metamorphosis. You will observe mealworms under two different environmental conditions and see whether metamorphosis is affected.

◆ Project Rules

◆ Have your teacher approve your conditions and plans before you obtain your mealworms.

◆ The condition you choose to study should not harm the animals.

◆ Remember that your animals are delicate, and treat them well.

◆ Follow the safety guidelines for handling animals.

◆ Suggested Materials

◆ Your teacher will provide you with mealworms.

◆ You will need two plastic or metal containers such as clean margarine tubs or bread pans. The beetles can't climb up the smooth sides, so no lid is necessary, but a screen may be used.

◆ You will need food for your mealworms. Wheat bran, rolled oats, and other cereals will usually work. Put about 2 inches of food in the container and add the mealworms.

◆ Your mealworms will need a moisture source such as a piece of apple, potato, or carrot.

◆ You will also need plastic spoons for moving and counting the mealworms.

CHAPTER 2 PROJECT OVERVIEW *(continued)*

◆ Project Hints

◆ Label your containers of mealworms so that you keep Condition 1 separate from Condition 2.

◆ When the piece of apple, potato, or carrot gets very dry, replace it with a fresh piece. In nature, mealworms live in places where there is not much water. Do not sprinkle water into their container—mold may develop and kill the mealworms.

◆ Project Time Line

Tasks	Date Due	Teacher's Initials
1. Bring two plastic or metal containers to class.	_____	_____
2. Choose the conditions you want to examine. Describe the two conditions you are examining. Get teacher approval for your plans.	_____	_____
3. Put mealworms into containers with food and a moisture source.	_____	_____
4. Count mealworm larvae, pupae, and adults daily.	_____	_____
5. Draw the mealworms in the larval, pupal, and adult stages of development.	_____	_____
6. Interpret data by making a graph.	_____	_____
7. Create your project display.	_____	_____

2

CHAPTER 2 PROJECT   **WORKSHEET 1**

Planning Your Mealworm Experiment

Choose the conditions you want to examine, and develop your experimental plan.
Write a description of the two conditions you will be examining in the spaces below.

Condition 1: _____

Condition 2: _____

◆ Recording Data

Make a table in your notebook, patterned after this one.

Date	Container 1 (Condition 1)			Container 2 (Condition 2)		
	Number of Larvae	Number of Pupae	Number of Beetles	Number of Larvae	Number of Pupae	Number of Beetles

Name _____ Date _____ Class _____

Organizing and Interpreting Your Data

Complete the following. When you have completed these exercises, you are ready to start planning your presentation.

1. a. Calculate and list the proportions of larvae, pupae, and beetles at the end of each week under Condition 1.

_____

_____

_____

_____

b. Calculate and list the proportions of larvae, pupae, and beetles at the end of each week under Condition 2.

_____

_____

_____

_____

2. Graph your data on the blank graphs below. At the end of each week, plot the data from Worksheet 1 and connect the data points to the previous week's data points. Use a different symbol for each life stage you are graphing. For example, you could use a dot for larvae, a circle for pupae, and a triangle for beetles.

3. Did the conditions you studied affect metamorphosis? Support your answer with evidence from your project.

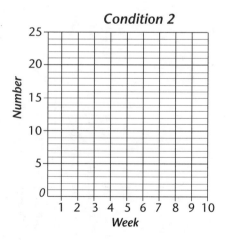

CHAPTER 2

Going Through Changes

In evaluating how well you complete the Chapter 2 Project, your teacher will judge your work in four categories. In each, a 4 is the best rating.

	4	3	2	1
Planning the Experiment	Accurately identifies and describes the two conditions to be examined. Plans the experiment. Obtains all needed materials.	Identifies two conditions to be examined. Plans the experiment but omits a step. Obtains most of the needed materials.	Identifies only one condition to be examined. Plans part of the experiment. Obtains some of the materials.	Identifies only one condition to examine. Plans a small part of the experiment. Obtains few of the materials.
Collecting Data	Collects data daily on the number of larvae, pupae, and adults in samples. Data are complete, clear, and accurate.	Collects data showing the number of larvae, pupae, and adults in samples. Data are complete and accurate.	Collects some data showing the number of larvae, pupae, and adults in samples. Data may be incomplete.	Collects occasional data showing the number of larvae, pupae, and adults in samples. Data may be unorganized or incomplete.
Presenting the Results	Display is clear and well-organized, and includes the conditions, a correct graph of the data, and an illustration of the stages of metamorphosis.	Display is adequate and includes the conditions, a graph of the data, and an illustration of the stages of metamorphosis.	Display is appropriate and includes at least two of the following: the conditions, a correct graph of the data, and an illustration of the stages of metamorphosis.	Display is inappropriate, incomplete, or incorrect. Includes only one of the following: the conditions, a graph of the data, or an illustration of the stages of metamorphosis.
Working Cooperatively	Takes a lead in planning, sharing data, and interpreting final results.	Actively participates in planning, sharing data, and interpreting final results.	Participates in some planning, shares some data, and interprets some results.	Does little planning, and shares little data and results.

Mollusks (pp. 48–53)

Objectives

After completing the lesson, students will be able to

- describe the main characteristics of mollusks;
- identify the major groups of mollusks.

1 Engage/Explore

- **Activating Prior Knowledge** Ask students if they have ever eaten clams, oysters, or squid as an introduction to mollusks.
- **Discover** Allow students to examine a variety of mollusk shells. Have them classify the shells into groups based on the characteristics they notice.

2 Facilitate

- **Building Inquiry Skills: Classifying** Have students list the characteristics of mollusks and segmented worms that are shared and those that are not shared between the two groups. Then ask students to say if they think mollusks and segmented worms are closely related, and to support their answer.
- **Integrating Earth Science** Demonstrate to students that limestone and marble both contain calcium carbonate, but that granite does not, by dripping a 10% solution of hydrochloric acid onto samples.
- **Sharpen Your Skills** Students imagine finding an animal that seems to be a mollusk in a stream. Elicit from students the characteristics of gastropods, bivalves, and cephalopods so that students would be able to classify the animal.
- **Cultural Diversity** Encourage students to research ethnic cookbooks to find out how mollusks are prepared and eaten in different cultures. Suggest that students prepare the recipes at home.
- **Including all Students** Help students that need extra help to pronounce gastropod, cephalopod, and bivalve.

- **Exploring a Snail** Allow students to observe live snails crawling in an aquarium. Direct them to examine the snail in the diagram and describe the function of the labeled parts. Then have them examine the snails in the aquarium, looking for the labeled parts.
- **Building Inquiry Skills: Observing** Give students closed and opened bivalves. Allow them to examine, draw, and label its internal parts.
- **Integrating Physics** Use a balloon filled with water to demonstrate how cephalopods move by jet propulsion.

3 Assess

- **Section 1 Review** Check students' understanding of mollusks by having them answer the section review questions.
- **Performance Assessment** Assess students' understanding of the characteristics that define an animal by asking them to draw one mollusk from each major group. Have students list three characteristics that make these animals mollusks. Finally, have students label one characteristic that distinguishes each group.

Lab

- **Skills Lab: Measuring** Allow students to practice measuring while investigating how environmental temperatures affect the activity level of a snail.

Mollusks

2

Guide for Reading

◆ What are the main characteristics of mollusks?

◆ What are the major groups of mollusks?

Mollusks are invertebrates with soft, unsegmented bodies often protected by hard outer shells. **In addition to soft bodies often covered with shells, mollusks have a thin layer of tissue called a mantle that covers their internal organs.** Most mollusks move using a muscular structure called a foot. Mollusks have bilateral symmetry. They do not have repeated body parts like segmented worms do. Instead, their internal organs are located in one area. The internal organs include a pair of **kidneys,** which remove wastes produced by the animal's cells.

Most water-dwelling mollusks have **gills,** organs that remove oxygen from water. Many have an organ called a **radula** (plural *radulae*), a flexible ribbon of tiny teeth. Mollusks use radulae to scrape food from a surface, such as a leaf.

The three major groups of mollusks are gastropods, bivalves, and cephalopods. Biologists classify mollusks into groups based on physical characteristics such as the presence of a shell, the type of shell, the type of foot, and the complexity of the nervous system.

Gastropods, such as snails and slugs, have a single shell or no shell. Most snails have a single coiled shell, while many slugs have no shell. Gastropods usually creep along on a broad foot. Gastropods can live nearly everywhere on Earth. Some gastropods are herbivores. Some are scavengers that feed on decaying material. Still others are carnivores.

Bivalves are mollusks that have two shells held together by hinges and strong muscles. Clams, oysters, scallops, and mussels are bivalves. Bivalves do not have radulae. Most bivalves are filter feeders; they strain their food from the water. Bivalves live in all kinds of watery environments. As adults, most bivalves stay in one place or move slowly. Bivalves, such as oysters, cover sand or grit lodged in their shells with a protective coat, which eventually forms a pearl.

Octopuses, cuttlefish, nautiluses, and squids are **cephalopods.** These animals have feet adapted to form tentacles around their mouths. They use their tentacles to capture food. Nautiluses have an external shell. Squids and cuttlefish have a small shell within their bodies. Octopuses do not have shells. Cephalopods have large eyes and excellent vision. They have the most complex nervous system, including a large brain, of any invertebrate. All cephalopods live in the ocean and swim by jet propulsion.

SECTION 2-1   **REVIEW AND REINFORCE**

Mollusks

◆ Understanding Main Ideas

Complete the table below with information about mollusks.

	Gastropods	Bivalves	Cephalopods
Common example			
How do they eat?			
How do they move?			
Do they have a shell?			
Adaptations of their feet			

◆ Building Vocabulary

From the list below, choose the term that best completes each sentence.

mantle   radula   cephalopod
gills   bivalve   kidneys
gastropod

1. A row of tiny teeth found in gastropods in called a _____ .

2. The most intelligent group of mollusks is the _____ group.

3. Waste is removed from a mollusk's body by its _____ .

4. The _____ produces a mollusk's shell and covers its internal organs.

5. A _____ is a two-shelled mollusk.

6. A snail is a _____ .

7. Most water-dwelling mollusks have _____ , organs that remove oxygen from water.

Describing Mollusk Shells

Shell collectors have admired the beauty and variety of mollusk shells for centuries. Three basic factors determine the general shape of most mollusk shells.

1. Almost every mollusk shell is **cone**-shaped. In some mollusks, the shell is nothing but a simple cone. It may be narrow (A) or wide (B).

2. Most mollusk shells are **coiled,** (C and D).

3. Often, the coiling is flat (C). In many cases, however, the coil is a three-dimensional spiral (D).

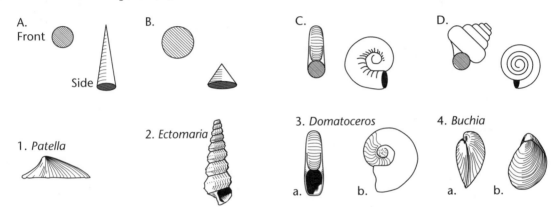

A. Front / Side   B.   C.   D.

1. Patella   2. Ectomaria   3. Domatoceros (a. b.)   4. Buchia (a. b.)

Complete the exercise by filling in the blanks in the following table, based on your observations of the fossil mollusk shells 1–4 above.

	Narrow or wide cone?	Coiling present?	Three-dimensional spiral present?
1. *Patella*			
2. *Ectomaria*			
3. *Domatoceras*			
4. *Buchia*			

Arthropods (pp. 54–61)

Objectives

After completing the lesson, students will be able to

- describe the major characteristics of arthropods;
- identify the main groups of arthropods.

1 Engage/Explore

- **Activating Prior Knowledge** Use students' prior knowledge of familiar arthropods to elicit important characteristics of arthropods.

- **Discover** Have students put a cardboard tube around their arms. Allow them to experience what it would be like to have a skeleton outside their bodies, and to understand the importance of joints in an external skeleton.

2 Facilitate

- **Including All Students** Provide students with crab legs and whole shrimp to explore the differences in the exoskeletons of these arthropods.

- **Integrating Chemistry** Invite students to examine hair or fingernails which are made of the polymer keratin.

- **Building Inquiry Skills: Modeling** Challenge students to invent their own arthropod by creating a three-dimensional model of it. Ask them to classify their arthropods as insects, arachnids, or crustaceans.

- **Including All Students** Help students to remember the meaning of *exoskeleton* by explaining the meaning of the prefixes *ex-* and *exo-*. Have students think of other words that begin with these prefixes.

- **Using the Visuals: Figure 6** Assign groups of students two of the three arthropod groups from the table. Direct each group of students to create Venn diagrams comparing and contrasting the two assigned arthropod groups using the information from the table.

- **Including All Students** Guide students to understand how arthropod antennae work by explaining the similarity to radio or television antennae.

- **Building Inquiry Skills: Inferring** Lead students to infer that the first arthropods had a hard exoskeleton that enabled them to become fossils.

- **Building Inquiry Skills: Observing** Allow students to examine a crustacean in order to discover which body parts it uses to protect itself.

- **Try This** Have students investigate whether pill bugs prefer a moist or dry environment.

- **Addressing Naive Conceptions** Lead students to see that not all spiders use webs to catch their prey and most spider bites aren't extremely dangerous to people.

- **Exploring a Crayfish** Have students use the art to identify anatomical features of a real crayfish.

- **Building Inquiry Skills: Making Generalizations** Have students use drinking straws and juicy oranges to simulate the way spiders eat.

- **Real-Life Learning** Discuss dust mites that live in houses and eat dead skin cells.

- **Using the Visuals: Figure 9** Direct students to draw a centipede and millipede, then label the visible characteristics.

3 Assess

- **Section 2 Review** Check students' understanding of arthropods by having them answer the section review questions.

- **Performance Assessment** Assess students' understanding of arthropods by having them describe a distinguishing characteristic of each of the following groups: crustaceans, arachnids, centipedes, and millipedes.

2

Arthropods

Guide for Reading

◆ What are the major characteristics of arthropods?

◆ What are the main groups of arthropods?

An arthropod is an invertebrate that has an external skeleton, a segmented body, and jointed attachments called appendages. Arthropods have open circulatory systems and reproduce sexually. Male and female reproductive organs are in separate individuals.

All arthropods have a waxy **exoskeleton,** or outer skeleton, that protects the animal and helps prevent evaporation of water. Arthropod exoskeletons are made of **chitin,** a long-chain molecule. Long-chain molecules like chitin are called polymers. An exoskeleton cannot grow with the animal. Arthropods shed their outgrown exoskeletons in a process called **molting.**

Arthropods have segmented bodies and jointed appendages that give them flexibility and enable them to move. These appendages are often highly specialized tools. For example, an **antenna** (plural *antennae*) is an appendage on the head that contains sense organs. The wings that most insects have are another type of appendage.

The major groups of arthropods are crustaceans, arachnids, centipedes, millipedes, and insects. A **crustacean** is an arthropod that has two or three body regions and usually has three pairs of appendages for chewing. Crustaceans have five or more pairs of legs. Each body segment has a pair of legs or modified legs attached to it. Crustaceans are the only arthropods that have two pairs of antennae.

Most crustaceans begin their lives as microscopic, swimming larvae. Crustacean larvae develop into adults by **metamorphosis,** a process in which an animal's body undergoes dramatic changes in form during its life cycle.

An **arachnid** is an arthropod that has two body sections, eight legs, and no antennae. The first body section is a combined head and chest. The hind section, called the **abdomen,** contains the arachnid's reproductive organs and part of its digestive tract. Spiders, mites, ticks, and scorpions are all arachnids. Spiders are predators and have hollow fangs, which are structures that inject venom into prey.

Centipedes and millipedes have highly segmented bodies. Centipedes have one pair of legs attached to each segment, and some centipedes have over 100 segments. Millipedes, which may have more than 80 segments, have two pairs of legs on each segment.

SECTION 2-2   **REVIEW AND REINFORCE**

Arthropods

◆ Understanding Main Ideas

Read each description. Decide which animal group from Section 2 best fits each question. Write your answers on a separate sheet of paper.

1. They are invertebrates with an exoskeleton, segmented body, and jointed appendages. They have an open circulatory system and reproduce sexually. Their name comes from the Greek for "joint-leg." What are they?

2. They have highly segmented bodies with one pair of legs attached to each segment. They are predators with venom and sharp jaws. They eat smaller animals. Some of them have over 100 segments. What are they?

3. They all have two body sections and eight legs. Some of them are predators with fangs or a stinger; others are parasites. None of them have antennae. What are they?

4. They have segmented bodies with two pairs of legs on each segment. They eat decaying leaves. They curl up into a ball when something disturbs them. What are they?

◆ Building Vocabulary

From the list below, choose the term that best completes each sentence. Use each term only once.

abdomen	antennae	chitin
exoskeleton	metamorphosis	molting

5. An arthropod's _____ protects it and keeps it from drying out. It is made of _____ and does not grow with the animal.

6. The heads of some arthropods have _____, which contain sense organs.

7. Some animals go through a process called _____ during their life cycle in which their bodies undergo dramatic changes in form as they develop.

8. The hind body section of an arachnid is called its _____.

9. The process of shedding an outgrown exoskeleton is called

_____.

The Arthropod Evolutionary Tree

2

When scientists say that two kinds of organisms are related, they mean that those two kinds of organisms had a common ancestor. The more recently that common ancestor lived, the more closely related the two kinds of organisms are.

A *cladogram* is a diagram that shows how closely related different kinds of organisms are to each other. It's a tree-shaped diagram with leaves, forks, and branches. The cladogram shows part of the arthropod evolutionary tree. At the top are the leaves, which are recent arthropods, such as insects, millipedes, and centipedes. Each fork in the diagram represents the shared ancestor of all arthropods above it. For example, fork D is the shared ancestor of millipedes and centipedes, while fork C is the shared ancestor of all insects, millipedes, and centipedes. Branches connect the ancestors with each other and with recent organisms.

To find the most recent ancestor of any two organisms just follow the branches down until you reach the first fork that connects them. You can also follow up from a fork, to find more and more recent organisms. The two organisms that have the same most recent ancestor are each other's closest relative.

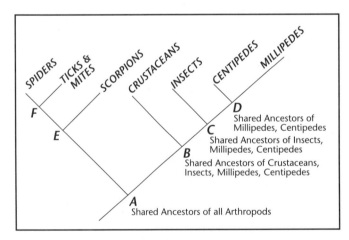

Answer the questions below on a separate sheet of paper.

1. Which fork occurred earlier, B or D? How do you know?

2. What does fork B represent?

3. What does fork E represent?

4. Which group are mites and ticks most closely related to? How do you know?

Insects (pp. 62–69)

Objectives

After completing the lesson, students will be able to

- describe the characteristics of insects;
- describe the overall impact of insects on humans;
- state and explain the life stages of insects.

1 Engage/Explore

- **Activating Prior Knowledge** Direct students to name as many insects as they can and then look for shared characteristics.
- **Discover** Allow students to observe an insect collection and to compare and contrast the characteristics of the insects.

2 Facilitate

- **Building Inquiry Skills: Interpreting Diagrams** Give students dead grasshoppers to examine and then use Figure 11 to identify external features of the specimen.
- **Addressing Naive Conceptions** Some students may think spiders are insects. Have them review insect characteristics and then examine a spider's body to verify it is not an insect.
- **Building Inquiry Skills: Comparing and Contrasting** Invite students to create a Venn diagram to distinguish complete and gradual metamorphosis.
- **Sharpen Your Skills** Direct students in creating a circle graph that shows the percentage of total insect species in each group.
- **Including All Students** Pronounce *pupa* and *nymph* aloud several times and suggest that students write two sentences using each word.
- **Real-Life Learning** Invite students working in groups to list examples of insect behavior and its results they have seen at home.

- **Exploring Insect Metamorphosis** Have students compare the different stages of complete and gradual metamorphosis.
- **Including All Students** Show pictures of insects that display various forms of defense such as camouflage, warning coloration, and adaptations for escape.
- **Social Studies Connection** After discussing the Black Death with students, have them do research to prepare for writing journal entries.
- **Integrating Environmental Science** Show students an insect trap and explain how it works.

3 Assess

- **Section 3 Review** Check students' understanding of insects by having them answer the section review questions.
- **Performance Assessment** Assess students' understanding by having students sketch an insect and label three characteristics that classify it in this group.

Lab

- **Real-World Lab: You and Your Environment** Students observe the organisms living in one specific soil environment.

Insects

Guide for Reading
◆ What are the characteristics of insects?
◆ What is the overall impact of insects on humans?

2

Insects are arthropods with three body sections, six legs, one pair of antennae, and usually one or two pairs of wings. The three body regions are the head, **thorax,** and abdomen. An insect's thorax, or mid-section, is the section to which wings and legs are attached. The abdomen contains many of the insect's internal organs. Sense organs, such as the eyes and antennae, are located on an insect's head. Most insects have two large compound eyes that are especially keen at seeing movement. Most also have simple eyes, which can distinguish between light and darkness.

Insects begin life as tiny, hard-shelled, fertilized eggs. After they hatch, insects begin a process of metamorphosis that eventually produces an adult insect. There are two types of metamorphosis. The first, called **complete metamorphosis,** has four stages: egg, larva, **pupa,** and adult. Insect larvae usually look something like worms. After a period of eating and growing, the larva goes into the second stage and becomes a pupa (plural *pupae*). During the pupal stage, the insect is enclosed in a protective covering and gradually changes from a larva to an adult.

In contrast, **gradual metamorphosis** has no distinctly different larval or pupal stages. An egg hatches into a **nymph** that often resembles the adult insect. A nymph may molt several times before becoming an adult.

Insects eat a wide variety of things. If something is alive, or was once living, some kind of insect will probably eat it. Insect mouthparts are tools adapted for a highly specific way of getting food.

Insects have many defenses against predators. **Camouflage,** or protective coloration, is one type. Insects have other defenses as well, such as hard exoskeletons or the ability to run or fly quickly. Some insects smell bad or taste bad to predators.

Many insects have an impact on humans. Some damage crops and some carry diseases. **The vast majority of insects, however, are harmless or beneficial to humans.** Many insects enable food crops and other plants to reproduce by carrying pollen from one plant to another. Some insects prey on harmful insects and help to reduce those insect populations. One method of controlling harmful insects is the use of biological controls. Biological controls introduce natural predators or diseases into insect populations.

SECTION 2-3   **REVIEW AND REINFORCE**

Insects

◆ Understanding Main Ideas

Answer the following questions.

1. How many body sections does an insect have? _____ Sketch an insect on a separate piece of paper. Name and label the body parts on your sketch.

2. How many legs does an insect have? _____ Show them on your sketch.

3. List two other features that most insects have. Show them on your sketch, and label them.

_____

4. Name two ways that insect mouthparts are used for feeding.

_____

_____

5. List at least three ways in which insects help humans.

_____

_____

6. What is one problem with using pesticides to kill insects?

_____

_____

◆ Building Vocabulary

From the list below, choose the term that best completes each sentence.

thorax	complete metamorphosis	nymph
pupa	gradual metamorphosis	camouflage

7. The wings and legs of an insect are attached to the _____ .

8. The four stages of _____ in order are egg, larva, _____ , and adult.

9. In the pattern of development known as _____ , the young insect, called a _____ , looks much like a miniature adult.

10. Some insects hide from predators by using _____ that allows them to blend into their surroundings.

Animals   Teaching Resources   **B ◆ 55**

SECTION 2-3   **ENRICH**

Warning Flares and False Colors

Mimicry happens when different animal species resemble one another. The animals that look alike are called *mimics*. Mimicry can protect insects and other animals against predators. There are two kinds of mimicry. In the first, called *Müllerian* mimicry, several species that have defenses against predators look similar to one another. When a predator learns to avoid one mimic, the predator will also avoid the others. For example, the butterflies in Figure 1 are Müllerian mimics. They look alike and all taste bad to predators.

In *Batesian* mimicry, the mimic species does not have a good defense against predators, but it looks like another animal that does. The predator confuses the two species and avoids both. In Figure 2, the lady-bird beetle tastes bad, but its Batesian mimic, a roach, tastes fine to predators.

Figure 1.
Müllerian mimcry

Mechanitis lysimnia   *Lycorea halia*   *Heliconius eurate*

Figure 2.
Batesian mimicry

Leis dunopi
**a kind of
lady-bird beetle**

Prosoplecta semperi
a kind of roach

Figure 3.

Alcraea aleiope   *Planema poggei*   *Planema macarista*

Figure 4.

Perrhybris pyrrha

Answer the following questions on a separate sheet of paper.

1. The butterflies in Figure 3 all taste bad to predators. What kind of mimicry is this?

2. The butterfly in Figure 4 is harmless to predators. Does it resemble any of the other insects pictured? What kind of mimicry is this?

3. What is the survival advantage to bees and wasps of having similar bright yellow stripes? What kind of mimicry is this?

4. The harmless kingsnake has markings like a poisonous coral snake. How does this help the kingsnake survive? What kind of mimicry is this?

Integrating Physics
The Sounds of Insects (pp. 70–72)

Objectives

After completing the lesson, students will be able to

◆ explain how sound is produced;

◆ describe one function that sound serves for many insects.

1 Engage/Explore

◆ **Activating Prior Knowledge** Challenge students to describe what insects sound like and list insects that make sounds.

◆ **Discover** Have students pluck a rubber band, listen to the sound it makes, and watch it vibrate. Help students conclude that the vibrations and sound are connected.

2 Facilitate

◆ **Building Inquiry Skills** Have students model how waves can travel through liquids by dropping a stone into a clear bowl of water.

◆ **Try This** Allow students to experiment with a tuning fork to see how vibrations cause sound. Challenge students to predict what will happen if a tuning fork is plunged into talcum powder.

◆ **Building Inquiry Skills: Inferring** Guide students to realize why most insects that produce sounds can also sense and interpret sounds.

3 Assess

◆ **Section 4 Review** Check students' understanding of the sounds of insects by having them answer the section review questions.

◆ **Performance Assessment** Assess students' understanding by asking them to draw a diagram illustrating how sound from a tuning fork reaches your ear.

The Sounds of Insects

Guide for Reading

2

◆ How is sound produced?

◆ What function does sound serve for many insects?

All sound is produced by vibrations that create waves that move outward from the source. For example, when a guitar string is pulled, it moves rapidly back and forth, bumping into air particles. This motion creates many alternating regions of compressed and spread-out air particles. These alternating regions are sound waves. The waves move outward from the vibrating object that produced them.

Sound waves must travel through a medium—a solid, a liquid, or a gas. The sound waves made by a guitar string usually travel through air. Sound waves can also travel through liquids, such as water, and solids, such as wood.

Insects make sound in a variety of ways. Different species of insects use different parts of their bodies to produce sound. Many insects rub a roughened part of their bodies against a sharp-edged part. For example, deathwatch beetles tap on the ground with their heads. Hissing cockroaches are among the few insects that make sounds by forcing air out of their bodies. This method is also used by humans and other vertebrates to make sounds.

Many insects use sound to attract mates. Usually the males make the sound that attracts females. That is the case with crickets, grasshoppers, and katydids. However, in a few types of insects, such as mosquitoes, the females make a sound to attract males.

The Sounds of Insects

◆ Understanding Main Ideas

Write the letter of the correct answer on the line at the left.

_____   **1.** A cricket's chirping is caused by
   a. hunger.
   b. its vocal chords.
   c. its wings vibrating back and forth.
   d. the wind.

_____   **2.** Sound can travel through all of the following *except*
   a. air.
   b. orange juice.
   c. wood.
   d. outer space.

_____   **3.** Insects make sound all of these ways *except* by
   a. tapping the ground with their head.
   b. forcing the air out of their body.
   c. rubbing their hind wings against rough patches on their abdomen.
   d. sitting still.

_____   **4.** Many insects use sound to
   a. express fear
   b. comunicate the location of food sources
   c. frighten predators
   d. attract mates

◆ Building Vocabulary

5. Define *sound* by explaining how a sound is produced.

_____

_____

_____

_____

_____

Sound Effects

Male crickets attract females by producing sound. The calls also sometimes attract a type of parasitic fly that lays its eggs inside the calling male. Their larvae live and grow inside the cricket, and the cricket eventually dies.

Biologist William Cade has studied these crickets and collected the following data. Measurements of the volume of the call are in decibels, the scientific unit of measurement for the volume of sound. Use the data to answer the questions.

Volume of call (in decibels)	Number of females attracted	Number of parasitic flies attracted
silent	0	0
80	7	3
90	21	18
100	30	36
110	32	42

Answer the questions below on a separate sheet of paper. Use graph paper if you wish.

1. On a graph, place the volume of the calls on the horizontal axis. Place the number of females attracted at each volume on the vertical axis. Plot the points. Use a colored pencil to connect these points with a line.

2. On the same graph, plot the number of parasitic flies that were attracted to the caller at each volume. Again, connect the points with a line. Use a pencil of a different color than the one you used for Step 1.

3. What is the relationship between the volume of sound and the number of females that the male cricket attracts?

4. What is the relationship between the volume of sound and the number of parasitic flies that come to the male cricket?

5. What is the loudest a male cricket can call and still attract more female crickets than parasitic flies?

Echinoderms (pp. 73–76)

Objectives

After completing the lesson, students will be able to

◆ describe the typical echinoderm characteristics.

1 Engage/Explore

◆ **Activating Prior Knowledge** Have students recall the definitions of radial and bilateral symmetry from the previous chapter. Show students the photographs in the section, and elicit that all these animals have radial symmetry.

◆ **Discover** Invite students to simulate the tube feet of sea stars using a plastic dropper and water.

2 Facilitate

◆ **Including All Students** Guide students whose native language is not English in the pronunciation of difficult words such as *vascular* and *echinoderm*. Allow them to practice saying the words with a partner.

◆ **Inquiry Challenge** Invite students to model the water vascular system of echinoderms using a surgical glove partly filled with water.

◆ **Exploring a Sea Star** Ask students to point out the parts of the water vascular system in the illustration and to trace a pathway water might travel through the system. Encourage them to describe the pathway to a partner.

◆ **Building Inquiry Skills: Interpreting a Photograph** Point out that the five-part symmetry of echinoderms is often difficult to see from certain angles. Tell students the symmetry of a sea cucumber is more easily seen when viewed from above. Challenge students to sketch what they think the sea cucumber in the figure looks like from the top.

3 Assess

◆ **Section 5 Review** Check students' understanding of echinoderms by having them answer the section review questions.

◆ **Performance Assessment** Assess students' understanding of echinoderm characteristics. Have them sketch a hypothetical echinoderm. Be sure student's sketches include the major characteristics of echinoderms.

2

SECTION 2-5   **SECTION SUMMARY**

Echinoderms

Guide for Reading

◆ What characteristics are typical of echinoderms?

2

An **echinoderm** is a radially symmetrical invertebrate that lives on the ocean floor. The skin of most echinoderms is supported by a spiny internal skeleton, or **endoskeleton.** Adult echinoderms are radially symmetrical. Their bodies usually have five parts, or multiples of five. These parts are arranged like the spokes on a wheel.

In addition to five-part radial symmetry and an endoskeleton, echinoderms also have an internal fluid system, called a water vascular system. The **water vascular system** consists of fluid-filled tubes within the echinoderm's body. Portions of the tubes can contract, squeezing water into structures called tube feet. Most echinoderms use their tube feet to move and to capture food.

Most echinoderms are either male or female. Eggs are usually fertilized externally, in the water. The fertilized eggs develop into larvae. The larvae eventually undergo metamorphosis and become adults.

A sea star is one type of echinoderm with five arms. It feeds by forcing its stomach out through its mouth and into the shell of its prey. Chemicals break down the prey. The sea star sucks in the partially-digested prey.

If a sea star loses an arm, it can grow a replacement. The process by which an animal grows a new part to replace a lost one is called **regeneration.**

Brittle stars are close relatives of sea stars. They have five arms, but their arms are long and slender, with flexible joints. Like sea stars, brittle stars can regenerate lost arms. Brittle stars use their arms to move rapidly along the ocean bottom.

Sand dollars and sea urchins have no arms. Sand dollars look like large coins. Their flat bodies are covered with very short spines. These spines help them burrow into sand. Sea urchins are covered by movable spines. The spines cover a central shell.

Sea cucumbers look a little bit like cucumbers. These animals live on ocean floors and are filter feeders. They use their tentacles to sweep food toward their mouths. They move by using five rows of tube feet on their underside. Their bodies are soft, flexible, and muscular.

SECTION 2-5   **REVIEW AND REINFORCE**

Echinoderms

◆ Understanding Main Ideas

Write the letter of the correct answer on the line at the left.

_____ **1.** Which of the following is *not* a characteristic of echinoderms?
  a. 5-part radial symmetry   **b.** endoskeleton
  c. segmented body   **d.** water vascular system

_____ **2.** Which of the following is *not* an echinoderm?
  a. fiddler crab   **b.** sand dollar
  c. sea urchin   **d.** sea cucumber

_____ **3.** Which of the following is *not* a function of tube feet?
  a. move along ocean floor   **b.** catch food
  c. grip surfaces   **d.** filter water

_____ **4.** Echinoderm means
  a. jointed legs   **b.** five arms
  c. spiny skin   **d.** spiny arms

Answer the following.

5. Describe how a sea star captures its food.

_____

_____

◆ Building Vocabulary

Fill in the blank to complete each statement.

6. The _____ consists of fluid-filled tubes within the echinoderm's body.

7. An echinoderm has a(n) _____ that supports its body.

8. Animals in the _____ phylum are radially symmetrical invertebrates that live on the ocean floor.

9. _____ is the process by which an animal grows a new part to replace a part that has been lost.

Sea Lilies

The five groups of echinoderms discussed in the text make up the vast majority of today's living echinoderms. There is another living group, however, the sea lilies, or *crinoids* (KRY-noydz). Although these echinoderms are rare today, their long history and complex fossil record make them important to scientists who study fossils.

Sea lilies are filter-feeders whose bodies vaguely resemble flowers. Instead of petals, however, these echinoderms have long arms lined with rows of tube feet that sweep food particles out of the water and move the particles toward the centrally located mouth. In most, their bodies have long stems. Unlike most modern echinoderms, sea lilies fasten themselves to solid objects on the bottom using the base of their stems. The sea lilies sometimes detach and move around.

Modern sea lilies live mostly in very deep water, though some live on coral reefs. During much of the last 530 million years, however, they were found in a greater variety of habitats, and they were much more abundant. In many places, the hard plates of the sea lilies' endoskeletons make up large portions of the rocks deposited in the seas in which they lived.

Sea Lily

Sand Dollar

Sea Star

Answer the questions below on the back of this sheet or on a separate sheet of paper.

1. Echinoderms have five-part radial symmetry, a water vascular system, and an internal skeleton. Which of these characteristics are visible in all three illustrations?

2. The endoskeletons of echinoderms are not visible in these illustrations. How do we know that ancient sea lilies had them?

3. What part of the water vascular system is visible in the illustration of the sea lily? How does the sea lily use this part in a different way then how the other echinoderms pictured use it?

4. While both sea lilies and sea cucumbers are filter feeding echinoderms, only sea lilies remain fastened to the sea floor. How do you think this difference would affect the habitats in which the two animals live?

CHAPTER 2   **SKILLS LAB**

Measuring

A Snail's Pace

In this lab, you will use the skill of measuring to investigate how fast a snail moves in different water temperatures.

◆ **Problem**   How do changes in environmental temperature affect the activity level of a snail?

◆ **Materials**

freshwater snail
plastic petri dish
spring water at three temperatures: cool (9–13°C); medium (18–22°C); warm (27–31°C)
thermometer
graph paper
ruler
timer

◆ **Procedure**

1. Use the data table on the next page to record your data.

2. On one sheet of graph paper labeled *Snail,* trace a circle using the base of an empty petri dish. Divide and label the circle as shown in the illustration. On a second sheet of graph paper labeled *Data,* draw three more circles like the one in the illustration.

3. Place the petri dish over the circle on the Snail page, fill it with cool water, and record the water temperature. Then place the snail in the water just above the "S" in the circle. Be sure to handle the snail gently.

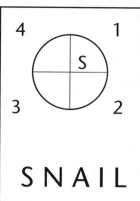

SKILLS LAB (*continued*)

4. For five minutes, observe the snail. Record its movements by drawing a line that shows its path in the first circle on the Data page.

5. Find the distance the snail moved by measuring the line you drew. You may need to measure all the parts of the line and add them together. Record the distance in the data table.

6. Repeat Steps 3 through 5 first with medium-temperature water and then with warm water. Record the snail's paths in the second circle and third circle on the Data page.

7. Return the snail to your teacher when you are done. Wash your hands thoroughly.

8. For each temperature, compute the class average for distance traveled.

◆ Data Table

	Cool	Medium	Warm
Water Temperature			
Distance			

◆ Analyze and Conclude

Write your answers on the back of this sheet or on a separate sheet of paper.

1. Make a bar graph showing the class average for each temperature. How does a snail's activity level change as temperature increases?

2. Do you think the pattern you found would continue at higher temperatures? Explain.

3. Think About It What factors in this lab were difficult to measure? How could you change the procedure to obtain more accurate measurements? Explain.

◆ Design an Experiment

Design an experiment to measure the rate at which a snail moves in an aquarium with gravel on the bottom. Obtain your teacher's permission before trying your experiment.

Animals

CHAPTER 2   REAL-WORLD LAB

You and Your Environment

What's Living in the Soil?

The soil beneath a tree, in a garden, or under a rock is home to many organisms, including a variety of arthropods. Each of these patches of soil can be thought of as a miniature environment with its own group of living residents. In this lab, you will examine one specific soil environment.

◆ **Problem**   What kinds of animals live in soil and leaf litter?

◆ **Skills Focus**   observing, classifying, inferring

◆ **Materials**

2-liter plastic bottle
coarse steel wool
cheesecloth
gooseneck lamp
large, wide-mouthed jar
fresh sample of soil and leaf litter
large scissors
trowel
large rubber band
hand lens
small jar

◆ **Procedure**

1. Select a location where your equipment can be set up and remain undisturbed for about 24 hours. At that location, place the small jar inside the center of the large jar.

2. Use scissors to cut a large plastic bottle in half. **CAUTION:** *Cut in a direction away from yourself and others.* Turn the top half of the bottle upside down to serve as a funnel.

3. Insert a small amount of coarse steel wool into the mouth of the funnel to keep the soil from falling out. Do not pack the steel wool too tightly. Leave spaces for small organisms to crawl through. Place the funnel into the large jar.

REAL-WORLD LAB (continued)

4. Using the trowel, fill the funnel with soil and surface leaf litter. When you finish handling the leaves and soil, wash your hands thoroughly.

5. Look closely to see whether the soil and litter are dry or wet. Record your observation.

6. Make a cover for your sample by placing a piece of cheesecloth over the top of the funnel. Hold the cheesecloth in place with a large rubber band. Immediately position a lamp about 15 cm above the funnel, and turn on the light. Allow this set-up to remain undisturbed for about 24 hours. **CAUTION:** *Hot light bulbs can cause burns. Do not touch the bulb.*

7. When you are ready to make your observations, turn off the lamp. Leave the funnel and jar in place while making your observations. Use a hand lens to examine each organism in the jar. **CAUTION:** *Do not touch any of the organisms.*

8. Use the data table below to sketch each type of organism and to record other observations. Be sure to include evidence that will help you classify the organisms. (*Hint:* Remember that some animals may be at different stages of metamorphosis.)

9. Examine the soil and leaf litter, and record whether this material is dry or wet.

10. When you are finished, follow your teacher's directions about returning the organisms to the soil. Wash your hands with soap.

◆ Data Table

Sketch of Organism	Number Found	Size	Important Characteristics	Probable Phylum

REAL-WORLD LAB (continued)

Sketch of Organism	Number Found	Size	Important Characteristics	Probable Phylum

◆ Analyze and Conclude

Write your answers on the back of this sheet or on a separate sheet of paper.

1. Describe the conditions of the soil environment at the beginning and end of the lab. What caused the change?

2. What types of animals did you collect in the small jar? What characteristics did you use to identify each type of animal? Which types of animals were the most common?

3. Why do you think the animals moved down the funnel away from the soil?

4. Apply Using what you have learned about arthropods and other animals, make an inference about the role that each animal you collected plays in the environment.

◆ More to Explore

What kinds of organisms might live in other soil types—for example, soil at the edge of a pond, dry sandy soil, or commercially prepared potting soil? Design an experiment to answer this question.

CHAPTER 3

Animal Adaptations

The following steps will walk you through the Chapter 3 Project. Use the hints as you guide your students through: planning; choosing an adaptation, a fish, an amphibian, and a reptile; constructing models; making a poster; and giving a presentation.

◆ Chapter Project Overview

◆ Before you introduce the project, allow students to pair off and search through the text for characteristics of fishes, amphibians, and reptiles. When they have finished brainstorming, ask each pair to report back to the class. Compile a list of characteristics on the board.

◆ Tell students they will be constructing models of fish, amphibians, and reptiles to show how they are adapted to live in their environments.

◆ Have students read the project description in the text. Then distribute the Chapter 3 Project Overview, pages 72–73. Review and discuss the project rules to make sure students understand what is expected of them. Encourage students to ask questions. You may want to hand out at this time the Chapter 3 Project Scoring Rubric, page 76, that you will use in evaluating student's work. Discuss the purpose of the project and your expectations of what the final product should include.

◆ Materials and Preparation

◆ Encyclopedias, books, the Internet, and magazines are useful for choosing animals and researching adaptations. Materials and tools for constructing models might include: toothpicks, pipe cleaners, polystyrene foam, cardboard, construction paper, chicken wire, balsa wood, balloons, modeling clay, papier mâché, glue, tape, scissors, paints, markers, and other decorating materials.

◆ Establish a date for the final project presentation and interim dates for project tasks.

Students' adaptations should be selected while studying Section 1. Each student's fish, amphibian, and reptile should be chosen during the study of Sections 2, 3, and 4, respectively. Give students a week to complete each model. Have students record these dates on their worksheet.

◆ Distribute Chapter 2 Worksheet 1, page 74. Students should be able to complete the chart based on the list that was compiled following the brainstorming activity.

◆ Distribute Chapter 3 Worksheet 2, page 75, which helps students plan their models. Each section of this worksheet should be completed prior to the construction of the related model. Students might need help thinking about how to construct their model. Also, having students start their model building in class might be helpful.

◆ Check Your Progress— Section 2 Review

◆ Explain to students that the adaptation they choose must be similar in each of the three animals, but might be different in specifics. For example, an adaptation for catching prey might be the many sharp teeth of a barracuda, the long sticky tongue of a bullfrog, and the teeth of a boa constrictor

◆ Direct students to choose a specific kind of fish to model. Remind students that each of the three main groups of fish has a different set of adaptations.

◆ Assist students in planning how to build their model fish given the materials available.

◆ Check Your Progress— Section 3 Review

◆ Make sure that students have finished their fish model.

◆ Check students' sketches of their model plans for building an amphibian. Each amphibian model must exhibit the same type of adaptation as shown in the fish model. The sketches should also include the specific kind of amphibian chosen.

◆ Check students' lists of materials that they plan on using to build their amphibian to make sure that these materials are available to the student.

◆ Check Your Progress— Section 4 Review

◆ Ensure that students have completed their fish and amphibian models.

◆ Check students' sketches of their model plans for building a reptile. Each reptile model must exhibit the same type of adaptation as shown in the fish and amphibian models. The sketches should also explain which specific reptile was chosen.

◆ Encourage students to begin working on their posters. They may need help thinking about what kinds of diagrams will be necessary to illustrate their adaptations. Remind students to label the diagrams.

◆ Chapter Project Wrap-Up

◆ As students make their presentations ask their classmates to take notes to add to their list of animal adaptations in Worksheet 1.

◆ Have students turn in all project products.

◆ An additional discussion of adaptations within each group of organisms—fishes, amphibians, and reptiles—might help students to use the compare and contrast skills they developed over the course of the project to review the chapter.

◆ Extensions/Options

◆ If time or building materials are limited, students could model only the part of the animal which shows the chosen adaptation. On their posters, students would illustrate the entire organism and show how the feature fits into the whole animal.

◆ Another option is to have students work in groups. If done in groups of three, each student in a group could do one of the three models. Students would work together to create a poster showing how their models demonstrate the adaptation.

◆ Allow students to model adaptations found within the same group of organisms. For example, a student could choose to model a jawless fish, cartilaginous fish, and a bony fish.

◆ Incorporate mathematical skills into this project. Require students to determine the size of their model in relation to the actual organism, e.g. 1/2 size, 1/10 size. Students should include the scale in their presentations.

◆ Suggest that students turn their poster and models into a display, and present them at a school or local science fair.

◆ Invite students to research how computer models of the human body are leading to advances in sports medicine.

◆ Encourage students to choose animals that live in the same habitat and have them construct a realistic diorama featuring their chosen animals, similar to what they might find in a natural history museum.

CHAPTER 3 PROJECT OVERVIEW

CHAPTER 3

Animal Adaptations

For this project you will study how different organisms are adapted to their own environments. You will choose one kind of adaptation and use models to demonstrate how it differs between a fish, an amphibian, and a reptile. The adaptation that you choose must be different in at least two of the three animals that you model. As an example, you might chose three organisms to show how they are adapted for moving. Or you could pick three organisms that have different adaptations for eating, or for surviving in a hot climate.

Your teacher will review your choice of adaptation and your choice of animals to model. You will design your models and decide what materials to use to build them.

◆ Project Rules

◆ You must model the same type of adaptation in all three of your models.

◆ Your models must include one fish, one amphibian, and one reptile. Since there are many variations within each of these groups, your models should be of a specific kind of organism. For example, your fish might be a lamprey, great white shark, or catfish.

◆ Make a sketch of each of your models and have your teacher approve it before you begin construction.

◆ Follow the safety guidelines for handling sharp tools in Appendix A of your textbook.

◆ Suggested Materials

◆ Materials and tools you might use to make your models include: toothpicks, pipe cleaners, polystyrene foam, cardboard, construction paper, chicken wire, balsa wood, balloons, modeling clay, papier mâché, glue, tape, scissors, paints, markers, and other decorating materials.

CHAPTER 3 PROJECT OVERVIEW *(continued)*

◆ Project Hints

◆ Encyclopedias, books, magazines, the Internet, pet stores, and zoos are all good places to look when trying to think about different adaptations and specific animals to model. They can also help you to think about how the adaptation that you choose makes your animal suited to its environment.

◆ Use a shoe box or other storage container to help you protect your models.

◆ Consider making a small model. Large models might take too long to complete, and you would need to use a large amount of materials. If your model is not life size, you should include information about the actual size of the organism in your poster and in your presentation.

◆ Project Time Line

Tasks	Due Date
1. Select adaptation and get teacher approval	_____
2. Select fish to model and get approval	_____
3. Sketch fish design	_____
4. Complete fish model	_____
5. Select amphibian to model and get approval	_____
6. Sketch amphibian design	_____
7. Complete amphibian model	_____
8. Select reptile to model and get approval	_____
9. Sketch reptile design	_____
10. Complete reptile model	_____
11. Make poster	_____
12. Do project presentation	_____

Animal Adaptations

All animals have adaptations that enable them to live in their own habitat and carry out necessary functions (such as eating). Chapter 3 examines three different types of organisms: fishes, amphibians, and reptiles. Completing the following chart is a good exercise for thinking about the different ways in which they are adapted to live in their habitats. As you fill it out, be thinking what type of adaptation you might pick for your three models. And remember, you don't have to pick an adaptation or animal from the book.

The first two rows of this chart have been done for you. Complete the rest. Skim through Chapter 3 for help. At the end of the project you will use the blank rows at the bottom of the chart to record information about other students' choice of adaptations.

3

Organism	Adaptation	Function
angelfish	fins	moving in water
balloon fish	spines	protection against predators
lamprey	sharp teeth and suction-cup mouth	
red-backed salamander		get oxygen from water
red-backed salamander	lungs	
spring peeper (frog)		find a mate
king cobra		keep from drying out
green iguana	sharp claws	

CHAPTER 3 PROJECT   **WORKSHEET 2**

Animal Adaptations

◆ Planning

Complete the following tasks using a separate sheet of paper. You should do each part after you have covered the corresponding section in the chapter.

◆ Part I: Choosing Your Adaptation

1. Describe the adaptation that you have chosen to study.

◆ Part II: Fishes

2. What fish have you chosen to model?

3. Make a sketch of your model fish. The sketch should be detailed enough to serve as the plan design for your model. You may need to do more than one sketch to show different views of your model. The sketches should include measurements of the height, width, and length of your model. Include a scale, if the sketch is not the actual size of the fish. Be sure that your sketches show the adaptation that you described in Part I.

4. What materials do you plan to use to build your model fish?

◆ Part III: Amphibians

5. What amphibian have you chosen to model?

6. Repeat step 3 for the amphibian you've chosen.

7. What materials do you plan to use to build your model amphibian?

◆ Part IV: Reptiles

8. What reptile have you chosen to model?

9. Repeat step 3 for the reptile you've chosen.

10. What materials do you plan to use to build your model reptile?

CHAPTER 3

Animal Adaptations

In evaluating how well you complete the Chapter 3 Project, your teacher will judge your work in four categories. In each, a score of 4 is the best rating.

	4	3	2	1
Planning	Thoroughly researches the adaptation and how it differs in the three animals. Makes useful sketches with appropriate measurements before attempting construction.	Adequately researches the adaptation and how it differs in the three animals. Makes sketches of the organisms before attempting construction.	Minimally researches the adaptation and how it differs in the three animals. Makes sketches of one or two organisms.	Does little or no research about the adaptation. Fails to make sketches before building model.
Model Building	All models are well designed and to scale. The chosen adaptations are apparent.	Most models well designed and to scale. The chosen adaptations are fairly easy to discern.	Models are moderately well designed, but are not to scale. The chosen adaptations are fairly easy to discern.	Models are poorly designed, not to scale, and adaptations are difficult to discern.
Poster	Written explanations accurately describe the adaptation. Labeled diagrams are included.	Written explanations accurately describe the adaptation. Partially labeled diagrams are included.	Written explanations partially describe the adaptation, but diagrams are unlabeled.	Written explanations fail to describe the adaptation and diagrams are missing.
Project Presentation	Presentation is thorough and well organized. Student demonstrates the adaptation using all three models.	Presentation is adequate. Student demonstrates the adaptation using two models.	Presentation is incomplete and disorganized. Student demonstrates the adaptation using a model.	The presentation is inappropriate and hard to follow. The student is unable to clearly demonstrate the adaptation.

What Is a Vertebrate? (pp. 82–86)

Objectives

After completing the lesson, students will be able to

◆ describe the main characteristics shared by all vertebrates and how vertebrates evolved;

◆ explain how vertebrates differ in the way they control body temperature.

1 Engage/Explore

◆ **Activating Prior Knowledge** Invite a volunteer to list all the kinds of vertebrates the student sees in a single day. Have them compare and contrast ways vertebrates and invertebrates are similar and ways they are different.

◆ **Discover** Help students understand the way the skeletal system provides support and gives shape to the body by comparing it to the ribs of an umbrella.

2 Facilitate

◆ **Demonstration** To help students visualize the notochord of chordates, show them a length of flexible garden hose.

◆ **Using the Visuals: Figure 2** Guide students in discovering which part of the endoskeleton is the backbone by instructing them to trace the cow skeleton from the neck until they come to where the tail begins.

◆ **Try This** Direct students to explore the flexibility of the backbone by creating a model with beads on a string.

◆ **Building Inquiry Skills: Relating Cause and Effect** Invite students to examine the insulating effects of feathers using down feathers insulating a small can.

◆ **Addressing Naive Conceptions** Explain to students that "coldblooded" animals are not always cold. Remind them that the temperature of an ectotherm can be greater than that of the typical endotherm. Elicit explanations to account for the rarity of land-dwelling ectotherms in cold regions.

◆ **Building Inquiry Skills: Inferring** Ask students why vertebrates may be better adapted to survive in many environments than are invertebrate chordates.

◆ **Using the Visuals: Figure 5** Help students understand the visual by asking them which evolved first, amphibians or reptiles. Also ask when mammals first evolved.

3 Assess

◆ **Section 1 Review** Check students' understanding of the characteristics of a vertebrate and how vertebrates differ in control of body temperature by having students answer the section review questions.

◆ **Performance Assessment** Have each student sketch a human skeleton and label its major structures. Then have each student decide whether the skeleton belongs to an ectotherm or an endotherm.

3

What Is a Vertebrate?

Guide for Reading

◆ What is the main characteristic shared by all vertebrates?

◆ How do vertebrates differ in the way in which they control body temperature?

3

Vertebrates are a subgroup within the phylum of animals known as **chordates.** All chordates share three characteristics: at some point in their development, they have a notochord, a nerve cord, and pharyngeal slits. A **notochord** is a flexible rod that supports the animal's back. In vertebrates, part or all of the notochord is replaced by a backbone. A few vertebrates have backbones made of **cartilage,** a tissue that is softer than bone, but flexible and strong. All chordates also have a nerve cord that runs down their backs. The nerve cord is the connection between the brain and the nerves. Also, chordates have pharyngeal slits, which are paired openings in the throat area, at some point in their lives.

Vertebrates have a backbone down the center of their backs. The backbone is formed by many similar bones called vertebrae (singular *vertebra*). **A vertebrate's backbone is part of an endoskeleton, or internal skeleton. The endoskeleton supports and protects the body, helps give it shape, and gives muscles a place to attach.** In addition to the backbone, the vertebrate's endoskeleton includes the skull, ribs, and in many cases, arm and leg bones. The skull protects the brain and sense organs. The ribs protect the heart and lungs.

One characteristic used to distinguish between the major groups of vertebrates is how they control body temperature. **Most fishes, amphibians, and reptiles have a body temperature that is close to the temperature of their environment. In contrast, birds and mammals have a stable body temperature that is typically much warmer than their environment.** Most fishes, amphibians, and reptiles are ectotherms. An **ectotherm** is an animal whose body does not produce much internal heat—its body temperature changes depending on the temperature of its environment. Birds and mammals are endotherms. An **endotherm** is an animal whose body controls and regulates its temperature by controlling the internal heat it produces and through adaptations such as fur, feathers, or sweat glands.

According to fossil evidence, the earliest vertebrates were fishes, which evolved about 530 million years ago. Later, amphibians developed from fishes, then reptiles developed from amphibians. Both mammals and birds are descended from reptiles. Birds were the latest group of vertebrates to arise, appearing about 150 million years ago. All vertebrates evolved from an invertebrate chordate ancestor. The pattern of vertebrate evolution looks something like the branching tree in Figure 5.

SECTION 3-1 **REVIEW AND REINFORCE**

What Is a Vertebrate?

◆ Understanding Main Ideas

Answer the following questions on a separate sheet of paper.

1. What three characteristics do all chordates share?

2. What is a vertebrate?

3. What are three functions of an endoskeleton?

4. In what order do scientists think the five main groups of vertebrates—
mammals, reptiles, fish, birds, and amphibians—developed? List the earliest
group first.

*State whether the following animals are ectotherms or endotherms. Write your
answer on the line provided.*

5. _____   **6.** _____   **7.** _____

◆ Building Vocabulary

From the list below, choose the term that best completes each sentence.

chordate   notochord   cartilage
ectotherm   endotherm   vertebra

8. The body of a(n) _____ doesn't produce much internal heat. Its
body temperature changes depending on the temperature of its environment.

9. The body of a(n) _____ controls and regulates its temperature.
Often its body temperature is higher than the temperature of its environment.

10. Some chordates keep the _____ all their lives, while others have
it only as larvae.

11. One of the bones of the spinal column is called a(n) _____ .

12. A notochord is made of _____ , the same material that the
human ear is made of.

13. Vertebrates are a subgroup of the phylum known as the _____
phylum.

Similar but Different

One of the characteristics that separate vertebrates from invertebrates is the presence of a backbone and endoskeleton. All vertebrates have an internal skeleton, but all vertebrate skeletons are not the same. Just as bodies of vertebrates vary in size and shape, so do vertebrate endoskeletons. Study the three diagrams of vertebrate skeletons below, and then answer the following questions.

3

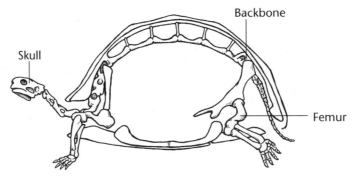

1. Look at the hind legs of the turtle and frog. Contrast the structures of the bone called the femur in both animals. Which animal's leg bones probably need to support a greater weight? How is this difference reflected in the bones' structures?

2. One function of an endoskeleton is to support the body against the downward pull of gravity. Which animal skeleton pictured above would have to support the least amount of weight? Explain your answer.

3. Do you think the turtle backbone allows as much movement as the backbone of the fish? Why or why not?

4. What bony body parts enable frogs and turtles to move on land? Can you see an adaptation for life in the water in the skeleton of the frog?

Fishes (pp. 87–94)

Objectives

After completing the lesson, students will be able to

◆ explain how fish use their gills, move, feed, and reproduce;

◆ name the three major groups of fishes;

◆ explain how fish provide food for people.

1 Engage/Explore

◆ **Activating Prior Knowledge** Encourage students to describe characteristics of fish they have observed.

◆ **Discover** Guide students' observations of a live aquarium fish so they notice the coordinated movements of the mouth and the gill flaps.

2 Facilitate

◆ **Addressing Naive Conceptions** Use the example of a carbonated beverage to help students understand that liquids can contain dissolved gases such as oxygen and carbon dioxide.

◆ **Sharpen Your Skills** Give students the opportunity to examine a preserved fish to see the connection between the mouth and the gill slits. Discuss the purpose of the feathery structure of the gills.

◆ **Real-Life Learning** Let students who have gone fishing share strategies they use to catch various types of fish.

◆ **Building Inquiry Skills: Applying Concepts** Challenge students to make inferences about the advantages and disadvantages of external and internal fertilization in fishes.

◆ **Using the Visuals: Figure 8** Direct the students to locate the mouth of the lamprey. Invite them to speculate how the specialized mouth aids the lamprey in feeding.

◆ **Building Inquiry Skills: Observation** Give chicken skeletons to students and guide them in distinguishing between the bones and cartilage.

◆ **Cultural Diversity** Using *cartilage* and *cartilaginous* as examples, have students find other examples of an adjective and noun sharing the same root.

◆ **Exploring a Bony Fish** As students study the visual essay, direct them to think of how the features described in the visual accomplish the functions that are described.

◆ **Integrating Physics** Explore the concepts of neutral buoyancy by inviting students to construct a model swim bladder using a balloon, string, and fishing weight.

◆ **Building Inquiry Skills: Observing** Allow students to conduct a scientific study of fish behavior in an aquarium or a fishpond. Give students a list of questions to direct their observations.

◆ **Integrating Environmental Science** Encourage students to brainstorm other ways that might be used to stop overfishing.

3 Assess

◆ **Section 2 Review** Check students' understanding of how fish use their gills and of the characteristics of the three major groups of fishes by having them answer the section review questions.

◆ **Performance Assessment** Assess students' understanding of the characteristics of fish by having them give a brief oral presentation about a particular species of fish.

Lab

◆ **Real-World Lab: How It Works** Guide students in building an aquarium for guppies. Lead students to see how an aquarium enables the fish to survive.

SECTION 3-2   **SECTION SUMMARY**

Fishes

3

Guide for Reading

◆ How do fish use their gills?

◆ What are the three groups of fishes?

A **fish** is an ectothermic vertebrate that lives in the water and has fins, which are structures used for moving. Most fishes obtain oxygen from the water through their gills and have scales. Scales are overlapping plates made of a hard substance. Nearly half of all vertebrate species are fishes. They evolved more than 500 million years ago.

Fishes get their oxygen from water. Water flows into a fish's mouth and over its gills. Gills contain many blood vessels. **As water flows over the gills, oxygen moves from the water into the fish's blood, while carbon dioxide, a waste product, moves out of the blood and into the water.**

Like all vertebrates, fishes have a closed circulatory system in which blood flows through blood vessels to all regions of the body. Most fishes have external fertilization.

Biologists classify fishes into three major groups: jawless fishes, cartilaginous fishes, and bony fishes. They are distinguished from one another by the structure of their mouths and the types of skeletons they have.

Jawless fishes have skeletons composed of cartilage. They have no scales, paired fins, or jaws. They feed by scraping, stabbing, and sucking their prey.

Sharks and their flat relatives—the rays and skates—are cartilaginous fishes. Their skeletons are made of cartilage, but unlike jawless fishes, they have scales, paired fins, and jaws. Cartilaginous fishes are carnivores.

Bony fishes make up 95 percent of all fish species. Exploring a Bony Fish shows the major characteristics of this group. Bony fishes have skeletons made of hard bone. The other major characteristics of bony fishes are tail fins, gills, paired fins, scales, a lateral line and a **swim bladder.**

A swim bladder is an internal gas-filled sac that helps a fish stabilize its body at different depths. The volume of gasses in the swim bladder affects the **buoyant force** on the fish. Buoyant force is the force that water exerts upward on any underwater object. By changing the volume of gas in its swim bladder, a bony fish adjusts its buoyancy and can float at different depths without using a large amount of energy.

Fishes are a valuable food resource for humans. Recently, overfishing has led to the decline of populations of some fishes. Some nations set limits on the amounts of certain fishes that can be caught. Also, some kinds of fishes are being raised in "fish farms."

SECTION 3-2   **REVIEW AND REINFORCE**

Fishes

◆ Understanding Main Ideas

Answer the following questions on a separate sheet of paper.

   1. What function do gills perform?

   2. How is the skeleton of a shark similar to the skeleton of a jawless fish?

   3. What are the three main groups of fishes?

   4. What kind of fertilization do most fish have?

   5. What is the function of a swim bladder?

   6. What is one way that people are trying to alleviate the problem of overfishing?

Determine whether each statement is true or false. If it is true, write true. If it is false, change the underlined word or words to make the statement true.

_____   **7.** Sharks are <u>bony</u> fishes.

_____   **8.** Fishes are <u>endotherms</u>.

_____   **9.** Fishes spend most of their time <u>hunting for food or feeding</u>.

_____   **10.** Most species of fishes belong to the <u>bony</u> fishes group.

◆ Building Vocabulary

Fill in the blank to complete each statement.

11. Most bony fishes have a gas-filled organ called a(n) _____ , which helps stabilize the fish at different levels in the water.

12. A balloonfish that swallows air will float because it weighs less than the _____ that water exerts upward against it.

Buoyancy in Fishes

You have learned that bony fishes use their swim bladders to adjust their buoyancy. Some fish have other methods to adjust or maintain their buoyancy, and still others have no method at all. Here is a summary:

◆ **No control:** The earliest fishes had no control over their buoyancy. Instead, they rested on the bottom and had to swim actively to rise off of it. Some modern fishes continue to live this way.

◆ **Oil:** The livers of many cartilaginous fishes make and store large amounts of oil. Because the oil is slightly more buoyant than water, its presence in the fish's tissues makes the entire fish more buoyant, so that it is easier for the fish to swim without sinking. Such fishes have very large livers.

◆ **Lungs:** Some fishes have lungs that are used to supplement the oxygen the fishes obtain from their gills. These lungs are connected to the esophagus. The esophagus is the tube that connects a fish's mouth to its stomach. The fishes get air by swimming to the surface and swallowing air. In addition to supplying oxygen, the air helps the fishes maintain buoyancy.

◆ **Swim bladder:** The swim bladder differs from lungs in that it is not connected to the esophagus. The fish inflates its swim bladder with gases removed from its bloodstream.

Write the method of buoyancy that each fish might use in the blank next to the number. For questions 5–7, write your answers on a separate sheet.

1. _____

2. _____

3. _____

4. _____

Fish live in many habitats. Questions 5–7 concern three of these habitats: (1) ponds that are low in oxygen; (2) near the surface of the ocean; and (3) thousands of meters deep in the ocean.

5. In which of these habitats would a lung not be a very useful way to adjust buoyancy? Explain.

6. In which of the habitats would a lung be a very useful adaptation? Explain.

7. In which of these habitats do you think it would be most important to maintain buoyancy? Explain.

Amphibians (pp. 95–100)

Objectives

After completing the lesson, students will be able to

◆ describe the characteristics of amphibians, their life cycle, and amphibian groups;

◆ explain how amphibians are adapted for movement on land and current threats to their survival.

1 Engage/Explore

◆ **Activating Prior Knowledge** Ask students to name animals they know that live both in water and on land during some part of their lives.

◆ **Discover** Have students explore the camouflage effect by displaying green and yellow dried peas on green construction paper.

2 Facilitate

◆ **Building Inquiry Skills: Inferring** Ask students to consider why water is essential for amphibian life and how amphibians' lives change after they acquire lungs.

◆ **Including All Students** Allow students to simulate the circulatory system of an amphibian by moving to stations representing the lungs, body, right atrium, left atrium, and ventricle. Use red balloons to represent oxygen.

◆ **Using the Visuals: Figure 15** Have students trace the stages of amphibian development, stating at least one difference between each pair of stages.

◆ **Language Arts Connection** Direct students as they write a guidebook that prepares tadpoles for life on land.

◆ **Try This** Have students experience the effect of webbed feet by enclosing their hands in plastic bags and moving them through water.

◆ **Including All Students** Have supervised students obtain additional information about frogs and toads from the Internet.

◆ **Addressing Naive Conceptions** Lead students to realize why touching a toad's skin will not cause warts.

◆ **Exploring a Frog** Guide students in comparing and contrasting this visual with that of *Exploring a Bony Fish* in Section 2.

◆ **Building Inquiry Skills: Relating Cause and Effect** Ask students to name animals other than the lungless salamander that absorb oxygen directly through their skin. Have students compare the sizes of these animals and discuss the size limitations of animals that breathe entirely through their skin.

◆ **Integrating Environmental Sciences** Have students research an amphibian that lives in their areas that is being threatened by loss of habitat.

3 Assess

◆ **Section 3 Review** Check students' understanding of amphibians' life cycles and how they are adapted for land by having them answer the section review questions.

◆ **Performance Assessment** Assess students' understanding of the life cycle of an amphibian by having students draw a diagram of the life cycle of a frog.

SECTION 3-3   **SECTION SUMMARY**

Amphibians

Guide for Reading

◆ What is the life cycle of an amphibian like?

◆ How are amphibians adapted for movement on land?

An **amphibian** is an ectothermic vertebrate that spends its early life in water. **After beginning their lives in water, most amphibians spend their adulthood on land, returning to water to reproduce.** Amphibian eggs hatch into larvae that swim and have gills for obtaining oxygen. Most adult amphibians have lungs rather than gills.

The circulatory system of adult amphibians has two loops. In the first loop, blood flows from the heart to the lungs and skin. In this loop blood picks up oxygen. In the second loop, the oxygen-rich blood flows to the rest of the body, where it delivers oxygen to body cells.

The hearts of most amphibians have three inner spaces, or chambers. The two upper chambers of the heart, called **atria** (singular *atrium*), receive blood. From the atria, blood moves into the lower chamber, the **ventricle,** which pumps blood out to the lungs and body.

Most frogs and toads have external fertilization. A female frog releases eggs into the water. Then the male's sperm fertilize the eggs. Most salamanders have internal fertilization. The eggs are fertilized inside the female's body before they are laid. Amphibian eggs are coated with clear jelly that keeps moisture in and helps protect them from infection. Frog larvae are called tadpoles and look very different from the adults. In contrast, the larvae of salamanders resemble adults.

Most adult amphibians have strong skeletons and muscular limbs adapted for movement on land. Frogs and toads have powerful hind-leg muscles for jumping. Some frogs have webbed feet that help them move through the water. Others have toe pads with adhesive suckers that help them climb and leap among twigs. Most adult frogs and toads are predators that feed on insects or other small animals. The skin of a frog is smooth and moist, while that of a toad is drier and bumpy.

Salamanders do not hop or jump as frogs do. Instead, they walk or run, and they catch their prey by stalking or ambushing it. Salamanders keep their tails as adults. Their bodies are long and usually slender. Most salamanders return to water each year to breed and lay their eggs.

Amphibian populations are declining all over the world. One reason is the destruction of their habitats. A **habitat** is the specific environment in which an animal lives. Other environmental factors, such as polluted water, are probably involved too.

Amphibians

◆ Understanding Main Ideas

Mark the diagram as directed.

1. Correctly label each stage of an amphibian's life—eggs, larva, adult.

2. Draw an X on the stage during which the amphibian breathes with gills.

3. Draw a circle around the life stage during which the amphibian breathes with lungs.

Answer the following questions on the back of this sheet or on a separate sheet of paper.

4. What are the two major groups of amphibians? Describe the characteristics of each group.

5. Identify two factors that are probably responsible for the decline in amphibian populations.

6. What are two adaptations amphibians have for moving on land?

◆ Building Vocabulary

Write an answer to the questions below in the spaces provided.

7. What are the main characteristics of amphibians?

_____

8. What is an animal's *habitat*?

_____

9. In the amphibian heart, what part is the *atrium* and what is it's function?

_____

10. In the amphibian heart, what part is the *ventricle* and what is it's function?

_____

SECTION 3-3   **ENRICH**

Amphibians Underground

All amphibians spend at least part of their lives in water. Their eggs are laid in water, and as adults they are susceptible to drying out. Surprisingly, some amphibians live in deserts, where it hardly ever rains.

The spadefoot toad of western North America is a master dry-land amphibian. For about nine months out of the year, it lives underground, sealed at the bottom of a burrow up to a meter deep in a state similar to hibernation. During this time, the toad does not eat anything and its metabolism slows. When it finally rains, the toads dig their way to the surface, eat, and lay eggs.

The spadefoot can survive underground by taking advantage of osmosis. Osmosis is the tendency of any liquid or gas to move into regions where it is less concentrated. Figure 1 shows a container of water, separated in half by a membrane. Water molecules can pass through the membrane, but salt particles cannot. Osmosis makes the water move from the side where it is more concentrated (i.e., fewer salt particles) to the side where it is less concentrated (more salt particles).

The spadefoot toad can absorb water from the surrounding soil through its skin by controlling the amount of salt particles in its own blood. Normally, the kidneys remove these salts from the blood so that the concentration of water in the blood is high. The salts are then expelled with the urine. While underground, the spadefoot's kidneys slow down, allowing the concentration of salt in the blood to increase to the point where even small amounts of water move from the soil into the body of the toad.

Answer the questions below on the back of this sheet or on a separate sheet of paper.

1. What would have to happen for the movement of water molecules pictured in Figure 1 to stop?

2. What would happen if the water were more highly concentrated in the spadefoot than in the surrounding soil?

3. Remember that urine contains water and salt. What two disadvantages would occur if the spadefoot were to expel urine while underground?

Reptiles (pp. 100–110)

Objectives

After completing the lesson, students will be able to

◆ describe some adaptations that allow reptiles to live on dry land;

◆ state how a reptile's egg is different from an amphibian's eggs;

◆ list and describe the major groups of reptiles.

1 Engage/Explore

◆ **Activating Prior Knowledge** After having students name characteristics of snakes, help them see which are myths and which are facts.

◆ **Discover** Allow students to simulate how a snake feeds by pulling a sock over a grapefruit.

2 Facilitate

◆ **Addressing Naive Conceptions** Allow students to touch the shed skin of a snake to discover that it is not slimy.

◆ **Building Inquiry Skills: Inferring** Allow students to model the membrane of an egg in order to discover the membrane's importance to the embryo.

◆ **Using the Visuals: Figure 13** To help students understand a reptile's two-loop circulation, refer them to Figure 13, which shows an amphibian's two-loop circulatory system.

◆ **Using the Visuals: Figure 18** Ask students to explain when and why a chameleon might change its color.

◆ **Exploring a Lizard** Challenge students to identify the characteristics iguanas and other vertebrates have in common.

◆ **Real-Life Learning** Arrange an opportunity for students to "meet a snake." Give students a checklist of key features to observe or have them write their own.

◆ **Addressing Naive Conceptions** Explain to students that some venomous snakes are relatively harmless to humans, and that venom is primarily an adaptation for capturing prey.

◆ **Using the Visuals: Figure 19** Point out that the kingsnake's color pattern mimics that of the venomous coral snake. Have students speculate on how this may benefit the kingsnake.

◆ **Including All Students: Demonstration** Have students observe how a turtle breathes.

◆ **Addressing Naive Conceptions** Explain that although they spend most of their time in water, sea turtles breathe like land-dwelling turtles.

◆ **Sharpen Your Skills** Guide students' interpretation of data regarding how incubation temperature affects the proportion of males to females in one species of alligator.

◆ **Addressing Naive Conceptions** Have students brainstorm characteristics of dinosaurs and evaluate their probable validity.

3 Assess

◆ **Section 4 Review** Check students' understanding of reptiles by having them answer the section review questions.

◆ **Performance Assessment** Assess students' understanding of reptile and amphibian adaptations by having students make compare/contrast tables.

Lab

◆ **Skills Lab: Interpreting Data** Allow students to examine and interpret data associated with an ectotherm while learning how some lizards control their body temperatures.

SECTION 3-4   **SECTION SUMMARY**

Reptiles

Guide for Reading

◆ What are some adaptations that allow reptiles to live on dry land?

◆ How is a reptile's egg different from an amphibian's egg?

3

A **reptile** is an ectothermic vertebrate that has lungs and scaly skin. Snakes, lizards, turtles, alligators, and crocodiles are all reptiles. Reptiles were the first vertebrates that were well adapted to live on land.

To live on land, an animal must be able to minimize water loss. **The eggs, skin, and kidneys of reptiles are adapted to conserve water.** Reptiles have dry, tough skin covered with scales that protects them and helps keep water in their bodies. The kidneys remove wastes from blood. The wastes are then excreted in a fluid called **urine.** Reptiles lose very little water in their urine.

The eggs of reptiles are fertilized internally. **Unlike an amphibian's egg, a reptile's egg has a shell and membranes that protect the developing embryo and keep it from drying out.** Most reptiles breathe entirely with lungs. Like adult amphibians, most reptiles have a three-chambered heart with two atria and one ventricle, and some mixing of oxygen-rich and oxygen-poor blood occurs.

Lizards usually are long and slender with long tails. Nearly all lizards are carnivores. Unlike snakes, lizards have external ears, movable eyelids, and most have four legs.

All snakes are carnivores. A snake's jawbones and skull bones can move to allow the snake to swallow an animal that is bigger around that it is. Some snakes kill their prey by injecting them with venom.

A turtle is a reptile whose body is covered by a protective shell. Some turtles can pull their legs and head into their shells for protection. While some turtles are carnivores, other turtles are herbivores. Turtles have sharp-edged beaks instead of teeth.

Alligators, crocodiles, and their relatives are the largest living reptiles. Alligators and crocodiles are carnivores that hunt mostly at night. Unlike most other reptiles, alligators and crocodiles care for their eggs and newly hatched young.

Reptiles, including dinosaurs, were the major form of vertebrate life on land from about 225 to 65 million years ago. Dinosaurs became extinct about 65 million years ago. Birds may be descended from dinosaurs.

Reptiles

◆ Understanding Main Ideas

Write the letter of the word or phrase that completes each statement.

1. Three adaptations that reptiles have for conserving water are
_____, _____, and _____.

2. The part of the egg that provides the reptile embryo with food is
called the _____.

3. Snakes have specialized _____ that enable them to eat large prey.

4. All reptiles breathe with _____.

5. Snakes look a lot like lizards, but snakes don't have _____ or
_____.

A. lungs

B. eyelids

C. eggs with shells

D. jaws

E. external ears

F. kidneys

G. yolk

H. thick skin

◆ Building Vocabulary

Write a definition for each of the following terms.

6. Reptile

_____

_____

_____

_____

7. Urine

_____

_____

_____

_____

How Snakes Get Around

Snakes can move in several different ways. There is no shape or texture of solid surface that snakes can't cross. Two types of snake movement are serpentine motion and linear motion.

◆ **Serpentine motion:** This is a very common way in which snakes move, and the fastest. The snake bends its body into curves. The outside rear part of each curve presses against surrounding objects, pushing the snake forward. The snake's head can easily be seen to move from side to side.

◆ **Linear motion:** The snake's body moves in a straight line, as if it were crawling. This is also called "caterpillar" motion. As the snake moves, small ripples of contracting muscles can be seen moving along its sides. At the same time, the broad belly scales grip against even tiny bumps or ridges on which the snake is crawling, in order to push the snake forward. A snake can't use linear motion on an extremely smooth or slippery surface, and it is only useful for moving slowly. A snake using linear motion is not easily seen.

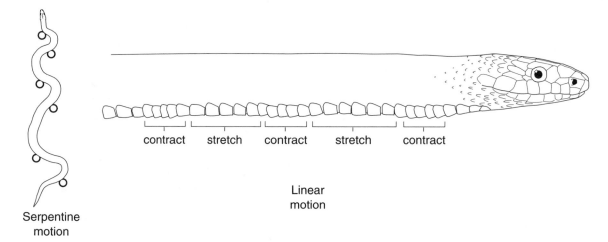

contract   stretch   contract   stretch   contract

Linear
motion

Serpentine
motion

Answer the following questions on a separate piece of paper.

1. Imagine that a small snake in a grassy yard sees you coming. Which type of motion would it probably use to move away quickly? Explain.

2. Which type of motion would a large snake probably use to sneak up on a motionless rabbit? Explain.

3. Which of the two kinds of motion would a snake have to use to move across deep water? Explain.

Integrating Earth Science
Vertebrate History in Rocks (pp. 111–114)

Objectives

After completing the lesson, students will be able to

◆ describe what scientists can learn from studying fossils.

1 Engage/Explore

◆ **Activating Prior Knowledge** Engage students' interest by having them describe fossils and infer about the organism that made the imprints and where it lived.

◆ **Discover** Give students hard and soft objects to use to make impressions in modeling clay. Lead students to notice what types of materials made the clearest impressions and also what information about the object the impression provides.

2 Facilitate

◆ **Including All Students** Allow students to simulate the effect of moving water on different sizes of rock fragments by shaking a jar of water that contains marbles, pea gravel, sand, and powdered clay. Ask students to observe the amount of time it took each type of material to fall out of suspension.

◆ **Building Inquiry Skills: Calculating** Have students consider the number of years it would take 4,000 m of limestone to accumulate at a rate of 1 cm every 50 years.

◆ **Science and History** Encourage students to add major events in world history to the timeline of major events in the history of vertebrate paleontology. Ask if they have heard of any recent paleontological discoveries that might be included in the timeline.

◆ **Real-Life Learning** Tell students that whole organisms may be preserved in materials such as ice, tar, and amber. Bring a piece of amber containing plant or animal remains to class for students to examine.

3 Assess

◆ **Section 5 Review** Check students' understanding of what scientists can learn from studying fossils by having them answer the section review questions.

◆ **Performance Assessment** Assess students' understanding of how fossils are formed by sediment by having students draw a flowchart showing the stages in the making of a fossil.

3

SECTION 3-5   **SECTION SUMMARY**

Vertebrate History in Rocks

A **fossil** is the hardened remains or other evidence of a living thing that existed a long time ago. A fossil can be an imprint in a rock, such as a footprint or outline of a leaf. Fossils can also be the remains of bones or other parts of living things. Very few organisms become fossils. Most just decay away.

Fossils usually occur in sedimentary rock. **Sedimentary rock** is made of hardened layers of sediments—particles of clay, sand, mud, or silt. Sediments can build up when muddy water stands still or when wind blows sand into dunes. Over a very long time, sediments can harden into rock. When a plant or animal dies and is buried by sediments, it is sometimes preserved as a fossil.

Paleontologists, the scientists who study extinct organisms, examine fossil structure and make comparisons to present-day organisms. **By studying fossils, paleontologists can infer how species changed over time.** Paleontologists use information gained from fossils to piece together the history of the major groups of vertebrates.

Paleontologists estimate the age of fossils. One way to do that is by studying the sedimentary rocks in which the fossils are found. Paleontologists know that the top layers of rock are usually younger than the bottom layers.

Radioactive chemical elements are also used to estimate the age of fossils. Over a long time, radioactive elements decay, or change into other elements. Scientists can measure the amount of the decayed element in the rock. The greater the amount of decayed element, the older the rock.

SECTION 3-5   **REVIEW AND REINFORCE**

Vertebrate History in Rocks

◆ Understanding Main Ideas

Answer the following questions on a separate sheet of paper.

1. How are sedimentary rocks formed?

2. What can paleontologists learn about present-day organisms from the study of fossils?

3. Describe two ways a paleontologist determines the approximate age of a fossil.

Use the diagram below to answer the question that follows.

4. Based on its position in the rock, which fossil is probably older? How do you know?

◆ Building Vocabulary

Write the term that best completes each sentence.

5. A _____ is a scientist who studies the remains or other evidence of things that lived in the past.

6. A _____ is the hardened remains or other evidence of organisms that died long ago.

7. Over many, many years, layers of clay, sand, mud, or silt may harden into

_____ .

SECTION 3-5   **ENRICH**

Telling Time with Fossils

Geologists (scientists who study rocks) use fossils to determine the age of the sedimentary rocks the fossils are found in. Each layer of rock will contain fossils of organisms living at that time. As time passes, some species die out or evolve into something else, many species survive, and some new species of animals appear. While the layers of rock contain many organisms similar to the layers above and below, a layer may also contain fossils not found in the layer above. Or it may contain other fossils not found in the layer below. So, each layer of rock has a set of fossils that is somewhat different from other layers. Geologists recognize that the set of all different fossils contained in a rock layer is like a fingerprint, identifying the time when the sediments forming that layer were deposited. Thus, geologists can determine the age of a rock layer and also tell that rocks in different parts of the world are the same age if they contain the same fossil "fingerprint."

The diagram below shows different layers of rock and the types of fossils found in them.

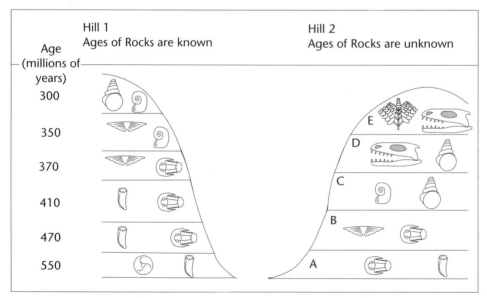

Answer the questions below on a separate sheet of paper.

1. Look at Hill 1. Many kinds of fossils are found in more than one layer, but do any two layers have all the same kinds of fossils? If so, which are they?

2. Which layer in Hill 1 is most similar to layer A in Hill 2?

3. Compare the fossil fingerprints of the layers in Hill 2 with those in Hill 1. About how old are layers A, B, and C, based on their fossils?

4. Assuming the layers of rock are in their original positions, is layer D older or younger than layer C?

CHAPTER 3   **REAL-WORLD LAB**

How It Works

Home Sweet Home

For an artificial environment to work, it must meet the needs of the organisms that live in it. In this lab, you will build an aquarium for guppies, whose natural environment is warm, fresh water.

◆ **Problem**   How does an aquarium enable a fish to survive?

◆ **Skills Focus**   making models, posing questions

◆ **Materials**

gravel
snails
tap water
aquarium filter
rectangular aquarium tank
(15 to 20 liters) with cover
metric ruler
guppy food
thermometer
aquarium heater
guppies
dip net
water plants

◆ **Procedure**

1. Wash the aquarium tank with lukewarm water—do not use soap. Then place it on a flat surface in indirect sunlight.

2. Rinse the gravel and spread it over the bottom of the tank to a depth of about 3 cm.

3. Fill the tank about two-thirds full with tap water. Position several water plants in the tank by gently pushing their roots into the gravel. Wash your hands after handling the plants.

REAL-WORLD LAB *(continued)*

4. Add more water until the level is about 5 cm from the top.

5. Place the filter in the water and turn it on. Insert an aquarium heater into the tank, and turn it on. Set the temperature to 25°C. **CAUTION:** *Do not touch electrical equipment with wet hands.*

6. Allow the water to "age" by letting it stand for 2 days. Aging allows chlorine to evaporate.

7. When the water has aged and is at the proper temperature, add guppies and snails to the tank. Include one guppy and one snail for each 4 liters of water. Cover the aquarium. Wash your hands after handling the animals.

8. Observe the aquarium every day for 2 weeks. Feed the guppies a small amount of food daily. Look for evidence that the fish and snails have adapted to their new environment. Also look for the ways they carry out their life activities, such as feeding and respiration. Record your observations on a separate sheet of paper.

9. Use a dip net to keep the gravel layer clean and to remove any dead plants or animals.

◆ Analyze and Conclude

Answer the following questions on the back of this sheet or on a separate sheet of paper.

1. How does the aquarium meet the following needs of the organisms living in it: (a) oxygen supply, (b) proper temperature, and (c) food?

2. What happens to the oxygen that the fish take in from the water in this aquarium? How is that oxygen replaced?

3. **Apply** How is an aquarium like a guppy's natural environment? How is it different?

◆ More to Explore

Write a plan for adding a different kind of fish to the aquarium. Include a list of questions that you would need to have answered before you could carry out your plan. Get the approval of your teacher before going ahead with your plan.

CHAPTER 3 | **SKILLS LAB**

Interpreting Data

Soaking Up Those Rays

In this lab, you will examine and interpret data associated with an ectotherm.

◆ **Problem** How do some lizards control their body temperatures in the extreme heat of a desert environment?

• **Suggested Materials**

paper
pencil

• **Procedure**

1. The data in the diagram below were collected by scientists studying how lizards control their body temperature. Examine the data.

2. Organize the data in the diagram by filling in the table, putting the appropriate information in each column. Begin by writing a brief description of each type of lizard behavior.

3. Complete the data table using the information in the diagram.

6 a.m.–7 a.m.

Emerging from burrow

Air temperature **20°C**

Top of rock **28°C**

Body temperature **25°C**

7 a.m.–9 a.m.

Basking

(lying on ground in sun)

Air temperature **27°C**

Top of rock **29°C**

Body temperature **32.6°C**

9 a.m.–12 p.m.

Active (moving about)

Air temperature **27°C**

Top of rock **30.8°C**

Body temperature **36.6°C**

SKILLS LAB (continued)

◆ Data Table

Activity	Description of Activity	Time of Day	Air Temp. (°C)	Ground Temp. (°C)	Body Temp. (°C)
1. Emerging					
2. Basking					
3. Active					
4. Retreat					
5. Stilting					
6. Retreat					

12 p.m.–2:30 p.m.	**2:30 p.m.–6 p.m.**	**6 p.m.–9 p.m.**
Retreat to burrow	*Stilting (belly off ground)*	*Retreat to burrow*
Air temperature **40.3°C**	Air temperature **34.2°C**	Air temperature **25°C**
Top of rock **53.8°C**	Top of rock **47.4°C**	Top of rock **26°C**
Body temperature **39.5°C**	Body temperature **39.5°C**	Body temperature **25°C**

SKILLS LAB *(continued)*

◆ Analyze and Conclude

Write your answers on the back of this sheet or on a separate sheet of paper.

1. How did the lizard's body temperature vary from 6 a.m. until 8 p.m.?

2. What are the three sources of heat that caused the lizard's body temperature to rise during the day?

3. During the hottest part of the day, what were the air and ground temperatures? Why do you think the lizard's temperature remained below 40°C?

4. Predict what the lizard's body temperature would have been from 8 p.m. to 6 a.m. Explain your prediction.

5. Based on what you learned from the data, explain why it is misleading to say that an ectotherm is a "coldblooded" animal.

6. Predict what would happen to your own body temperature if you spend a brief period outdoors in the desert at noon. Predict what your temperature would be if you spend time in a burrow at 7 p.m. Explain your predictions.

7. Think About It Why is it helpful to organize data in a data table before you try to interpret the data?

◆ More to Explore

Make one or more bar graphs of the temperature data. Explain what the graphs show you. How do these graphs help you interpret the data?

Bird Watch

The following steps will walk you through the Chapter 4 Project. Use the hints as you guide your students through planning, observing, recording data, and making presentations.

◆ Chapter Project Overview

◆ Before introducing the project, bring a bird identification guidebook to class and show the students how to use the book to identify birds. Show students how to use the range maps or a checklist of local birds to see if a bird is actually found in your area. Group students. Have them use field guides and checklists to make a list of birds commonly found in your area. Review different types of bird feeders and foods that birds eat.

◆ Have students read the project description in the text. Then distribute the Chapter 4 Project Overview, pages 104–105. Review and discuss the project rules to make sure students understand what is expected of them. Encourage students to ask questions. At this time, you may want to hand out the Chapter 4 Project Scoring Rubric, page 108, that you will use in evaluating students' work. Discuss the purpose of the project and your expectations of what the final product should include.

◆ Discuss methods for identifying and observing birds. Using binoculars may help students observe birds in detail, especially at the beginning of the project, but they are not necessary.

◆ Materials and Preparation

◆ Students can watch a feeder that is already in place. If they decide to install a bird feeder, they can use a ready-made one or build their own. Libraries and the Internet are good sources for suggestions on building bird feeders from inexpensive materials.

◆ The Cornell Lab of Ornithology is an excellent resource for teachers. Their projects include Cornell Nest Box Network, Project Pigeon Watch, and Project Feeder Watch. Get more information on these and other programs by mail from Cornell Laboratory of Ornithology, 159 Sapsucker Woods Road, Ithaca, NY 14850-1999, or on the World Wide Web at www.ornith.cornell.edu.

◆ Two widely available bird identification guides are *A Field Guide to the Birds*, by Roger Tory Peterson, and *Field Guide to the Birds of North America*, published by the National Geographic Society. In many cities, checklists of local birds are available from the chapters of the National Audubon Society. Donald and Lillian Stokes are authors of useful books on bird behavior: *A Guide to Bird Behavior, Volumes I, II, and III.*

◆ Bird seed can be purchased in bulk to save money.

◆ Birds can choke on peanut butter unless it is mixed with corn meal, grain, or sand.

◆ Establish a date for the final project presentation and interim dates for project tasks. Have students record these dates on their worksheet.

◆ Hand out Chapter 4 Project Worksheet 1, page 106, which helps students plan their bird feeder and its proper placement.

◆ Hand out Chapter 4 Project Worksheet 2, page 107, which provides a sample data table each student should copy into a project notebook. Worksheet 2 also describes some specific behaviors. At the completion of the observation phase of this project, students should use the questions on Worksheet 2 to help in analyzing their data.

◆ Check Your Progress— Section 1 Review

◆ Check that an adequate number of birds are coming to students' feeders. If there are problems, review that the placement and food are suitable and that the feeders are being observed at different times of the day.

◆ Encourage students to record what they actually observe at their feeders rather than ascribing human feelings or motivation to what they see.

◆ Check students' data sheets for correct bird identifications or adequate descriptions of the birds. Correct their misidentifications and review how to use field guides, checklists, and range maps.

◆ Remind students that their observation time should be long enough to note the interactions among the different species of birds and mammals. Students may observe that some species are usually dominant.

◆ Check Your Progress— Section 2 Review

◆ Check students' observation records on a regular basis. Be sure students include details about the feeding habits of different species of birds.

◆ Encourage students to draw the different beak shapes of birds that visit the feeder.

◆ Invite students to identify which type of food each bird species prefers to eat. Students can test this idea by separating different types of food and observing which food each type of bird eats.

◆ Check Your Progress— Section 4 Review

◆ Explain to students that analyzing their data means examining their records, summarizing their observations, finding patterns, and deciding what these patterns imply about the birds visiting their feeder.

◆ Remind students they will be presenting their findings to the class. Tell students that their presentations can be supported with drawings, graphs, details of bird behaviors, and any other interesting observations. Encourage students to be creative, as well as accurate.

◆ Chapter Project Wrap-Up

◆ After students give their presentations, group students and have them compare observations in order to identify similarities and differences in behaviors observed.

◆ Have students turn in any written work you require.

◆ Extensions/Options

◆ Interested students may want to set up specialized feeders to attract specific birds. Examples are hummingbird feeders, suet feeders, and thistle feeders. Birds are also attracted by birdbaths and dripping water.

◆ Interested students may want to set up birdhouses. Encourage students to research the requirements for different types of birds. Students can build birdhouses out of simple materials.

◆ Make a bar graph using data on bird numbers from the whole class to estimate which kinds of birds are most common in your area.

◆ Suggest that interested students continue their observations through the school year.

◆ Invite a member of the local chapter of the National Audubon Society to make a presentation on common and not-so-common birds or other topic to the class.

◆ If space and time are limited, you may want to keep a bird feeder at school and allow time during class for students to regularly observe the feeder.

◆ Rain will ruin birdseed. Suggest that students install a cover over their feeders if necessary.

◆ Some students may not have a practical place to put a bird feeder near where they live. Suggest that these students use the house of a relative or neighbor. If they do this, make sure they get permission before setting up the feeder.

◆ Allow students to work in pairs to observe the same feeder.

4

CHAPTER 4 PROJECT   OVERVIEW

CHAPTER 4

Bird Watch

For this project, you will choose an existing bird feeder or install your own to attract birds.

You will then identify and make a list of the different birds that come to your feeder. You will also observe interactions between birds and also between birds and any mammals at the feeder. Different kinds of birds may have different feeding behaviors and food preferences. Your observations will be recorded on data sheets. Later, you will analyze your observations, summarize what you have learned about the birds at your feeder. Finally, you report your findings to the class in a brief presentation.

◆ Project Rules

◆ Have your teacher approve your choice of bird feeder, whether it is an already established feeder or one you will put up yourself.

◆ Check the bird feeder daily and keep it clean and filled with birdseed.

◆ Make regular observations and take notes on what you observe.

◆ Suggested Materials

◆ If you are going to observe a feeder you put out yourself, you will need materials to construct the bird feeder, or you can buy or borrow a feeder already made.

◆ Bird feeders can be constructed from milk cartons, milk jugs, plastic bottles, or wood. Cut the carton or bottle in half to make a tray. Use string or a coat hanger to hang the feeder.

◆ In rainy areas, it may be helpful to make a cover to keep rain out of the seed tray. Punching small holes in the bottom of the feeder will also help drain any water that gets in the tray.

◆ Binoculars may be useful in making observations.

◆ You will need data tables in a notebook to record your observations.

◆ Project Hints

◆ Libraries and local birding clubs are good places to find information about birds in your area.

◆ If you install your own feeder, install it as soon as possible so birds can learn where it is.

CHAPTER 4 PROJECT OVERVIEW (*continued*)

◆ If you decide to build your feeder, you can choose from various materials and designs. The feeder does not need to be elaborate or expensive. The library is a good source for feeder designs.

◆ The feeder should be located so that you can easily observe it and keep it filled with food. You'll probably have more birds coming to your feeder it you put it near a tree or bushes for shelter. Have your teacher approve your feeder placement. Try to design and locate the feeder so squirrels cannot get to the food easily.

◆ Make your observations at various times of the day. You may find that some birds are more active at particular times.

◆ Your observations will include the date and time of observation and the kind of bird observed. If you don't know what kind of bird is at your feeder, write a description of the bird so you can identify it later. You will record whatever happens at your feeder: what food the birds eat, what happens when other birds are nearby, and whether the birds eat in groups or only individually. Also, list things that you think might affect a bird's behavior, such as the temperature and the weather.

◆ When trying to see which birds prefer which type of food, it may be helpful to add partitions to your feeder to separate the different kinds of food. By keeping track of which partitions are emptied first, you can infer which type of food is most popular. Suggestions for different foods are birdseed, sunflower seeds, breakfast cereal, and grains.

◆ There are many ways to present what you have learned. You might write a report, give an oral presentation, make labeled drawings on a poster, or record a summary on videotape.

4

◆ Project Time Line

Tasks	Date Due	Teacher's Initials
1. Bird feeder chosen, acquired, or constructed	_____	_____
2. Bird feeder location approved by teacher	_____	_____
3. Research of common area birds completed	_____	
4. Observation of birds feeding and interacting among themselves and with animals.	ongoing	
5. Bird and feeding observations completed	_____	
6. Analysis of observations completed	_____	
7. Presentation of observations	_____	

CHAPTER 4 PROJECT   **WORKSHEET 1**

Planning for Your Bird Feeder Observations

Use this worksheet to help you prepare for your bird feeder observations.

1. Research the birds of your area using field guides, the library, an encyclopedia, or the Internet. Make a list of common birds in your area.

2. Write down what books or other references you will use to identify the birds.

4

3. If you plan to make your own feeder, decide on a design. Make a list of materials needed.

4. If you will be installing your own bird feeder, make a sketch of the feeder you will use. Indicate on the sketch the kind of bird food, where the food goes, and any other important features of the feeder.

5. Research what is needed for a good location to hang your feeder. Whether you will be observing an existing feeder or putting up a new one, write a description of the location and whether it is safe for birds, easy to observe, easy to keep filled with birdseed, and difficult for other animals to get to.

CHAPTER 4 PROJECT   **WORKSHEET 2**

Recording Bird Feeder Observations

First, in your notebook, write a brief description of the bird feeder and its surroundings, such as height from the ground, distance from buildings, observer's
distance, and so on. A sketch would be helpful.

   Record your observations in a data table organized like the one below. If you
are unsure what kinds of birds you are watching, write down a description. Your
observations should include what a bird does by itself, such as eating or groom-
ing, and also behaviors that the bird does only when near other birds.

   As your observations continue, you may notice that certain behaviors are
repeated. After first describing the repeated behavior in your data table, you can
give it a name to make note-taking easier. For example, many birds make a display called "head-forward," in which one bird gets ready to peck another bird, but
the birds don't actually make contact. Other behaviors between birds include
"crest-raise" and "wing-droop." Make up your own names for different behaviors
you see.

4

Observer _____

Location _____

Date	Time	Bird(s)	Observations

◆ Analyzing and Presenting

*Complete the following tasks using a separate sheet of paper. When they have been
completed, you are ready to start planning your presentation.*

1. Write a few sentences which summarize your research methods. Describe the
   location and surroundings of the study site. Include the approximate distance
   between you and the feeder.

2. Write a paragraph or two, summarizing your observations from the data chart.

3. Decide how you want to communicate what you have learned to your
   classmates.

Bird Watch

In evaluating how well you complete the Chapter 4 Project, your teacher will judge your work in three categories. In each, a score of 4 is the best rating.

	4	3	2	1
Planning	Thoroughly researches local birds. Chooses an appropriate established bird feeder or chooses appropriate design and location for new feeder.	Adequately researches local birds. Chooses an appropriate established bird feeder or chooses an adequate design and location for new feeder.	Minimally researches local birds. Chooses an adequate established bird feeder or builds an adequate bird feeder and places it in a reasonable location.	Does little or no research about local birds. Bird feeder is inadequate or placement is poor.
Making Bird Observations	Makes more than 10 complete observation entries. Each entry includes what birds appeared, interactions, and foods eaten if appropriate. Applies chapter concepts to the observations.	Makes at least 7 complete observation entries. Each entry includes what birds appeared at the feeder, interactions, and foods eaten if appropriate.	Makes at least 3 observation entries. Data may be unorganized or incomplete.	Makes less than 3 observation entries. Entries may be unorganized or incomplete.
Presenting the Results	Makes a thorough, well-organized presentation. Written analysis of birds' behavior is thoughtful, well organized, and follows directly from the observation entries.	Presentation is adequate. Written analysis of birds' behavior is mostly complete, and follows directly from the observation entries.	Presentation is appropriate, but disorganized or hard to follow. Analysis of birds' behavior is incomplete.	Presentation is inappropriate and hard to follow. Written analysis is missing or unsupported by the bird observation data.

Animals

Birds (pp. 120–129)

Objectives

After completing the lesson, students will be able to

◆ identify the common characteristics of birds;

◆ explain how birds are adapted to their environments.

1 Engage/Explore

◆ **Activating Prior Knowledge** Challenge students to list expressions about birds and ask them whether these are scientifically valid.

◆ **Discover** Encourage students to examine a feather and observe what happens when the barbs are separated and rejoined.

2 Facilitate

◆ **Including All Students** Challenge student pairs to write definitions of endothermic, vertebrate, feathers, four-chambered heart, and egg-laying. Have them list three or four animals that share these characteristics.

◆ **Visual Arts Connection** Invite students to compare a specific bird's picture in The Birds of America with one in a field guide.

◆ **Integrating Physics** Guide students in testing the effectiveness of different insulators such as down feathers.

◆ **Including All Students** Encourage students who have difficulty seeing to model a gizzard with a jar and pebbles.

◆ **Exploring a Bird** Reinforce the information presented in the visual by directing students to consider the structures that help a bird fly.

◆ **Cultural Diversity** Describe to students examples of birds and feathers that appear in folklore of different cultures.

Lab

◆ **Skills Lab: Drawing Conclusions** Provide the opportunity for students to examine pellets coughed up by an owl allowing them to gather evidence and draw conclusions about its diet.

◆ **Inquiry Challenge** Emphasize the connection between vigorous physical activity and oxygen needs by having students check their pulse and breathing rates before and after physical activity.

◆ **Building Inquiry Skills: Observing** Let students observe birds outside to identify the senses the bird uses.

◆ **Demonstration** Demonstrate the strength of eggs by placing a heavy book on three eggs.

◆ **Try This** Have students examine a chicken egg with a hand lens.

◆ **Building Inquiry Skills: Classifying** Show students pictures of birds' legs and feet and direct them to classify the pictures into groups based on characteristics.

◆ **Exploring Birds** Lead students to see how the bill and feet of birds are adapted to help the bird survive.

◆ **Integrating Environmental Science** Emphasize to students the important roles birds play in helping to pollinate plants and eliminate pests.

3 Assess

◆ **Section 1 Review** Check students' understanding of section content by having them answer the section review questions.

◆ **Performance Assessment** Assess students' understanding of the characteristics of birds by having them select a type of bird and make a presentation describing their bird's appearance, habitat, and survival adaptations.

Birds

Guide for Reading

◆ What characteristics do birds have in common?

◆ How are birds adapted to their environments?

A bird is an endothermic vertebrate that has feathers and a four-chambered heart, and lays eggs. The bodies of birds are adapted for flight. For example, the bones of a bird's front limbs form wings. Many bones in the bird's body are hollow, which makes the skeleton light. Flying birds have large chest muscles. Finally, birds have feathers. Some modern birds cannot fly, but all modern birds evolved from ancestors that could fly.

All birds have feathers. A **contour feather** is a large feather that gives shape to a bird's body. The long contour feathers on the wings and tail are called flight feathers. When a bird flies, these feathers help it balance and steer. Birds also have short, fluffy **down feathers** specialized to trap air against the skin and keep the bird warm. Air is a good **insulator**—a material that does not conduct heat well and therefore helps prevent it from escaping.

Birds have no teeth. Instead, they have bills that are shaped according to the type of food they eat. For example, a finch has a short, thick bill that helps it crack open and eat seeds.

After a bird eats its food, digestion begins. Many birds have an internal storage tank, or **crop,** that allows them to store food inside the body after swallowing it. Birds also have a stomach where food is bathed in chemicals that help to break it down. This food then moves into a thick-walled, muscular part of the stomach, the **gizzard,** which squeezes and grinds the partially digested food.

Flying takes a lot of oxygen. Birds have a system of air sacs inside their bodies that connect to their lungs. Air sacs enable birds to get more oxygen from each breath than other animals can.

A bird's heart has four chambers—two atria and two ventricles. Because there is no mixing of oxygen-rich and oxygen-poor blood in a four-chambered heart, blood that arrives in the bird's tissues has plenty of oxygen.

Birds have internal fertilization and lay eggs. Bird eggs will develop only at a temperature close to the body temperature of the parent. Most parent birds care for their young at least until they are able to fly.

Birds are the most diverse land-dwelling vertebrates. **In addition to adaptations for flight, birds have adaptations—such as the shapes of their legs, claws, and beaks—for living in widely diverse environments.**

Birds play important roles in the environment. They act as pollinators, seed dispersers, and predators.

SECTION 4-1   **REVIEW AND REINFORCE**

Birds

◆ Understanding Main Ideas

Answer the following questions. Use the back of this sheet if you need more room.

1. What are four characteristics that all birds share?

_____

2. What are three adaptations that enable birds to fly?

_____

3. What are two functions of feathers?

_____

4. Briefly describe a bird's heart and circulatory system.

_____

5. Give two examples that show how the bills of birds allow them to live in diverse environments.

_____

4

◆ Building Vocabulary

From the list below, choose the term that best completes each sentence.

contour feather   insulator   crop
gizzard   down feather

6. A bird's food is stored in its _____ before it is digested.

7. A _____ is soft and used for insulation.

8. Air is a good _____ , which means it doesn't conduct heat well.

9. The _____ is a muscular, thick-walled part of a bird's stomach where partially digested food is ground up.

10. A _____ gives shape to a bird's body and helps a bird balance and steer during flight.

SECTION 4-1   **ENRICH**

What Does That Bird Do?

Birds come in different shapes, sizes, and colors. They also live in different habitats and eat different foods. Emperor penguins, for example, are nearly a meter tall and live in Antarctica. They can dive deeper than 200 m to catch the fish they eat, and they are protected from the bitter cold by dense feathers and an insulating layer of blubber.

Sometimes a bird's size, the shape of its bill, and other physical characteristics enable you to infer what a bird's habitat is like, what it eats, how it eats, or how it flies. Examine the drawings of the five birds shown below. All of them live in the United States. Note their characteristics.

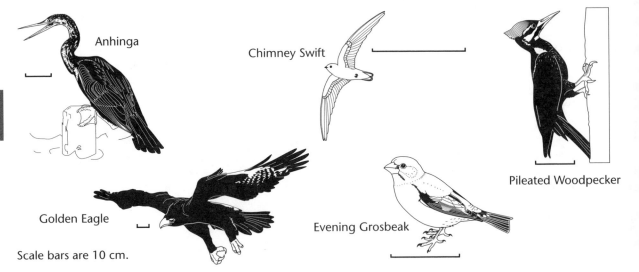

Scale bars are 10 cm.

Answer the questions below on a separate sheet of paper.

1. Make a chart with five columns to show the differences in bird size, bill size and shape, foot shape, and wing size and shape. Put the names of the birds in the first column. The headings of the other four columns should be "Bird Size," "Bill Size and Shape," "Foot Shape," and "Wing Size and Shape." Some of the information about the birds can't be determined from the drawings, so you won't be able to fill in the entire chart.

2. For each bird, use the chart of characteristics and make one inference about the bird. Include the reason for each inference. For example, the evening grosbeak probably flies mainly by flapping because it has small wings.

Integrating Physics
The Physics of Bird Flight (pp. 130–132)

Objectives

After completing the lesson, students will be able to

◆ explain how a bird is able to fly.

1 Engage/Explore

◆ **Activating Prior Knowledge** Guide students to notice the differences in the flight of birds they have seen fly before. Encourage them to speculate how some birds seem to fly without putting forth any effort at all.

◆ **Discover** Allow students to simulate air flowing over the wing of an airplane or bird using a book and strip of paper. Lead students to see how the air flowing across the top of a wing lifts the airplane or bird.

2 Facilitate

◆ **Using the Visual: Figure 6** Emphasize that the high pressure under the wing creates an upward force. Guide students to trace the air flow in the figure with their fingers.

◆ **Try This** Encourage students to design a paper airplane with wings shaped like those of a bird. Guide them to discover how wing shape is important for flight. Have them assess which designs were most successful.

◆ **Addressing Naive Conceptions** Help students understand that a bird's flapping is not a simple up and down movement. Point out the differences between the movements of the upward strokes and downward strokes and how they affect the movement of the bird.

3 Assess

◆ **Section 2 Review** Check students' understanding of section content by having them answer the section review questions.

◆ **Performance Assessment** Assess students' understanding of how a bird is able to fly by having them draw and label the wing of a flying bird. Tell them to show the direction in which the air moves over the wing using arrows, and clearly label areas of high and low pressure.

4

The Physics of Bird Flight

Guide for Reading

◆ How is a bird able to fly?

4

Birds that fly are lightweight. Also, their wings have a special shape. Air is a mixture of gas molecules which exert pressure on the objects they surround. Moving air exerts less pressure than air that is not moving. The faster air moves, the less pressure it exerts. With birds and airplanes, the lower surface of the wing is flatter than the upper surface of the wing. This means that the curved upper surface of a wing is a little longer than the flatter lower surface. When the wing moves forward, air travels the longer distance over the top of the wing in the same amount of time as it takes air to travel the shorter distance under the wing.

Since fast-moving air over a wing exerts less pressure than air that is moving slowly, the air above the wing exerts less pressure than does the air beneath the wing. **The difference in pressure above and below the bird's wing produces an upward force that causes the wing to rise.** That upward force is called **lift.**

However, wing shape alone does not enable birds to fly. They must get off the ground. To get off the ground, birds push off with their legs as they pull their wings down. The downstroke provides the power that pushes birds forward and upward.

Birds fly in a variety of ways. Some, like sparrows, flap nearly constantly. Others, like vultures and albatrosses, will glide or soar without flapping after they get in the air. When birds glide, they coast downward through the air. When birds soar, they rise up into the sky on currents of warm air.

SECTION 4-2   **REVIEW AND REINFORCE**

The Physics of Bird Flight

◆ Understanding Main Ideas

1. The diagram below shows the wing on a bird that is moving from left to right. Indicate on the diagram the area of lower air pressure and the area of higher air pressure.

Answer the following questions.

2. What in air causes air pressure?

3. How is the speed of moving air related to its air pressure?

4. Classify the three types of flying—flapping, gliding, and soaring—as using either a lot of energy or not much energy.

_____

_____

_____

5. Which do you think would experience more lift, the wing of a slow-flying bird or the wing of a fast-flying bird? Explain your reasoning.

_____

◆ Building Vocabulary

Write a definition for the following term.

6. lift

_____

_____

SECTION 4-2   **ENRICH**

How Do They Do That?

Hummingbirds are tiny birds, often just 8 to 10 cm long or smaller, that can *hover*—they can stay in one place in the air by flapping their wings rapidly. They flap so fast, 50 or 60 times a second, that their wings become a blur.

When any bird flies forward, its wings flap up and down. By pushing against air, the downstroke of the wing moves the bird forward and helps to keep the bird up. The function of the upstroke is simply to prepare the wing for another downstroke.

Hummingbirds use their wings differently when they hover than when they are flying forward. They don't just flap their wings up and down, they move them in a figure-eight pattern, with the "eight" lying on its side. The wings actually move forward and backward as well as up and down. In this way, both the downstroke and the upstroke serve to keep the bird aloft.

Make two giant hummingbird wings out of stiff paper and two dowel rods. Attach the long side of each paper wing to a dowel rod, so that it hangs down, as indicated in the diagram. Holding your arm out horizontal to the side, label the front of each wing "A" and the back "B". While walking forward, hold the dowel rods out and slowly "flap" the wings like a bird would in forward flight. Then stand still and flap them as shown in the diagram—in a horizontal figure-eight motion like the hummingbird does when it's hovering.

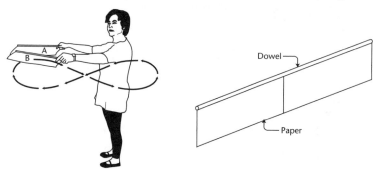

Answer the following questions on a separate sheet of paper.

1. When you flapped the wings as in normal forward flight, which side of the wing faced down on the downstroke? Did that side face down on the upstroke, too?

2. When you flapped the wings as in hovering flight, which side faced down on the forward stroke? Did that side face down on the backward stroke, too?

3. Hummingbirds feed on the nectar of flowers. How might the ability to hover be an advantage to the hummingbird?

What is a Mammal? (pp. 133–140)

Objectives

After completing the lesson, students will be able to

◆ describe the characteristics all mammals share.

1 Engage/Explore

◆ **Activating Prior Knowledge** Engage students' interest in mammals by encouraging them to discuss what their pets look like and any special experiences they've had with their pets.

◆ **Discover** As students examine the shapes of their teeth, lead them to see the advantages of the different shapes.

2 Facilitate

◆ **Building Inquiry Skills: Inferring** Guide students to infer some advantages to being a small animal living during the time of the dinosaurs.

◆ **Cultural Diversity** Describe some uses of domesticated mammals that various cultures rely on their daily lives.

◆ **Building Inquiry Skills: Comparing and Contrasting** Show students pictures of different mammals and ask them if there are some kinds of hair that all the mammals have.

◆ **Try This** Let students discover fat as an insulator by sticking a shortening-coated and noncoated rubber glove into icy water.

◆ **Including All Students** Emphasize the differences in herbivores and carnivores teeth and jaws by showing students jaw models.

◆ **Building Inquiry Skills: Observing** Have students observe the movement of their diaphragms as they breathe in and out.

◆ **Inquiry Challenge** Provide students with orange peels, cloves, vanilla extract, and blindfolds. Instruct students to design an experiment to answer a question about the senses using the materials.

◆ **Sharpen Your Skills: Classifying** Have students examine the diagram and decide if bats are more closely related to birds or to humans.

◆ **Building Inquiry Skills: Comparing and Contrasting** Show students photos of mammals with interesting styles of movement. Ask them to infer what adaptations each animal has that helps or affects its movement.

◆ **Addressing Naive Conceptions** Ensure students realize that young mammals are more likely to survive because they receive protection and food from a parent.

3 Assess

◆ **Section 3 Review** Check students' understanding of section content by having them answer the section review questions.

◆ **Performance Assessment** Assess students' understanding of the characteristics of mammals by having them sketch a mammal, label its body parts, and list the characters unique to mammals.

Lab

◆ **Real World Lab: You, the Consumer** Challenge students to test the claim that wool keeps you warm when dry or wet.

Science and Society

◆ **Animals and Medical Research** Have students list the benefits and drawbacks of using or not using animals in medical research.

4

What Is a Mammal?

Guide for Reading

◆ What characteristics do all mammals share?

Mammals are a diverse group of vertebrates that share many characteristics. **All mammals are endothermic vertebrates with a four-chambered heart, and skin covered with fur or hair. The young of most mammals are born alive, and every young mammal is fed with milk produced in its mother's body.** In addition, mammals have teeth of different shapes that are adapted to the type of food they eat.

The earliest mammals were small, mouse-sized animals that lived in habitats dominated by dinosaurs. Large mammals first evolved after the dinosaurs disappeared.

All mammals have fur or hair at some point in their lives. Thick fur provides lightweight insulation that prevents body heat from escaping. Mammals that live in cold climates usually have thicker fur than mammals that live in warm climates.

Most mammals have teeth of four different shapes to tear and chew their food. **Incisors** are flat-edged teeth used to bite off and cut parts of food. **Canines** are sharply pointed teeth that stab food and tear into it. **Premolars** and **molars** grind and shred food into tiny bits.

Mammals breathe with lungs. Mammals breathe in and out because of the combined action of rib muscles and a large muscle called the **diaphragm** located at the bottom of the chest. The lungs have a huge, moist surface area where oxygen can dissolve and then move into the bloodstream. Mammals have a four-chambered heart and a two-loop circulatory system like birds. One loop of the circulatory system carries blood from the heart to the lungs and back to the heart. The other loop carries blood to the rest of the body and back to the heart.

The brains of mammals enable them to learn, remember, and behave in complex ways. The senses of mammals are highly developed and adapted for the ways that individual species live. For example, many mammals that are active at night have eyes adapted for seeing in the dark. Most mammals also have highly developed senses of smell and hearing.

Mammals have internal fertilization. Some mammals lay eggs, but the young of most mammals develop inside their mothers' bodies. All mammals feed their young with milk produced in **mammary glands.** Young mammals usually stay with their mother or both parents for an extended time.

What Is a Mammal?

◆ Understanding Main Ideas

Answer the following questions.

1. What are four characteristics shared by all mammals?

_____

_____

2. If a mammal has a dense coat of fur, what might you infer about the climate where that mammal lives?

_____

3. Where in a mammal's body does oxygen enter the bloodstream?

_____

4. Briefly describe a mammal's heart and circulatory system.

_____

_____

5. What information can you infer from the size and shape of a mammal's teeth?

_____

_____

◆ Building Vocabulary

From the list below, choose the term that best completes each sentence.

canine   molar   premolar   diaphragm
mammal   incisor   mammary gland

6. _____ teeth are used to stab and tear into food.

7. _____ teeth are used to bite off and cut parts of food.

8. _____ and _____ teeth are used to grind and shred food into tiny bits.

9. A large muscle called the _____ helps mammals breathe.

10. The _____ is a structure in which milk is produced for the young.

11. Every _____ has hair or fur, but sometimes not very much.

SECTION 4-3   **ENRICH**

Identifying Mammal-like Fossils

Many of the characteristics that scientists use to identify an animal as being
a mammal are seldom or never preserved as fossils. Some of these are a four-
chambered heart, skin covered with fur or hair, and giving birth to live young. So
how do paleontologists recognize the fossils of mammals and their close relatives?

Not surprisingly, paleontologists use characteristics of the skeleton to identify
both mammals and their "mammal-like reptile" relatives. For example, Figure 1
shows the skull of the very early "mammal-like reptile" *Dimetrodon*. Like most
other vertebrate skulls, it has paired openings in the front for nostrils and near
the middle for eyes. Unlike most vertebrates, it also has an extra paired opening
at the back of the skull, behind the eye. This opening is an adaptation that makes
room for the jaw muscles that fill the back of the skull to bulge outward, allowing
the animal to bite harder. It is a characteristic found both in living mammals and
in their extinct relatives.

4

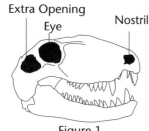

Extra Opening
Eye   Nostril

Figure 1

A

B   C

Figure 2

*Study Figure 2 and fill in the table, answering "yes" or "no." Then answer the
questions below on the back of this sheet or on a separate sheet of paper.*

Specimen	Nostril opening present?	Eye opening present?	Extra opening behind eye present?
A			
B			
C			

1. Based on the information you have recorded in the table, which of the skulls in
   Figure 2 do you think belong to mammals or "mammal-like reptiles"? Why?

2. What other characteristic of mammals do you see in the skulls in Figure 2?
   Does this characteristic appear in all of the specimens, or only in mammals
   and "mammal-like reptiles"?

Diversity of Mammals (pp. 141–146)

Objectives

After completing the lesson, students will be able to

◆ identify the characteristic used to classify mammals as monotremes, marsupials, or placental mammals.

1 Engage/Explore

◆ **Activating Prior Knowledge** After having students list methods for the development of young animals, lead them to conclude that mammals can be classified based on their adaptations for the development of their young.

◆ **Discover** Encourage students to discover the advantage of having thumbs by immobilizing their thumb for 5 minutes while they do everyday activities which normally utilizes their thumb.

2 Facilitate

◆ **Using the Visuals: Figure 12** Have students study the photographs to see what characteristics make the animals look different from each other. Lead students to realize the important characteristic they have in common—laying eggs—can't be seen. Guide students to understand that mammals are classified into different groups based on how their young develop, not how the adults look.

◆ **Building Inquiry Skills: Inferring** Encourage students infer the functions of a female marsupial's pouch.

◆ **Building Inquiry Skills: Observing** Obtain a breeding pair of mice so students can observe the reproduction and development of placental mammals in the classroom. Encourage students to make predictions about how the parents will care for their offspring.

◆ **Exploring Placental Mammals** Organize students into small groups so that they can share any observations they make about the mammals in *Exploring Placental Mammals*. Direct students to make flash cards with the name of each mammal along with several of its observable characteristics.

◆ **Inquiry Challenge** Instruct students to cut out pictures of mammals from magazines and infer in which of the groups shown in *Exploring Placental Mammals* it belongs.

◆ **Addressing Naive Conceptions** Stress the fact that bats and dolphins are mammals, not birds or fish, because they nurse their young.

◆ **Including All Students** Remind students that the English word *mammal* comes from the same Latin root as the word *mammary*. Discuss words in other languages used for mammal and try to identify any root word similarities.

3 Assess

◆ **Section 4 Review** Check students' understanding of section content by having them answer the section review questions.

◆ **Performance Assessment** Assess students' understanding of the characteristics used to classify mammals as monotremes, marsupials, or placental mammals by directing them to create a flowchart.

4

Diversity of Mammals

Guide for Reading

◆ What characteristic is used to classify mammals into three groups?

4

Members of the three groups of mammals—monotremes, marsupials, and placental mammals—are classified on the basis of how their young develop.

Monotremes are mammals that lay eggs. There are only two types of monotremes—the spiny anteater and the duck-billed platypus. Spiny anteaters are monotremes that look like pincushions with long noses. A female spiny anteater lays one to three leathery-shelled eggs directly into the pouch on her belly. The young drink milk and stay in the pouch until they are six to eight weeks old.

Duck-billed platypuses are the other type of monotreme. They have webbed feet, a bill, fur, and milk glands. The female lays her eggs in an underground nest. The offspring drink mother's milk and dig their way out of the nest when they are about six weeks old.

Marsupials are mammals whose young are born alive but are at an early stage of development. The babies usually continue to develop in a pouch on their mother's body. Opossums and kangaroos are marsupials.

Marsupials usually have a very short **gestation period,** the length of time between fertilization and birth. Newborn marsupials are tiny, blind, hairless, and pink. They remain in the pouch at least until they are big enough to peer out of the pouch opening.

Unlike a monotreme or a marsupial, a **placental mammal** develops inside its mother's body until its body systems can function independently. The name of this group comes from the **placenta,** an organ in pregnant female mammals that passes materials between the mother and the developing embryo. Food and oxygen pass from the mother to her young through the placenta. Wastes pass from the young through the placenta to the mother. The umbilical cord connects the young to the placenta. Most mammals, including humans, are placental mammals.

Placental mammals are classified into groups on the basis of characteristics such as how they eat, how they move, and where they live. Two examples of groups of placental mammals are carnivores and primates.

The gestation period of placental mammals varies with the animal group. Generally, the larger the placental mammal, the longer will be its gestation period.

Diversity of Mammals

◆ Understanding Main Ideas

Write the following characteristics on the lines in the concept map:

    All have a pouch   Feed young milk

    All lay eggs   Have relatively long gestation period

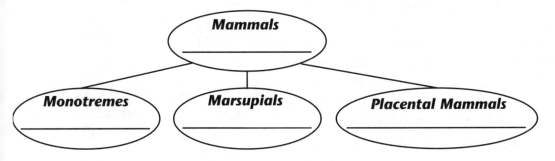

◆ Building Vocabulary

From the list below, choose the term that best completes each sentence.

    gestation period   marsupial   monotreme

    placenta   placental mammal

1. The organ through which materials pass between a pregnant female mammal and the developing embryo is a _____ .

2. Mammals that lay eggs belong to the _____ group.

3. A _____ develops inside its mother's body until its body systems can function independently.

4. The length of time between fertilization and birth is called the

    _____ .

5. A _____ carries its young in a pouch.

Limbs for Speed and Limbs for Strength

Animals' bodies are living things, but they are also machines. An animal's abilities depend on the shapes, sizes, and positions of its parts.

Fig. 1
Fulcrum
Out-lever arm   In-lever arm   A
B

Levers are simple machines that change the direction of a force. A seesaw is an example. Imagine a seesaw (Figure 1) with one side slightly longer than the other. Pushing down on one end (A) causes the seesaw to rotate around a *fulcrum*. This makes the other end (B) move up. In this case, end B moves farther and faster than end A does. The distance from the fulcrum to end A is the *in-lever arm* and from the fulcrum to end B is the *out-lever arm*.

Fig. 2   Fig. 3

O   I   O   I

You can learn about the speed and strength of an out-lever arm by dividing its length by the length of the in-lever. A high ratio says it will move fast, but it will not be as strong. A small ratio says it will move slowly but it will be strong. Imagine two seesaws. One has a very long out-lever arm and the other has a very short one. If you push their in-levers equal distances, the long out-lever would move faster, but it would be easier to stop with your hand. It would be fast but weak. The seesaw with the short out-lever would be slow but strong.

Fig. 4   Fig. 5

I
O   I
O

I = In-lever arm
O = Out-lever arm

The limbs of animals are also levers. Like the seesaw, they can be fast and weak or slow and strong. The limbs of fast-moving mammals like deer have high ratios of lever arm length. Slow-moving mammals with very powerful digging limbs have low ratios.

Answer the questions below on a separate sheet of paper.

1. Measure the in-lever arms and out-lever arms shown in Figures 2 through 5 in millimeters and calculate the ratios of out-lever arm to in-lever arm lengths for each.

2. Figures 2 and 3 show the leg bones of two mammals. Which one do you think would be able to run faster? Why?

3. Figures 4 and 5 show the shoulder and upper arm bones of two species of cat. Which do you think would be able to run faster? Why?

4. In Figures 4 and 5, which arm do you think could be moved with more power? (Assume the cats are the same size.)

5. Compare the arrangement of lever arms and fulcrum in the legs in Figures 2 and 3 with that of the arms in Figures 4 and 5. How are they different?

CHAPTER 4   **SKILLS LAB**

Drawing Conclusions

Looking at an Owl's Leftovers

In this lab, you will gather evidence and draw conclusions about an owl's diet.

◆ **Problem**   What can you learn about owls' diets from studying the pellets that they cough up?

◆ **Materials**

owl pellet
metric ruler
hand lens
forceps
dissecting needle

◆ **Procedure**

1. An owl pellet is a collection of undigested materials that an owl coughs up after a meal. Write a hypothesis describing what items you expect an owl pellet to contain. List the reasons for your hypothesis.

2. Use a hand lens to observe the outside of an owl pellet. Record your observations.

3. Use one hand to grasp the owl pellet with forceps. Hold a dissecting needle in your other hand, and use it to gently separate the pellet into pieces. **CAUTION:** *Dissecting needles are sharp. Never cut material toward you; always cut away from your body.*

4. Using the forceps and dissecting needle, carefully separate the bones from the rest of the pellet. Remove any fur that might be attached to bones.

5. Group similar bones together in separate piles. Observe the skulls, and draw them. Record the number of skulls, their length, and the number, shape, and color of the teeth.

6. Use the chart on the next page to determine what kinds of skulls you found. If any skulls do not match the chart exactly, record which animal the skulls resemble most.

Animals   Teaching Resources   **B ◆ 125**

SKILLS LAB *(continued)*

7. Try to fit together any of the remaining bones to form complete or partial skeletons. Sketch your results.

8. Wash your hands thoroughly with soap when you are finished.

Shrew   House mouse   Meadow vole   Mole   Rat

Shrew	House Mouse	Meadow Vole	Mole	Rat
Upper jaw has at least 18 teeth; tips of the teeth are brown	Upper jaw has 2 biting teeth and extends past lower jaw.	Upper jaw has 2 biting teeth that are smooth, not grooved.	Upper jaw has at least 18 teeth.	Upper jaw has 2 biting teeth. Upper jaw extends past lower jaw.
Skull is 23 mm or less.	Skull length is 22 mm or less.	Skull length is 23 mm or more.	Skull length is 23 mm or more.	Skull length is 22 mm or more.

4

Record your observations in the space below .

SKILLS LAB *(continued)*

◆ Analyze and Conclude

Write your answers on the back of this sheet or on a separate sheet of paper.

1. How many animals' remains were in the pellet? What data led you to that conclusion?

2. Combine your results with those of your classmates. Which three animals were eaten most frequently? How do these results compare to your hypothesis?

3. Owls cough up about two pellets a day. Based on your class's data, what can you conclude about the number of animals an owl might eat in one month?

4. **Think About It** In this lab, you were able to examine only the part of the owl's diet that it did not digest. How might this fact affect your confidence in the conclusions you reached?

◆ More to Explore

Design a study that might tell you how an owl's diet varies at different times of the year. Give an example of a conclusion you might expect to draw from such a study.

4

CHAPTER 4

Keeping Warm

Any time you wear a sweater or socks made of wool, you are using a mammalian adaptation to keep yourself warm. Suppose a manufacturer claims that its wool socks keep your feet as warm when the socks are wet as when they are dry. In this investigation, you will test that claim.

◆ **Problem**   Do wool products provide insulation from the cold? How well does wool insulate when it is wet?

◆ **Skills Focus**   controlling variables, interpreting data

◆ **Materials**

hot tap water
beaker, 1-L
clock or watch
a pair of wool socks
graph paper

tap water, room temperature
3 containers, 250-mL, with lids
scissors
3 thermometers

◆ **Procedure**

1. Put one container into a dry woolen sock. Soak a second sock with water at room temperature, wring it out so it's not dripping, and then slide the second container into the wet sock. Both containers should stand upright. Leave the third container uncovered.

2. Use scissors to carefully cut a small "X" in the center of each lid, making the X just large enough for a thermometer to pass through.

3. Fill a beaker with about 800 mL of hot tap water. Then pour hot water nearly to the top of each of the three containers. **CAUTION:** *Avoid spilling hot water on yourself or others.*

4. Place a lid on each of the containers, and insert a thermometer into the water through the hole in each lid. Gather the socks around the thermometers above the first two containers so that the containers are completely covered.

5. Immediately measure the temperature of the water in each container, and record it in the data table. Take temperature readings every 5 minutes for at least 15 minutes.

REAL-WORLD LAB *(continued)*

◆ Data Table

	Starting Temperature	5 Minute Temperature	10 Minute Temperature	15 Minute Temperature
Dry Sock Container				
Wet Sock Container				
No Sock Container				

◆ Analyze and Conclude

4

Answer the following questions on the back of this sheet or on a separate sheet of paper.

1. Graph your results using a different color to represent each container. Graph time in minutes on the horizontal axis and temperature on the vertical axis.

2. Compare the temperature chages in the three containers. Relate your findings to the insulation characteristics of mammal skin coverings.

3. **Apply** Suppose an ad for wool gloves claims that the gloves keep you warm even if they get wet. Do your findings support this claim? Why or why not?

◆ More to Explore

Design an experiment to compare how wool's insulating properties compare with those of other natural materials (such as cotton) or manufactured materials (such as acrylic). Obtain your teacher's approval before conducting your experiment.

Learning New Tricks

The following steps will walk you through the Chapter 5 Project. Use the hints as you guide your students through planning, animal observations, and presentations.

◆ Chapter Project Overview

◆ Before you introduce the project, bring an animal into the classroom and show the students a conditioned response that it knows. Talk about who trained the animal, how it was trained, and any difficulties encountered during the training process.

◆ Have students read the Chapter 5 Project Overview, pages 132–133. Review the project's rules, and hand out the Chapter 5 Scoring Rubric, page 136, that you will use for scoring students' work. Discuss with students what will be expected of them.

◆ Explain to students that a required part of the project is to observe their chosen animals before training them to find out whether and how often the behavior they want to teach is already performed by the untrained animals. Make it clear that students are training their animals to respond to a stimulus with a behavior. In the case of pets, students should test to be sure that the animals do not already know the new skill.

◆ Set a deadline for the project presentation and interim dates for the Check Your Progress at the end of Section 1 and Section 3. Encourage students to copy the appropriate dates in the Project Time Line.

◆ Distribute Chapter 5 Project Worksheet 1. This worksheet will help students to think about possible project ideas. You might want to have students work together in groups so that they can brainstorm possible ideas. Review students' ideas to clarify any misconceptions.

◆ Distribute Chapter 5 Project Worksheet 2. Completion of steps 1–4 prepares students for making the Training Plan. Steps 5–7 are the Training Plan itself. In step 8, the students decide how they will present the results of the training to the class. You should look over the completed worksheet before allowing the student to begin the animal training. Make sure the project poses no danger to the student or the animal. Also make sure the project is reasonable and that it is possible for the animal to learn the proposed behavior.

◆ Material and Preparation

◆ Make sure students are not exposed to animals they are allergic to.

◆ Students who train an animal belonging to another person must have the owner's permission. If the owner is a child, an adult must be present during training.

◆ Check Your Progress— Section 1 Review

◆ Review students' training plans. Make sure the expectations they have of their animals' learning abilities are reasonable.

◆ Check that students have scheduled specific training times and dates, and that rewards they have chosen for their animals will not cause the animals harm. Caution students not to mistreat animals. Remind students that consistent use of a positive reward when the desired behavior is performed after the stimulus is the best way to achieve training.

◆ Make sure students have thought about how they will observe learning in their animals. The students should have thought of specific ways in which they will monitor the training process. They should be able to predict how they will know their animals have learned the response to the stimulus.

CHAPTER 5 PROJECT (*continued*)

◆ Check Your Progress— Section 3 Review

◆ Check students' training records frequently. Make sure students are recording their observations of the animals' behavior during the training trials.

◆ Some students may run into difficulties with their training. Help them think of different approaches or rewards to use to overcome obstacles.

◆ Students should begin thinking about how they will present their results to the class. Inform students whether you will allow them to bring animals into the classroom. If so, animals should be on leashes or in cages. Also, remember that normally well-behaved animals may become agitated around other animals. If you will not allow animals in the classroom, help students to think of other ways to illustrate their animals' learning. They might choose to make posters to display data, drawings, and/or photographs, or they might show videotapes of their animals performing the behavior on command.

◆ Chapter Project Wrap-Up

◆ Allow each student to present his or her project, and encourage class members to ask questions about how they conducted their training trials.

◆ Be sensitive to students who were unable to train their animals. Encourage these students to think about what they could have done differently. Was the training period too short? Was that particular animal unable to do the behavior on command? Perhaps the behavior chosen was too complex and the student was asking too much of their animal.

◆ After all students have had a chance to present their projects, hold a class discussion on animal learning. What did students learn about the process of learning? Are there some things that are easier to teach to certain animals? Guide a discussion of how inherited traits may permit or limit an animal's ability to learn.

◆ Extensions/Options

◆ You may wish to restrict students' animal choices to animals that can be maintained and trained in the classroom. Or, you may wish to restrict students' choices to nonmammals to familiarize them with learning in situations other than the standard "train a pet" situation.

◆ Invite someone who uses an animal in his or her work to bring the animal to class and talk about how it was trained. A police dog or a service dog would be a perfect example of an animal that has been trained by conditioning.

5

CHAPTER 5 PROJECT   **OVERVIEW**

Learning New Tricks

In this project, you will train an animal to perform a behavior or new skill in response to a stimulus. After choosing your animal, you will observe your animal's behavior before training. Then you will devise a training plan, have your teacher review the plan, and begin training trials. At the end of the project, you will analyze your observations, summarize what you have learned, and demonstrate your animal's new skill or make a class presentation about the training.

◆ Project Rules

◆ If the animal is not your own, obtain permission from the animal's owner before attempting to train it. If a child owns the animal, an adult must be present when you train the animal.

◆ In this project, you may be training an animal to do a behavior as a response to a stimulus that it would sometimes do occasionally without the stimulus. Record your observations of the animal before you begin training. Note whether your animal performs on its own the behavior you are going to teach it. If so, record how often your animal performs the behavior.

◆ Have your teacher approve your training plans before you begin training your animal.

◆ Always treat your animal well. You are responsible for the well-being of your animal, and you must care for it properly.

◆ Realize that learning is a complex process, and it may not be possible for your animal to learn what you are trying to teach it. If you are having problems training your animal, discuss possible solutions with your teacher.

◆ Do not attempt to train or handle a wild animal. Some animals are protected by law, and others may carry diseases.

◆ Planning

◆ You will need access to an animal. Your family's or a neighbor's pet such as a dog, cat, hamster, or bird is a good choice.

◆ Choose a stimulus to which your animal will respond. Don't limit your thinking to spoken words. You could also use visual or sound signals such as a hand signal, a flash of a light, or a hand clap.

◆ Decide on a reward that will encourage your animal to learn the trick. Some examples of good rewards are a morsel of food, affection (like a pat on the head), and encouragement.

CHAPTER 5 PROJECT OVERVIEW *(continued)*

◆ If you decide to teach an animal to run a maze, you will need to design and build a maze. Include a materials list and the design in your plan.

◆ Project Hints

◆ The ability to perform certain behaviors depends on inherited traits. You are able to pick up a pencil and write your name because you inherited an opposable thumb. Think about the abilities of your animal before you select a behavior so that you can be sure the animal is capable of doing what you want it to do.

◆ Make sure you know all the behaviors your animal already performs on command, and what the commands are. Do not try to elicit different responses from the same stimulus. If your dog already associates a knock with somebody at the front door, do not confuse it by attempting to condition it to come when you knock.

◆ Learn to recognize the animal's inborn behaviors and use these as a basis for training. It is much easier to teach an animal to do something on command that it already does occasionally on its own than it is to teach it to do something entirely new.

◆ Be patient. Short but frequent training sessions are more effective than long ones.

◆ Be considerate. Your animal won't learn very well if it isn't treated well.

◆ Keep the training simple. Complex behaviors are taught one small step at a time. For this project, stick to small steps.

◆ You may not be able to bring your animal to class to demonstrate its new skill. Think about other ways that you could illustrate the new skill to the class, such as through drawings, photographs, or a videotape.

◆ Project Time Line

Tasks	Date Due	Teacher's Initials
1. Animal selected	_____	_____
2. Behavior selected	_____	_____
3. Pre-training observation completed	_____	_____
4. Stimulus or command selected	_____	_____
5. Training plan completed	_____	_____
6. All training completed	_____	_____
7. Class presentation	_____	_____

CHAPTER 5 PROJECT   **WORKSHEET 1**

Learning New Tricks

◆ Brainstorming Ideas

The chart below gives examples of stimuli, responses, and rewards you could use to train an animal. Fill in the numbered blanks. This will help you to understand the training process and plan this project. Fill in the last three rows with your own ideas.

Animal	Stimulus	Response	Reward
Dog	Bell rings	Dog barks	Pat on the head
Parrot	Presentation of red square, blue square, and yellow square	Bird pecks at red square.	**1.**
Hamster	Lights blink	**2.**	Sunflower seed
Cat	Snap your fingers	Cat comes to you.	**3.**
Fish	**4.**	Fish swims to surface.	Fish food

Learning New Tricks

◆ Planning

Complete the following on a separate sheet of paper. This is your training plan. Have your teacher approve your plan and initial your Project Time Line as you complete the tasks.

1. Choose an animal you would like to train for this project. Write a few sentences describing this animal and why you chose it. Who is the animal's owner? Have you obtained the owner's permission to use the animal in the project?

2. What behavior or new skill are you going to teach your animal to do? Write a few sentences describing why you have chosen this behavior and why you think the animal is capable of learning to do it in response to a stimulus.

3. Observe your animal. Does your animal do on its own the behavior you will teach it to do on command?

4. Identify the stimulus and the reward you will use to elicit the desired response from your animal. Why did you choose that stimulus? Why did you choose that reward?

5. How will you present the stimulus? When and how will you reward the animal?

6. How long will you spend training your animal during each training trial? How many training trials do you predict it will take to train your animal? Do you have prior experience with this animal on which you base your prediction?

7. What problems do you expect to encounter during training? How will you deal with these problems?

8. How will you demonstrate your animal's learning to the class? Will your teacher allow you to bring your animal into the classroom? If so, do you have the animal owner's permission to bring the animal into the classroom? If not, what kind of class presentation will you make?

Learning New Tricks

In evaluating how well you complete the Chapter 5 Project, your teacher will judge your work in three categories. In each, a score of 4 is the best rating.

	4	3	2	1
Planning	Chooses completely appropriate animal, trick, stimulus, and reward. Thoroughly plans a workable training regimen with short but frequent training sessions.	Chooses mostly appropriate animal, trick, stimulus, and reward. Plans a workable training regimen.	Chooses partly appropriate animal, trick, stimulus, and reward. One of those choices may be deeply flawed. Plans a somewhat workable training regimen.	Chooses inappropriate animal, trick, stimulus, and reward. Plan for training regimen is deeply flawed.
Making Observations	Makes pre-training observations that carefully note when and how often animal performs activity.	Makes pre-training observations that generally note when and how often animal performs activity.	Makes pre-training observations that note whether or not the animal performs the activity but not the frequency of activity.	Makes pre-training observations that fail to note when and how often animal performs activity.
Presenting the Project	Makes a thorough, well-organized presentation that explains the training method and indicates a thorough understanding of learning in animals. Stimulus produces response in animal.	Makes a presentation that mostly explains the training method and indicates an adequate understanding of learning in animals. Stimulus usually produces response in animal.	Presentation hard to follow. Explains only part of the training method and indicates minimal understanding of learning in animals. Stimulus may produce a minimal response in the animal.	Presentation is minimal or very disorganized. Fails to show that student understands learning process in animals. Stimulus produces no response in animal.

Why Do Animals Behave as They Do?

(pp. 152–159)

Objectives

After completing the lesson, students will be able to

◆ explain the functions of most of an animal's behaviors;

◆ compare instinctive and learned behavior.

1 Engage/Explore

◆ **Activating Prior Knowledge** Invite students to share examples of animal behaviors they have observed. Have the class suggest reasons for each behavior.

◆ **Discover** Allow students to observe the behavior of a small vertebrate for a few minutes.

2 Facilitate

◆ **Demonstration** Allow students to examine the involuntary blink response by tossing soft foam balls at sheets of clear plastic held in front of students' faces.

◆ **Including All Students** Point out that the word *behavior* can have more then one meaning. Elicit other words with more than one meaning.

◆ **Addressing Naïve Conceptions** Lead students to see that not only simple behaviors are instinctive. Provide them with examples of complex instinctive behaviors of animals. Then direct them to make a list of their own complex behaviors that may be partly or wholly instinctive.

◆ **Sharpen Your Skills** Lead students to predict how older gull chicks will behave when they see various bird shadows.

◆ **Using the Visuals: Figure 3** Have students describe what is happening in the figure without looking at the captions.

◆ **Real-Life Learning** Have students describe their response to the school's fire alarm. Have them problem-solve to decide whether the

described response is an example of learning or conditioning.

◆ **Inquiry Challenge** Challenge students to design an experiment to test a particular animal's ability to learn a specific behavior.

◆ **Including All Students** Emphasize the meanings of trial-and-error and insight learning by modeling them with students.

◆ **Integrating Technology** Encourage students to explore the abilities and limits of artificial intelligence by allowing them to play a computer checkers program.

◆ **Try This** Direct students to discuss the kinds of learning they used when solving a logic problem.

◆ **Real-Life Learning** Explain to students the danger for the condor if it imprinted on humans.

3 Assess

◆ **Section 1 Review** Check students' understanding of animal behavior by having them answer the section review questions.

◆ **Performance Assessment** Assess students' understanding of animal behavior by having them write short fictional accounts of a day in the life of a specific animal.

Lab

◆ **Skills Lab: Designing Experiments** Provide the opportunity for students to design an experiment to investigate how people learn.

SECTION 5-1   SECTION SUMMARY

Why Do Animals Behave as They Do?

Guide for Reading

◆ What are the functions of most of an animal's behaviors?

◆ How does instinctive behavior compare with learned behavior?

An animal's **behavior** consists of all the actions it performs. Some behaviors are very complex. To understand an animal, you need to know about both its behaviors and its body structure.

Most behaviors help an animal survive or reproduce. For example, catching food is an important behavior for survival.

Behavior is a complicated process of response to a stimulus, a signal that causes an animal to react in some way. Some stimuli come from outside the animal's body, while other stimuli, like thirst, come from inside the animal's body. The animal's reaction to the stimulus is called a **response.**

Some animal behaviors must be learned, while others are inborn. Inborn behaviors are called **instincts.** Instincts are usually done correctly the first time.

Learning is the process that leads to changes in behavior based on practice or experience. **Unlike instincts, learned behaviors result from an animal's experience and are not usually done perfectly the first time.**

Learned behaviors depend in part on inherited traits. For example, a lion cub is born with an instinct to catch moving objects, but it learns how to do it well by imitating its mother and by practicing.

Animals learn new behaviors in different ways. These include **conditioning, trial-and-error learning,** and **insight learning.**

Learning to connect some sort of stimulus with a good or bad event is called **conditioning.** Conditioning is often used to train animals. **Trial-and-error learning** occurs when an animal, through repeated practice, learns to perform a behavior more and more skillfully. **Insight learning** is when an animal solves a problem or learns how to do something new by applying what it already knows.

Some computers can learn and solve problems. **Artificial intelligence** is the capacity of a computer to perform tasks beyond its programming.

Imprinting is a behavior in a newborn animal in which it learns to recognize and follow the first moving object it sees, which is usually its mother.

Why Do Animals Behave as They Do?

◆ Understanding Main Ideas

Answer the following question.

1. What are two important functions of behavior?

_____

Label the following behaviors L for "learned" or I for "instinctive."

2. _____ A dog sits when you command him to "sit."

3. _____ A spider spins a web.

In the table below, fill in the blanks in the left-hand column with one of the three types of learning. Fill in the blanks in the right-hand column with an example of the type of learning named on the left.

Type of Learning	Example
4. _____	A bird stops eating orange butterflies because they taste bad. **5.** _____
Trial-and-error	**6.** _____ **7.** _____
8. _____	You stand on a chair to reach a jar of cookies.

◆ Building Vocabulary

Match each term with its definition by writing the letter of the correct definition in the right column on the line beside the term in the left column.

_____ **9.** stimulus

_____ **10.** response

_____ **11.** imprinting

_____ **12.** learning

_____ **13.** behavior

_____ **14.** instinct

_____ **15.** artificial intelligence

a. A reaction to a stimulus

b. All the actions that an animal performs

c. Allows computers to perform tasks beyond their programming

d. The process that leads to changes in behavior, based on practice or experience

e. A signal that causes an organism to react

f. Inborn behavior

g. When a baby animal learns to recognize and follow the first moving object it sees

Name _____ Date _____ Class _____

A Simple Insight

Insight learning involves the ability to apply what you already know to solve a new problem. The biologist L. V. Krushinsky tested animals' insight learning in a simple experiment.

The experimental setup is shown below. Animals looked through an opening in the middle of a partition and saw two dishes, one empty and the other full of food. Both dishes were then pulled away behind swinging doors, where they were no longer visible. In this experiment, what the animal already knows is, "Follow moving food to get it." The new situation in this experiment was, "The moving food goes out of sight." Any animal that used insight to walk around the correct side of the partition could locate and eat the food. When the dishes were pulled away, Krushinsky would record how many animals walked around the correct side of the partition and found the food, how many walked to the wrong side and how many wandered aimlessly. The table shows the results of his trials with several different kinds of animals.

A
Swinging door

B

To food dish   To empty dish

Aimless behavior

Species	Number of animals tested	Walked to food side	Walked to wrong side	Walked aimlessly
Pigeons	27	7%	0%	93%
Chickens	129	27%	25%	48%
Rabbits	33	24%	3%	73%
Cats	42	50%	36%	14%
Dogs	18	78%	11%	11%

Answer the following questions on a separate sheet of paper.

1. Which animals found the food most often? Which animals found it least often?

2. Which animals walked to the correct and incorrect sides of the partition almost equally often? Do you think these animals understood how to find the food?

3. What situation might cause an animal that had achieved the insight of how to find the food to still not walk toward it? How would you design the experiment to prevent this from happening?

Patterns of Behavior (pp. 160–169)

Objectives

After completing the lesson, students will be able to

◆ describe some ways in which animals relate to one another and explain the functions of those behaviors;

◆ describe animal behavior cycles and explain how they are important for an animal's survival.

1 Engage/Explore

◆ **Activating Prior Knowledge** Instruct students to stop what they are doing. Ask what they think was the purpose of their behaviors at that moment.

◆ **Discover** Have students communicate a feeling or situation without words. Others should infer what is being communicated.

2 Facilitate

◆ **Demonstration** Demonstrate competition and aggression in animals with Siamese fighting fish. Have students observe and record the fish's behavior.

◆ **Building Inquiry Skills: Predicting** Challenge students to predict what would happen to a male blackbird whose red wing patches were dyed black.

◆ **Building Inquiry Skills: Inferring** Lead students to see that territorial markings don't warn *all* animals.

◆ **Addressing Naive Conceptions** Explain that human behavior is often determined by culture.

◆ **Try This** Direct students to discover if it is more productive to work alone or in a group.

◆ **Building Inquiry Skills: Applying Concepts** Have students describe groups of animals and how living in a group benefits the individual.

◆ **Cultural Diversity** Provide examples of expressions from various cultures.

◆ **Exploring a Honeybee Society** Encourage students to discuss the importance of the role of each type of honeybee.

◆ **Real-Life Learning** Ask students for examples of circadian rhythms in their lives.

◆ **Including All Students** Have students discuss trouble waking up when it's dark.

◆ **Social Studies Connection** Have students use a map to compare migration routes.

◆ **Building Inquiry Skills: Comparing and Contrasting** Have students compare and contrast hibernation and migration as survival adaptations.

◆ **Integrating Environmental Science** Describe how migratory animals are threatened and how they can be protected.

3 Assess

◆ **Section 2 Review** Check students' understanding of section content by having them answer the section review questions.

◆ **Performance Assessment** Assess students' understanding of behavior patterns by having them prepare charts describing behavior patterns.

Lab

◆ **Real World Lab: You and Your Environment** Allow students to study an ant colony to observe organization and cooperative behavior.

5

SECTION 5-2   **SECTION SUMMARY**

Patterns of Behavior

Guide for Reading

◆ What is the function of courtship behavior?

◆ How do animals benefit from living in groups?

◆ How is migration important for an animal's survival?

Scientists classify patterns of behavior into different types. Aggression is a threatening pattern of behavior that one animal uses to gain control over another. Animals may be aggressive when they compete for limited resources such as food, water, space, shelter, or mates. Another reason animals may be aggressive is to protect their **territory,** an area that is occupied and defended by an animal or group of animals.

Courtship behavior is behavior in which males and females of the same species prepare for mating. **Courtship behavior ensures that the males and females of the same species recognize one another, so that mating can take place.**

Some animals live alone, while others live in groups. **Living in a group usually helps animals survive—group members protect each other and work together to find food.** A **society** is a group of closely related animals of the same species that work together for the benefit of the whole group.

Although animals don't all use language, they do communicate. They use sounds, body positions, movements, and scents to communicate information. Communication is used for courtship, defense, aggression, and finding food.

Some animal behavior occurs in predictable patterns. For example, some animals are active at night while others are active during the day. Daily behavior cycles are examples of **circadian rhythms.** Other behavior cycles are related to seasons, such as **hibernation.** Hibernation is a state of greatly reduced body activity that occurs during the winter.

Migration is a periodic journey of an animal from one place to another and back again. Migration is usually related to the change of seasons. **Animals usually migrate to an area that provides abundant food, a favorable environment for reproduction, or both.** Sometimes, human activity interferes with animal migration. For example, dams interfere with the migration of salmon, and city lights can confuse migrating birds at night.

SECTION 5-2 **REVIEW AND REINFORCE**

Patterns of Behavior

◆ Understanding Main Ideas

Answer the following questions on a separate sheet of paper.

1. What are two things animals might compete for?

2. Instead of using language, what are two ways that animals communicate?

3. What are two reasons that some animals migrate?

4. What two behaviors must an animal do to secure a territory?

5. What is one function of courtship behavior?

6. What are two benefits to animals of living in groups?

Diagram A shows two male Siamese fighting fish separated by a board. In diagram B the board has been removed. Write a paragraph to answer the following questions about the fishes' behavior in diagram B.

7. How are the fish communicating? What might the fish be communicating?

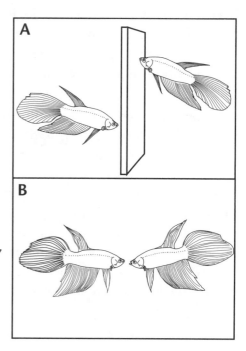

_____

_____

_____

◆ Building Vocabulary

Fill in the blank to complete each sentence.

8. The periodic journey by animals from one place to another and then back again is called _____ .

9. A period of inactivity during the winter is _____ .

10. A group of animals that work together for the benefit of the whole group is called a(n) _____ .

11. A behavior cycle that occurs over the period of about one day is _____ .

12. A dog will show _____ by barking and growling at other dogs that approach its territory.

SECTION 5-2   **ENRICH**

The Language of Honeybees

Karl von Frisch, an Austrian biologist, studied honey bees. He made the remarkable discovery that inside their hive, honey bees can communicate the direction, distance, and quality of food sources.

When a honeybee returns home from a food source, she performs a "waggle-dance" that gives information about the food's location and quality. She repeatedly walks in the pattern of a squashed figure-8 on the wall of the honeycomb (Figure 1). In the middle of the figure-8, she makes a straight run, waggling her abdomen back and forth. The distance she walks while waggling tells her sisters how far away the food is. She waggles more vigorously if the food source is very good.

The dancing bee cannot point in the direction of the food, however. It is dark inside the hive, and the bee is dancing on a vertical surface. Instead, the angle between straight up and the direction of her straight run indicates the angle between the sun and the food source. For example, if the food were located in the direction of the sun, her straight run would be vertical. Armed with this information about the direction, distance, and quality of the food, other bees can then go to it.

Answer the questions below on a separate sheet of paper.

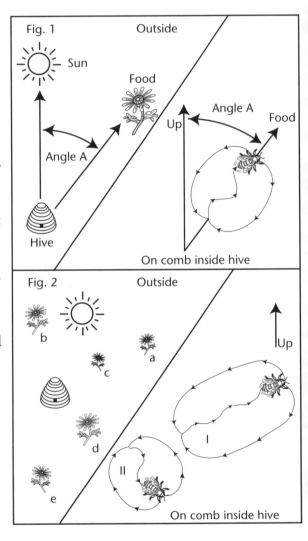

1. Figure 2 shows the location of several food sources (pictured as flowers), and the direction of the sun in relation to a beehive. Inside the hive, two bees are performing waggle-dances. Which food source is each one dancing about?

   a. Bee I:

   b. Bee II:

2. Based on the two bees' dances, which food source is closer to the hive?

3. Based on the two bees' dances, which is a better food source?

4. Which food source would you expect the other bees in the hive to fly to?

5. During the waggle-dance, what does the vertical direction stand for?

Integrating Chemistry

The Chemistry of Communication (pp. 170–172)

Objectives

After completing the lesson, students will be able to

◆ describe how animals use pheromones to communicate.

1 Engage/Explore

◆ **Activating Prior Knowledge** Hide a strong-smelling object somewhere in the classroom. Challenge students to find the object using some sense other than sight. After they have located the object, ask them what sense they used.

◆ **Discover** Have students sniff the unknown contents of a container and try to find the other container in the classroom whose scent matches it.

2 Facilitate

◆ **Including All Students** Explain to students how the term bioluminescence was formed. Allow students to use a dictionary to determine how the word pheromone was formed.

◆ **Building Inquiry Skills: Inferring** Have students fit paper cutouts together to model pheromones attaching to receptors.

◆ **Integrating Environmental Science** Discuss with students the advantage of pheromone-based pest traps.

◆ **Building Inquiry Skills: Inferring** Allow groups of students to attempt to communicate with each other across the room using a code they devised. Then have them attempt to communicate with members of other groups.

3 Assess

◆ **Section 3 Review** Check students' understanding of the chemistry of communication by having them answer the section review questions.

◆ **Performance Assessment** Assess students' understanding of pheromone communication by having students write fictional accounts of a day in the life of an animal that communicates with pheromones.

5

SECTION 5-3   **SECTION SUMMARY**

The Chemistry of Communication

A **pheromone** is a chemical released by one animal that affects the behavior of another animal of the same species. **Animals communicate with pheromones in order to establish territories, locate food, attract mates, and distinguish members of their own group from members of another group.**

Each pheromone contains a unique combination of atoms. Because the atoms join together in specific ways, each pheromone has a specific chemical shape. This means that an animal's pheromone usually only causes a response in other animals of the same species.

Pheromones enable many animals to recognize group members and establish territories. Every ant colony, for example, has its own specific pheromone that identifies colony members.

Pheromones also play an important role in mating and reproduction. For example, the female of some moths releases a pheromone to attract a male.

Some pheromones can be made in laboratories and then used to attract and eliminate pest insects. The insect pests are attracted to manufactured pheromones inside traps. Some traps expose male insects to X-rays to make them sterile. Other traps kill the insects.

Some animals, such as fireflies and some species of fish, use light to communicate. **Bioluminescence** is the production of light by a living organism. Male and female fireflies use such light to signal each other during courtship.

5

Animal Behavior

◆ Understanding Main Ideas

Answer the following questions.

1. What is a pheromone?

_____

_____

2. What are two functions of pheromones?

_____

_____

3. How are pheromones used in insect control?

_____

_____

4. What is one way animals use pheromones to communicate?

_____

_____

5. What is the function of bioluminescence in fireflies?

_____

_____

◆ Building Vocabulary

Fill in the blank to complete each sentence.

6. Animals that communicate with _____ are relying on their sense of smell.

7. Animals that communicate with _____ are relying on their sense of sight.

SECTION 5-3 **ENRICH**

Pheromones and Honeybee Communities

In some species of animals, pheromones coordinate the complex actions of thousands of individuals. The honeybee is one example. Often, when a colony of honeybees becomes large, the queen prepares to leave by laying eggs for new queens. Larvae hatch from those eggs and worker bees raise new queens by feeding them special foods. Meanwhile, the workers feed the current queen less and eventually push her out of the hive. She leaves, taking with her up to half of the workers in a process called *swarming*. For a short time, the hive is queenless, but soon the first new queen emerges. As her sister queens emerge from their cells, she kills them or drives them away and she becomes the new queen of the hive.

All this complex behavior is controlled by a pheromone called *queen substance,* and depends on the amount of queen substance available to each worker. Queen substance is produced by the queen and is spread throughout the colony. The workers constantly use it up, but as long as there is a queen present, the pheromone is produced.

Queen substance has an important effect on workers. When there is enough queen substance available for each worker, the workers do not raise new queens. The diagram shows the relationship between the amount of queen substance in the nest and swarming.

Answer the following questions on a separate sheet of paper.

1. Where in the cycle is the most queen substance being produced?

2. Why is no queen substance being produced in the old colony between points 2 and 4?

3. If the old queen died at point 2 instead of swarming, what would happen to the amount of queen substance available to each worker in the old colony? How would workers react? Would this be different from their normal behavior?

4. If the new queen died at point 5, what would happen to the amount of queen substance available to each worker? How would workers react? Would this be different from their normal behavior?

CHAPTER 5   **SKILLS LAB**

Designing Experiments

Become a Learning Detective

In this lab, you will design an experiment to investigate how people learn.

◆ **Problem**   What are some factors that make it easier for people to learn new things?

◆ **Suggested Materials**

paper and pencil

◆ **Design a Plan**

1. Look over the two lists of words in the table. Researchers use groups of words like these to investigate how people learn. Notice the way the two groups differ. The words in List A have no meanings in ordinary English. List B contains familiar, but unrelated, words.

2. What do you think will happen if people try to learn the words in each list? Write a hypothesis about which list will be easier to learn. How much easier will it be to learn that list?

3. With a partner, design an experiment to test your hypothesis. Brainstorm a list of the variables you will need to control in order to make your results reliable. Then write out your plan and present it to your teacher.

4. If necessary, revise your plan according to your teacher's instructions. Then perform your experiment using people your teacher has approved as test subjects. Keep careful records of your results.

List A	List B
zop	bug
rud	rag
tig	den
wab	hot
hev	fur
paf	wax
mel	beg
kib	cut
col	sip
nug	job

SKILLS LAB *(continued)*

◆ Data Table

List A	zop	rud	tig	wab	hev	paf	mel	kib	col	nug	Total

List B	bug	rag	den	hot	fur	wax	beg	cut	sip	job	Total

5

◆ Analyze and Conclude

Write your answers on the back of this sheet or on a separate sheet of paper.

1. Find the average (mean) number of words people learned from each list. How did these results compare with your hypothesis?

2. What factors may have made one list easier to learn than the other?

3. Share your results with the rest of the class. How do the results of the different experiments in your class compare? What might explain the similarities or differences?

4. **Think About It** Look back at your experimental plan and think about how well you were able to carry it out in the actual experiment. What difficulties did you encounter? What improvements could you make, either in your plan or in the way you carried it out?

◆ More to Explore

Plan an experiment to investigate how long people remember what they learn. Write a hypothesis, and design an experiment to test your hypothesis. Obtain your teacher's permission before carrying out this experiment.

CHAPTER 5   **REAL-WORLD LAB**

You and Your Environment

One For All

Have you ever stopped to watch a group of busy ants? In this lab, you will find out what goes on in an ant colony.

◆ **Problem**   How does an ant society show organization and cooperative behavior?

◆ **Skills Focus**   observing, inferring, posing questions

◆ **Materials**

large glass jar	large, thick rubber band	shallow pan
water	sandy soil	sponge
20–30 ants	wire screen	bread crumbs
sugar	hand lens	tape
glass-marking pencil	black paper	forceps

◆ **Procedure**

1. Read over the entire lab to preview the kinds of observations you will be making.

2. Mark the outside of a large jar with four evenly spaced vertical lines, as shown in the diagram. Label the sections with the letters A, B, C, and D. You can use these labels to identify the sections of soil on and below the surface.

3. Fill the jar about three-fourths full with soil. Place the jar in a shallow pan of water to prevent any ants from escaping. Place a wet sponge on the surface of the soil as a water source for the ants.

4. Observe the condition of the soil, both on the surface and along the sides of the jar. Record your observations.

5. Add the ants to the jar. Immediately cover the jar with the wire screen, using the rubber band to hold the screen firmly in place.

6. Observe the ants for at least 10 minutes. Look for differences in the appearance of adult ants, and look for eggs, larvae, and pupae. Examine both individual behavior and interactions between the ants.

REAL-WORLD LAB *(continued)*

7. Remove the screen cover, and add small amounts of bread crumbs and sugar to the soil surface. Close the cover. Observe the ants for at least 10 minutes.

8. Create dark conditions for the ants by covering the jar with black paper above the water line. Remove the paper only when you are making your observations.

9. Observe the ant colony every day for two weeks. Remove the dark paper, and make and record your observations. Look at the soil as well as the ants, and always examine the food. If any food has started to mold, use forceps to remove it. Place the moldy food in a plastic bag, seal the bag, and throw it away. Add more food as necessary, and keep the sponge moist. When you finish your observations, replace the dark paper.

10. At the end of the lab, follow your teacher's directions for returning the ants.

◆ Data Table

Date	Section A	Section B	Section C	Section D

REAL-WORLD LAB *(continued)*

◆ Analyze and Conclude

Answer the following questions on the back of this sheet or on a separate sheet of paper.

1. Describe the various types of ants you observed. What differences, if any, did you observe in their behavior? What evidence did you observe that different kinds of ants perform different tasks?

2. How do the different behaviors you observed contribute to the survival of the colony?

3. How did the soil change over the period of your observations? What caused those changes? How do you know?

4. Apply What kinds of environmental conditions do you think ant colonies need to thrive outdoors? Use the evidence obtained in this lab to support your answer.

◆ More to Explore

Design an experiment to investigate how an ant colony responds when there is a change in the ants' environment, such as the introduction of a new type of food. Obtain your teacher's approval before carrying out your experiment.

5

INTERDISCIPLINARY EXPLORATION · SCIENCE

Ways the Chinese Use Insects

The ancient Chinese people learned how to raise silkworms very successfully. But silkworms raised for their silk were not the only insects the Chinese knew about. Here is a list of insects that we know were kept by the ancient Chinese. Each of these insects creates a substance or performs an action that humans have considered useful. See if you can match the product or function with the name of the animal.

Write the letter of the product or function on the line next to the name of the animal.

_____ **1.** bee

_____ **2.** silkworm

_____ **3.** lac insect

_____ **4.** cricket

_____ **5.** firefly

a. This insect produces a thread used to make a rich material used for ties, scarves, and expensive clothing.

b. This insect makes a wax used for candles and sculptures.

c. This insect secretes shellac, which is used in lipstick, glue, and dye.

d. This insect was raised and then released in large numbers to amuse royalty.

e. This insect is kept as a pet because it sings.

6. What other useful things do we get from bees?

_____

_____

7. If the silkworm is not a worm, what is it? Why is it called a worm?

_____

_____

8. Why do you think the silkworm eats only mulberry leaves?

_____

_____

INTERDISCIPLINARY EXPLORATION   **SCIENCE**

Spider Silk

Read the paragraphs below. Then answer the following questions on the lines below.

In October 1994, scientists at Cornell University announced that they were a step closer to raising genetically engineered plants that could grow fibers as strong as steel.

The scientists have been studying the molecular structure of the spider silk produced by the golden orb-weaving spider. This material is used by the spider to spin a web to catch insects. The fibers of this web have the strength of steel fiber of the same diameter, but spider thread can stretch to ten times its original length. No metal or synthetic fiber yet made can stretch that length.

Scientists hope to engineer plants to produce the silk fiber, as it is not practical to have spiders produce it. You need more than 400 spiders to produce enough silk for one square yard of cloth.

In the future, scientists hope they will be able to use this special fiber to make items such as bulletproof vests or ultralight parachutes.

1. Do the scientists already know how to raise the plants?

_____

_____

2. For what purpose does the spider produce silk?

_____

_____

3. In what two ways is the silk of the spider better than any fiber that people use?

_____

_____

_____

4. Why do you think it would be useful to have a very strong fiber that can stretch?

_____

_____

5. In what ways are plants easier to raise than spiders?

_____

_____

_____

INTERDISCIPLINARY EXPLORATION   **MATHEMATICS**

Graphing Mountain Heights

The table below shows the height of the nine highest peaks in the Pamir Mountains. Complete the bar graph below. When you finish the graph, answer the following questions.

Peaks of the Pamir Mountains

Name of Peak	Height (meters)
Communism Peak	7,495
Garmo Peak	6,595
Karl Marx Peak	6,726
Korzhenevski Peak	7,105
Kurumba	6,610
Moscow Peak	6,785
Revolution Peak	6,974
Victory Peak	7,439
Vudor Peak	6,132

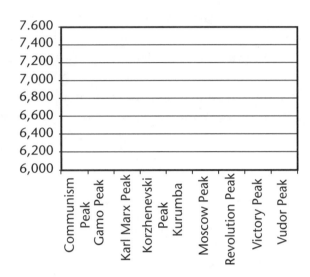

1. Which are the highest and lowest peaks?

_____

2. What is the difference in height between the highest and lowest peaks?

_____

3. Look at your bar graph and determine which two peaks are closest to each other in height.

_____

INTERDISCIPLINARY EXPLORATION ████████ **MATHEMATICS**

Your Weight in Food

Over its lifetime, a silkworm eats about 20 times its own mass. Help Kim calculate what mass she eats in food. Kim has a mass of about 45 kilograms. Kim determines that all the food she eats and drinks in one day has a mass of about 1.5 kilograms. Answer the following questions on the lines below.

1. If Kim consumes 1.5 kilograms a day, how many days will it take her to consume her body mass?

_____

2. How much will Kim consume in 50 days?

_____

3. How many times Kim's body mass will Kim consume in 50 days?

_____

4. If Kim wants to consume 20 times her body mass, how much must she consume?

_____

5. If Kim consumes 1.5 kilograms a day, how many days will it take her to consume 20 times her body mass?

_____

6. About how many weeks is this?

_____

7. How many pounds will Kim consume in 1 year?

_____

8. How many pounds will Kim consume in 5 years?

_____

INTERDISCIPLINARY EXPLORATION   MATHEMATICS

A Trip on the Silk Road

Imagine that you are a merchant in ancient China who is planning a trip on the silk road. To help plan the trip, you need to solve some problems involving proportion. Use the strategy described on page 182 of your textbook. Use the spaces below the questions for your calculations.

1. Suppose it takes about 3 days for a caravan to travel a distance of 50 kilometers through the mountains. How long would it take the caravan to make the journey between 2 cities that are 125 km apart?

2. In 15 days, how great a distance would the caravan travel?

3. During 6 hours of traveling, the caravan needs to stop 2 times so the animals can rest. If a day's journey lasts 9 hours, how many times must the caravan stop?

4. On a previous journey, 5 yaks were able to carry a total of 375 kg of spices. On this trip, you want to carry 600 kg of spices. How many yaks will you need?

5. Once you get to Europe, you can trade 4 rolls of silk for 15 rolls of wool cloth. If you take 48 rolls of silk with you, how much wool can you expect in return?

INTERDISCIPLINARY EXPLORATION   SOCIAL STUDIES

World Populations

This table below compares the populations of ten countries near or along the Silk Road. Use the table to answer the questions that follow.

Population Change

	1996	2000 (estimated)
China	1,210,005,000	1,253,438,000
Greece	10,539,000	10,735,000
India	952,108,000	1,012,909,000
Iran	66,094,000	71,879,000
Iraq	21,422,000	24,731,000
Italy	57,460,000	57,807,000
Russia	148,178,000	147,938,000
Saudi Arabia	19,409,000	22,246,000
Turkey	62,484,000	66,618,000
Uzbekistan	23,418,000	25,245,000

1. Which country had the lowest population in 1996?

_____

2. Which country is expected to have the second-highest population in 2000?

_____

3. Which country had a population closest to 65 million in 1996?

_____

4. Which country's population is expected to decline from 1996 to 2000?

_____

5. Which country's population is expected to increase by the smallest number?

_____

6. Write the ten countries in increasing order of population in 1996.

_____

_____

7. Which country's population is expected to increase by 60.8 million?

_____

INTERDISCIPLINARY EXPLORATION **SOCIAL STUDIES**

Interpreting a Map

Identify each place described below. Use the map on page 179 of your book to find the answers.

1. This sea is north of Antioch.

_____

2. This sea is west of Antioch.

_____

3. The route from Ch'ang-an to Dunhuang is just north of these mountains.

_____

4. This city is about 1,500 kilometers west of Dunhuang.

_____

5. To get from Kashgar to Parthia, you would have to cross these mountains.

_____

6. This bay is about 2,000 kilometers south of Dunhuang.

_____

7. If you were a Silk Road trader, and you began sailing from Antioch, you would most likely be heading to this city.

_____

8. The country in which you find the city of Rome is part of this continent.

_____

9. If you are climbing the Himalaya Mountains, what continent are you in?

_____

10. If you wanted to travel from Antioch to Parthia, you would travel in this direction.

_____

Animals

INTERDISCIPLINARY EXPLORATION   SOCIAL STUDIES

Finding Cities Along the Silk Road

The map on the next page shows ten cities near or along the Silk Road. This table below gives the latitude and longitude of the ten cities. On the line next to the name of the city, write the corresponding letter of the city from the map. Then answer the following questions on the lines below.

Cites of the Silk Road

		Latitude	Longitude
_____	Almaty	43:15 N	76:57 E
_____	Ankara	40:01 N	32:54 E
_____	Athens	38:01 N	23:44 E
_____	Baghdad	33:14 N	44:22 E
_____	Beirut	33:53 N	35:30 E
_____	Dushanbe	38:35 N	68:48 E
_____	Kabul	34:34 N	69:13 E
_____	Nicosia	35:09 N	33:16 E
_____	Rome	41:52 N	12:37 E
_____	Tehran	35:45 N	51:30 E

1. Which city is farthest east?

_____

2. Which city is farthest south?

_____

3. Which two cities are closest in latitude?

_____

4. Which two cities are farthest apart in longitude?

_____

INTERDISCIPLINARY EXPLORATION   SOCIAL STUDIES

INTERDISCIPLINARY EXPLORATION   LANGUAGE ARTS

Silk Vocabulary

Complete each sentence with a term from the list below.

treacherous   shimmer
pack animals   caravan
wasteland   harness
whinny   snout
ceremonial   suture

1. A _____ is the sound a horse makes when it is grumbling.

2. Animals, such as camels, llamas, horses, and donkeys, that are trained to carry things for people are called _____ .

3. A group of camels and riders traveling together is called a

_____ .

4. A _____ is a small delicate stitch that surgeons use to sew people back together.

5. A horse wears a _____ so the rider can more easily control the animal.

6. A vast deserted region that appears to have no plants or animals of any kind living in it is called a _____ .

7. The hikers felt that crossing the rope bridge would be _____ because of the strong wind.

8. The dancing _____ of the lights on the water was beautiful and hypnotic.

9. The formal costume a princess might wear to a very important occasion would be called her _____ robes.

10. The long nose of a horse is called a _____ ; some dogs also have these.

INTERDISCIPLINARY EXPLORATION   LANGUAGE ARTS

Writing Your Own Myth

In 1902, author Rudyard Kipling wrote a humorous story to explain how the camel got its hump. Read the outline of the story on the left. On the right, write an outline for a story you would write to explain how the yak got its thick fur.

How the Camel Got His Hump by Rudyard Kipling	How Yak Got His Fur by
Three animals, Horse, Dog, and Ox, told the Camel he had to work along with them, but Camel didn't want to. Whatever they asked Camel to do, he would say "Humph."	Introduce the character's setting:
Horse, Dog, and Ox were angry because Man told them they would have to do Camel's work for him.	Present the problem:
The three animals had a meeting. During their meeting, a magic Djinn came along. They told him about lazy Camel. The Djinn found Camel. He talked to Camel and got "Humph" in reply to everything.	
Djinn warned Camel to start working but Camel said "Humph." So the Djinn made some magic.	
The next time Camel said "Humph" and puffed up his back, the Djinn sent the magic to Camel's back. Camel's "Humph" turned into a hump.	Develop the humorous solution:
Djinn told Camel that because he now had a hump, he could do all the work he had been avoiding for three days without stopping for food.	
However, Camel was still so lazy that he never caught up on the work he missed, so he will always wear his hump.	

INTERDISCIPLINARY EXPLORATION   LANGUAGE ARTS

A Broken Promise

On page 181 in the textbook, you are asked to write a story about a broken promise. The following prewriting questions and strategies will help you plan your story.

1. When and where does your story take place?

_____

2. What is the name of your main character? What character traits does he or she have?

_____

_____

_____

3. What other characters will appear in your story? What are they like?

_____

_____

_____

4. In most stories, the main character is faced with a conflict. In your story, the conflict will involve a broken promise. What is the promise, and who breaks it?

_____

_____

5. The plot of a story is the events that happen, in the order in which they occur. The beginning of a story sets the scene and establishes the conflict. The middle of the story shows what happens after the conflict starts. The story's climax shows the final result or resolution of the conflict. The story ends shortly after the climax. Use the table below to describe the plot of your story.

Story Plot	
Beginning	
Middle	
Climax and Ending	

CHAPTER
1   Planarians and Light

Students are asked the question, "Do planarians prefer darkness or light?" To answer this question, each student will formulate a hypothesis, design an experiment, and collect data which will support or refute the hypothesis. Then students will use their observations to infer how and why planarians respond to light in nature.

◆ Expected Outcome

Students should formulate hypotheses that answer the given question. Hypotheses should address one of three possibilities: Planarians respond to light using a seeking behavior, an avoidance behavior, or planarians do not respond to light. Students' experiments must be designed to test their hypotheses. A typical setup would be to place the planarian in a dish of water which is half-covered with foil or paper. There should be a light shining on the setup. The variable factor would be the lighting conditions. The control factors would be the conditions that are identical for all worms. For example, the worms are in the same water, in the same petri dish, have the same oxygen conditions, are under the same temperature, and so forth. Students will evaluate their hypotheses based on the reaction of the planarian. Expect planarians to prefer darkness.

◆ Content Assessed

This activity assesses students' understanding of the characteristics of animals and how animals respond to their environment.

◆ Skills Assessed

developing a hypothesis, designing an experiment, controlling variables, applying concepts, drawing conclusions

◆ Materials

◆ Provide students with aluminum foil, black construction paper, flashlight or other light source, hand lens, and planarians in a petri dish of pond water or dechlorinated water

◆ Advance Preparation

◆ Live planarians may be obtained from a biological supply house.

◆ Have sufficient quantities of aluminum foil and construction paper available for students.

◆ Distribute the planarians carefully. Use a small paintbrush to put them into the petri dish for students. Caution students to handle the planarians carefully.

◆ Time

one class period

◆ Safety

Students should thoroughly wash their hands after completing their experiment and cleaning their equipment.

◆ Monitoring the Task

◆ Discuss possible procedures with the class or individual groups before students begin the Performance Assessment.

◆ Check experimental designs to see if they are safe and will actually test the hypothesis. Do not allow a student to begin his or her experiment before you check the planned procedure.

CHAPTER 1

Planarians and Light

In assessing students' performance, use the following rubric.

	4	3	2	1
Developing a Hypothesis	Student's hypothesis is clearly and specifically stated as a possible answer to the experimental problem.	Student's hypothesis is general, but does address the experimental problem.	Student's hypothesis is vague, but demonstrates some understanding of the experimental problem.	Student's hypothesis does not address the experimental problem.
Designing an Experiment	Student's experimental design clearly tests the hypothesis. Variables are precisely identified and the procedure controls for them.	Student's experimental design is adequate. Variables are identified correctly but are not completely controlled.	Student's experimental design demonstrates only a partial understanding of hypothesis testing. Procedure shows a serious flaw with control of variables or variables are not correctly identified.	Student's experimental design demonstrates little or no comprehension of hypothesis testing. Variables are incorrectly identified.
Concept Understanding	Student demonstrates complete understanding of chapter concepts.	Student demonstrates adequate understanding of chapter concepts.	Student demonstrates some understanding of chapter concepts.	Student demonstrates minimal understanding of chapter concepts.
Drawing Conclusions	Student bases acceptance or rejection of hypothesis on valid data from experiment.	Student loosely bases acceptance or rejection of hypothesis on valid data from experiment but uses some conjecture.	Student loosely bases acceptance or rejection of hypothesis on data from experiment. Data are invalid.	Student's acceptance or rejection of hypothesis irrelevant to data from experiment. Data are invalid.

CHAPTER 1   **PERFORMANCE ASSESSMENT**

Planarians and Light

1

Animals respond to changes in their environment. The way an animal responds may be an adaptation for escaping predators, catching prey, survival, or reproduction. In this performance assessment, you will explore how a planarian responds to a change in its environment.

Eyespots

◆ **Problem**   Do planarians prefer darkness or light?

◆ **Suggested Materials**

aluminum foil	planarians	hand lens
flashlight or light source	construction paper, black	petri dish
pond water or dechlorinated tap water		

◆ **Safety** Handle the planarians gently. Thoroughly wash your hands after completing the Performance Assessment.

◆ **Devise a Plan**

1. Form a hypothesis about how planarians respond to light. Record your hypothesis on a data sheet on a separate sheet of paper.

2. Decide how to use the materials to test your hypothesis. Write down what you want to do on your data sheet.

3. Draw a diagram of your experimental setup on your data sheet.

4. Discuss your plan with your teacher. If your teacher approves, perform the experiment.

◆ **Analyze and Conclude**

After completing your plan, answer the following questions on a separate sheet.

1. How did the planarians respond to light?

2. Was your hypothesis correct? Do your observations support or reject your hypothesis? What factors are controlled in your experiment? What is the variable?

3. How do you think the planarian's response to light helps it to survive in nature?

4. Do you think a cnidarian would have the same response to light in nature? Explain.

CHAPTER 1   **TEST**

Sponges, Cnidarians, and Worms

◆ Multiple Choice

Write the letter of the correct answer on the line at the left.

_____ **1.** A group of organisms that can mate with each other and produce off-
    spring who in turn can mate and reproduce is called a(n)
    a. phylum.   **b.** invertebrate.
    c. species.   **d.** heterotroph.

_____ **2.** _____ are invertebrates that have two different body plans—a
    polyp and a medusa.
    a. sponges   **b.** cnidarians
    c. roundworms   **d.** flatworms

_____ **3.** Budding is a form of
    a. sexual reproduction.   **b.** movement.
    c. larva.   **d.** asexual reproduction.

_____ **4.** One characteristic by which animals are classified is
    a. their body structure.
    b. where they are found.
    c. how they get oxygen.
    d. the time of year they are born.

_____ **5.** An invertebrate is an animal with
    a. a backbone.
    b. no backbone.
    c. only sexual reproduction.
    d. only asexual reproduction.

_____ **6.** Which of the following is *not* a characteristic of a sponge?
    a. filters water   **b.** has collar cells
    c. has stinging cells   **d.** is a heterotroph

_____ **7.** Cnidarians detect food and defend themselves by
    a. using stinging cells.
    b. using collar cells.
    c. budding
    d. forming a hard skeleton.

_____ **8.** Sponges obtain food and _____ from the water.
    a. shelter   **b.** oxygen
    c. DNA   **d.** carbon dioxide

CHAPTER 1 TEST *(continued)*

_____ **9.** Cnidarians are
  a. omnivores.
  b. herbivores.
  c. carnivores.
  d. filter feeders.

_____ **10.** The ability to regrow a body part is called
  a. budding.
  b. asexual reproduction.
  c. regeneration.
  d. sexual reproduction.

◆ Completion

Fill in the line to complete each statement.

11. Three major worm phyla are flatworms, roundworms, and

  _____ .

12. A(n) adaptation is a characteristic that helps an organism survive in its environment or _____ .

13. The organism that supports a parasite is called the _____ .

14. Roundworms have a digestive tract with _____ opening(s).

15. To crawl forward, an earthworm uses its segments, well-developed muscles, and _____ .

◆ True or False

If the statement is true, write true. If it is false, change the underlined word or words to make the statement true.

_____ **16.** Roundworms have <u>radial</u> symmetry.

_____ **17.** An animal that eats both plants and animals is an <u>omnivore</u>.

_____ **18.** <u>Collar cells</u> help move water through sponges.

_____ **19.** Corals spend their adult lives as <u>medusas</u>.

_____ **20.** <u>Heterotrophs</u> make their own food.

CHAPTER 1 TEST *(continued)*

◆ Using Science Skills

Use the diagram below to answer the following questions.

21. Classify To which of the large groups of organisms discussed in the text does the larger animal belong? How do you know?

_____

_____

22. Inferring How does the larger animal obtain and digest food?

_____

_____

◆ Essay

Write an answer for each of the following. Use the back of this sheet if you need more room.

23. Describe how coral reefs form.

_____

_____

24. Describe the circulatory system of an earthworm. Explain how this type of system benefits the earthworm.

_____

_____

25. Predators have many special adaptations to catch prey. List four adaptations and tell how they help the predator.

_____

_____

_____

_____

Name _____ Date _____ Class _____

CHAPTER 1 TEST *(continued)*

◆ Using Science Skills

Use the diagram below to answer the following questions.

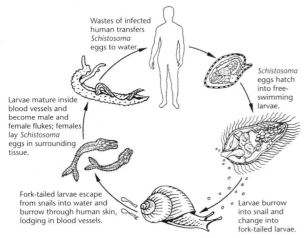

Wastes of infected
human transfers
Schistosoma
eggs to water.

Schistosoma
eggs hatch
into free-
swimming
larvae.

Larvae mature inside
blood vessels and
become male and
female flukes; females
lay *Schistosoma*
eggs in surrounding
tissue.

Fork-tailed larvae escape
from snails into water and
burrow through human skin,
lodging in blood vessels.

Larvae burrow
into snail and
change into
fork-tailed larvae.

Schistosoma, a parasitic flatworm, affects hundreds of millions of people in Africa, South America, the Caribbean, the Middle East, and Asia. In humans, the eggs of this flatworm block blood vessels, causing inflammation, swelling, pain, and tissue damage.

26. Interpreting Diagrams What organisms are hosts for *Schistosoma*?

_____

27. Relating Cause and Effect What are two ways in which the life cycle of the
Schistosoma can be broken?

_____

_____

◆ Essay

Write an answer for each of the following.

28. Describe four characteristics of animals.

_____

_____

29. Describe the advantages that bilateral symmetry gives an animal.

_____

_____

30. What characteristics do scientists use when they classify an animal?

_____

_____

CHAPTER
2   Imprint Inquiry

Students are asked to examine simulated fossils you create and to identify the kind of animal from Chapter 2 that left the imprint. Students must use their knowledge of the characteristics of mollusks, arthropods, and echinoderms to infer what kind of animal made each imprint.

◆ Expected Outcome

Students will infer which animals' imprints produced the simulated fossils by observing the characteristics of each organism obtained from the imprints and classifying the organism based on those characteristics.

◆ Content Assessed

This Performance Assessment tests students' knowledge of the physical characteristics of mollusks, arthropods, and echinoderms and their ability to infer from observations.

◆ Skills Assessed

applying concepts, observing, inferring

◆ Materials

- ◆ mollusk shells
- ◆ dried arthropods or arthropod models
- ◆ dried echinoderms or echinoderm models
- ◆ hand lens
- ◆ clay

◆ Advance Preparation

- ◆ Prepare materials at least a week in advance to allow clay "fossils" plenty of time to dry.
- ◆ Obtain specimens or models and clay.
- ◆ Choose several mollusks, arthropods, and echinoderms to use to make the "fossils." Each student should receive a set of three

"fossils" including one of each kind. The sets should be somewhat different.

- ◆ Prepare the imprints by rolling clay into sheets. Place each specimen on the clay. Using a small block of wood or other object, gently press the specimen into the clay. Remove the specimen. If the arthropod or echinoderm breaks into pieces, press the individual pieces into the clay and remove them. (This more closely resembles an actual fossil.) If models of arthropods and echinoderms are used, be sure they are accurate. Students must have enough information to infer whether the animal is a mollusk, an arthropod, or an echinoderm from the imprint. Allow the clay to dry.

◆ Time

Allow one class period for this Performance Assessment.

◆ Safety

The dried clay is brittle and fragile, so students should handle the models carefully.

◆ Monitoring the Task

- ◆ Student inferences must be logically supported or refuted. If no inference is made, the student must clearly indicate what additional information is necessary.

CHAPTER 2

Imprint Inquiry

In assessing students' work, use the following rubric.

	4	3	2	1
Observing	Observations are thorough, accurate, and will allow the student to classify the organism. There are six or more observations.	Observations are accurate and sufficient to allow the animal to be classified. There are fewer than six observations.	Several observations are incomplete or inaccurate.	Most observations are incorrect or are unrelated to the fossils.
Inferring	All inferences are logical and based on observed characteristics of the fossil.	Most inferences are logical and based on observed characteristics.	All but two or three inferences are logical and based on observed characteristics.	Most inferences do not make sense and are not related to the fossil.
Applying Concepts	Demonstrates thorough knowledge of the physical characteristics of mollusks, arthropods, and echinoderms by listing six or more appropriate observations.	Demonstrates adequate knowledge of the physical characteristics of mollusks, arthropods, and echinoderms by listing four or five appropriate observations.	Demonstrates some knowledge of the physical characteristics of mollusks, arthropods, and echinoderms by listing two or three appropriate observations.	Demonstrates little knowledge of the physical characteristics of mollusks, arthropods, and echinoderms.

CHAPTER 2   **PERFORMANCE ASSESSMENT**

Imprint Inquiry

Hiking in the Texas Hill Country, you find a rock with an imprint of a shell on it. This is an *imprint fossil.* Imprint fossils happen when hard parts of an animal are trapped in layers of sediment, and the hard part of the animal decomposes completely, leaving an imprint.

Examine the simulated fossils made from the same types of animals you studied in this chapter. In this activity you will use your knowledge of the animals of Chapter 2 to classify the mystery animals that made the simulated imprint fossils as echinoderms, mollusks, or arthropods.

◆ Problem   What kind of animals produced the clay simulated fossils?

◆ Suggested Materials

simulated fossils   hand lens

◆ Safety   Thoroughly wash your hands after handling the simulated fossils. Handle all simulated fossils with care.

◆ Devise a Plan

1. Decide what information you need to determine which kind of animal made each imprint, and decide where you will obtain this information.

2. Write down the procedure you will follow on a separate sheet of paper.

◆ Analyze and Conclude

After following the plan you devised, answer the following questions on a separate sheet of paper.

1. What information did you need to classify each fossil?

2. What kind of animal do you think made each imprint?

3. If you were unable to classify an imprint, what additional information would you need?

4. The hard parts of animals are usually the ones that make fossils. Using what you've learned from Chapter 2, what parts of a mollusk, an arthropod, and an echinoderm would leave the best imprint fossil?

5. List the characteristics of organisms that probably would not be preserved in fossils.

CHAPTER 2   **TEST**

Mollusks, Arthropods, and Echinoderms

◆ Multiple Choice

Write the letter of the correct answer on the line at the left.

2

_____ **1.** A squid is an example of a(n)
    a. arachnid.   **b.** cephalopod.
    c. octopus.   **d.** bivalve.

_____ **2.** In complete metamorphosis, an insect goes through all of the follow-
    ing stages except
    a. larva   **b.** nymph.
    c. pupa.   **d.** adult.

_____ **3.** Crustaceans are the only arthropods that have
    a. two body segments.   **b.** appendages.
    c. two pairs of antennae.   **d.** an exoskeleton.

_____ **4.** A male cricket uses sound to
    a. defend itself against predators.
    b. blend into the surroundings.
    c. attract a mate.
    d. trap prey for food.

_____ **5.** Which of the following is *not* a characteristic of mollusks?
    a. They have a mantle.
    b. They are invertebrates.
    c. They have radial symmetry.
    d. They eliminate waste with kidneys.

_____ **6.** Spiders, ticks, and scorpions are all
    a. gastropods.   **b.** parasites.
    c. arthropods.   **d.** herbivores.

_____ **7.** Which of the following is *not* a body segment of an insect?
    a. radula   **b.** thorax
    c. abdomen   **d.** head

_____ **8.** If a sea star loses an arm, it can grow a new one by a process called
    a. molting.   **b.** metamorphosis.
    c. camouflage.   **d.** regeneration.

CHAPTER 2 TEST *(continued)*

_____ **9.** Which of the following is not a way in which mollusks gather food?
    a. using tube feet to pry apart bivalves
    b. using tentacles to detect and grab prey
    c. using radulae to collect food
    d. using gills to collect food

_____ **10.** If an animal has one pair of antennae and six legs, it could be a(n)
    a. insect.   **b.** arachnid.
    c. octopus.   **d.** crustacean.

◆ Completion

Fill in the line to complete each statement.

11. A mollusk's _____ covers its internal organs and produces its shell if it has one.

12. During gradual metamorphosis, an egg hatches into a stage called a _____ .

13. The skin of most echinoderms is supported by a spiny internal skeleton, called a(n) _____ .

◆ True or False

Determine whether each statement is true or false. If it is true, write true. If it is false, change the underlined word or words to make the statement true.

_____ **14.** If a mollusk has two shells, it is a <u>gastropod</u>.

_____ **15.** The wings of an insect are attached to its <u>abdomen</u>.

_____ **16.** Tube feet, which most echinoderms use to grasp objects, move around, and catch food are part of the <u>circulatory system</u>.

_____ **17.** An echinoderm has <u>radial</u> symmetry.

CHAPTER 2 TEST *(continued)*

◆ Essay

Write a brief paragraph to answer each of the following.

18. Describe how the water vascular system of an echinoderm works.

_____

_____

_____

19. Describe how sound is produced.

2

_____

_____

_____

◆ Using Science Skills

20. Classifying Place a check mark in the column under the name of the group or groups which have each characteristic.

	Mollusks	Arthropods	Echinoderms
exoskeleton			
mantle			
muscular foot			
invertebrate			
jointed appendages			
water vascular system			
segmented bodies			
radial symmetry			
molting			
endoskeleton			

CHAPTER 2 TEST *(continued)*

◆ Using Science Skills

21. Interpreting a Diagram Label the following parts on the diagram.

   a. legs

   b. antenna

   c. compound eye

   d. wing

22. Classifying Based on what you know about the animal pictured, is it a mollusk, an arthropod, or an echinoderm? In what more specific group would you classify this animal? Explain what characteristic(s) you used to classify the animal. Use a separate sheet of paper if you need more space.

_____

_____

_____

_____

◆ Essay

On a separate sheet of paper, discuss each of the following statements in a brief paragraph.

23. Describe gradual metamorphosis.

24. Describe the main differences between gastropods, bivalves, and cephalopods with regard to their shells.

25. What is biological control of insects? Give an example. What is an advantage of the use of biological controls over the use of pesticides?

CHAPTER

3   **Making a Zoo Poster**

Students display their knowledge of the concepts in the chapter by creating a poster for a zoo.

◆ Expected Outcome

Each poster should show an example of each type of organism with the characteristics of each displayed in some way.

◆ Content Assessed

This activity assesses students' understanding of characteristics of fishes, reptiles, and amphibians.

◆ Skills Assessed

communicating, applying concepts

◆ Materials

◆ poster board, tempera paint, colored marking pens, white glue, tape, pencils, rulers, photographs cut from magazines

◆ Advance Preparation

◆ Acquire sufficient materials for the students who will be completing the task.

◆ Time

45 minutes

◆ Safety

Caution students to be careful with glue. Some students may be sensitive to fumes from the marking pens.

◆ Monitoring the Task

◆ Make sure students have included sufficient characteristics and that these include ways of distinguishing the different types of animals.

◆ As students are planning their posters, suggest that they consider what information they want to communicate with words, such as in lists or compare/contrast tables, and what information is effectively communicated visually.

CHAPTER

3

Making a Zoo Poster

In assessing students' performance, use the following rubric.

	4	3	2	1
Planning	Plan is clearly a very useful preparatory step for making the poster.	Plan is a useful preparatory step for making the poster.	Plan is a somewhat useful step for making the poster.	Plan is a barely useful step for making the poster.
Communicating	Poster is organized and neat and effectively uses both pictures and words, and includes descriptions, lists, and compare/contrast tables.	Poster is fairly well organized and neat and makes effective use of pictures and words, and includes descriptions and lists, but lacks compare/contrast tables.	Poster is somewhat organized and makes fair use of pictures and words but lacks compare/contrast tables.	Poster is disorganized and messy. Use of pictures and words is ineffective.
Concept Understanding	Poster shows more than four characteristics for each main animal group. Student communicates exemplary knowledge of the similarities and differences between the animal groups, including characteristics which are internal or can't be drawn.	Poster shows four characteristics for each main animal group. Student communicates adequate knowledge of the similarities and differences between the animal groups, including characteristics which are internal or can't be drawn.	Poster shows three characteristics for each main animal group. Student communicates some knowledge of the similarities and differences between the animal groups, but little on characteristics which are internal or can't be drawn.	Poster shows two characteristics for each main animal group. Student communicates little knowledge of the similarities and differences between the animal groups, including characteristics which are internal or can't be drawn.

CHAPTER 3   **PERFORMANCE ASSESSMENT**

Making a Zoo Poster

You are the new Education Coordinator at the zoo. Your first project is to design a poster to teach visitors about the characteristics of fish, amphibians, and reptiles.

◆ **Problem**   How can you design a poster to teach zoo visitors about the characteristics of fish, amphibians, and reptiles?

◆ **Suggested Materials**

poster board   tempera paint   colored marking pens
white glue   tape   pencils   rulers

◆ **Devise a Plan**

1. Think about what you know about the characteristics of each animal and how you want to show these characteristics. What will most help a zoo visitor identify and understand each kind of animal? Make a list of at least four or five characteristics for each animal that you want to include on your poster.

2. Make a quick sketch of your design. Decide how you will present the information you plan to include on your poster. Experiment with different layouts of the information to get the most effective display.

3. Position objects on the poster board, lightly sketch pictures, and letter in pencil first so you can still change things if you need to. When you are satisfied with your design, complete your poster.

4. Look at your poster. Will zoo visitors be able to tell how fish, amphibians and reptiles are similar? Will they be able to tell how the animals are different?

5. Is there a way you could include more information or display information more effectively?

◆ **Analyze and Conclude**

After following the plan that you devised, answer the questions below on a separate sheet of paper.

1. Describe how your poster teaches visitors about the characteristics of fish, amphibians, and reptiles.

2. What are the most important pieces of information that you want zoo visitors to learn from your poster?

CHAPTER 3   **TEST**

Fishes, Amphibians, and Reptiles

◆ Multiple Choice

Write the letter of the correct answer on the line at the left.

_____ **1.** Some chordates do not have
   a. a notochord at some point in life.
   b. a spinal column.
   c. a nerve cord.
   d. pharyngeal slits at some point in life.

_____ **2.** An animal whose body temperature changes depending on the environment is called a(n)
   a. ectotherm.   **b.** endotherm.
   c. vertebrate.   **d.** invertebrate.

_____ **3.** The three major groups of fishes are distinguished from one another by the types of _____ they have.
   a. fins   **b.** scales
   c. eggs   **d.** skeletons

_____ **4.** An object whose buoyancy is less than its weight
   a. can easily move up in the water.
   b. will remain floating at the same depth.
   c. will sink to the bottom.
   d. can easily move sideways in the water.

_____ **5.** Gills and lungs enable _____ to get into an animal's blood.
   a. oxygen   **b.** carbon dioxide
   c. urine   **d.** albumen

_____ **6.** *Amphibian* means
   a. "two tails."   **b.** "double life."
   c. "red-backed."   **d.** "three chambers."

_____ **7.** The amphibian heart has _____ chamber(s).
   a. one   **b.** two
   c. three   **d.** four

_____ **8.** All snakes have only one
   a. external ear.   **b.** eye.
   c. rib.   **d.** lung.

CHAPTER 3 TEST (*continued*)

_____ **9.** Which of the following groups evolved from reptiles?
     a. fishes and amphibians
     b. amphibians and mammals
     c. mammals and birds
     d. no new groups

_____ **10.** Unlike most fishes, sharks
     a. have skeletons of hard bone.
     b. have a two-loop circulatory system.
     c. cannot pump water over their gills.
     d. reproduce through external fertilization.

◆ Completion

Fill in the line to complete each statement.

11. Small bones called _____ line up in a row to form the backbone.

12. The skeletons of lampreys and hagfishes are made of _____ .

13. A _____ helps a bony fish stabilize its body at different depths in the water.

14. The upper chambers of an amphibian's heart are called _____ .

15. _____ are reptiles whose bodies are covered by a protective shell.

◆ True or False

If the statement is true, write true. If it is false, change the underlined word or words to make the statement true.

_____ **16.** Most fishes have <u>external</u> fertilization.

_____ **17.** A paleontologist is a scientist who studies <u>reptiles</u>.

_____ **18.** During metamorphosis, most salamander larvae lose their <u>lungs</u>.

_____ **19.** The yolk provides an embryo with the <u>food</u> it needs to grow.

_____ **20.** An animal's teeth are more likely to become fossils than its internal organs because they are <u>more numerous</u>.

CHAPTER 3 TEST *(continued)*

◆ Using Science Skills

Imagine you are an ocean biologist. One afternoon, a very excited fisherman calls to tell you that he thinks he has caught a shark in a nearby freshwater lake. What are two questions you could ask him about the structure of his fish to determine whether or not he actually caught a shark?

21. Posing Questions Question #1 for fisherman:

_____

_____

22. Posing Questions Question #2 for fisherman:

_____

_____

◆ Essay

Write an answer for each of the following.

23. Describe the differences between ectothermic and endothermic animals.

_____

_____

_____

_____

24. Compare and contrast the eggs of amphibians and reptiles.

_____

_____

_____

_____

25. Describe three adaptations that reptiles have for conserving water.

_____

_____

_____

_____

CHAPTER 3 TEST (*continued*)

◆ Using Science Skills

Answer the following questions using the graph below.

Rock Records

26. **Interpreting Data** If the layers are undisturbed, which rock layer is probably older, B or C? Explain your answer.

_____

_____

_____

27. **Relating Cause and Effect** Layer D contains a vertebrate skull. Give a reason to explain why there are no vertebrate skulls in layers A, B, or C.

_____

_____

_____

28. **Applying Concepts** Which layer in site 2 is probably the same age as site B? Explain your answer.

_____

_____

_____

◆ Essay

On a separate sheet of paper, discuss each of the following statements in a brief paragraph.

29. Describe how an ectotherm could warm up when the air temperature is cold or cool down when the air temperature is hot.

30. Explain why amphibians are more sensitive than reptiles to changes in the environment.

CHAPTER
4   Bird or Mammal?

This activity invites students to make comparisons between two animals whose superficial characteristics are identical. Students must extract more information from the diagrams or determine which additional information they would need. To successfully complete this activity, students must apply concepts from the chapter, comparing and contrasting the defining characteristics of birds and mammals.

◆ Expected Outcome

Students will first list the characteristics of each animal. Then they will list the additional characteristics that can be obtained from the diagrams. Students should then be able to determine that the platypus is a mammal because it has fur, and that the penguin is a bird because it has feathers. If students are unable to make the determination because the fur and feathers are not obvious, they can still successfully complete the activity by listing the additional information they would need, such as whether the animal has fur, produces milk, or its forelimbs are modified as wings.

◆ Content Assessed

This activity assesses students' ability to compare and contrast the characteristics of birds and mammals.

◆ Skills Assessed

comparing and contrasting, applying concepts, making models

◆ Materials

◆ drawing paper

◆ colored pencils, pastels, or crayons

◆ Advance Preparation

◆ Obtain drawing paper and colored pencils, pastels, or crayons.

◆ Time

One class period

◆ Monitoring the Task

◆ To introduce the Performance Assessment, review the defining characteristics of birds as presented in Section 1.

◆ Note the picture of the platypus in Section 4. Students may use this picture as a model.

◆ Remind students that although they may recognize the animals and know which is which, to successfully complete the activity they must justify their choices and make complete and defining lists.

4

CHAPTER 4

Bird or Mammal?

In assessing students' performance, use the following rubric.

	4	3	2	1
Developing a Hypothesis	Hypothesis is clearly stated or additional information needed is clearly stated. Four or more of the defining characteristics of birds or mammals are included.	Hypothesis is adequate or additional information needed is clearly stated. Three defining characteristics of birds or mammals are included.	Hypothesis is vague or additional information needed is vague. Two defining characteristics of birds or mammals are included.	Hypothesis is incorrectly stated or additional information is missing. Most characteristics are incorrect or missing.
Making Models	Sketches fully illustrate the hypothesis and are completely labeled.	One trait from the hypothesis may be missing from the sketch. One trait on the sketch is not labeled.	Two traits from hypothesis are missing from the sketch. Two traits on the sketch are not labeled.	More than two traits from hypothesis are missing from the sketch. Traits on the sketch are not labeled.
Comparing and Contrasting	Sketches, written answers, and Venn diagram reflect a comprehensive knowledge of the similarities and differences of mammals and birds.	Sketches, written answers, and Venn diagram reflect adequate knowledge of the similarities and differences of mammals and birds.	Sketches, written answers, and Venn diagram reflect some knowledge of the similarities and differences of mammals and birds. Some key points are missing.	Sketches, written answers, and Venn diagram reflect little knowledge of the similarities and differences of mammals and birds. Most key points are missing.

Animals

CHAPTER 4   **PERFORMANCE ASSESSMENT**

Bird or Mammal?

◆ Problem

While strolling through the zoo one day, you observe an animal that has a bill and webbed feet; swims underwater; lays eggs, eats small fish and crustaceans, and is endothermic. Now you walk to a different part of the zoo. You see another animal that has a bill and webbed feet; swims underwater; lays eggs, eats small fish and crustaceans, and is endothermic. One of these animals is a bird and one is a mammal, but which is which?

◆ Suggested Materials

drawing paper   colored pencils, pastels, or crayons

◆ Devise a Plan

1. On a separate sheet of paper, make a chart with two columns. Label one column "First Animal" and the other "Second Animal." Write what you know about each animal in the columns of the chart. Include information from the pictures as well as from the problem statement.

2. Make a hypothesis about which animal is a bird and which is a mammal. Or, if you do not have enough information to determine which is a bird and which is a mammal, make a list of the additional information you would need.

3. Sketch or trace each animal on a separate sheet of paper. Label the characteristics you know of each. Based on the characteristics, decide which animal is a bird and which is a mammal. If you cannot decide, list the additional information you need.

◆ Analyze and Conclude

After completing your labeled sketches, answer the following questions on the back of this sheet or on a separate sheet of paper.

1. What characteristics do all birds and mammals share?

2. What characteristics distinguish birds from mammals?

3. Construct a Venn diagram showing the characteristics of birds, the characteristics of mammals, and the characteristics they have in common.

CHAPTER 4   **TEST**

Birds and Mammals

◆ Multiple Choice

Write the letter of the correct answer on the line at the left.

_____ **1.** All kinds of birds and all kinds of mammals
      a. have teeth.   **b.** lay eggs.
      c. have three-chambered hearts.   **d.** are endotherms.

_____ **2.** The difference in _____ above and below a wing causes lift.
      a. temperature   **b.** air pressure
      c. feather density   **d.** weight

_____ **3.** Placental mammals are divided into groups based on adaptations such as
      a. how they eat.   **b.** how their young develop.
      c. how they sleep.   **d.** size.

_____ **4.** A gestation period is the length of time
      a. a bird sits on its eggs.
      b. a baby marsupial spends in the pouch.
      c. between birth and maturity.
      d. between fertilization and birth.

_____ **5.** Birds usually sit on their eggs to
      a. feel the chicks hatch.   **b.** keep the eggs cool.
      c. keep them warm.   **d.** keep the eggs moist.

_____ **6.** All kinds of birds
      a. fly.   **b.** lay eggs.
      c. have three-chambered hearts.   **d.** are ectotherms.

_____ **7.** All mammals feed their young with
      a. worms.   **b.** milk
      c. plants.   **d.** other animals.

_____ **8.** Mammals are classified as monotremes, marsupials, or placental mammals according to
      a. how they move and feed.
      b. how they hunt.
      c. how their young develop.
      d. their size and how many legs they have.

CHAPTER 4 TEST (continued)

_____ **9.** Both a mammal's fur and a bird's feathers function to help the animal
   a. fly.   **b.** keep warm.
   c. hatch eggs.   **d.** climb.

_____ **10.** No mammal
   a. can lay eggs.
   b. can fly.
   c. spends its entire life in water.
   d. has a three-chambered heart.

◆ Completion

Fill in the line to complete each statement.

11. _____ feathers trap air next to a bird's body, keeping the bird warm.

12. The _____ is an organ through which some mammals receive food and oxygen from their mothers during gestation.

13. Mammals are assisted in breathing by a large muscle located under the lungs called the _____ .

14. Birds can store food in an organ called a _____ before the food goes to the stomach.

15. Koalas, kangaroos, and opossums belong to the _____ group of mammals.

◆ True or False

If the statement is true, write true. If it is false, change the underlined word or words to make the statement true.

_____ **16.** All mammals are <u>invertebrates</u>.

_____ **17.** The young of marsupials are <u>more</u> developed at birth than the young of placental mammals.

_____ **18.** <u>Contour feathers</u> help a bird keep its balance during flight.

_____ **19.** <u>Monotremes</u> are mammals that lay eggs.

_____ **20.** A wing provides lift because its top surface is <u>straight</u>.

CHAPTER 4 TEST *(continued)*

◆ Essay

On a separate sheet of paper, write a brief paragraph to answer each of the following.

21. Compare and contrast the shape and function of the four kinds of mammal teeth.

22. What is a placenta and what is its function?

23. Discuss the similarities and differences in the development from birth of a marsupial with that of a placental mammal.

◆ Using Science Skills

Use the diagram below to answer the following questions. Write the letter of the correct answer for question 24 on the line at the left. Write your answer for question 25 on a separate sheet of paper.

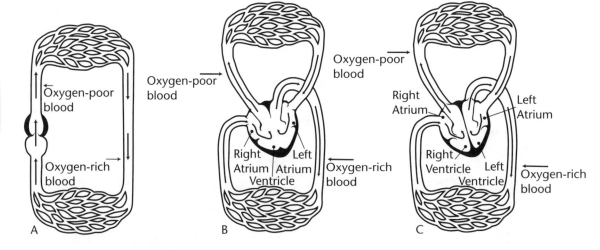

_____ **24. Interpreting Diagrams** Which diagram represents the circulatory system of a bird?

25. Interpreting Diagrams What advantages does the bird circulatory system provide over the others?

◆ Essay

Write an answer for each of the following. Use the back of this sheet if you need more room.

26. Compare and contrast the three kinds of bird flight—flapping, gliding, and soaring. Include information on which form or forms use a lot of energy and which use a little.

_____

_____

Animals

CHAPTER 4 TEST *(continued)*

27. Describe what happens to a seed from the time it is eaten by a sparrow until it leaves the stomach.

_____

_____

_____

28. Explain how reproduction in birds and reptiles is similar.

_____

_____

_____

29. In addition to wings and feathers, birds have other adaptations that help them fly. Describe at least two of these adaptations.

_____

_____

_____

◆ Using Science Skills

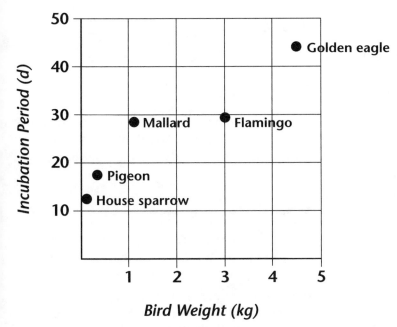

30. Making Generalizations What seems to be the relationship between the size of a bird species and its incubation time?

CHAPTER
5   Observing Pillbug Behavior

Students will observe the behavior of pillbugs, common terrestrial crustaceans. Students will observe at least three behaviors. Each student will then choose one of the observed behaviors, formulate a hypothesis to explain its survival value, and suggest an experiment to test his or her hypothesis.

◆ Expected Outcome

Students will observe several behaviors of pillbugs in the natural habitat container. Then they will write a hypothesis to investigate a cause and effect relationship between stimulus and behavior. Using material you provide, students should create new habitats and use stimuli to study behaviors such as a preference for moist environments, and aversion to light, cold, or touch. Students should look for presence or absence of territoriality, competition, sociality, communication, and/or other interactions between pillbugs. Students will use their ability to observe and their knowledge of animal behavior from the chapter to analyze the behavior and design experiments, and to explain how the studied behavior could help pillbugs survive.

◆ Content Assessed

This Performance Assessment tests students' knowledge of animal behavior and their understanding of the scientific method.

◆ Skills Assessed

observing, developing a hypothesis, designing an experiment

◆ Materials

◆ Sowbugs are related to pillbugs and may be used instead. Pillbugs curl up into balls. Sowbugs do not.

◆ Provide students with pillbugs, containers to hold the pillbugs during observations (such as petri dishes or other small containers), flashlights, toothpicks, ice, sand, soil, compost, and peat.

◆ Advance Preparation

◆ When not being observed, pillbugs should be kept in a warm, moist, dark environment with plenty of organic material. Place soil, leaf litter, and compost in a plastic tray with an opaque cover. Keep the soil slightly damp with strips of newspaper and a spray bottle. Pillbugs or sowbugs can be collected locally, obtained from your school district's living materials center, or purchased from a scientific supply company.

◆ Prepare enough natural habitat containers for each student or group. Put 5 to 10 pillbugs in each natural habitat container.

◆ Time

Allow at least 50 minutes for the activity.

◆ Safety

Pillbugs and sowbugs are harmless, but students should wash their hands if they touch them. Make sure that students take care not to harm the animals.

◆ Monitoring the Task

◆ Students should transfer pillbugs with a spoon or by holding them gently with their fingertips or in their palms.

◆ Monitor students to see if they are making accurate observations. In the Analyze and Conclude section, some students may get "stuck" on a question. If this happens, they will not be able to answer subsequent questions. To help these students, you may want to suggest ways of proceeding. Make sure students record their observations on a separate sheet of paper.

Observing Pillbug Behavior

In assessing students' performance, use the following rubric.

	4	3	2	1
Understanding Concepts	Description of stimuli, observed responses, and the survival value of the chosen behavior indicate complete understanding of behavior in animals.	Description of stimuli, observed responses, and the survival value of the chosen behavior indicate good understanding of behavior in animals.	Description of stimuli, observed responses, and the survival value of the chosen behavior indicate some understanding of behavior in animals.	Description of stimuli, observed responses, and the survival value of the chosen behavior indicate little understanding of behavior in animals.
Making Observations	Five or more observations are listed. Observations are relevant.	Four observations are listed. Observations are relevant.	Three observations are listed or observations are unrelated to actual behavior.	Less than three observations are listed and observations are unrelated to actual behavior.
Developing a Hypothesis	Hypothesis is well stated and related to observation.	Reasonable hypothesis is stated.	Hypothesis is given, but hypothesis may not be related to observation.	Hypothesis is absent or supplied by teacher.
Designing an Experiment	Experiment design is complete, including data table, environments, and stimuli, and clearly tests the hypothesis. The variable and all the controls are identified.	Experiment design is adequate, but some elements of data table, environment description, and stimuli are missing, and may test more than the hypothesis. The variable and most of the controls are identified.	Experiment design is missing a significant number of elements of data table, environment description, and/or stimuli, and demonstrates only a partial understanding of hypothesis testing. The variable and one control are identified.	Experiment design is missing most of the required elements and demonstrates little or no comprehension of hypothesis testing. Neither the variable nor a control is identified.

CHAPTER 5   **PERFORMANCE ASSESSMENT**

Observing Pillbug Behavior

In both instinctive and learned behaviors, animals respond to many different stimuli, or cues in their environment. You will observe various behaviors of pillbugs as they respond to different stimuli.

◆ **Problem**   Can you observe a behavior of pillbugs that helps them to survive?

◆ **Suggested Materials**

small test containers	ice cubes	water	flashlight
sand or soil	organic material	toothpicks	spoon

◆ **Safety**   🦺   Pillbugs are harmless, but they should not be handled more than necessary. Be careful not to harm your test animals. Wash your hands after handling the pillbugs.

◆ **Devise a Plan**

1. Your teacher has supplied several pillbugs and placed them in a natural habitat. These will be your test animals. Your teacher has also provided you with a variety of materials to use in devising your plan. Look at these materials and decide how they relate to pillbug behavior.

2. Observe the test animals in their natural habitat. Record three to five pillbug behaviors. Be specific and give details. Describe the actual behavior, not what you think the animal is doing.

3. Based on the natural behaviors you observed, write a plan to test a particular pillbug preference as indicated by its behavior. In your plan, include how you will make test environments and what stimuli you will use. Also include a hypothesis about how the animal will behave.

4. Prepare a data table to record your observations.

5. Have your teacher approve your plan.

◆ **Analyze and Conclude**

After following the plan you devised, answer the following questions on a separate sheet of paper.

1. Was your hypothesis supported?

2. Suggest an explanation for how the behavior that you observed helps pillbugs survive.

3. What are the controls in your experiment? What is the variable?

CHAPTER 5   **TEST**

Animal Behavior

◆ Multiple Choice

Write the letter of the correct answer on the line at the left.

_____ **1.** An animal's reaction to a stimulus is a(n)
  a. artificial intelligence.
  b. instinct.
  c. response.
  d. behavior.

_____ **2.** In _____ , an animal uses what it already knows to figure out a new problem.
  a. imprinting
  b. conditioning
  c. instinct learning
  d. insight learning

_____ **3.** Pavlov's dog is an example of an animal that has been subjected to
  a. instinct.
  b. migration.
  c. conditioning.
  d. hibernation.

_____ **4.** An area occupied and defended by an animal or group of animals is a
  a. neighborhood.
  b. district.
  c. home.
  d. territory.

_____ **5.** In order to ensure that mating and reproduction occur, some animals perform
  a. migration.
  b. courtship behavior.
  c. hibernation.
  d. behavior.

5

CHAPTER 5 TEST *(continued)*

_____ **6.** When some birds fly south in the winter, they are showing _____ behavior.
  a. migration
  b. hibernation
  c. territorial
  d. circadian

_____ **7.** Ants are animals that live in a special group called a(n) _____ , where all the individuals work for the good of the community.
  a. territory
  b. society
  c. group
  d. herd

_____ **8.** Chemical means of communication include
  a. sight
  b. hearing.
  c. pheromones.
  d. speaking.

_____ **9.** Pheromones are not used for
  a. identifying other animals.
  b. attracting mates.
  c. locating food.
  d. poisoning prey.

5

_____ **10.** _____ occurs in some birds and mammals when they recognize and follow the first moving object they see.
  a. Imprinting
  b. Conditioning
  c. Response
  d. Learning

CHAPTER 5 TEST *(continued)*

◆ Completion

Fill in the line to complete each statement.

11. Animals may compete for food by showing _____ , which is a threatening behavior.

12. Fireflies use a type of chemical communication called _____ .

13. Learning is a change in _____ based on practice or experience.

14. _____ is a state of greatly reduced body activity in the winter.

15. Behavior patterns that follow a daily cycle are called _____ .

◆ True or False

If the statement is true, write true. If it is false, change the underlined word or words to make the statement true.

_____ **16.** Some birds <u>hibernate</u> in the winter, when they fly to warmer areas to find food.

_____ **17.** When you learned to ride a bike, you became better the more you practiced. This is an example of <u>trial-and-error</u> learning.

_____ **18.** Animals sometimes travel in <u>groups</u> because they are less likely to be attacked by predators.

_____ **19.** Most behaviors of invertebrates are <u>learned</u>.

_____ **20.** <u>Instincts</u> are behaviors that are inborn and performed correctly the first time.

5

CHAPTER 5 TEST *(continued)*

◆ Using Science Skills: Interpreting Diagrams

The diagram below represents a dog being trained to "dance," or walk in a circle. Use the diagram to answer the questions below.

A. ⎯OX⎯⎯⎯⎯⎯OX⎯⎯⎯⎯⎯OX⎯→
　　　　　　Time

X = dog walks in a circle
O = command given to "dance"
▲ = dog receives treat

B. ⎯OX▲⎯⎯⎯⎯OX▲⎯⎯⎯⎯OX▲⎯→
　　　　　　Time

21. Which line comes first in time? _____

Use the terms *stimulus, response,* and *reward* to answer Questions 22–24.

22. After the dog learns the trick, **X** is called the _____ .

23. O is called the _____ .

24. ▲ is called the _____ .

25. What kind of learning does the diagram represent? _____

ANIMALS   **BOOK TEST**

Animals

◆ Multiple Choice

Write the letter of the correct answer on the line at the left.

_____ **1.** The arthropod's outer skeleton that protects the animal and helps
prevent evaporation of water is called an
   a. ectotherm.   **b.** endotherm.
   c. exoskeleton.   **d.** endoskeleton.

_____ **2.** _____ is an example of sexual reproduction.
   a. Budding   **b.** Regeneration
   c. Adaptation   **d.** Fertilization

_____ **3.** A cnidarian body plan that is shaped like a vase is a
   a. pupa.   **b.** polyp.
   c. medusa.   **d.** larva.

_____ **4.** Sea stars, sea urchins, sand dollars, and sea cucumbers are classified in
the _____ phylum.
   a. echinoderm   **b.** arthropod
   c. mollusk   **d.** reptile

_____ **5.** The bones of a spinal column are called
   a. vertebrae.   **b.** cartilage.
   c. notochord.   **d.** chordate.

_____ **6.** A paleontologist is a scientist who studies
   a. fish.   **b.** reptiles.
   c. mammals.   **d.** fossils.

_____ **7.** Short, fluffy feathers that are specialized to trap a bird's body heat are
called _____ feathers.
   a. flight   **b.** contour
   c. down   **d.** crop

_____ **8.** Mammals that lay eggs are called
   a. marsupials.   **b.** monotremes.
   c. omnivores.   **d.** placental mammals.

_____ **9.** A behavior that is inborn and performed correctly the first time is a(n)
   a. insight.   **b.** stimulus.
   c. response.   **d.** instinct.

_____ **10.** Reptiles have leathery eggs, scaly skin, and kidneys. These three adaptations help the reptile conserve
   a. water.   **b.** heat.
   c. oxygen.   **d.** waste.

BOOK TEST *(continued)*

◆ Completion

Fill in the line to complete each statement.

11. Humans, fish, and birds each have only one line of symmetry. This type of symmetry is called _____ .

12. Mollusks that have two shells held together by hinges and strong muscles are called _____ .

13. The three major groups of fishes are distinguished from one another by the structure of their mouths and by their _____ .

14. Sharply pointed teeth that are used to stab food and tear into it are called

_____ .

15. Reproduction and mating are ensured through _____ behavior between males and females of the same species.

◆ True or False

Determine whether each statement is true or false. If it is true, write true. If it is false, change the underlined word or words to make the statement true.

_____ **16.** Segmented worms have an <u>open</u> circulatory system.

_____ **17.** The transformation from egg to an adult butterfly is called a <u>gradual metamorphosis</u>.

_____ **18.** Amphibian <u>larvae</u> breathe with gills.

_____ **19.** Birds fly in three basic ways. <u>Flapping flight</u> is the type of flight that requires the most energy.

_____ **20.** Pheromones are <u>behaviors</u> that some animals use to communicate.

◆ Essay

On a separate sheet of paper, write a brief paragraph to answer easch of the following.

21. One characteristic of mammals is a diaphragm. What is a diaphragm and what function does it serve?

22. Name three adaptations that can help keep endothermic animals warm. Explain how the adaptations work.

BOOK TEST (continued)

◆ Using Science Skills

Use the tree diagram of major animal phyla below and your knowledge of animal characteristics to help identify the animals described.

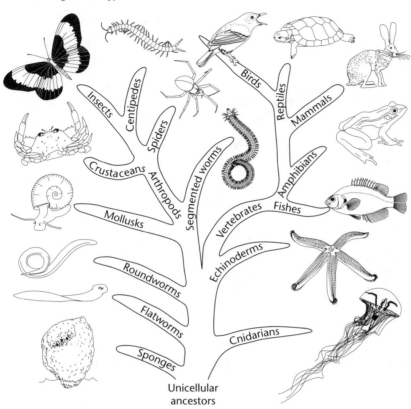

23. **Classifying** To which major phyla do the following animals belong?

   a. This animal obtains food by straining water taken in through its pores. It has no tissues, organs, or symmetry. _____

   b. This arthropod has twelve legs and two pair of antennae. _____

   c. This vertebrate is an endotherm. It has two legs and is not covered in fur or hair. _____

   d. This vertebrate is an ectotherm. It begins its life with gills, but breathes through its lungs as an adult. _____

24. **Interpreting Diagrams** In the tree diagram above, sea stars, sometimes known as starfish, are not shown on the same branch as the fishes. Explain, citing at least one major difference between the two.

   _____

   _____

   _____

BOOK TEST *(continued)*

25. Drawing Conclusions Can an animal be both an arthropod and a vertebrate? Explain.

_____

_____

◆ Using Science Skills

Use the Venn diagram to answer the following questions.

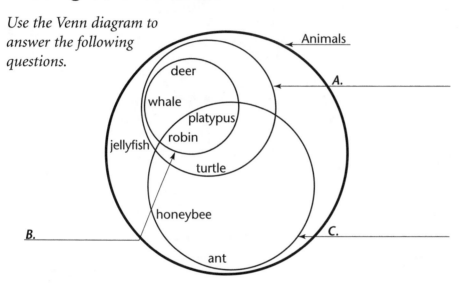

26. Interpreting Diagrams Write the name of each of the lettered sets on the Venn diagram above. Choose from the following list.

endotherms	ectotherms	egg-layers
flyers	invertebrates	vertebrates

27. Classifying Add the following animals to the chart above.

   a. king cobra   **b.** butterfly

   c. sponge   **d.** rabbit

◆ Essay

On a separate sheet of paper, discuss each of the following statements in a brief paragraph.

28. What are the differences and similarities between an endoskeleton and an exoskeleton?

29. Explain what imprinting is and how it is a combination of instinctive behavior and learning. Tell why imprinting is valuable to animals.

30. Frog, snakes, and birds all lay eggs. Explain how the eggs are different, and how they are similar.

Chapter 1

Chapter 1 Project Worksheet 1 (p. 14)

1–6. Answers will vary.

Chapter 1 Project Worksheet 2 (p. 15)

1. Answers will vary.

Section 1-1 Review and Reinforce (p. 19)

1. autotroph
2. phyla
3. species
4. omnivore
5. predator; prey
6. adaptation
7. invertebrate
8. asexual reproduction
9. herbivore

Section 1-1 Enrich (p. 20)

1. Most of the time it wasn't moving. Its top speed was 30 kph, but it moved at this speed only for very short amounts of time.

2. Its average speed was about 2 kph. It was active during the day. It stopped to rest only during the night. During the day it kept moving.

3. Animal 3 was active during the day. It usually moved at low speed or not at all. Its top speed was about 10 kph. It kept up that speed for close to 2 hours. It would have traveled about 25 km.

4. Animal 4 was active at night and slept during the day. Only animal 2 was active throughout the heat of the afternoon.

5. a. sit-and-wait predator
   b. herbivore or omnivore
   c. predator that pursues its prey long distances.
   d. sit-and-wait predator

Section 1-2 Review and Reinforce (p. 23)

1. radially symmetrical
2. asymmetrical
3. bilaterally symmetrical
4. bilaterally symmetrical
5. radially symmetrical
6. bilaterally symmetrical
7. bilateral symmetry
8. radial symmetry
9. many
10. one

Section 1-2 Enrich (p. 24)

1. bilateral symmetry; one
2. radial symmetry; many
3. The fish is the faster swimmer. A bilaterally symmetrical animal is more streamlined and can move faster than a radially symmetrical animal.
4. The single body parts occur roughly on the line of symmetry. Each paired body part lies on one side of the line of symmetry.

Section 1-3 Review and Reinforce (p. 27)

1. Sponges filter small food particles from the water as it passes through their bodies. Also, sponge cells get oxygen from the water. Reproduction takes place in water.

2. Sponges have spikes to protect them. Some also produce poisons.

3. Sponges reproduce asexually through budding. They reproduce sexually by releasing eggs or sperm into the water.

4. A coral polyp attaches itself to a hard surface on the ocean floor. The polyp produces a hard external skeleton. After a very long time, many, many polyps living together will create a coral reef.

5. Cnidarians reproduce asexually and sexually. Asexual reproduction is by budding. The manner of sexual reproduction depends on the species. Some species have both sexes in one individual; in other species some individuals are male and others are female.

6. Students should label A as a medusa, B as a polyp. The mouth on A is at the bottom, on B at the top. The medusa is free swimming.

7. Cnidarians, which include jellyfish, hydras, and corals, are carnivores that use their stinging cells to capture prey. They live in watery environments.

8. A larva is an immature form of an animal that looks very different from an adult.

Section 1-3 Enrich
(p. 28)

1. **A.** Cnidoblast is ready for firing. Thread is coiled.
B. Cnidocil is touched, and operculum pops open. Coiled thread begins to shoot out.
C. Coiled thread penetrates prey and injects venom. Prey is paralyzed or killed.
D. Tentacles pull food into mouth. Cnidarian digests food.

2. Although the jellyfish is dead, the stinging cells are still activated when a person steps on them.

3. defense

Section 1-4 Review and Reinforce
(p. 31)

1. segmented worms
2. through sexual and asexual reproduction
3. T
4. T
5. segmented worms
6. T
7. one-way
8. T
9. T
10. closed
11. Bristles
12. b
13. e
14. a
15. d
16. c

Section 1-4 Enrich
(p. 32)

1. about 16 cm

2. Drawing should indicate rocks 16 cm beneath surface, still in a layer.

3. About 91 years

4. Rocks continue to sink only as long as worms remove soil from beneath them and deposit it on the surface. The rocks would stop at a meter deep because there are no worms below that depth.

Chapter 1 Real-World Lab
(pp. 33–34)

For answers, see Teacher's Edition, pp. 26–27.

Chapter 1 Skills Lab
(pp. 35–37)

For answers, see Teacher's Edition, pp. 42–43.

Chapter 2

Section 2-1 Review and Reinforce
(p. 47)

Gastropods: snails or slugs; gather food with radulae; large foot; none or one; one broad foot adapted for creeping

Bivalves: clams, mussels, scallops, oysters; gather food with cilia on gills; burrow with a foot; yes, two; one thin foot adapted for digging

Cephalopods: squids, octopuses, nautiluses; gather food with tentacles; jet propulsion; some do, but not all; foot adapted to form tentacles around the mouth

1. radula
2. cephalopod
3. kidneys
4. mantle
5. bivalve
6. gastropod
7. gills

Section 2-1 Enrich
(p. 48)

1. *Patella:* wide cone, coiling absent, three-dimensional spiral absent
2. *Ectomaria:* narrow cone, coiling tight, three-dimensional spiral present

3. *Domatoceras:* narrow cone, tight coiling, three-dimensional spiral absent

4. *Buchia:* This is a special case, a bivalve, but the same principles apply. The smaller shell is similar to *Patella:* wide cone, coiling absent, three-dimensional spiral absent. The larger shell: wide cone, very loose coiling, three-dimensional spiral absent.

Section 2-2 Review and Reinforce
(p. 51)

1. arthropods; Answers may vary. Samples: mosquito, lobster, spider
2. centipedes; Answers may vary. Sample: centipede
3. arachnids; Answers may vary. Samples: spider, mite, tick, scorpion
4. millipedes; Answers may vary. Sample: millipede
5. exoskeleton; chitin
6. antennae
7. metamorphosis
8. abdomen
9. molting

Section 2-2 Enrich
(p. 52)

1. Fork B, because it is lower on the tree
2. The most recent common ancestor of crustaceans, insects, centipedes, and millipedes
3. The most recent common ancestor of spiders, ticks, mites, and scorpions. (Also accept: the last common ancestor of arachnids.)
4. Spiders. The most recent common ancestor of mites, ticks, and spiders is at fork F. It is higher on the tree, and therefore more recent, than any of their other common ancestors.

Section 2-3 Review and Reinforce
(p. 55)

1. Three body sections; students should label the head, thorax, and abdomen on the insect.
2. 6
3. Answers will vary. Students must list two features common to most insects. Possible answers will include an exoskeleton, one or two pairs of wings, and one pair of antennae.

4. Answers may vary: Samples: A bee has a bristly tongue that laps nectar from flowers; a mosquito's sharp mouthparts are used for jabbing and sucking blood.
5. Answers will vary. Sample: Some insects make substances that humans can use. For example, bees make honey and larvae of the silkworm moth spin fibers that can be made into silk. Bees also pollinate food crops and other plants. Some insects eat other insects that are harmful to humans.
6. Accept any of these: pesticides kill beneficial insects; they can harm other animals, such as birds; after a while, insects become resistant.
7. thorax
8. complete metamorphosis; pupa
9. gradual metamorphosis; nymph
10. camouflage

Section 2-3 Enrich
(p. 56)

1. It is Müllerian mimicry.
2. It looks like the bad-tasting butterflies in Figure 1. It is Batesian mimicry.
3. Because bees and wasps share one color pattern, predators are more likely to encounter that pattern and learn to avoid those bees and wasps. It is Müllerian mimicry.
4. Predators mistake them for dangerous coral snakes and avoid them. It is Batesian mimicry.

Section 2-4 Review and Reinforce
(p. 59)

1. c
2. d
3. d
4. To attract mates; also accept: to communicate.
5. Sample: Sound is produced by vibrations that create waves that move outward from the source.

Section 2-4 Enrich
(p. 60)

1. and **2.**

Volume of Call
(decibels)

3. the louder the sound, the more females are attracted

4. the louder the sound, the more parasitic flies

5. about 93 decibels.

Section 2-5 Review and Reinforce
(p. 63)

1. c

2. a

3. d

4. c

5. A sea star uses its arms and tube feet to capture its prey.

6. water vascular system

7. endoskeleton

8. echinoderm

9. regeneration

Section 2-5 Enrich
(p. 64)

1. The water vascular system (the tube feet) and five-part symmetry are visible.

2. We know ancient sea lilies had endoskeletons because their fossil remains are common and consist of pieces of the endoskeleton.

3. Tube feet are visible. The sea lily uses these to filter food particles from the water. The other echinoderms pictured use them for moving about.

4. Answers may vary. Sample: The sea lily attaches to solid objects on the bottom. The sea cucumber spends its life moving about. The sea lily must have solid objects such as rocks and shells to attach to, while the sea cucumber can travel across soft mud.

Chapter 2 Skills Lab
(pp. 65–66)

For answers, see Teacher's Edition, p. 53.

Chapter 2 Real-World Lab
(pp. 67–69)

For answers, see Teacher's Edition, pp. 68–69.

Chapter 3

Chapter 3 Project Worksheet 1
(p. 74)

feed on other fish

gills

get oxygen from the air

inflatable throat for loud voice

thick, scaled skin

climb trees

Chapter 3 Project Worksheet 2
(p. 75)
Part I:

Answers may vary. Sample: My adaptation is the tail fin of a barracuda, the hind leg of a bullfrog, and the tail of an alligator. Each one is an adaptation for moving the animal through the water, so each has a flat surface with which the animal pushes against water to move forward. Also, the bullfrog's leg has powerful muscles for jumping long distances on land. The alligator's tail is heavy and powerful and can be used as a weapon.

Section 3-1 Review and Reinforce
(p. 79)

1. Notochord, a nerve cord running down their back, pharyngeal slits at some life stage

2. A vertebrate is an animal with a backbone.

3. An endoskeleton supports and protects the body, helps give it shape, and gives muscles a place to attach.

4. Fish, amphibians, reptiles, mammals, birds

5. ectotherm

6. endotherm

7. ectotherm

8. ectotherm

9. endotherm

10. notochord

11. vertebra

12. cartilage

13. chordate

Section 3-1 Enrich (p. 80)

1. The turtle's femur looks relatively thicker than the frog's. The turtle's femur seems to be an adaptation for supporting the greater weight of the turtle.

2. The endoskeleton of the fish supports the least amount of weight. The downward pull of gravity would be partially offset by the buoyancy of the body of a fish, because it lives in the water and not on land.

3. The turtle backbone does not allow for as much movement as the backbone of the fish. You can see that the fish backbone is divided into smaller and more divisions than the backbone of the turtle, allowing the backbone to bend in more places.

4. Frogs and turtles have 4 legs. Frogs have large webbed feet for swimming.

Section 3-2 Review and Reinforce (p. 83)

1. To get oxygen from water

2. Both are made of cartilage.

3. jawless fishes, cartilaginous fishes (sharks and rays), bony fishes

4. external

5. A swim bladder helps a fish stabilize its body at different depths.

6. Answers may vary. Sample: limiting fishing through quotas; growing fish in fish farms

7. cartilaginous

8. ectotherms

9. true

10. true

11. swim bladder

12. buoyant force

Section 3-2 Enrich (p. 84)

1. lungs

2. oil

3. no control

4. swim bladder

5. The deep ocean. A fish with lungs must swim to the surface to get air. A deep-sea fish would not be able to do this. For a deep-sea fish, a swim bladder would be more useful.

6. An oxygen poor pond. A fish with lungs could live in water that did not contain very much oxygen by gulping air at the surface.

7. Near the surface of the ocean. A fish without a method to maintain buoyancy would have to swim constantly to stay afloat.

Section 3-3 Review and Reinforce (p. 87)

1–3.

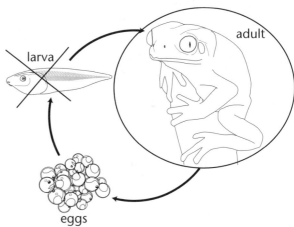

4. frogs and toads, salamanders. As adults, frogs and toads have four legs. The hind legs are adapted for jumping. They breathe with lungs and most are predators. Toads have dry, warty skins. Frogs' skins are moist and smooth. Adult frogs and toads lay eggs in water that hatch into larvae called tadpoles. Tadpoles live in water, breathe with gills, and are generally vegetarian. They gradually develop legs and lungs and become adult frogs.

An adult salamander has four legs adapted for walking, moist skin, lungs, and a tail. Salamanders are predators. Reproduction is similar to frogs and toads, but most have internal fertilization, while frogs and toads have external fertilization.

5. One reason is the loss of habitat. Another reason is that amphibians are particularly sensitive to pollution because their skins are thin and their eggs lack hard shells. Human-caused pollution is becoming more common.

6. Amphibian have strong skeletons and muscular limbs adapted for moving on land.

7. Amphibians are ectothermic vertebrates. They have three-chambered hearts. Their life cycle includes three stages—eggs laid in water hatch into swimming, gilled tadpoles which metamorphose into air-breathing adults with legs.

8. specific environment in which an animal lives

9. upper chamber of heart; receives blood

10. lower chamber of heart; pumps blood out

Section 3-3 Enrich
(p. 88)

1. Enough water would have to move through the membrane for the concentration of the water on either side to be equal.

2. Water would move out of the toad into the soil.

3. If the toad were to urinate, it would: (1) lose the salts it needs to keep its water concentration lower than that of the surrounding soil, and (2) it would expel water in its urine. Both of these results would cause the toad to dry out.

Section 3-4 Review and Reinforce
(p. 91)

1. C, F, H
2. G
3. D
4. A
5. B, E
6. Reptiles are ectothermic vertebrates with thick skins. They breathe with lungs and have four-chambered hearts and two-loop circulatory systems. Most lay thick-shelled eggs. The major groups of reptiles are lizards, snakes, turtles, and alligators and crocodiles. Most reptiles are predators.
7. Urine is a fluid of concentrated wastes that helps an animal reduce water loss.

Section 3-4 Enrich
(p. 92)

1. Serpentine motion. The snake could push off the grass quickly. Moving like a caterpillar would be slow.

2. If the snake used serpentine motion, its head would move side to side. The snake would probably use linear motion because it would be less likely to seen by the rabbit.

3. The snake would have to use serpentine motion because deep water wouldn't have any surface for its belly scales to grip. It could push off of water, as a fish pushes water with its fins.

Section 3-5 Review and Reinforce
(p. 95)

1. Sedimentary rocks are formed when layers of sediment such as mud or sand undergo a hardening process.

2. Answers may vary. Samples: They learn about the relationships between organisms; they learn when the present-day organisms might have developed.

3. The relative age of a fossil can be determined from its position in the rock. Usually, lower layers are older. Absolute age can be determined by measuring radioactive elements that have decayed.

4. Fossil B is older because it is in older rock. This is so because the rock on top was formed from layers of sediment that were deposited later.

5. paleontologist
6. fossil
7. sedimentary rock

Section 3-5 Enrich
(p. 96)

1. Yes, 410 and 470 million years.
2. The 410- and 470-million-year-old layers are both similar to layer A.
3. Layer A: 410 million years old
   Layer B: 370 million years old
   Layer C: 300 million years old
4. Layer D is younger than layer C.

Chapter 3 Skills Lab
(pp. 97–98)

For answers, see Teacher's Edition, p. 106.

Chapter 3 Real-World Lab
(pp. 99–101)

For answers, see Teacher's Edition, p. 94.

Chapter 4

Chapter 4 Project Worksheet 1
(p. 106)

1. Answers may vary. Examples of birds with widespread distribution in the U.S. include house sparrow, cardinal, blue jay, starling, house wren, and mourning dove.
2.–5. Answers will vary.

Chapter 4 Project Worksheet 2
(p. 107)

1.–3. Answers will vary.

Section 4-1 Review and Reinforce
(p. 111)

1. Answers may vary. Samples: endothermic, feathers, four-chambered heart, lay eggs
2. Answers may vary. Samples: wings, feathers, hollow bones, strong chest muscles, air sacs
3. Steering and balancing in flight (contour feathers); keeping warm (down feathers)
4. The heart has four chambers—two atria and two ventricles. The circulatory system has two loops. One loop carries blood from the heart to the lungs, The other loop carries blood from the heart to the rest of the body.
5. Answers may vary. Samples: A woodpecker's bill enables it to find insects by chiseling holes into trees. The bill of a spoonbill enables it to feed on small snimals in water.
6. crop
7. down feather
8. insulator
9. gizzard
10. contour feather

Section 4-1 Enrich
(p. 112)

1. Answers may vary. Sample:

Bird	Bird size	Bill size and shape
anhinga	large	long and pointed
turkey vulture	large	large, curved at end
chimney swift	small	short and wide*
pileated woodpecker	medium	long, narrow, and strong
evening grosbeak	small	heavy and powerful

Bird	Feet shape	Wing size and shape
anhinga	webbed	large*
turkey vulture	large and heavy	large and wide
chimney swift	small*	small and narrow
pileated woodpecker	large	medium
evening grosbeak	small	medium

*This information can't be determined from the drawing.

2. Answers may vary. Students' inferences should be supported by an observed characteristic. Sample answers: **A.** The Anhinga lives in or near water because it has webbed feet. **B.** The turkey vulture glides and soars because it has large and heavy wings. **C.** The chimney swift mostly flaps when flying because it has small wings. **D.** The pileated woodpecker eats insects that it finds through digging into dead wood with its long, narrow, and strong bill. **E.** The evening grosbeak eats seeds with its heavy, powerful bill.

Section 4-2 Review and Reinforce
(p. 115)

1.

Lower air pressure

Higher air pressure

2. Air molecules pushing

3. The faster air moves, the less pressure it exerts.

4. Flapping uses a lot of energy. Gliding and soaring don't use much energy.

5. A fast-flying bird. Since fast-moving air exerts less pressure than air that is moving slowly, the air above the wing exerts less pressure than the air beneath the wing, producing lift. The faster air moves the less pressure it exerts. The difference in air pressure between the top and bottom of the wing is greater when the bird flies faster than when it flies slower, so lift is greater.

6. An upward force that causes a bird or other object to rise; caused by lower air pressure on top of a wing than beneath the wing

Section 4-2 Enrich
(p. 116)

1. The "A" side faced down. Yes, it faced down on the upstroke, too.

2. The "A" side faced down. No, on the backward stroke, the "B" side faced down.

3. Answers may vary. Sample: Hovering would allow the hummingbird to feed in midair and quickly fly between flowers to feed. If a hummingbird couldn't hover, it might have to land on the flower to feed, but that might cause the bird and flower to fall from the bird's weight.

Section 4-3 Review and Reinforce
(p. 119)

1. Answers may vary. Samples: endothermic, hair, four-chambered heart, young fed on mother's milk

2. It is probably cold.

3. The lungs

4. Answers may vary. Sample: Mammals have a four-chambered heart and a two-loop circulatory system.

5. Answers may vary. Sample: You can infer what it eats.

6. Canine

7. Incisor

8. Molar/premolar

9. diaphragm

10. mammary gland

11. mammal

Section 4-3 Enrich
(p. 120)

	Nostril?	Eye?	Extra opening?
A	yes	yes	yes
B	yes	yes	no
C	yes	yes	yes

1. Specimens A and C are mammals or "mammal-like reptiles," because they have the extra opening, Specimen 2 does not look like a close relative of mammals.

2. In specimens A and C, there are big differences in the shapes of the teeth in different parts of the mouth. Incisors, canines, and teeth that could be either molars or premolars are visible. Specimen B doesn't have that characteristic—the teeth are all the same shape.

Note: For the information of interested students, the animals figured are:

Fig. 1. *Dimetrodon*, a "mammal-like reptile"

Fig. 2.A *Ptilocerus*, an extinct tree shrew, a mammal

Fig. 2.B *Paleothyris*, an extinct reptile

Fig. 2.C *Thrinaxodon*, an extinct "mammal-like reptile."

Section 4-4 Review and Reinforce
(p. 123)

1. placenta
2. monotreme
3. placental mammal
4. gestation period
5. marsupial

Section 4-4 Enrich
(p. 124)
1. Ratios of out-lever arms to in-lever arms
   Figure 2 —19 : 4 = 4.75
   Figure 3 —13 : 4 = 3.25
   Figure 4 —18 : 3 = 6
   Figure 5 —17 : 4 = 4.25
   (Accept any reasonable approximation.)
2. The animal in Figure 2 is probably faster because its out-lever arm/in-lever arm ratio is greater.
3. The animal in Figure 4 is probably faster because its out-lever arm/in-lever arm ratio is greater.
4. The animal in Figure 5 is probably more powerful because its out-lever arm/in-lever arm ratio is smaller.
5. In Figures 2 and 3, the in-lever arms and out-lever arms are on opposite sides of the fulcrum. In Figures 4 and 5, they are on the same side.

Chapter 4 Skills Lab
(pp. 125–127)
For answers, see Teacher's Edition, pp. 124–125.

Chapter 4 Real-World Lab
(pp. 128–129)
For answers, see Teacher's Edition, pp. 139.

Chapter 5

Chapter 5 Project Worksheet 1
(p. 134)
Answers will vary. Samples:
1. Sunflower seed
2. Crawls through cardboard tube
3. Pat on head
4. You tap lightly on glass of aquarium.

Dog; You say "Come."; Dog comes.; Dog treat

Guinea pig; You show a carrot; Guinea pig climbs on small box; bite of carrot

Parakeet; You say "Home."; Parakeet flies into cage; Sunflower seed

Chapter 5 Project Worksheet 2
(p. 135)
Answers will vary. Samples:
1. I will train my cat, Asta. He's smart, for a cat. I've taken care of Asta for three years, so he's comfortable around me. He is not afraid of me and lets me pick him up. He is my cat so I don't need to get the owner's permission to train him.
2. I will teach him to sit up on his hind legs like a trained lion. I chose this behavior because I think he can do it, since a lion is a big cat. It will look really cool.
3. Actually, I've never seen him sit up on his hind legs like a trained lion. But I've seen him reach up to sharpen his claws on the back of the sofa, so I know he is capable of doing the behavior.
4. The stimulus will be me waving a little "teaser" on a stick that I use to get him to jump and play. I'll also say "up." The reward will be a cat treat. I chose that stimulus and reward because I know he will notice the stimulus, and I know he likes cat treats.
5. I will be in a room without other people so he won't be distracted. First I will hold the treat up and let him eat out of my hand. Later I will wave the teaser while he eats out of my hand. I will let him stay on his hind feet longer and longer before actually letting him eat the treat. Finally, I will just wave the teaser, and I will reward Asta with a treat when he performs the trick.

6. 10 minutes, three times a day. In the morning before school (and before Asta eats), in the afternoon after school, and in the evening after dinner.

7. I'll have to make sure he is hungry when I train him so he'll be more likely to want the treat. Also, he might just want to play with the teaser, so I may have to use a different stimulus.

8. My parents will videotape me and Asta before I do any training. I'll use the teaser and say "up" but he won't know what to do. During the middle of the project, my parents will videotape Asta and me when he is partly trained. At the end of the project they will videotape us again. Hopefully, Asta will know the behavior by then and will respond like a lion at the circus.

Section 5-1 Review and Reinforce (p. 139)

1. to survive, to reproduce
2. L
3. I
4. conditioning
5. Answers will vary. Example: A dog learns to come when called after it gets a treat for doing it several times.
6. Answers will vary. Example: A man learns to type by practicing.
7. Answers will vary. Example: A girl learns to do a back flip off the diving board by practicing.
8. insight learning
9. e
10. a
11. g
12. d
13. b
14. f
15. c

Section 5-1 Enrich (p. 140)

1. Dogs moved to the food side most often. Pigeons moved to the food side least often.
2. Chickens. They did not seem to understand how to find the food. If they had, they would have walked to the food side more often.

3. If an animal were not hungry, if might not go after the food, even if it knew how. To avoid this, one might withhold food from the animals for a while before testing them.

Section 5-2 Review and Reinforce (p. 143)

1. Any two: food, water, space, shelter, and mates
2. Any two: sounds, scents, body position, and movements
3. Any two: to find food, to avoid cold, to reproduce
4. Define its boundaries by marking or advertising them in some manner, defend it
5. Answers may vary. Sample answer: It ensures that males and females of the same species recognize each other so that mating and reproduction can take place.
6. Answers may vary. Sample answers: Group members protect each other and work together to find food.
7. Answers may vary. Sample answers: The fish are communicating visually, by displaying their fins. They might be communicating aggression toward each other, or they might be competing for food, territory, or mates.
8. migration
9. hibernation
10. society
11. circadian rhythm
12. aggression

Section 5-2 Enrich (p. 144)

1. a. Bee I—source a
   b. Bee I—source d
2. Source d is closer.
3. Source d looks better because the bee is waggling more vigorously.
4. Source d makes sense. It's closer and better than source a.
5. The vertical stands for the direction to the sun.

Section 5-3 Review and Reinforce (p. 147)

1. A pheromone is a chemical released by one animal that affects the behavior of another animal of the same species.

2. Answers may vary. Samples: establish territories, locate food, attract a mate, and identify group members

3. The pheromone that attracts the male of a species is manufactured and put in a trap. Males are attracted by the pheromone, go into the trap, and can't get out.

4. Answers may vary. Sample: All ants of one colony have the same pheromone, which is different from the pheromone of ants from other colonies. If an ant wanders into another ant's colony, the intruder ant's pheromones will be recognized as foreign.

5. to attract or recognize mates

6. pheromone

7. bioluminescence

Section 5-3 Enrich
(p. 148)

1. Between points 5 and 1.

2. No queen substance is being produced because there are no queens to produce it.

3. The amount of queen substance would drop to zero. This would cause workers to raise new queens, just as they would do in a normal cycle.

4. The amount of queen substance would drop to zero. This would cause workers to raise new queens. This would be unlike their behavior in a normal cycle, when they would be prevented from raising queens by a lot of queen substance being available to each worker.

Chapter 5 Skills Lab
(pp. 149–150)

For answers, see Teacher's Edition, p. 159.

Chapter 5 Real-World Lab
(pp. 151–153)

For answers, see Teacher's Edition, pp. 168–169.

Interdisciplinary Explorations

Science: Ways the Chinese Use Insects
(p. 154)

1. b

2. a

3. c

4. e

5. d

6. Bees aid agriculture by pollinating flowers. Many people eat the honey collected by bees.

7. The silkworm is not a worm. It is the larvae of a moth. It is incorrectly called a worm because it is long and thin. Unlike a true worm, it has legs.

8. Answers will vary. Sample: The silkworm obtains some chemical from the mulberry leaf required to manufacture silk.

Science: Spider Silk
(p. 155)

1. No, but they are a step closer to knowing how to raise them.

2. The spider spins a web to capture insects. The insects are trapped by sticky material on some of the threads of the web.

3. The silk is stronger than steel. The silk can stretch more than 10 times its own length.

4. Answers may vary. Sample: Fabrics made from spider silk might not break as easily.

5. Answers may vary. Sample: Plants need good soil, sunlight, and water. They can be quite easy to grow. Spiders need to be fed and to have space to live and to spin their webs. It takes many spiders to make a small amount of cloth.

Mathematics: Graphing Mountain Heights
(p. 156)

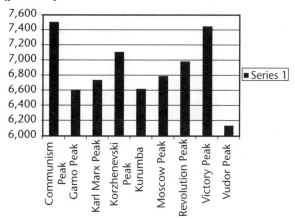

1. Communism is highest, Vudor is lowest.

2. 1,363 meters

3. Kurumba and Garmo Peak

Mathematics: Your Weight in Food (p. 157)

1. 30 days
2. 75 kilograms
3. 1.67 times
4. 900 kilograms
5. 600 days
6. about 87 weeks
7. 547.5 kilograms
8. 2,737.5 kilograms

Mathematics: A Trip on the Silk Road (p. 158)

1. 7.5 days
2. 250 kilometers
3. 3 times
4. 8 yaks
5. 180 rolls

Social Studies: World Populations (p. 159)

1. Greece
2. India
3. Iran
4. Russia
5. Greece
6. Greece, Saudi Arabia, Iraq, Uzbekistan, Italy, Turkey, Iran, Russia, India, China
7. India

Social Studies: Interpreting a Map (p. 160)

1. Black Sea
2. Mediterranean Sea
3. Nan Shan Mountains
4. Kashgar
5. Pamir Mountains
6. Bay of Bengal
7. Rome
8. Europe
9. Asia
10. East

Social Studies: Finding Cities Along the Silk Road (p. 161)

j Almaty
h Ankara
f Athens
a Baghdad
b Beirut
g Dushanbe
c Kabul
d Nicosia
i Rome
e Tehran

1. Almaty
2. Baghdad
3. Athens and Dushanbe
4. Rome and Almaty

Language Arts: Silk Vocabulary (p. 163)

1. whinny
2. pack animals
3. caravan
4. suture
5. harness
6. wasteland
7. treacherous
8. shimmer
9. ceremonial
10. snout

Language Arts: Writing Your Own Myth (p. 164)

Student essays will vary. Make sure they explain in some way how the yak got his fur. Look for creativity, humor, and imagination. Also look for a believable setting, a good statement of the problem, and a humorous solution to the problem

Language Arts: A Broken Promise
(p. 165)

1. The time and place of the setting should be clearly identified.
2. Students should identify several traits of the main character.
3. Students should describe other characters and their traits.
4. The conflict should be one that is focused enough to explore in a short story.
5. Plots should be described clearly. Events should be linked by cause-and-effect relationships.

Assessment

Chapter 1 Performance Assessment
(p. 168)

1. Planarians move away from light.
2. Answers may vary. Sample: When a light is shined on a planarian, it moves toward the light. My observations did not support my hypothesis. I controlled the temperature of the container (except for the amount of extra heat from the flashlight), the presence and arrangement of objects in the container, and I was careful not to jar the table or disturb the planarian as I did the experiment. The variable was the presence or absence of light shining on the planarian.
3. Answers will vary. Sample: If planarians avoid light in nature, they might be safer because there are fewer predators. Also, they might find food in dark crevices. Or they might get sunburned since they don't have a thick skin.
4. Answers may vary. Sample: Since cnidarians have stinging cells, they might not have very many predators, so they might not have to worry much about escaping predators. Some cnidarians live in the ocean in very bright places, so they must have some adaptation to withstand the light. The textbook doesn't say that cnidarians have eyespots, so maybe they don't sense light.

Chapter 1 Test
(p. 169–172)

1. c
2. b
3. d
4. a
5. b
6. c
7. a
8. b
9. c
10. c
11. segmented worms
12. habitat
13. host
14. two
15. bristles
16. bilateral
17. T
18. T
19. polyps
20. Autotrophs
21. The animal is a cnidarian (also accept jellyfish). It has long tentacles, a bowl-shaped body, and a mouth that faces downward.
22. The stinging cells in the tentacles inject venom into the fish. Then the tentacles draw the fish into the mouth. The digestive system eats the food and expels the waste out the mouth.
23. Coral reefs form when a free-swimming coral larva attaches to a solid surface. The coral larva becomes a polyp and secretes a hard, stony skeleton. Over time, many coral larvae attach to the surface and the polyps reproduce asexually. As more and more polyps secrete stony skeletons, the colony eventually forms a coral reef.
24. Earthworms have a closed circulatory system. In this type of system, blood flows through a network of blood tubes called vessels. A closed circulatory system benefits the earthworm because is more efficient than an open circulatory system. A closed system can move blood more quickly. This allows the worms to grow large and be active.
25. Answers could include adaptations such as sharp teeth, sharp claws, the ability to run fast, good vision, and good hearing. Sharp teeth allow predators to hold, kill, and eat prey. Sharp claws help predators catch and hold their prey. The ability to run fast helps predators chase down and catch their prey. Good

vision helps predators spot their prey at great distances. Good hearing helps predators hear their prey.

26. humans, snails
27. Accept any two: By keeping human waste from reaching the water, by keeping people away from contaminated water, by controlling the snail population, by developing drugs to treat victims.
28. Animals are multicellular. They must eat other organisms for food. They can reproduce sexually, asexually, or both. Most animals can move from place to place.
29. Animals with bilateral symmetry can move quickly and efficiently because they have balanced, streamlined bodies. Also, they have sense organs concentrated at their front ends, so they are able to get information about food or predators that are in front of them. Efficient movement and sense organs help them get food and avoid enemies.
30. Scientists study the structure of animals' bodies, the way they develop as embryos, and their DNA.

Chapter 2 Performance Assessment (pp. 173–175)

1. Answers will vary, depending on the exact nature of each simulated fossil, but should only include actually observed characteristics. Sample: For the first fossil I saw the imprint of the smooth exoskeleton. I needed to see that the animal had 5 pairs of jointed legs rather than 4 pairs or 3 pairs, which meant it was a crustacean, rather than a different kind of arthropod.
2. Answers will depend on the imprint fossils the students observed. Sample: The first simulated fossil was made by a crustacean, in the arthropod phylum. It is a crab.
3. Answers will vary. Sample: I thought one fossil was a type of echinoderm called a sea urchin because the little dents in the fossil were caused by bumps like the echinoderm shell had, but I really needed to see that it had 5-part symmetry to be sure.
4. Shells of mollusks; exoskeletons, segmented bodies, bilateral symmetry, and paired legs of arthropods; and exoskeletons and five-part radial symmetry of echinoderms. Students

may be more specific—hard legs of arthropods, pattern of bumps on sea star—but should also include the group characteristics.

5. Answers should include many of the soft body parts of mollusks, arthropods, and echinoderms.

Chapter 2 Test (pp. 176–179)

1. b
2. b
3. c
4. c
5. c
6. c
7. a
8. d
9. a
10. a
11. mantle
12. nymph
13. endoskeleton
14. bivalve
15. thorax
16. water vascular system
17. true
18. Answers may vary. Sample: The water vascular system is a system of water-filled tubes. Water is forced through tube feet which have sticky pads on the animal's arms. When moistened, they act as suction cups, allowing the animal to grasp objects or move around.
19. Sound is produced by vibrations that create waves that move outward from the source.

20.

	Mollusks	Arthropods	Echinoderms
exoskeleton		✔	
mantle	✔		
muscular foot	✔		
invertebrate	✔	✔	✔
jointed appendages	✔		
water vascular system			✔
segmented bodies		✔	
radial symmetry			✔
molting		✔	
endoskeleton			✔

21.

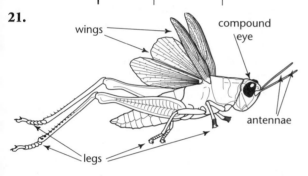

wings — compound eye — antennae — legs

22. It is an arthropod. It is an insect. Supporting characteristics listed will vary. Samples: It's an arthropod because it has an exoskeleton and jointed legs. It's an insect because it has three body segments, six legs, two antennae, compound eyes, and two pairs of wings.

23. During gradual metamorphosis, an insect hatches from an egg, emerges as a nymph, which looks like a small adult with a few missing characteristics. As it grows and matures it molts into larger nymphs until reaching its final adult form.

24. Gastropods usually have one shell, but sometimes none. Bivalves have two shells. Cephalopods have an internal shell or none.

25. Answers will vary. Example: Biological control is the use of a natural predator to kill a harmful insect. For example, ladybug beetles, which feed on harmful aphids, can be added to fields where crops are grown. Biological controls kill only one or a few pest species, but pesticides can kill other organisms and pollute the envoronment.

Chapter 3 Performance Assessment (p. 182) ·

Analyze and Conclude

1. Answers will vary. Sample: My poster uses words and pictures to teach visitors about the characteristics of fish, amphibians, and reptiles. The poster is divided into four sections—one that deals with all vertebrates and an individual section for each type of animal. Each animal section uses words and pictures to teach visitors about that type of animal. The lists include characteristics of each type of animal, including internal characteristics and others that can't be drawn. I have drawn pictures of the main types of fish, amphibians, and reptiles so a person could recognize one of these animals if he or she saw one.

2. Answers will vary. Sample: Fish, amphibians, and reptiles are vertebrates. They have skeletons, two-loop circulatory systems, and adaptations for moving, feeding, getting oxygen, and reproducing. These vertebrates are ectotherms, which means their bodies don't produce a lot of heat, and they move to warmer or cooler parts of their habitats to control their internal temperature. The main kinds of fish are jawless fishes, cartilaginous fishes, and bony fishes. Only bony fishes have bony skeletons, but all have gills for getting oxygen from water and fins for moving. Compared to the other fishes, there aren't many kinds of jawless fishes. They don't have teeth, but have teethlike parts in their mouths for feeding on other fish. Sharks are cartilaginous fishes. They have rough skins and many teeth, and they have to swim to make water pass over their gills. Bony fish have swim bladders that they use to adjust their buoyancy. Many fish reproduce by laying eggs. Fish eggs don't have shells.

   The two main groups of amphibians are salamanders and frogs and toads. Amphibians lay eggs in water that hatch into larvae which breath with gills. Most amphibians metamorphose into adults that breath with lungs and can live on land. Adults have legs that allow them to move about on land. Amphibians are sensitive to pollution because they have thin skins and because their eggs don't have shells.

Reptiles have a thick, scaly skin that protects them against loss of water. Also, their eggs have a leathery shell that helps protect against water loss. Another adaptation to reduce water loss is a kidney that produces concentrated urine. A reptile egg hatches into a baby that resembles the adult. The main kinds of reptiles are alligators and crocodiles, snakes, lizards, and turtles. Snakes don't have legs, but other reptiles (except for some lizards) have four legs to move on land. Snakes are carnivores. Alligators and crocodiles look somewhat like lizards but are generally much bigger and live in and near water. Turtles' bodies are protected by a shell.

Chapter 3 Test
(pp. 183–186)

1. b
2. a
3. d
4. c
5. a
6. b
7. b
8. d
9. c
10. a
11. vertebrae
12. cartilage
13. swim bladder
14. atria
15. Turtles
16. true
17. false; fossils
18. false; gills
19. true
20. harder
21. Answers may vary. Sample: Does the fish have a cartilaginous skeleton?
22. Answers may vary. Sample: Is the skin rough, like sandpaper?
23. Answers may vary. Ectothermic animals do not produce much internal body heat. They regulate their body temperature by moving to warm or cool places. Their body temperature is usually about the same as the temperature of their environment. Endothermic animals produce their own body heat. They keep a constant body temperature by controlling the heat they produce. Their body temperature is usually warmer than the environment.
24. Answers may vary. The eggs of fishes and amphibians are similar. They are laid in water, and they are surrounded by a kind of jelly. Reptile eggs have adaptations for conserving water, including a leathery shell and membranes. They are laid on land and have a yoke.
25. Answers may vary. They have thick, tough skins covered with scales, eggs with shells and membranes, and kidneys.
26. B is probably older. Since the layers are undisturbed, layer B had to be in place before layer C could be laid on top of it.
27. Answers will vary. Sample: Vertebrates did not exist when layers A, B, and C were laid down.
28. Layer H is probably the same age as layer B, because the same two organisms were alive when both layers were laid down..
29. Answers may vary. Samples: It might move into the sunlight to warm up. It might crawl into water or dig underground to cool down.
30. Amphibians have thin skin and their eggs lack shells, so their bodies more easily absorb pollutants from the water. Reptiles have thick skin and eggs with shells, which provide more protection from pollutants.

Chapter 4 Performance Assessment
(p. 189)
Analyze and Conclude

1. Both mammals and birds are endothermic vertebrates with four-chambered hearts and two-loop circulatory systems.
2. All birds lay eggs, have feathers, and have forelimbs modified as wings. All mammals have fur at some stage of development and feed their young with milk from the mother's body.
3. Answers will vary. Sample:

Characteristics of Birds | Characteristics of Mammals

Note: "Lays eggs" should not be listed in the part of the circle for Characteristics of Birds outside the area of overlap because egg-laying is not unique to birds.

Chapter 4 Test
(pp. 190–193)

1. d
2. b
3. a
4. d
5. c
6. b
7. b
8. c
9. b
10. d
11. Down
12. placenta
13. diaphragm
14. crop
15. marsupial
16. vertebrates
17. less
18. true
19. true
20. curved
21. Incisors have a sharp edge. They are used to cut and bite off food. Canines are pointed and are used for stabbing and tearing. Premolars and molars have a broad, flattened surface for grinding food.

22. The placenta is an internal organ in pregnant females that one group of mammals has. Food and oxygen pass from the mother to her young through the placenta, and wastes pass from the young through the placenta to the mother, where they are eliminated by her body.
23. Both are born alive and both are fed milk. Newborn marsupials are very small. They stay in a pouch and nurse until they develop enough to come out. Newborn placental mammals are relatively more developed than new born marsupials. Newborn palcental mammals do not live in a pouch.
24. c
25. The bird circulatory system has two loops and a four-chambered heart. The advantage of a four-chambered heart is that there is no mixing of oxygen-rich and oxygen-poor blood between the two loops. Therefore, blood that arrives in the body's tissues has plenty of oxygen.
26. In flapping flight, the bird continuously flaps its wings and uses a lot of energy. Gliding and soaring use much less energy. A gliding bird keeps its wings outstretched as it flies downward. A soaring bird keeps its wings outstretched and flies upward as the air surrounding it moves upward.
27. Answers may vary. Sample: The seed is picked up by the bill but can't be chewed. From the mouth the seed passes into the crop where it is stored. Next, it passes to the stomach where digestive juices are added. It is crushed by the muscular gizzard before passing out of the stomach.
28. Like reptiles, birds have internal fertilization and lay eggs. Bird eggs are similar to reptile eggs, except that their shells are harder. In most bird species, the female lays the eggs in a nest that has been prepared by one or both parents. Most reptiles do not care for their eggs after laying them.
29. Answers may vary. Sample: Other adaptations are hollow bones, which help make the birds lighter; air sacs, which enable birds to extract much more oxygen from each breath than other animals can; and large chest muscles, which move the wings.
30. In general, the larger the bird species, the longer its incubation time.

Chapter 5 Performance Assessment
(p. 196)

Analyze and Conclude

1. Check to see that the student's answer is consistent with their data.
2. Answers will vary. Example: The pillbug moved away from bright light. In nature, this behavior might help keep the pillbugs out of sight of predators.
3. Check to see that students have controlled all variables except the manipulated variable.

Chapter 5 Test
(pp. 197–200)

1. c
2. d
3. c
4. d
5. b
6. a
7. b
8. c
9. d
10. a
11. aggression
12. bioluminescence
13. behavior
14. hibernation
15. circadian rhythms
16. migrate
17. true
18. true
19. instinctive
20. true
21. B
22. response
23. stimulus
24. reward
25. conditioning

Book B Test

(pp. 201–204)

1. c
2. d
3. b

4. a
5. a
6. d
7. c
8. b
9. d
10. a
11. bilateral symmetry
12. bivalves
13. skeletons
14. canines
15. courtship
16. closed
17. complete metamorphosis
18. true
19. true
20. chemicals
21. The diaphragm is a large muscle at the bottom of the chest which aids in breathing in and out.
22. Birds have down feathers, and mammals are covered in either fur or hair. These all trap air next to the animal's skin, and the air acts as an insulator. Fat also acts as an insulator for endotherms.
23. **a.** sponge
    b. crustacean
    c. bird
    d. amphibian
24. Answers may vary. Sample: Fish are vertebrates because they have a backbone. Sea stars have an endoskeleton but they do not have a backbone. They are echinoderms.
25. No, an arthropod has an exoskeleton and a vertebrate has an endoskeleton.
26–27.

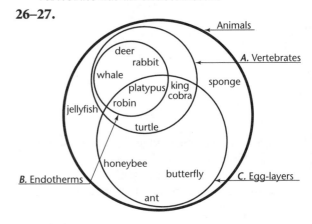

28. Sample answer: Both an endoskeleton and an exoskeleton help protect the animal and give shape to the body. An endoskeleton is a framework inside the body. An exoskeleton surrounds the body and conserves water. The endoskeleton grows with the animal while the exoskeleton must be molted.

29. The young animal has an instinct to follow a moving object, but it must learn from experience which object to follow, hopefully the mother. Imprinting is valuable to animals because babies stay close to their mother, who raises and protects them.

30. Sample answer: Frog eggs are laid in water and are coated in a clear jelly. They are fertilized externally. Snake eggs are leathery and are fertilized internally. Bird eggs are also fertilized internally but they have a hard shell. All of the eggs have some type of shell or coating that helps protect them.

PSAT/
NMSQT®
Prep
2021

Editors-in-Chief

M. Dominic Eggert; Alexandra Strelka, MA

Contributing Editors

Dr. Brandon Deason, MD; Kathryn Sollenberger, MEd; Glen Stohr, JD

Special thanks to our faculty authors and reviewers

Michael Cook; Christopher Cosci; Boris Dvorkin; John Evans; Chason Goldschmitz; Emily Graves; Jonathan Habermacher; Jack Hayes; Jo L'Abbate; Bird Marathe; Karen McCulloch; Melissa McLaughlin; Gail Rivers; Anne Marie Salloum; Jason Selzer; Gordon Spector; Caroline Sykes; Bob Verini, MFA; Bonnie Wang; and Ethan Weber

Additional special thanks to

Laura Aitcheson; Matthew Callan; Mark Feery; Paula L. Fleming, MA, MBA; Joanna Graham; Adam Grey; Rebekah Hawthorne; Rebecca Knauer; Abnia Loriston, MEd; Mandy Luk; Kristen Murner, PhD; Aishwarya Pillai; and the countless others who made this project possible

PSAT/NMSQT® is a registered trademark of the College Board and the National Merit Scholarship Corporation, which were not involved in the production of, and do not endorse, this product.

TABLE OF CONTENTS

GO ONLINE

*www.kaptest.com/
moreonline*

How to Use This Book

Congratulations on taking this important step in your college admissions process! By studying with Kaplan, you'll maximize your score on the PSAT/NMSQT, a major factor in your overall college application.

Our experience shows that the greatest PSAT score increases result from active engagement in the preparation process. Kaplan will give you direction, focus your preparation, and teach you the specific skills and effective test-taking strategies you need to know for the PSAT. We will help you achieve your top performance on test day, but your effort is crucial. The more you invest in preparing for the PSAT, the greater your chances of achieving your target score and getting into your top-choice college.

Are you registered for the PSAT? Kaplan cannot register you for the official PSAT. If you have not already registered for the upcoming PSAT, talk to your high school guidance counselor or visit the College Board's website at www.collegeboard.org to register online and for information on registration deadlines, test sites, accommodations for students with disabilities, and fees.

The PSAT/NMSQT is traditionally administered on only two days in mid-October. This year, the College Board has also scheduled an additional test date on January 26, 2021. Students should be registered well in advance of the test dates. Your high school guidance counselor may also have more information about registering for the PSAT. Homeschooled students can contact the guidance office of a local high school to make arrangements to take the exam at that school.

Practice Test

Kaplan's Practice Tests are just like the actual PSAT. By taking a practice exam, you will prepare yourself for the actual test day experience. One of your Practice Tests is included in this book and the other one can be accessed online. See the "Digital Resources" section below to learn how to access your online Practice Test.

Chapter Organization

The chapters in this book follow a standard format to make this book as easy to use as possible. Most chapters in this book start with a section called "How Much Do You Know?" that allows you to get a sense of how comfortable you already are with the material in the chapter. Answers and explanations follow immediately in the "Check Your Work" section. Each lesson in a chapter starts with a question typical of the way the PSAT tests a given topic and ends with a set of practice questions called "Try on Your Own." There is yet another practice set at the end of each chapter called "How Much Have You Learned?" to reinforce the concepts explained in the chapter. Answers and Explanations for the "Try on Your Own" and "How Much Have You Learned?" sections are provided at the end of each chapter for easy reference.

SmartPoints®

Different topics are worth different numbers of points on the PSAT because they show up more or less frequently in questions. By studying the information released by the College Board, Kaplan has been able to determine how often certain topics are likely to show up on the PSAT, and therefore how many points these topics are worth on test day. If you master a given topic, you can expect to earn the corresponding number of SmartPoints® on test day.

We have used a 600-point scale for SmartPoints® because that's the number of points you can earn within the Math and Verbal subscores: the PSAT scoring scale is 160–760, so there are $760 - 160 = 600$ points to be earned within each major section of the test. The breakdown of SmartPoints® for Math, Reading, and Writing and Language are summarized in the following tables. Keep in mind that these values are approximate because testing administrations differ.

Math		
SmartPoints® Category	# of Points	Sub-Categories
Linear Equations	110	Linear equations, linear graphs, word problems
Functions	105	Functions, graphs of functions, functions in word problems
Ratios, Proportions, and Percents	80	Setting up a proportion to solve for an unknown, unit conversion, calculating percent and percent change
Quadratics	60	Quadratic equations, parabolas, modeling data, mixed systems of equations
Statistics and Probability	60	Descriptive statistics, probability, tables and charts, data samples
Systems of Linear Equations	45	Systems of equations, number of possible solutions
Geometry	35	Triangles, circles, 3-dimensional figures
Inequalities	35	Inequalities, graphical representations of inequalities
Scatterplots	35	Scatterplots, lines of best fit, modeling data
Exponents, Radicals, Polynomials, and Radical Expressions	25	Exponents, radicals, polynomial operations, graphs of polynomials, modeling growth and decay, rational expressions/equations
Imaginary Numbers	5	Adding, subtracting, multiplying, and dividing complex numbers
Trigonometry	5	Sine, cosine, tangent
TOTAL	**600**	

Reading		
SmartPoints® Category	# of Points	Sub-Categories
Inference questions	90	Making deductions
Command of Evidence questions	60	Citing evidence
Detail questions	45	Finding details in the text
Vocab-in-Context questions	45	Determining the meaning of a word as it is used in the passage
Function questions	40	Explaining *why* the author included a certain detail
Global questions	20	Determining central ideas and themes, summarizing
TOTAL	**300**	

Writing & Language		
SmartPoints® Category	# of Points	Sub-Categories
Sentence Structure	85	Correcting run-ons and fragments, using correct conjunctions, punctuation
Development	85	Word choice, relevance, revising text
Agreement	60	Subject-verb agreement, verb tense, pronoun agreement, modifiers, idioms
Organization	40	Transitions, sentence placement
Conciseness	20	Avoiding wordiness and redundancy
Graphs	10	Drawing inferences from a graph included with a passage
TOTAL	**300**	

Extra Chapters

The chapters in this book will help you answer most questions on test day, but there is some additional content that will be covered on the PSAT. To cover this content and take your preparation to the next level, we have provided 12 additional chapters online. See Digital Resources below to learn how to access these helpful extra materials.

Digital Resources

To access the online resources that accompany this book, which include extra practice sets and study planning guidance, follow the steps below:

1. Go to kaptest.com/moreonline.

2. Have this book available as you complete the on-screen instructions.

The PSAT and You

Inside the PSAT

PSAT Structure

The PSAT, like any standardized test, is predictable. The more comfortable you are with the test structure, the more confidently you will approach each question type, thus maximizing your score.

The PSAT is 2 hours and 45 minutes long and is made up mostly of multiple-choice questions that test two subject areas: Evidence-Based Reading and Writing, and Math. The former is broken into a Reading Test and a Writing and Language Test.

Test	Allotted Time (min.)	Question Count
Reading	60	47
Writing and Language	35	44
Math	70	48
Total	165	139

PSAT Scoring

PSAT scoring can be pretty complex. You will receive one score ranging from 160–760 for Evidence-Based Reading and Writing and another for Math. Your overall PSAT score will range from 320–1520 and is calculated by adding these two scores together.

In addition to your overall scores, you will receive subscores that provide a deeper analysis of your PSAT performance. The PSAT also gives you a percentile ranking, which allows you to compare your scores with those of other test takers. For example, a student who scored in the 63rd percentile did better than 63 percent of all others who took that test.

How to Maximize Your Score

What is most important to remember while taking the test is that maximizing all the various scores and subscores depends on getting the most points you can out of every section. You'll find advice on test-taking strategies below and in the section management chapters at the end of the Math, Reading, and Writing and Language sections of this book. However, if you still have a meaningful amount of time to prepare for the PSAT, the best advice we can give you is to improve the skills you need to answer Math and Verbal questions correctly and efficiently. That's what this book is for. Use it in any order you like; you don't need to start with Math. But do use it. Read the instructional text for those topics you feel weak in and work your way through the practice questions. There are hundreds of them in this book, and they are very similar to those that you will see on test day. Practice will not only improve your skills, but also raise your confidence—and that's very important to test day success.

Where and When to Take the PSAT

The PSAT is offered every year in mid-October. It is administered at your high school, not at a testing center. Homeschooled students can sign up at the nearest local high school. Most high schools administer the exam on a Wednesday; some offer it on a Saturday. Some high schools recommend that their sophomores take the test for additional practice, but sophomores who take the PSAT are not eligible to qualify for the National Merit Scholarship unless they are in an accelerated program and are preparing to graduate the following year. However, some schools will administer the test to their students only once (at the beginning of junior year). If this is the case, sophomores wanting to take the PSAT need to get permission from their guidance counselors.

Why Take the PSAT?

The PSAT/NMSQT stands for the Preliminary SAT/National Merit Scholarship Qualifying Test. It has three main functions:

1. The PSAT is excellent practice for the SAT. Although shorter than the SAT, it contains the same types of math, reading, and writing questions. It does not, however, contain an essay component. The PSAT also measures your score against those of your classmates and peers across the country, just as the SAT does.

2. Taking the PSAT also gives you a chance to qualify for several scholarship programs, most notably the National Merit Scholarship Program. Aside from the possibility of receiving tuition for college, the National Merit Scholarship program gives you recognition that is an impressive addition to your college applications.

3. The PSAT can help you stand out to colleges. Many schools purchase lists of high-scoring students and encourage these students to apply. A great score on the PSAT could get you noticed by colleges and earn you small perks like meals during visits and waived application fees.

The top 50,000 scorers on the PSAT are recognized by the National Merit program and sent letters of commendation. More than 10,000 of these students share more than $41 million in National Merit Scholarship money. Only juniors who take the PSAT are eligible for National Merit Scholarships. The top 16,000 scorers become semifinalists, and approximately 15,000 semifinalists become finalists. Finally, almost 8,500 National Merit finalists receive National Merit Scholarships, with each award being up to $2,500 a year toward a college education. Many high scorers who don't receive National Merit Scholarships are awarded merit scholarships from the schools to which they apply based on their high scores. Whether you qualify as a Commended Student, a Semifinalist, a Finalist, or a full-fledged National Merit Scholar, it's definitely worth noting this achievement on your college applications.

For more information on the National Merit Scholarships and Special Scholarships, visit www.nationalmerit.org.

The PSAT Math Test

The PSAT Math Test is broken down into a calculator section and a no-calculator section. Questions across the sections consist of multiple-choice, student-produced response (Grid-in), and more comprehensive multi-part question sets.

	No-Calculator Section	Calculator Section	Total
Duration (minutes)	25	45	70
Multiple-choice	13	27	40
Grid-in	4	4	8
Total Questions	17	31	48

The PSAT Math Test is divided into four content areas: Heart of Algebra, Problem Solving and Data Analysis, Passport to Advanced Math, and Additional Topics in Math.

PSAT Math Test Content Area Distribution	
Heart of Algebra (16 questions)	Analyzing and fluently solving equations and systems of equations; creating expressions, equations, and inequalities to represent relationships between quantities and to solve problems; rearranging and interpreting formulas
Problem Solving and Data Analysis (16 questions)	Creating and analyzing relationships using ratios, proportions, percentages, and units; describing relationships shown graphically; summarizing qualitative and quantitative data
Passport to Advanced Math (14 questions)	Rewriting expressions using their structure; creating, analyzing, and fluently solving quadratic and higher-order equations; purposefully manipulating polynomials to solve problems
Additional Topics in Math (2 questions)	Making area and volume calculations in context; investigating lines, angles, triangles, and circles using theorems

A few math questions might look like something you'd expect to see on a science or history test. These "crossover" questions are designed to test your ability to use math in real-world scenarios. There are a total of 14 "crossover" questions that will contribute to subscores that span multiple tests. Seven of the questions will contribute to the Analysis in Science subscore and seven will contribute to the Analysis in History/Social Studies subscore.

The PSAT Reading Test

The PSAT Reading Test will focus on your comprehension and reasoning skills when you are presented with challenging extended prose passages taken from a variety of content areas.

PSAT Reading Test Overview	
Timing	60 minutes
Questions	47 passage-based multiple-choice questions
Passages	4 single passages; 1 set of paired passages
Passage Length	500–750 words per passage or passage set

Passages will draw from U.S. and World Literature, History/Social Studies, and Science. One set of History/Social Studies or Science passages will be paired. History/Social Studies and Science passages can also be accompanied by graphical representations of data such as charts, graphs, tables, and the like. One of the History/Social Studies passages (or pair of passages) will be taken from primary sources, such as U.S. founding documents like the Constitution.

Reading Test Passage Types	
U.S. and World Literature	1 passage with 9 questions
History/Social Studies	2 passages or 1 passage and 1 paired-passage set with 9–10 questions each
Science	2 passages or 1 passage and 1 paired-passage set with 9–10 questions each

The multiple-choice questions for each passage will typically be arranged with main idea questions at the beginning of the set so that you can consider the entire passage before answering questions about details.

Skills Tested by Reading Test Questions	
Reading for Detail	Finding details in the passage, citing textual evidence
Summarizing	Determining central ideas and themes, understanding how a passage is structured, understanding relationships
Drawing Inferences	Understanding relationships, drawing conclusions from facts stated in a passage, interpreting words and phrases in context
Rhetorical Analysis	Analyzing word choice, analyzing point of view, determining why a fact is included, analyzing arguments
Synthesis	Analyzing multiple texts, analyzing quantitative information

The PSAT Writing and Language Test

The PSAT Writing and Language Test will focus on your ability to revise and edit text from a range of content areas.

PSAT Writing and Language Test Overview	
Timing	35 minutes
Questions	44 passage-based multiple-choice questions
Passages	4 single passages with 11 questions each
Passage Length	400–450 words per passage

The PSAT Writing and Language Test will contain four single passages, one from each of the following subject areas: Careers, Humanities, History/Social Studies, and Science.

Writing and Language Passage Types	
Careers	Hot topics in "major fields of work" such as information technology and health care
Humanities	Texts about literature, art, history, music, and philosophy pertaining to human culture
History/Social Studies	Discussion of historical or social sciences topics such as anthropology, communication studies, economics, education, human geography, law, linguistics, political science, psychology, and sociology
Science	Exploration of concepts, findings, and discoveries in the natural sciences including Earth science, biology, chemistry, and physics

Passages will also vary in the "type" of text. A passage can be an argument, an informative or explanatory text, or a nonfiction narrative.

Writing and Language Passage Text Type Distribution	
Argument	1–2 passages
Informative/Explanatory Text	1–2 passages
Nonfiction Narrative	1 passage

Some passages and/or questions will refer to one or more data tables or charts. Questions associated with these graphics will ask you to revise and edit the passage based on the data presented in the graphic.

The most prevalent question format on the PSAT Writing and Language Test will ask you to choose the best of three alternatives to an underlined portion of the passage or to decide that the current version is the best option. You will be asked to improve the development, organization, and diction in the passages to ensure they conform to conventional standards of English grammar, usage, and style.

Skills Tested by Writing and Language Test Questions	
Expression of Ideas (24 questions)	Development, organization, and effective language use
Standard English Conventions (20 questions)	Sentence structure, conventions of usage, and conventions of punctuation

Test-Taking Strategies

You have already learned about the overall structure of the PSAT as well as the structure of the three main areas it entails: Math, Reading, and Writing and Language. The strategies outlined in this section can be applied to any of these tests.

The PSAT is different from the tests you are used to taking in school. The good news is that you can use the PSAT's particular structure to your advantage.

For example, on a test given in school, you probably go through the questions in order. You spend more time on the harder questions than on the easier ones because harder questions are usually worth more points. You also probably show your work because your teacher tells you that how you approach a question is as important as getting the correct answer.

This approach is not optimal for the PSAT. On the PSAT, you benefit from moving around within a section if you come across tough questions, because the harder questions are worth the same number of points as the easier questions. Similarly, showing your work is unimportant. It doesn't matter how you arrive at the correct answer—only that you bubble in the correct answer choice.

Strategy #1: Triaging the Test

You do not need to complete questions on the PSAT in order. Every student has different strengths and should attack the test with those strengths in mind. Your main objective on the PSAT should be to score as many points as you can. While approaching questions out of order may seem counterintuitive, it is a surefire way to achieve your best score.

Just remember, you can skip around within each section, but you cannot work on a section other than the one you've been instructed to work on.

To triage a section effectively, do the following:

- First, work through all the easy questions that you can do quickly. Skip questions that are hard or time-consuming.
  - For the Reading Test, start with the passage you find most manageable and work toward the one you find most challenging. You do not need to go in order.
- Second, work through the questions that are doable but time-consuming.
- Third, work through the hard questions.

Strategy #2: Elimination

Even though there is no wrong-answer penalty on the PSAT, elimination is still a crucial strategy. If you can determine that one or more answer choices are definitely incorrect, you can increase your chances of getting the correct answer by paring down the selection.

To eliminate answer choices, do the following:

- Read each answer choice.
- Cross out the answer choices that are incorrect.
- There is no wrong-answer penalty, so take your best guess.

Strategy #3: Guessing

Each multiple-choice question on the PSAT has four answer choices and no wrong-answer penalty. That means if you have no idea how to approach a question, you have a 25 percent chance of randomly choosing the correct answer. Even though there's a 75 percent chance of selecting an incorrect answer, you won't lose any points for doing so. The worst that can happen on the PSAT is that you'll earn zero points on a question, which means you should *always* at least take a guess, even when you have no idea what to do.

When guessing on a question, do the following:

- Try to strategically eliminate answer choices before guessing.
- If you run out of time, or have no idea what a question is asking, pick a Letter of the Day.

LETTER OF THE DAY

A Letter of the Day is an answer choice letter (A, B, C, or D) that you choose before test day to select for questions you guess on.

PART 2

PSAT Math

CHAPTER 2

Prerequisite Skills and Calculator Use

Math Fundamentals

Test Prerequisites

This book focuses on the skills that are tested on the PSAT. It assumes a working knowledge of arithmetic, algebra, and geometry. Before you dive into the subsequent chapters where you'll try testlike questions, there are a number of concepts—ranging from basic arithmetic to geometry—that you should master. The following sections contain a brief review of these concepts.

Algebra and Arithmetic

- **Order of operations** is one of the most fundamental of all arithmetic rules. A well-known mnemonic device for remembering this order is PEMDAS: Please Excuse My Dear Aunt Sally. This translates to Parentheses, Exponents, Multiplication/Division, Addition/Subtraction. Perform multiplication and division from left to right (even if it means division before multiplication) and treat addition and subtraction the same way, as shown here:

$$(14 - 4 \div 2)^2 - 3 + (2 - 1)$$
$$= (14 - 2)^2 - 3 + (1)$$
$$= 12^2 - 3 + 1$$
$$= 144 - 3 + 1$$
$$= 141 + 1$$
$$= 142$$

- Three basic properties of number (and variable) manipulation—commutative, associative, and distributive—will assist you with algebra on test day:

  1. **Commutative:** Numbers can swap places and still provide the same mathematical result. This is valid only for addition and multiplication. For example:

  $$a + b = b + a \rightarrow 3 + 4 = 4 + 3$$
  $$a \times b = b \times a \rightarrow 3 \times 4 = 4 \times 3$$

  BUT: $3 - 4 \neq 4 - 3$ and $3 \div 4 \neq 4 \div 3$

  2. **Associative:** Different number groupings will provide the same mathematical result. This is valid only for addition and multiplication. For example:

  $$(a + b) + c = a + (b + c) \rightarrow (4 + 5) + 6 = 4 + (5 + 6)$$
  $$(a \times b) \times c = a \times (b \times c) \rightarrow (4 \times 5) \times 6 = 4 \times (5 \times 6)$$

  BUT: $(4 - 5) - 6 \neq 4 - (5 - 6)$ and $(4 \div 5) \div 6 \neq 4 \div (5 \div 6)$

  3. **Distributive:** A number that is multiplied by the sum or difference of two other numbers can be rewritten as the first number multiplied by the two others individually. This does *not* work with division. For example:

  $$a(b + c) = ab + ac \rightarrow 6(x + 3) = 6x + 6(3)$$
  $$a(b - c) = ab - ac \rightarrow 3(y - 2) = 3y + 3(-2)$$

  BUT: $12 \div (6 + 2) \neq 12 \div 6 + 12 \div 2$

  Note: When subtracting an expression in parentheses, such as in $4 - (x + 3)$, distribute the negative sign outside the parentheses first: $4 + (-x - 3) \rightarrow 1 - x$.

- Subtracting a positive number is the same as adding its negative. Likewise, subtracting a negative number is the same as adding its positive:

$$r - s = r + (-s) \rightarrow 22 - 15 = 7 \text{ and } 22 + (-15) = 7$$
$$r - (-s) = r + s \rightarrow 22 - (-15) = 37 \text{ and } 22 + 15 = 37$$

- You should be comfortable manipulating both proper and improper fractions.
  - To add and subtract fractions, first find a common denominator, then add the numerators together:

$$\frac{2}{3} + \frac{5}{4} \rightarrow \left(\frac{2}{3} \times \frac{4}{4}\right) + \left(\frac{5}{4} \times \frac{3}{3}\right) = \frac{8}{12} + \frac{15}{12} = \frac{23}{12}$$

○ Multiplying fractions is straightforward: multiply the numerators together, then repeat for the denominators. Cancel when possible to simplify the answer:

$$\frac{5}{8} \times \frac{8}{3} = \frac{5}{\cancel{8}} \times \frac{\cancel{8}^{1}}{3} = \frac{5 \times 1}{1 \times 3} = \frac{5}{3}$$

○ Dividing by a fraction is the same as multiplying by its reciprocal. Once you've rewritten a division problem as multiplication, follow the rules for fraction multiplication to simplify:

$$\frac{3}{4} \div \frac{3}{2} = \frac{\cancel{3}^{1}}{\cancel{4}_{2}} \times \frac{\cancel{2}^{1}}{\cancel{3}_{1}} = \frac{1 \times 1}{2 \times 1} = \frac{1}{2}$$

- **Absolute value** means the distance a number is from 0 on a number line. Because absolute value is a distance, it is always positive or 0. Absolute value can *never* be negative. For example:

$$|-17| = 17, \ |21| = 21, \ |0| = 0$$

- Whatever you do to one side of an equation, you must do to the other. For instance, if you multiply one side by 3, you must multiply the other side by 3 as well.

- The ability to solve straightforward, one-variable equations is critical on the PSAT. For example:

$$\frac{4x}{5} - 2 = 10$$
$$\frac{4x}{5} = 12$$
$$\frac{5}{4} \times \frac{4x}{5} = 12 \times \frac{5}{4}$$
$$x = 15$$

Note: $\frac{4x}{5}$ is the same as $\frac{4}{5}x$. You could see either form on the PSAT.

- You will encounter **irrational numbers**, such as common radicals and π, on test day. You can carry an irrational number through your calculations as you would a variable (e.g., $4 \times \sqrt{2} = 4\sqrt{2}$). Only convert to a decimal when you have finished any intermediate steps and when the question asks you to provide an *approximate* value.

Mental Math

Even if you're a math whiz, you need to adjust your thought process in terms of the PSAT to give yourself the biggest advantage you can. Knowing a few extra things, such as the below, will boost your speed on test day:

- Don't abuse your calculator by using it to determine something as simple as $15 \div 3$ (we've seen it many times). Besides, what if you're in the middle of the no-calculator section? Save time on test day by reviewing multiplication tables. At a bare minimum, work up through the 10s. If you know them through 12 or 15, that's even better!

- You can save a few seconds of number crunching by memorizing **perfect squares**. Knowing perfect squares through 10 is a good start; go for 15 or even 20 if you can.

- **Percent** means "out of a hundred." For example, $27\% = \frac{27}{100}$. You can write percents as decimals (e.g., $27\% = 0.27$).

- The ability to recognize a few simple fractions masquerading in decimal or percent form will save you time on test day because you won't have to turn to your calculator to convert them. Memorize the content of the following table.

Fraction	Decimal	Percent
$\frac{1}{10}$	0.1	10%
$\frac{1}{5}$	0.2	20%
$\frac{1}{4}$	0.25	25%
$\frac{1}{3}$	0.333̄	33.33̄%
$\frac{1}{2}$	0.5	50%
$\frac{3}{4}$	0.75	75%

Tip: If you don't have the decimal (or percent) form of a multiple of one of the fractions shown in the table memorized, such as $\frac{2}{5}$, just take the fraction with the corresponding denominator ($\frac{1}{5}$ in this case), convert to a decimal (0.2), and multiply by the numerator of the desired fraction to get its decimal equivalent:

$$\frac{2}{5} = \frac{1}{5} \times 2 = 0.2 \times 2 = 0.4 = 40\%$$

Graphing

- Basic two-dimensional graphing is performed on a **coordinate plane**. There are two **axes,** x and y, that meet at a central point called the **origin.** Each axis has both positive and negative values that extend outward from the origin at evenly spaced intervals. The axes divide the space into four sections called **quadrants,** which are labeled I, II, III, and IV. Quadrant I is always the upper-right section, and the rest follow counterclockwise:

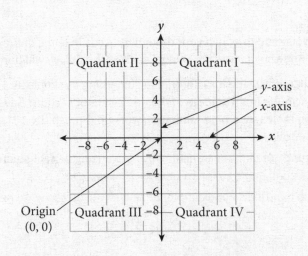

- To plot points on the coordinate plane, you need their coordinates. The **x-coordinate** is where the point falls along the x-axis, and the **y-coordinate** is where the point falls along the y-axis. The two coordinates together make an **ordered pair** written as (x, y). When writing ordered pairs, the x-coordinate is always listed first (think alphabetical order). Four points are plotted in the following figure as examples:

- When two points are vertically or horizontally aligned, calculating the distance between them is easy. For a horizontal distance, only the x-value changes; for a vertical distance, only the y-value changes. Take the positive difference of the x-coordinates (or y-coordinates) to determine the distance—that is, subtract the smaller number from the larger number so that the difference is positive. Two examples are presented here:

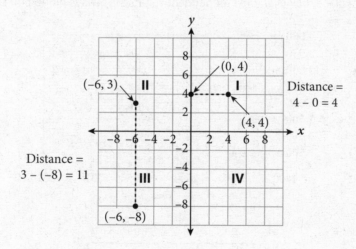

- Two-variable equations have an **independent variable** (input) and a **dependent variable** (output). The dependent variable (often y), depends on the independent variable (often x). For example, in the equation $y = 3x + 4$, x is the independent variable; any y-value depends on what you plug in for x. You can construct a table of values for the equation, which can then be plotted. For example:

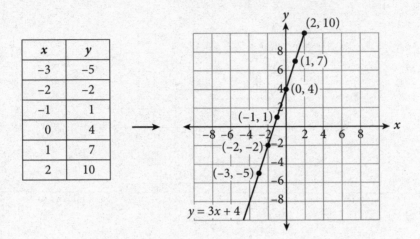

x	y
−3	−5
−2	−2
−1	1
0	4
1	7
2	10

$y = 3x + 4$

- You may be asked to infer relationships from graphs. In the first of the following graphs, the two variables are time and population. Clearly, the year does not depend on how many people live in the town; rather, the population increases over time and thus depends on the year. In the second graph, you can infer that plant height depends on the amount of rain; thus, rainfall is the independent variable. Note that the independent variable for the second graph is the vertical axis; this can happen with certain nonstandard graphs. On the standard coordinate plane, however, the independent variable is always plotted on the horizontal axis.

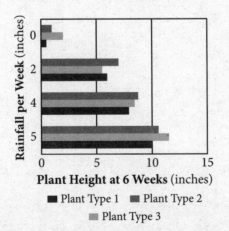

- When two straight lines are graphed simultaneously, one of three possible scenarios will occur:
  1. The lines will not intersect at all (no solution).
  2. The lines will intersect at one point (one solution).
  3. The lines will lie on top of each other (infinitely many solutions).

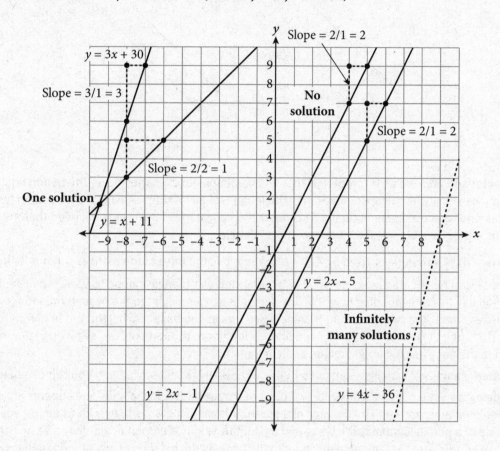

Geometry

- **Adjacent angles** can be added to find the measure of a larger angle. The following diagram demonstrates this:

- Two angles that sum to 90° are called **complementary angles**. Two angles that sum to 180° are called **supplementary angles**.

- Two distinct lines in a plane will either intersect at one point or extend indefinitely without intersecting. If two lines intersect at a right angle (90°), they are **perpendicular** and are denoted with ⊥. If the lines never intersect, they are **parallel** and are denoted with ||. For example:

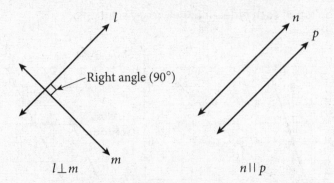

$l \perp m$ $n \parallel p$

- **Perimeter** and **area** are basic properties that all two-dimensional shapes have. The perimeter of a polygon can easily be calculated by adding the lengths of all its sides. Area is the amount of two-dimensional space a shape occupies. The most common shapes for which you'll need these two properties on test day are triangles, parallelograms, and circles.

- The **area (A) of a triangle** is given by $A = \frac{1}{2}bh$, where b is the base of the triangle and h is its height.

  The base and height are always perpendicular. Any side of a triangle can be used as the base; just make sure you use its corresponding height (a line segment perpendicular to the base, terminating in the opposite vertex). You can use a right triangle's two legs as the base and height, but in non-right triangles, if the height is not given, you'll need to draw it in (from the vertex of the angle opposite the base down to the base itself at a right angle) and compute it.

- The **interior angles** of a triangle sum to 180°. If you know any two interior angles, you can calculate the third.

- **Parallelograms** are quadrilaterals with two pairs of parallel sides. Rectangles and squares are subsets of parallelograms. You can find the **area of a parallelogram** using $A = bh$. As with triangles, you can use any side of a parallelogram as the base, and again, the height is perpendicular to the base. For a rectangle or square, use the side perpendicular to the base as the height. For any other parallelogram, the height (or enough information to find it) will be given.

- A circle's perimeter is known as its **circumference (C)** and is found using $C = 2\pi r$, where r is the **radius** (distance from the center of the circle to its edge). The **area of a circle** is given by $A = \pi r^2$. The strange symbol is the lowercase Greek letter pi (π, pronounced "pie"), which is approximately 3.14. As mentioned in the algebra section, you should carry π throughout your calculations without rounding unless instructed otherwise.

- A **tangent line** touches a circle at exactly one point and is perpendicular to a circle's radius at the point of contact, as shown here:

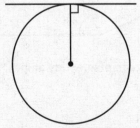

The presence of a right angle opens up the opportunity to draw otherwise hidden shapes, so pay special attention to tangents when they're mentioned.

- A shape is said to have **symmetry** when it can be split by a line (called an **axis of symmetry**) into two identical parts. Consider folding a shape along a line: if all sides and vertices align once the shape is folded in half, the shape is symmetrical about that line. Some shapes have no axis of symmetry, some have one, some have multiple axes, and still others can have infinite axes of symmetry (e.g., a circle):

Sample axis of symmetry   Not an axis of symmetry

Sample shapes with corresponding axes of symmetry

- **Congruence** is simply a geometry term that means identical. Angles, lines, and shapes can be congruent. Congruence is indicated by using hash marks. Everything with the same number of hash marks is congruent:

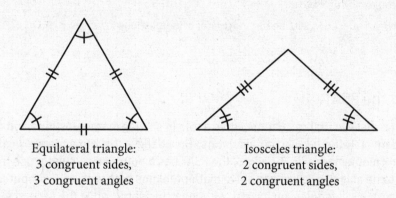

Equilateral triangle: Isosceles triangle:
3 congruent sides,   2 congruent sides,
3 congruent angles   2 congruent angles

- **Similarity** between shapes indicates that they have identical angles and proportional sides. Think of taking a shape and stretching or shrinking each side by the same ratio. The resulting shape will have the same angles as the original. While the sides will not be identical, they will be proportional. For example:

Multiply each side by 2

If you're comfortable with these concepts, read on for tips on calculator use. If not, review this lesson and remember to refer to it for help if you get stuck in a later chapter.

Calculator Use

LEARNING OBJECTIVE

After this lesson, you will be able to:

- Distinguish between questions that need a calculator and questions in which manual calculations are more efficient

Calculators and the PSAT

Educators and parents believe that calculators serve a role in solving math questions, but they are sometimes concerned that students rely too heavily on calculators. They believe this dependence weakens students' overall ability to think mathematically. Therefore, the PSAT has a policy on calculator use to promote the idea that students need to be able to analyze and solve math problems both with and without a calculator. The first math section you see will require you to work without a calculator, while the second math section will allow you to use one.

Many students never stop to ask whether using a calculator is the most efficient way to solve a problem. This chapter will show you how the strongest test takers use their calculators strategically; that is, they carefully evaluate when to use the calculator and when to skip it in favor of a more streamlined approach. As you will see, even though you can use a calculator, sometimes it's more beneficial to save your energy by approaching a question more strategically. Work smarter, not harder.

Which Calculator Should You Use?

The PSAT allows four-function, scientific, and graphing calculators. No matter which calculator you choose, start practicing with it now. You don't want to waste valuable time on test day looking for the exponent button or figuring out how to correctly graph equations. Due to the wide range of math topics you'll encounter on test day, **we recommend using a graphing calculator**, such as the TI-83/84. If you don't already own one, see if you can borrow one from your school's math department or a local library.

A graphing calculator's capabilities extend well beyond what you'll need for the test, so don't worry about memorizing every function. The next few pages will cover which calculator functions you'll want to know how to use for the PSAT. If you're not already familiar with your graphing calculator, you'll want to get the user manual; you can find this on the Internet by searching for your calculator's model number. Identify the calculator functions necessary to answer various PSAT Math questions, then write down the directions for each to make a handy study sheet.

When Should You Use a Calculator?

Some PSAT question types are designed based on the idea that students will do some or all of the work using a calculator. As a master test taker, you want to know what to look for so you can identify when calculator use is advantageous. Questions involving statistics, determining roots of complicated quadratic equations, and other topics are generally designed with calculator use in mind.

Other questions aren't intentionally designed to involve calculator use. Solving some with a calculator can save you time and energy, but you'll waste both if you go for the calculator on others. You will have to decide which method is best when you encounter the following topics:

- Long division and other extensive calculations
- Graphing quadratics
- Simplifying radicals and calculating roots
- Plane and coordinate geometry

Practicing **long computations** by hand and with the calculator will not only boost your focus and mental math prowess, but it will also help you determine whether it's faster to do the work for a given question by hand or reach for the calculator on test day.

Graphing quadratic equations may be a big reason you got that fancy calculator in the first place; it makes answering these questions a snap! This is definitely an area where you need to have an in-depth knowledge of your calculator's functions. The key to making these questions easy with the calculator is being meticulous when entering the equation.

Another stressful area for many students is **radicals**, especially when the answer choices are written as decimals. Those two elements are big red flags that trigger a reach for the calculator. Beware: not all graphing calculators have a built-in radical simplification function, so consider familiarizing yourself with this process.

Geometry can be a gray area for students when it comes to calculator use. Consider working by hand when dealing with angles and lines, specifically when filling in information on complementary, supplementary, and congruent angles. You should be able to work fluidly through those questions without using your calculator.

If you choose to use **trigonometric functions** to get to the answer on triangle questions, make sure you have your calculator set to degrees or radians as required by the question.

To Use or Not to Use?

A calculator is a double-edged sword on the PSAT: using one can be an asset for verifying work if you struggle when doing math by hand, but turning to it for the simplest computations will cost you time that you could devote to more complex questions. Practice solving questions with and without a calculator to get a sense of your personal style as well as your strengths and weaknesses. Think critically about when a calculator saves you time and when mental math is faster. Use the exercises in this book to practice your calculations so that by the time test day arrives, you'll be in the habit of using your calculator as effectively as possible.

CHAPTER 3

The Method for PSAT Math Questions

LEARNING OBJECTIVE

After completing this chapter, you will be able to:

- Efficiently apply the Math Method to PSAT Math questions

How to Do PSAT Math

PSAT Math questions can seem more difficult than they actually are, especially when you are working under time pressure. The method we are about to describe will help you answer PSAT questions, whether you are comfortable with the math content or not. This method is designed to give you the confidence you need to get the right answers on the PSAT by helping you think through each question logically, one piece at a time.

Take a look at this question and take a minute to think about how you would attack it if you saw it on test day:

> The Collins Library is one of four public libraries in Madison County. According to data maintained by the county's public library system, 58 percent of the 15,000 books in Collins Library are fiction titles. If Collins Library is representative of the public libraries in Madison County with regard to the number of fiction vs. nonfiction titles, and the average number of books per public library in Madison County is 15,000, then which of the following is the best estimate of the total number of nonfiction titles held by public libraries in Madison County?
>
> A) 8,700
> B) 25,200
> C) 34,800
> D) 60,000

Many test takers will see a question like this and panic. Others will waste a great deal of time reading and rereading without a clear goal. You want to avoid both of those outcomes.

Start by defining clearly for yourself **what the question is actually asking**. What do the answer choices represent? In this question, they represent *the number of nonfiction books in all the public libraries in Madison County*.

Next, **examine the information** that you have and organize it logically. The question asks about the number of nonfiction books. Okay, then what information do you have about numbers of books? You know that 58% of the 15,000 books in Collins Library are fiction. That's the opposite of nonfiction. You can deduce that 100% − 58% = 42% of the 15,000 books in Collins Library are nonfiction books.

Now, **make a strategic decision** about how to proceed. The answer choices are far apart, so you might consider rounding 42% to $\frac{4}{10}$ and estimating. However, this question appears on the calculator section, and it's a quick calculation. Let's say that you decide to use your calculator. Plug the numbers into your calculator and jot down what you know so far:

Nonfiction total in Collins Library: 0.42 × 15,000 = 6,300

The question asks for the number of nonfiction books *in Madison County*, so hunt for information tying Collins Library to Madison County. You're told that the average number of books per public library in Madison County is 15,000, which is identical to the number of books in Collins Library, and that Collins Library is "representative" of the libraries in Madison County. Translation: what is true for Collins Library is also true for all public libraries in Madison County. You also know that there are four public libraries in Madison County. You can deduce that the number of nonfiction books in Collins Library (6,300) times the total number of public libraries in Madison County (4) will give you the number of nonfiction books in all of Madison County. Plug that into your calculator:

6,300 × 4 = 25,200

Finally, **confirm** that you answered the right question: you want the number of nonfiction books in all public libraries in Madison County. That's what you calculated, so you're done; the correct answer is **(B)**.

Here are the steps of the method we just used:

Method for PSAT Math Questions	
Step 1.	State what the question is asking
Step 2.	Examine the given information
Step 3.	Choose your approach
Step 4.	Confirm that you answered the right question

You can think of these steps as a series of questions to ask yourself: What do they want? What are they giving me to work with? How should I approach this? Did I answer the right question?

Not all PSAT Math questions will require time spent on all of the steps. The question above, because it is a word problem, required a fair amount of analysis in steps 1 and 2, but choosing an approach (step 3) was straightforward; the calculations were quick to do on a calculator, so there was no need to estimate. Other questions will require very little thought in steps 1 and 2, but will benefit from a careful strategy decision in step 3. Step 4 is always quick, but you should always do it: just make sure you answered the question that was actually asked before you bubble in your response. Doing so will save you from speed mistakes on questions that you know how to do and should be getting credit for.

There are several approaches you can choose from in step 3: doing the traditional math, as we did in the question above; Picking Numbers; Backsolving; estimating; or taking a strategic guess. In the next two examples, you'll see Picking Numbers and Backsolving in action.

Here's another example. This one is not a word problem, so steps 1 and 2 require negligible mental energy, but pay attention when you get to step 3:

Which of the following expressions is equivalent to $\dfrac{6x+8}{x-1}$?

A) $6 - \dfrac{14}{x-1}$

B) $6 + \dfrac{8}{x-1}$

C) $6 + \dfrac{14}{x-1}$

D) $\dfrac{6+8}{-1}$

Step 1: What do they want? An expression equivalent to $\dfrac{6x+8}{x-1}$.

Step 2: What do they give you? Only the expression $\dfrac{6x+8}{x-1}$.

Step 3: What approach will you use?

Here's where it gets interesting. The creator of this question may be expecting you to use polynomial long division to solve, and we'll cover that technique in the online appendix included with this book because you may want to have it in your arsenal. But if you don't know how to do polynomial long division, there's no need to panic. You could use an alternate approach called **Picking Numbers** that will work just as well: choose a number to substitute for x in the question, then substitute the same number in for x in the choices and see which one matches. Like this:

Pick a small number for x, say 2. When $x = 2$, the original expression becomes the following:

$$\frac{6x+8}{x-1} = \frac{6(2)+8}{2-1} = \frac{20}{1} = 20$$

Now, plug $x = 2$ into the choices:

A) $6 - \dfrac{14}{x-1} = 6 - \dfrac{14}{2-1} = 6 - 14 = -8$

Not 20, so eliminate (A).

B) $6 + \dfrac{8}{x-1} = 6 + \dfrac{8}{2-1} = 14$

Eliminate (B).

C) $6 + \dfrac{14}{x-1} = 6 + 14 = 20$

This is a match. When using Picking Numbers, it is possible that another answer choice can produce the same result, so check (D) to be sure there isn't another match when $x = 2$. (If there is, go back and pick another number to distinguish between the choices that match.)

D) $\dfrac{6+8}{-1} = -14$

Eliminate (D).

Step 4: Did you solve for the right thing? You found the equivalent expression, so yes. Only **(C)** is a match, and therefore it is correct.

When picking numbers, use numbers that are **permissible** and **manageable**. That is, use numbers that are allowed by the stipulations of the question and that are easy to work with. In this question, you could have picked any real number because x was not defined as positive, negative, odd, even, a fraction, etc. A small positive integer is usually the best choice in this situation. In other questions, other kinds of numbers may be more manageable. For example, in percents questions, 100 is typically a smart number to pick.

Try one more:

A child is arranging plates of apples to serve at a party. If the child places 6 apples on each plate, there will be 5 apples left over. In order to place 7 apples on each plate, with no apples left over, 5 more apples are needed. How many apples does the child have to arrange?

A) 32
B) 41
C) 56
D) 65

Step 1: What do they want? The number of apples.

Step 2: What do they give you? Two unknowns (the number of plates and the number of apples) and sufficient information to set up a system of equations.

Step 3: What approach will you use? You could set up the system of equations, but it might be faster to use a technique called **Backsolving**: plug the answer choices in for the unknown and see which one works. Here, you need an answer choice that will leave a remainder of 5 when divided by 6. Choices (A) and (C) don't meet this condition, so the answer must be (B) or (D).

Check (B). If there are 41 apples, and they are distributed 6 to a plate, there will indeed be 5 apples left over since $41 \div 6 = 6\ R5$. Now, what happens in the other situation? With an extra 5 apples, there should be enough to distribute 7 to a plate with none left over. But $41 + 5 = 46$, which is not evenly divisible by 7. There would be 4 apples left over. Eliminate (B).

You've now eliminated every choice but **(D)**, so it must be correct—you don't even need to test it! For the record:

(D) If there are 65 apples and they are distributed 6 to a plate, there would indeed be 5 left over since $65 \div 6 = 10\ R5$. With an extra 5 apples, it should be possible to distribute them evenly to 7 plates, and this is in fact what happens: $65 + 5 = 70$, which is evenly divisible by 7.

Step 4: Did you solve for the right thing? The question asked for the number of apples. You found that 65 apples satisfies all conditions of the problem. Choose **(D)** and move on.

Although it wasn't the case in this question, when backsolving it often makes sense to start with (B) or (C) in case you can tell from the context whether you'll need a larger or smaller answer choice if the one you're testing fails.

Now, it's your turn. Be deliberate with these questions. If there is analysis to do up front, do it. If there is more than one way to do a question, consider carefully before choosing your approach. And be sure to check whether you answered the right question. Forming good habits now, in slow and careful practice, will build your confidence for test day.

Try on Your Own

Directions: Take as much time as you need on these questions. Work carefully and methodically. There will be opportunities for timed practice in future chapters.

1. $4 + \sqrt{y + 2} = 7$

   In the equation above, what is the value of y?

   A) 3
   B) 7
   C) 9
   D) 11

2. A tractor trailer has a maximum capacity of 8,000 pounds. The equipment needed to load and unload the trailer must travel with the trailer and weighs a combined 1,500 pounds. The trailer will be loaded with x containers, each of which weighs 300 pounds. What is the largest value of x such that the trailer's capacity is not exceeded?

   A) 5
   B) 15
   C) 21
   D) 26

3. A certain vacuum cleaner is priced at $450 at a local appliance store. The same model of vacuum cleaner sells online for $\frac{7}{10}$ of the price at the appliance store. At a department store, the same model vacuum cleaner sells for $\frac{6}{5}$ of the appliance store's price. How many dollars more is the price of the vacuum cleaner at the department store than at the online retailer?

   A) 90
   B) 135
   C) 180
   D) 225

4. A stack of 50 kitchen serving trays forms a column that is approximately $7\frac{1}{4}$ inches tall. What is closest to the number of kitchen trays that would be needed to form a column that is 14 inches tall?

   A) 70
   B) 83
   C) 100
   D) 113

5. Last month, Keith ran 18 more miles than Mick ran. If they ran a total of 76 miles, how many miles did Keith run?

   A) 29
   B) 38
   C) 42
   D) 47

6. If $\frac{3x}{2y} = 6$, what is the value of $\frac{y}{2x}$?

   A) $\frac{1}{8}$
   B) $\frac{1}{2}$
   C) $\frac{2}{3}$
   D) 1

x	y
1	$\dfrac{5}{3}$
3	3
5	$\dfrac{13}{3}$
7	$\dfrac{17}{3}$

7. Which of the following equations relates y to x according to the values in the table above?

A) $y = \dfrac{2}{3}x + 1$

B) $y = x + \dfrac{2}{3}$

C) $y = \left(\dfrac{2}{3}x\right)^2 + 1$

D) $y = \left(\dfrac{2}{5}\right)^x - \dfrac{3}{5}$

8. In a restaurant's kitchen, c cakes are made by adding s cups of sugar to a mix of eggs and butter. If $s = 3c + 5$, how many more cups of sugar are needed to make one additional cake?

A) 0

B) $\dfrac{1}{3}$

C) 1

D) 3

9. A bowling league charges a one-time membership fee of \$25, plus x dollars each month. If a bowler has paid \$53 for the first 4 months, including the membership fee, what is the value of x?

A) 4

B) 7

C) 10

D) 13

10. If $x > 0$, which of the following is equivalent to $\dfrac{3}{\dfrac{1}{x+5} + \dfrac{1}{x+3}}$?

A) $(x+5)^2$

B) $\dfrac{3(x+5)(x+3)}{2(x+4)}$

C) $3(x+4)$

D) $\dfrac{(x+4)}{(x+5)^2}$

A Note about Grid-ins

You will see an occasional question without answer choices throughout the Math chapters of this book, starting in the next chapter. On the PSAT, several of these Grid-in questions appear at the end of each Math section. Instead of bubbling in a letter, you'll enter your responses to these questions into a grid that looks like this:

If you are gridding a value that doesn't take up the whole grid, such as 50, you can enter it anywhere in the grid as long as the digits are consecutive; it doesn't matter which column you start in. Gridding mixed numbers and decimals requires some care. Anything to the left of the fraction bar will be read as the numerator of a fraction, so you must grid mixed numbers as improper fractions. For instance, say you want to grid the mixed fraction $5\frac{1}{2}$. If you enter 5 1/2 into the grid, your answer will be read as $\frac{51}{2}$. Instead, enter your response as 11/2, which will be read (correctly) as $\frac{11}{2}$. Alternatively, you could grid this answer as 5.5.

A repeating decimal can either be rounded or truncated, but it must be entered to as many decimal places as possible. This means it must fill the entire grid. For example, you can grid $\frac{1}{6}$ as .166 or .167 but not as .16 or .17.

Note that you cannot grid a minus sign or any value larger than 9,999, so if you get an answer that is negative or larger than 9,999 to a grid-in question, you've made a mistake and should check your work.

Reflect

Directions: Take a few minutes to recall what you've learned and what you've been practicing in this chapter. Consider the following questions, jot down your best answer for each one, and then compare your reflections to the expert responses on the following page. Use your level of confidence to determine what to do next.

Think about your current habits when attacking PSAT questions. Are you a strategic test taker? Do you take the time to think through what would be the fastest way to the answer?

_____

_____

_____

Do word problems give you trouble?

_____

_____

_____

What are the steps of the Method for PSAT Math and why is each step important?

_____

_____

_____

Expert Responses

Think about your current habits when attacking PSAT questions. Are you a strategic test taker? Do you take the time to think through what would be the fastest way to the answer?

If yes, good for you! If not, we recommend doing questions more than one way whenever possible as part of your PSAT prep. If you can discover now, while you're still practicing, that Picking Numbers is faster for you on certain types of questions but not on others, you'll be that much more efficient on test day.

Do word problems give you trouble?

If word problems are difficult for you, get into the habit of taking an inventory, before you do any math, of what the question is asking for and what information you have.

What are the steps of the Method for PSAT Math and why is each step important?

Here are the steps:

Step 1. *State what the question is asking*

Step 2. *Examine the given information*

(Taking an inventory is especially important in word problems.)

Step 3. *Choose your approach*

(Taking a moment to decide what approach will be the fastest way to the answer will ultimately save you time.)

Step 4. *Confirm that you answered the right question*

(Making sure you solved for the right thing will save you from losing points to speed mistakes on questions that you know how to do and should be getting credit for.)

Next Steps

If you answered most questions correctly in the "How Much Have You Learned?" section, and if your responses to the Reflect questions were similar to those of the PSAT expert, then consider the Method for PSAT Math an area of strength and move on to the next chapter. Do keep using the method as you work on the questions in future chapters.

If you don't yet feel confident, review those parts of this chapter that you have not yet mastered and try the questions you missed again. As always, be sure to review the explanations closely.

Answers and Explanations

1. B

Difficulty: Medium

Category: Radicals

Strategic Advice: Backsolve by plugging the answer choices in for y to determine which one makes the given equation true.

Getting to the Answer: Simplify the equation by subtracting 4 from both sides to get $\sqrt{y+2} = 3$. Now, check the answer choices, starting with (B) or (C). If the answer you choose is too large or too small, you'll know which direction to go when testing the next choice.

(B): $\sqrt{7+2} = 3$. This is the correct answer.

If you prefer the algebraic approach, here it is:

$$\sqrt{y+2} = 3$$
$$y + 2 = 9$$
$$y = 7$$

Again, **(B)** is the correct answer.

2. C

Difficulty: Medium

Category: Solving Equations

Strategic Advice: Break apart the question into its mathematical parts; determine what information you have and what value you need to find and then determine how you'll find that value.

Getting to the Answer: To answer this question, organize the information you know. The capacity of the trailer is 8,000 pounds. However, equipment that is already on the trailer weighs 1,500 pounds, so there is only $8,000 - 1,500 = 6,500$ pounds of remaining capacity. Each container weighs 300 pounds, so divide 6,500 by 300 to determine the maximum number of containers that can be packed: $\frac{6,500}{300} = 21\frac{200}{300} = 21\frac{2}{3}$. Partial containers may not be packed, so round down to 21, which is **(C)**.

3. D

Difficulty: Medium

Category: Solving Equations

Strategic Advice: Begin by determining what you are being asked to find—the difference between the online retailer's price and the department store's price. Next, use the information you're given—the price at the appliance store, as well as fractions that represent the prices at the other two retailers.

Getting to the Answer: To answer this question, determine the price of the vacuum cleaner at each retailer. Online, the vacuum cleaner sells for $\frac{7}{10}$ of the price at the appliance store, or $\frac{7}{10}(450) = 315$. The department store sells the vacuum cleaner for $\frac{6}{5}$ the price of the appliance store, so the department store's price is $\frac{6}{5}(450) = 540$. Now that you know the price of the vacuum cleaner at each store, simply subtract: $540 - 315 = 225$, which is **(D)**.

4. C

Difficulty: Easy

Category: Proportions

Strategic Advice: Because the answer choices are widely spaced apart, and the question asks for the answer that is "closest to the number," estimation will be a better approach than wading into unnecessarily detailed and tedious calculations.

Getting to the Answer: Notice the relationship between the stack of trays in the question and the stack of trays you are asked to solve for: you are given a stack of $7\frac{1}{4}$ inches, and you are asked how many plates are needed for a 14-inch stack. The number 14 is very close to twice $7\frac{1}{4}$, so you will need nearly twice the 50 plates given in the question. Thus, 100 is the correct answer, which is **(C)**.

5. D

Difficulty: Medium

Category: Systems of Linear Equations

Strategic Advice: Use the answer choices to your advantage to quickly find Keith's distance.

Getting to the Answer: The question gives two unknowns and enough information so that a system of equations could be formed. Traditional algebra could be used to solve this system of equations.

However, there is a more efficient way to answer the question: examine the answer choices to see which answers make sense for Keith's distance. The question states that Keith ran 18 more miles than Mick; thus, Keith must have run more than half of the 76 miles that the two of them ran. Since one-half of 76 is 38, you can eliminate (A) and (B) immediately.

Now, you just have to check either (C) or (D). For (C), if Keith ran 42 miles, then Mick ran $42 - 18 = 24$ miles, and $42 + 24 = 66$ miles, which isn't correct. Thus, **(D)** is the correct answer. For the record, if Keith ran 47 miles, then Mick ran $47 - 18 = 29$ miles, and $47 + 29 = 76$, which is correct.

If you are curious about the algebraic approach, let k represent the number of miles Keith ran. Since Keith ran 18 miles more than Mick, Mick ran 18 miles fewer, or $k - 18$ miles. They ran a combined 76 miles, so the following equation can be created and solved:

$$k + (k - 18) = 76$$
$$2k - 18 = 76$$
$$2k = 94$$
$$k = 47$$

Again, this matches **(D)**.

6. A

Difficulty: Medium

Category: Solving Equations

Strategic Advice: You have two variables, but only one equation, so solving for each variable will not be possible. Instead, pick numbers for x and y that will make the equation true.

Getting to the Answer: Pick a simple number for x and solve for y. Hopefully, y will also be easy to work with so you can plug them into the expression you are

trying to find. Say $x = 4$; this gives $\frac{3(4)}{2y} = 6$, or $\frac{12}{2y} = 6$. Multiplying both sides by $2y$ gives $12 = 12y$, so $y = 1$. Both numbers are very manageable, so plug them into the expression $\frac{y}{2x}$. This yields $\frac{1}{2(4)} = \frac{1}{8}$, which is **(A)**.

7. A

Difficulty: Medium

Category: Linear Graphs

Strategic Advice: The answer choices are split into two types. The first two are linear equations and the second two are nonlinear. They are quadratic and exponential, respectively. Thus, examine the table to determine whether the relationship between x and y is linear or nonlinear.

Getting to the Answer: Notice that for every increase of 2 in x, y increases by $\frac{4}{3}$. Thus, the relationship is linear, meaning you can eliminate (C) and (D). To determine whether (A) or (B) is correct, substitution could be used. However, note that if y increases by $\frac{4}{3}$ for every 2 unit increase in x, then dividing both values by 2 shows that y increases by $\frac{2}{3}$ for every 1 unit increase in x. This is the definition of slope, and the only equation that is a line with a slope of $\frac{2}{3}$ is **(A)**.

8. D

Difficulty: Medium

Category: Word Problems

Strategic Advice: Pick a number for c to see how many cups of sugar will be needed, then pick another number for c to see how the number of cups of sugar changes.

Getting to the Answer: Pick a number for c; let's say $c = 2$. This means that $3(2) + 5 = 11$ cups of sugar are needed for two cakes. Now, try $c = 3$: $3(3) + 5 = 14$ cups of sugar needed for 3 cakes. To go from 2 cakes to 3 cakes, 3 additional cups of sugar were needed, which is **(D)**. You can try $c = 4$ to confirm: $3(4) + 5 = 17$, which is another 3 cups of sugar.

9. B

Difficulty: Medium

Category: Word Problems

Strategic Advice: Backsolve by plugging in answer choices for x to determine which answer matches the cost of four months of membership.

Getting to the Answer: Examine the answer choices, starting with (B) or (C). If the answer you choose is too large or too small, you will know which direction to go. Multiply the answer choice by 4 and add the $25 membership fee.

(B): $7 \times \$4 = \$28 \rightarrow \$28 + \$25 = \$53$. This is a match, so **(B)** is the correct answer.

Algebra could also be used here:

$$\$25 + 4x = \$53$$
$$4x = \$28$$
$$x = \$7$$

Algebra also leads to $7, which is **(B)**.

10. B

Difficulty: Medium

Category: Rational Expressions and Equations

Strategic Advice: Pick a number for x to determine the numerical value of the given expression, then plug the same number into the answer choices to find the one that matches.

Getting to the Answer: Pick something easy, like $x = 1$: $\dfrac{3}{\dfrac{1}{1+5} + \dfrac{1}{1+3}}$. This simplifies to

$\dfrac{3}{\dfrac{1}{6} + \dfrac{1}{4}} = \dfrac{3}{\dfrac{2}{12} + \dfrac{3}{12}} = \dfrac{3}{\dfrac{5}{12}}$. This fraction can be rewritten

as $3 \times \dfrac{12}{5} = \dfrac{36}{5}$.

Now, plug 1 in for x in each of the answer choices to see which one gives you the same value:

(A): $((1) + 5)^2 = 36$. Eliminate.

(B): $\dfrac{3[(1) + 5][(1) + 3]}{2[(1) + 4]} = \dfrac{3(6)(4)}{2(5)} = \dfrac{72}{10} = \dfrac{36}{5}$. Correct!

Just to be sure, check the other two answers.

(C): $3((1) + 4) = 3(5) = 15$. Eliminate.

(D): $\dfrac{[(1) + 4]}{[(1) + 5]^2} = \dfrac{5}{6^2} = \dfrac{5}{36}$. Eliminate.

Since **(B)** is the only answer that matched the calculated value, it must be the correct answer.

The Heart of Algebra

CHAPTER 4

Linear Equations and Graphs

LEARNING OBJECTIVES

After completing this chapter, you will be able to:

- Isolate a variable
- Translate word problems into equations
- Calculate the slope of a line given two points
- Write the equation of a line in slope-intercept form
- Discern whether the slope of a line is positive, negative, zero, or undefined based on its graph
- Describe the slopes of parallel and perpendicular lines

110/600 SmartPoints® (Very High Yield)

How Much Do You Know?

Directions: Try the questions that follow. Show your work so that you can compare your solutions to the ones found in the Check Your Work section immediately after this question set. The "Category" heading in the explanation for each question gives the title of the lesson that covers how to solve it. If you answered the question(s) for a given lesson correctly, and if your scratchwork looks like ours, you may be able to move quickly through that lesson. If you answered incorrectly or used a different approach, you may want to take your time on that lesson.

$$\frac{1}{2}(3x + 17) = \frac{1}{6}(8x - 10)$$

1. Which value of x satisfies the equation above?

    A) -61

    B) -55

    C) -41

    D) -35

2. Jenna is renting a car while on a business trip. The cost is $54.95 per day, which is taxed at a rate of 6 percent. The car rental company charges an additional one-time, untaxed environmental impact fee of $10. Which of the following equations represents Jenna's total cost, in dollars, for renting the car for d days?

    A) $c = (54.95 + 0.06d) + 10$

    B) $c = 1.06(54.95d) + 10$

    C) $c = 1.06(54.95d + 10)$

    D) $c = 1.06(54.95 + 10)d$

3. What was the initial amount of water in a barrel, in liters, if x liters remain after y liters were spilled and 6 liters were added?

    A) $x - y + 6$

    B) $y - x + 6$

    C) $x + y + 6$

    D) $y + x - 6$

Price of One Can	Projected Number of Cans Sold
$0.75	10,000
$0.80	9,000
$0.85	8,000
$0.90	7,000
$0.95	6,000
$1.00	5,000

4. Which of the following equations best describes the relationship shown in the table, where n indicates the number of cans sold and p represents the price in dollars of one can?

    A) $n = -20{,}000p + 25{,}000$

    B) $n = -200p + 250$

    C) $n = 200p + 250$

    D) $n = 20{,}000p + 25{,}000$

Shipping Cost

5. A freight company charges a flat insurance fee to deliver a package anywhere in the continental United States, plus an additional charge for each pound the package weighs. The graph shows the relationship between the weight of the package and the total cost to ship it. Based on the graph, how much would it cost to ship a 25-pound box?

    A) $37.00

    B) $48.00

    C) $62.50

    D) $74.50

Check Your Work

1. A

Difficulty: Easy

Category: Solving Equations

Getting to the Answer: Look for a way to make the algebra manipulations easier (and quicker). Begin by multiplying both sides by 6 to eliminate the fractions. So, $3(3x + 17) = 8x - 10$. Then, distribute to get $9x + 51 = 8x - 10$. Combining like terms yields $9x - 8x = -10 - 51$, and solving for x reveals that $x = -61$, which is **(A)**.

2. B

Difficulty: Medium

Category: Word Problems

Getting to the Answer: Use the information in the question to write your own equation, then look for the answer choice that matches. Simplify your equation only if you don't find a match. Start with the cost, not including tax or the environmental impact fee. If Jenna rents a car for d days at a daily rate of $54.95, the untaxed total is $54.95d$. There is a 6% tax added to this amount, so multiply by 1.06 to get $1.06(54.95d)$. The $10.00 environmental impact fee is *not* taxed, so simply add 10 to your expression. The total cost is $c = 1.06(54.95d) + 10$, which matches **(B)**, so you do not need to simplify.

3. D

Difficulty: Medium

Category: Word Problems

Getting to the Answer: Write an equation in words first, then translate from English to math. Finally, rearrange your equation to find what you're interested in, which is the initial amount. Call the initial amount A. After you've written your equation, solve for A.

Amount now (x) = initial amount (A) minus y plus 6:

$$x = A - y + 6$$
$$x + y - 6 = A$$

This is the same as $y + x - 6$, so **(D)** is correct.

You could also pick numbers to answer this question.

4. A

Difficulty: Medium

Category: Linear Graphs

Getting to the Answer: The answer choices are given in slope-intercept form, so start by finding the slope. To do this, substitute two pairs of values from the table into the slope formula, $m = \dfrac{y_2 - y_1}{x_2 - x_1}$. Keep in mind that the projected number of cans sold *depends* on the price, so the price is the independent variable (x) and the projected number is the dependent variable (y). Using the points $(0.75, 10{,}000)$ and $(1.0, 5{,}000)$, the slope is:

$$m = \frac{5{,}000 - 10{,}000}{1.00 - 0.75}$$
$$= \frac{-5{,}000}{0.25}$$
$$= -20{,}000$$

This means that **(A)** must be correct because it is the only one that has a slope of $-20{,}000$. Don't let (D) fool you—the projected number of cans sold goes *down* as the price goes *up*, so there is an inverse relationship, and the slope must be negative.

5. D

Difficulty: Hard

Category: Linear Graphs

Getting to the Answer: In a real-world scenario, the y-intercept of a graph usually represents a flat fee or an initial value. The slope of the line represents a unit rate, such as the cost per pound. The y-intercept of the graph is 12, so the flat fee is $12. To find the cost per pound (the unit rate), substitute two points from the graph into the slope formula. Using the points $(0, 12)$ and $(2, 17)$, the unit rate is $\dfrac{17 - 12}{2 - 0} = \dfrac{5}{2} = 2.5$, which means $2.50 per pound will be added to the cost.

The total cost to ship a 25-pound box is $12 + 2.50(25) = 12 + 62.50 = 74.50$, which is **(D)**.

Solving Equations

To answer a question like this:

$$\frac{1}{3}(3x + 12) = \frac{1}{6}(5x - 12)$$

Which of the following values is equal to x ?

A) -36

B) 4

C) 12

D) 20

You need to know this:

Isolating a variable means getting that variable by itself on one side of the equation. To do this, use inverse operations to manipulate the equation, remembering that whatever you do to one side of the equation, you must do to *both* sides.

You need to do this:

It usually makes sense to proceed in this order:

1. Eliminate any fractions.

2. Collect and combine like terms.

3. Divide to leave the desired variable by itself.

Explanation:

Eliminate the fractions by multiplying both sides of the equation by 6:

$$\left(\frac{6}{1}\right)\frac{1}{3}(3x+12)=\left(\frac{6}{1}\right)\frac{1}{6}(5x-12)$$

$$2(3x+12)=(5x-12)$$

In order to collect all the x terms on one side, you'll first need to distribute the 2 on the left side of the equation:

$$6x+24=5x-12$$

Next, subtract $5x$ from both sides:

$$x+24=-12$$

Finally, subtract 24 from both sides:

$$x=-36$$

Therefore, **(A)** is correct.

Try on Your Own

Directions: Take as much time as you need on these questions. Work carefully and methodically. There will be an opportunity for timed practice at the end of the chapter.

HINT: Since the answer choices in Q1 involve decimals, convert the fractions to decimals.

$$\frac{8}{7}\left(x - \frac{101}{220}\right) + 4\left(x + \frac{8}{9}\right) = 38$$

1. Which approximate value of x satisfies the equation shown?

   A)   4.3

   B)   4.6

   C)   6.6

   D)   6.8

HINT: Is there a simpler way to solve Q2 than finding the value for n?

---

2. If $3(n - 2) = 6$, then what does $\dfrac{n - 2}{n + 2}$ equal?

$$\frac{7(n - 3) + 11}{6} = \frac{18 - (6 + 2n)}{8}$$

3. In the equation shown, what is the value of n ?

   A) $\dfrac{38}{17}$

   B) $\dfrac{38}{11}$

   C) $\dfrac{56}{11}$

   D) $\dfrac{94}{17}$

4. If $36 + 3(4x - 9) = c(2x + 1) + 25$ has no solution and c is a constant, what is the value of c ?

   A) -3

   B)   3

   C)   6

   D)   12

HINT: There's no need to try to isolate the variable in the equation for Q5.

---

5. In the equation $x - 4 = \dfrac{5}{x - 4}$, which of the following is a possible value of $x - 4$?

   A) $\sqrt{5}$

   B)   4

   C) $4 + \sqrt{5}$

   D)   5

Word Problems

LEARNING OBJECTIVE

After this lesson, you will be able to:

• Translate word problems into equations

To answer a question like this:

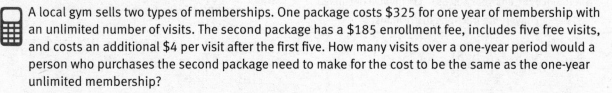

A local gym sells two types of memberships. One package costs $325 for one year of membership with an unlimited number of visits. The second package has a $185 enrollment fee, includes five free visits, and costs an additional $4 per visit after the first five. How many visits over a one-year period would a person who purchases the second package need to make for the cost to be the same as the one-year unlimited membership?

A) 30

B) 35

C) 40

D) 45

You need to know this:

The PSAT likes to test your understanding of how to describe real-world situations using math equations. For some questions, it will be up to you to extract and solve an equation; for others, you'll have to interpret an equation in a real-life context. The following table shows some of the most common phrases and mathematical equivalents you're likely to see on the PSAT.

Word Problems Translation Table	
English	**Math**
equals, is, equivalent to, was, will be, has, costs, adds up to, the same as, as much as	$=$
times, of, multiplied by, product of, twice, double	$\times$
divided by, out of, ratio	$\div$
plus, added to, sum, combined, increased by	$+$
minus, subtracted from, smaller than, less than, fewer, decreased by, difference between	$-$
a number, how much, how many, what	x, n, etc.

You need to do this:

When translating from English to math, *start by defining the variables,* choosing letters that make sense. Then, *break the question down into small pieces,* writing down the translation for one phrase at a time.

Explanation:

The phrase "how many visits" indicates an unknown, so you need a variable. Use an intuitive letter to represent the number of visits; call it v. The question asks when the two memberships will cost the "same amount," so write an equation that sets the total membership costs equal to each other.

The first membership type costs \$325 for unlimited visits, so write 325 on one side of the equal sign. The second type costs \$4 per visit (not including the first 5 visits), or $4(v - 5)$, plus a flat \$185 enrollment fee, so write $4(v - 5) + 185$ on the other side of the equal sign. That's it! Now, solve for v:

$$325 = 4(v - 5) + 185$$
$$140 = 4v - 20$$
$$160 = 4v$$
$$40 = v$$

The answer is **(C)**.

Try on Your Own

Directions: Take as much time as you need on these questions. Work carefully and methodically. There will be an opportunity for timed practice at the end of the chapter.

6. An automotive insurer computes the charge for an insurance policy by starting with a fixed fee for administrative expenses and then adding a percentage of the value of the car, v. If the total price for an automobile policy is given by the function $T = 0.02v + 25$, then the value 0.02 best represents which of the following?

    A) The fee for the administrative expenses

    B) The value of the car

    C) The total price of the policy

    D) The percentage of the value of the car

7. Ibrahim has a contract for a cell phone plan that includes the following rates: the plan has a fixed cost of $50 per month, a data plan that provides 2 gigabytes (GB) of data for free and $8 for each GB of data after that, and a text message plan that costs $0.10 per text message sent. Which of the following equations represents the amount of money, in dollars, that Ibrahim will spend as long as he uses at least 2 GB of data? (Assume $d = $ dollars, $g = $ number of GB of data used, and $t = $ number of text messages sent.)

    A) $d = 50 + 8g + 0.1t$

    B) $d = 50 + (8g - 2) + 0.1t$

    C) $d = 50 + 8(g - 2) + 0.1t$

    D) $d = 5{,}000 + 800g + 10t$

HINT: For Q8, take the time to determine which number goes with which variable before attempting to build the entire equation.

8. An online video game service has two different packages available. The first is an Unlimited Rental Package that costs $250 for 3 months and allows customers to rent as many games as they want. The second is the Standard Rental Package that initially has a flat fee of $130 but costs $4 per rental in the 3-month period. How many rentals on the Standard Rental Package would it take for both packages to equal the same price over 3 months?

    A) 2

    B) 30

    C) 96

    D) 120

9. A produce stand normally sells watermelons for $0.60 per pound. On Mondays, it sells watermelons at a 20 percent discount. The stand also sells sweet potatoes for $0.79 each. Which of the following represents the total cost, c, if a customer buys 4 sweet potatoes and a watermelon weighing p pounds on a Monday?

    A) $c = 0.2p + 0.79$

    B) $c = 0.48p + 3.16$

    C) $c = 0.6p + 0.79$

    D) $c = 0.6p + 3.16$

HINT: For Q10, if *a* arrows hit the inner circle, how many
hit the outer circle in terms of *a*?

---

10. Juan is on his school's archery team. In a match, he
gets 12 arrows to shoot at a target. He gets 8 points
if the arrow hits the inner circle of the target and
4 points if it hits the outer circle. Which of the
following equations represents Juan's total score if
a of his arrows hit the inner circle and the rest hit
the outer circle?

A) $p = 8a$

B) $p = 8a + 4$

C) $p = 48 + 4a$

D) $p = 96 - 4a$

Linear Graphs

To answer a question like this:

Which of the following equations describes the line that passes through the points $(2, -4)$ and $(-2, 2)$?

A) $y = \frac{3}{2}x + 1$

B) $y = \frac{3}{2}x - 1$

C) $y = -\frac{3}{2}x + 1$

D) $y = -\frac{3}{2}x - 1$

You need to know this:

The answer choices in this question are written in slope-intercept form: $y = mx + b$. In this form of a linear equation, m represents the **slope** of the line and b represents the **y-intercept**. You can think of the slope of a line as how steep it is. The y-intercept is the point at which the line crosses the y-axis and can be written as the ordered pair $(0, y)$.

You can calculate the slope of a line if you know any two points on the line. The formula is $m = \frac{y_2 - y_1}{x_2 - x_1}$, where (x_1, y_1) and (x_2, y_2) are the coordinates of the two points on the line.

A line that moves from the bottom left to the top right has a positive slope. A line that moves from the top left to the bottom right has a negative slope. A horizontal line has a slope of zero and a vertical line has an undefined slope.

Some PSAT questions ask about parallel or perpendicular lines. Parallel lines have the same slope, while perpendicular lines have negative reciprocal slopes.

You need to do this:

- Find the slope of the line.
- Write the equation in slope-intercept form, substituting the value of the slope you found and one of the known points for *x* and *y*.
- Solve for the *y*-intercept.

Explanation:

In the question above, $m = \dfrac{-4-2}{2-(-2)} = \dfrac{-6}{4} = -\dfrac{3}{2}$. Of the answer choices, only (C) and (D) have negative slopes, so rule out (A) and (B).

To find the *y*-intercept of the line, write the equation for the line in slope-intercept form and plug in one of the known points for *x* and *y*:

$$y = -\frac{3}{2}x + b$$
$$2 = -\frac{3}{2}(-2) + b$$
$$2 = 3 + b$$
$$-1 = b$$

Therefore, **(D)** is correct.

Another way to solve this question would be to plot the two points, graph the line, check where it crosses the *y*-axis to find the *y*-intercept, and count how many spaces the line moves up for each space it moves to the right to find the slope.

Try on Your Own

Directions: Take as much time as you need on these questions. Work carefully and methodically. There will be an opportunity for timed practice at the end of the chapter.

HINT: For Q11, remember that parallel lines have the same slope and perpendicular lines have opposite sign reciprocal slopes.

---

11. A line, t, is perpendicular to $y = -\dfrac{3}{4}x + 5$ and passes through the point $(3, 5)$. What is the equation of line t?

    A) $y = \dfrac{4}{3}x + 1$

    B) $y = -\dfrac{4}{3}x + 1$

    C) $y = \dfrac{4}{3}x + 5$

    D) $y = -\dfrac{3}{4}x + 1$

HINT: Convert the word problem in Q12 to an equation in slope-intercept form, $y = mx + b$.

Months after June	4	8	10
Price of Gas	2	3.33	4

12. In June, Marie notices that the price of gas is increasing. She records the price of gas 4, 8, and 10 months after her initial observation. If y is the price of gas, in dollars per gallon, and x is the number of months after June, which linear equation represents the correct relationship between y and x?

    A) $y = 0.33x + 0.67$

    B) $y = 0.67x + 1.33$

    C) $y = 1.33x + 2$

    D) $y = 2.67x + 5.67$

HINT: For Q13, focus on where the answer choices differ in their equations: the y-intercept.

---

13. The graph above shows the volume of a sample of gas as it is cooled. If T is the temperature of the gas in degrees Celsius and V is the volume in liters, which of the following equations, when plotted, could produce the graph shown?

    A) $V = 0.004T + 100$

    B) $V = 0.004T$

    C) $V = 0.004T + 1$

    D) $V = 0.004T - 0.25$

Golf Balls

14. A driving range sells golf balls in different quantities. The figure shows the costs of the various quantities. According to the figure, what is the cost of a single golf ball?

A) $0.60

B) $1.67

C) $3.00

D) $5.00

15. For what value of y does the graph of $4x - \frac{1}{2}y = -12$ cross the y-axis?

On Test Day

Remember that the PSAT doesn't ask you to show your work. If you find the algebra in a question challenging, there is often another way to get to the answer.

Try this question first using algebra and then using the Picking Numbers strategy you learned in chapter 3. Time yourself. Which approach do you find easier? Which one was faster? Did you get the correct answer both times? Remember your preferred approach and try it first if you see a question like this on test day.

$$\frac{2(a-4)}{b} = \frac{4}{5}$$

16. Which of the following statements is NOT true if the above equation is true?

   A) $\dfrac{b}{a-4} = \dfrac{5}{2}$

   B) $\dfrac{2a}{b} = -\dfrac{12}{5}$

   C) $10a - 4b = 40$

   D) $\dfrac{a-4}{b} = \dfrac{2}{5}$

The answer and explanation can be found at the end of this chapter.

How Much Have You Learned?

Directions: For testlike practice, give yourself 15 minutes to complete this question set. Be sure to study the explanations, even for questions you answered correctly. They can be found at the end of this chapter.

17. Line m is parallel to line k and passes through $(5, 5)$. The slope of line k is $-\frac{2}{5}$ and line k passes through the origin. Which of the following is the equation for line m?

    A) $y = -\frac{2}{5}x$

    B) $y = \frac{5}{2}x + 7$

    C) $y = \frac{5}{2}x$

    D) $y = -\frac{2}{5}x + 7$

18. Which value of x makes the equation $\frac{2}{3}(x - 1) = 12$ true?

    A) 7

    B) 9

    C) 17

    D) 19

$$\frac{5 + 3z - (1 + 2z)}{3} = \frac{-3z - 2(5 - 3)}{9}$$

19. What is the value of z in the equation above?

    A) $-\frac{8}{3}$

    B) $-\frac{61}{27}$

    C) $\frac{61}{27}$

    D) $\frac{8}{3}$

20. Sandy works at a tire store. She gets paid $70 for a day's work, plus a commission of $14 for each tire she sells. Which of the following equations represents the relationship between one day of Sandy's pay, y, and the number of tires she sells, x?

    A) $x = 14y + 70$

    B) $x = 70y + 14$

    C) $y = 14x + 70$

    D) $y = 70x + 14$

Carnival Spending

21. The figure above shows the cost of going to a certain carnival. What does the y-intercept most likely represent?

    A) A flat entrance fee

    B) The cost of riding 8 rides

    C) The cost of attending the carnival 8 times

    D) The total cost of attending the carnival and riding 1 ride

22. For a car, depreciation is a reduction in value due to use or age. The value of a new car starts to depreciate as soon as the car is purchased and driven for the first time. If the equation $y = -0.15x + 27,000$ represents the estimated value of a certain car, taking into account depreciation over time, what does 27,000 most likely represent?

    A) The depreciation rate

    B) The current value of the car

    C) The original purchase price of the car

    D) The value of the car after 0.15 years of ownership

$$\frac{2}{3}(3h) - \frac{5}{2}(h-1) = -\frac{1}{3}\left(\frac{3}{2}h\right) + 8$$

23. What is the value of h in the equation above?

    A) $h = -5.5$

    B) $h = 5.5$

    C) There is no value of h for which the equation is true.

    D) There are infinitely many values of h for which the equation is true.

$$\frac{9}{4}(y - 8) = \frac{27}{2}$$

24. What value of y satisfies the equation above?

25. A cybercafe is a place that provides Internet access to the public, usually for a fee, along with snacks and drinks. Suppose a cybercafe charges a base rate of $25 to join for a year, an additional $0.30 per visit for the first 50 visits, and $0.10 for every visit after that. How much does the cybercafe charge for a year in which 72 visits are made?

    A) $32.20

    B) $36.60

    C) $42.20

    D) $46.60

26. An Internet provider charges k dollars for the first hour of use in a month and m dollars per hour for every additional hour used that month. If Jared paid $65.50 for his Internet use in one month, which of the following expressions represents the number of hours he used the Internet that month?

A) $\dfrac{65.50}{k+m}$

B) $\dfrac{65.50-k}{m}$

C) $\dfrac{65.50-k-m}{m}$

D) $\dfrac{65.50-k+m}{m}$

Reflect

Directions: Take a few minutes to recall what you've learned and what you've been practicing in this chapter. Consider the following questions, jot down your best answer for each one, and then compare your reflections to the expert responses on the following page. Use your level of confidence to determine what to do next.

What should you do to isolate a particular variable in an equation?

_____

_____

_____

What types of keywords should you look for when translating English into math?

_____

_____

_____

What is the most useful equation for a line in the coordinate plane? Why?

_____

_____

_____

When the PSAT gives you two points on a line, what can you figure out?

_____

_____

_____

How are parallel and perpendicular lines related to each other?

_____

_____

_____

Expert Responses

What should you do to isolate a particular variable in an equation?

Perform inverse operations until the variable is by itself on one side of the equal sign. If the equation has fractions, make them disappear by multiplying both sides of the equation by the denominator(s). If like terms appear on different sides of the equation, collect them on the same side so that you can combine them.

What types of keywords should you look for when translating English into math?

Look for keywords that signal equality ("is," "has," "was"), variable names ("Marina's age," "the cost of one bathtub"), or one of the four arithmetic operations (addition, subtraction, multiplication, and division).

What is the most useful equation for a line in the coordinate plane? Why?

The best equation is slope-intercept form, $y = mx + b$, because it tells you the slope (m) and the y-intercept (b). Conversely, if you need to derive an equation yourself, you can plug the slope and y-intercept into slope-intercept form and you're done.

When the PSAT gives you two points on a line, what can you figure out?

If you know two points, you can figure out the slope of the line with the equation $m = \dfrac{y_2 - y_1}{x_2 - x_1}$. From there, you can plug one of the points and the slope into slope-intercept form and find the y-intercept.

How are parallel and perpendicular lines related to each other?

Parallel lines never intersect and they have equal slopes. Perpendicular lines intersect at a 90° angle and they have negative reciprocal slopes.

Next Steps

If you answered most questions correctly in the "How Much Have You Learned?" section, and if your responses to the Reflect questions were similar to those of the PSAT expert, then consider Linear Equations and Graphs an area of strength and move on to the next chapter. Come back to this topic periodically to prevent yourself from getting rusty.

If you don't yet feel confident, review those parts of this chapter that you have not yet mastered. In particular, review the variable isolation example in the Solving Equations lesson and the definition of slope-intercept form in the Linear Graphs lesson. Then, try the questions you missed again. As always, be sure to review the explanations closely.

Math

Answers and Explanations

1.   D

Difficulty: Medium

Getting to the Answer: Multiply both sides by 7 to eliminate the fraction outside the parentheses. Then, because the choices are decimals, convert all fractions to decimal form: $8(x - 0.46) + 28(x + 0.89) = 266$. Distribute to get $8x - 3.68 + 28x + 24.92 = 266$, then combine like terms to yield $36x = 266 + 3.68 - 24.92$, or $36x = 244.76$. Divide both sides by 36 to find that $x = 6.8$, which is **(D)**.

2.   1/3 or .333

Difficulty: Medium

Getting to the Answer: Notice that $n - 2$ is in both the equation and the desired expression, so isolate $n - 2$ and plug it into the expression. Determine the value of $n - 2$ by dividing both sides of $3(n - 2) = 6$ by 3. Now you know that $n - 2 = 2$, so plug 2 into the numerator of the desired expression. To find the value of the denominator, add 2 to both sides of the given equation to find that $n = 4$. Plug 4 into $n + 2$, which leaves $\frac{2}{4 + 2} = \frac{2}{6} = \frac{1}{3}$. Grid in **1/3 or .333** and move on to the next question.

Note that you could also solve the equation for n and substitute the result into the desired expression, but this may take a bit more time.

3.   A

Difficulty: Medium

Getting to the Answer: Start by simplifying the numerators. Don't forget to distribute the negative to both terms inside the parentheses on the right side of the equation:

$$\frac{7(n - 3) + 11}{6} = \frac{18 - (6 + 2n)}{8}$$
$$\frac{7n - 21 + 11}{6} = \frac{18 - 6 - 2n}{8}$$
$$\frac{7n - 10}{6} = \frac{12 - 2n}{8}$$
$$\frac{7n - 10}{6} = \frac{6 - n}{4}$$

Next, cross-multiply and solve for n using inverse operations:

$$4(7n - 10) = 6(6 - n)$$
$$28n - 40 = 36 - 6n$$
$$34n = 76$$
$$n = \frac{76}{34} = \frac{38}{17}$$

This matches **(A)**.

4.   C

Difficulty: Medium

Getting to the Answer: If a linear equation has no solution, the variables cancel out, leaving two numbers that are not equal to each other. Start by simplifying the left side of the equation:

$$36 + 3(4x - 9) = c(2x + 1) + 25$$
$$36 + 12x - 27 = c(2x + 1) + 25$$

The variable term on the left is $12x$. Because the variable terms must cancel, the right side of the equation must also have a $12x$, so it must be that $c = 6$, which is **(C)**.

5.   A

Difficulty: Medium

Strategic Advice: When a question asks for a value of an expression, isolate that expression on one side of the equation. Do not solve for the variable because you'll have the extra step of plugging that value into the expression.

Getting to the Answer: Notice that the question asks for a possible value of $x - 4$, not a possible value of x. Isolate $x - 4$ on one side of the equation by multiplying both sides by $x - 4$ and taking the square root of both sides:

$$(x - 4)(x - 4) = \frac{5}{x - 4}(x - 4)$$
$$(x - 4)^2 = 5$$
$$\sqrt{(x - 4)^2} = \sqrt{5}$$
$$x - 4 = \pm\sqrt{5}$$

Thus, **(A)** is correct. Watch out for traps like (C), which is a possible value of x.

An alternative strategy is to backsolve, plugging each choice in for $x - 4$ to see which results in a true statement.

6. D

Difficulty: Easy

Getting to the Answer: The total insurance bill consists of a flat fee and a percentage of the value of the car. The administrative fee does not depend on the value of the car and therefore should not be multiplied by v. This means that 25 is the administrative fee. The other expression in the equation, $0.02v$, represents the percentage of the value of the car times the car's value (which the question tells you is v). Therefore, 0.02 must represent the value of the car as a percentage, which is **(D)**.

7. C

Difficulty: Medium

Getting to the Answer: You know there will be a flat fee of $50, and for text messages you'll be looking for $0.1t$. This eliminates (D). If you're stuck on the data plan cost, plug in some numbers. For $g = 2$, you wouldn't expect there to be an additional fee for data usage. For $g = 3$, you'd expect to see an $8 charge, and for $g = 4$, you'd expect to see a $16 charge. The only choice that reflects this is **(C)**.

8. B

Difficulty: Medium

Getting to the Answer: Translate from English into math by assembling equations and setting them equal to each other. Let $u =$ Unlimited Rental Package, $s =$ Standard Rental Package, and $r =$ number of rentals. Using the information about each package, you know that $u = 250$ and $s = 130 + 4r$. Now, solve for r when $u = s$:

$$250 = 130 + 4r$$
$$120 = 4r$$
$$30 = r$$

Choice **(B)** is correct.

9. B

Difficulty: Medium

Getting to the Answer: Write the equation in words first, then translate from English to math. The total cost, c, is the weight of the watermelon in pounds, p, multiplied by the sale price. Since the purchase is made on Monday, the sale price is: $\$0.60 \times 80\% = 0.6 \times 0.8 = 0.48$. This gives the cost of the watermelons: $0.48p$. Now, add the cost of four sweet potatoes, $0.79 \times 4 = 3.16$, to get the equation $c = 0.48p + 3.16$, which matches **(B)**.

You could also use the Picking Numbers strategy: pick a number for the weight of the watermelon and calculate how much it would cost (on sale). Next, add the cost of four sweet potatoes. Finally, find the equation that gives the same amount.

10. C

Difficulty: Hard

Getting to the Answer: The key to answering this question is to determine how many arrows hit each circle. If there are 12 arrows total and a hit the inner circle, the rest, or $12 - a$, must hit the outer circle. Now, write the expression in words: points per inner circle, 8, times number of arrows in inner circle, a, plus points per outer circle, 4, times number of arrows in outer circle, $12 - a$. Next, translate the words into numbers, variables, and operations: $8a + 4(12 - a)$. This is not one of the answer choices, so simplify the expression by distributing the 4 and then combining like terms: $8a + 4(12 - a) = 8a + 48 - 4a = 4a + 48$, so the equation is $p = 4a + 48$. Rearrange the order of the terms on the right side to arrive at **(C)**.

11. A

Difficulty: Medium

Getting to the Answer: The first useful piece of information is that the slope of the line perpendicular to line t is $-\frac{3}{4}$. Perpendicular lines have negative reciprocal slopes, so the slope of line t is $\frac{4}{3}$. Eliminate (B) and (D) because they have the incorrect slopes.

Plug the values for the slope and the coordinate point $(3, 5)$ into the slope-intercept equation to solve for b:

$$5 = \frac{4}{3}(3) + b$$
$$5 = 4 + b$$
$$5 - 4 = b$$
$$b = 1$$

Eliminate (C) because it does not have the correct y-intercept. Choice **(A)** is correct.

12. A

Difficulty: Medium

Getting to the Answer: The question tells you that the relationship is linear, so start by finding the the slope, m, using any two pairs of values from the table and the slope formula. Next, substitute the slope and any pair of values from the table, such as $(4, 2)$ and $(10, 4)$, into the equation $y = mx + b$ and solve for b. Finally, use the values of m and b to write the function:

$$m = \frac{y_2 - y_1}{x_2 - x_1} = \frac{4 - 2}{10 - 4} = \frac{2}{6} = \frac{1}{3}$$

You can stop right there! Only **(A)** has a slope of 0.33, so it must be the correct answer. For the record:

$$2 = \frac{1}{3}(4) + b$$
$$2 = \frac{4}{3} + b$$
$$\frac{2}{3} = b$$

13. C

Difficulty: Medium

Getting to the Answer: Temperature, T, is the independent variable on the x-axis, and volume, V, is the dependent variable on the y-axis. Therefore, the skeleton of the equation you're looking for is $V = mT + b$. Because each answer choice has a different y-intercept, finding b is enough to get the right answer; there is no need to determine the slope. Although the graph is not centered around the origin, you can still find the y-intercept. In this case, it's 1. This eliminates every answer choice except **(C)**, which is correct.

14. B

Difficulty: Medium

Getting to the Answer: The x-axis represents the number of golf balls, so find 1 on the x-axis and trace up to where it meets the graph of the line. The y-value is somewhere between \$1 and \$2, so the only possible correct answer is \$1.67, which is **(B)**.

You could also find the unit rate by calculating the slope of the line using two of the points shown on the graph. The graph rises 5 units and runs 3 units from one point to the next, so the slope is $\frac{5}{3}$, or 1.67.

15. 24

Difficulty: Medium

Getting to the Answer: The place where the line crosses the y-axis is the y-intercept, or b when the equation is written in slope-intercept form ($y = mx + b$), so rewrite the equation in this form:

$$4x - \frac{1}{2}y = -12$$
$$-\frac{1}{2}y = -4x - 12$$
$$-2\left(-\frac{1}{2}y\right) = -2(-4x - 12)$$
$$y = 8x + 24$$

The y-intercept is **24**.

Because the y-intercept of a graph is always of the form $(0, y)$, you could also substitute 0 for x in the original equation and solve for y.

16. B

Difficulty: Hard

Category: Solving Equations

Strategic Advice: Watch out for the word NOT in the question stem.

Getting to the Answer: To find the answer using Picking Numbers, take advantage of the fact that the equation is a proportion (that is, two fractions equal to each other). If $b = 5$ and $2(a - 4) = 4$, then both fractions will be the same and the numbers you've picked will be valid. Solve for a: $a - 4 = 2$, so $a = 6$. Now, plug $b = 5$ and $a = 6$ into the choices, looking for the one that is NOT true:

(A) $\dfrac{b}{a-4} = \dfrac{5}{6-4} = \dfrac{5}{2}$, eliminate.

(B) $\dfrac{2a}{b} = \dfrac{2(6)}{5} = \dfrac{12}{5} \neq -\dfrac{12}{5}$

You're done: pick **(B)** and move on. For the record:

(C) $10a - 4b = 10(6) - 4(5) = 60 - 20 = 40$, eliminate.

(D) $\dfrac{a-4}{b} = \dfrac{6-4}{5} = \dfrac{2}{5}$, eliminate.

To solve this question using algebra, first cross-multiply and simplify the original equation:

$$\frac{2(a-4)}{b} = \frac{4}{5}$$
$$10(a-4) = 4b$$
$$5(a-4) = 2b$$
$$5a - 20 = 2b$$
$$5a - 2b = 20$$

Then, repeat this process for each answer choice, looking for the one that does NOT yield the same equation:

(A) $\dfrac{b}{a-4} = \dfrac{5}{2}$, $2b = 5a - 20$, $20 = 5a - 2b$, eliminate.

(B) $\dfrac{2a}{b} = -\dfrac{12}{5}$, $10a = -12b$, $5a = -6b$, $5a + 6b = 0$

This equation is different from the one in the question, so **(B)** is correct. For the record:

(C) $10a - 4b = 40$, $5a - 2b = 20$, eliminate.

(D) $\dfrac{a-4}{b} = \dfrac{2}{5}$, $5a - 20 = 2b$, $5a - 2b = 20$, eliminate.

17. D

Difficulty: Medium

Category: Linear Graphs

Getting to the Answer: This question provides an equation for a line parallel to line m and a coordinate point for line m, $(5, 5)$. The slope of the parallel line, which is $-\dfrac{2}{5}$, is the same as the slope of line m. Eliminate (B) and (C) because they have the incorrect slope.

Plug the values for the slope and the coordinate point $(5, 5)$ into the slope-intercept equation to solve for b:

$$5 = -\frac{2}{5}(5) + b$$
$$5 = -2 + b$$
$$5 + 2 = b$$
$$b = 7$$

Eliminate (A) because it does not have the correct y-intercept. Only **(D)** is left and is correct. To confirm, plug the values for the slope and the y-intercept into the slope-intercept equation to get $y = -\dfrac{2}{5}x + 7$.

18. D

Difficulty: Easy

Category: Solving Equations

Getting to the Answer: Distributing the $\dfrac{2}{3}$ will result in messy calculations, so clear the fraction instead. Multiply both sides of the equation by the reciprocal of $\dfrac{2}{3}$, which is $\dfrac{3}{2}$, and isolate x:

$$\frac{3}{2} \cdot \frac{2}{3}(x-1) = 12 \cdot \frac{3}{2}$$
$$x - 1 = 18$$
$$x = 19$$

Choice **(D)** is correct.

Alternatively, you could backsolve. Say you started with (B). The left side of the equation would become $\dfrac{2}{3}(9-1) = \dfrac{2}{3}(8) = \dfrac{16}{3}$, which is smaller than 12, so you would move to (C) next. Plugging in 17 gives $\dfrac{2}{3}(17-1) = \dfrac{2}{3}(16) = \dfrac{32}{3}$. This is still smaller than 12 since $12(3) = 36$, so the correct answer again must be **(D)**.

19. A

Difficulty: Medium

Category: Solving Equations

Getting to the Answer: Simplify the numerators as much as possible, then isolate the variable. Begin by combining like terms on both sides of the equation. Once complete, cross-multiply and solve for z:

$$\frac{5 + 3z - (1 + 2z)}{3} = \frac{-3z - 2(5 - 3)}{9}$$

$$\frac{4 + z}{3} = \frac{-3z - 4}{9}$$

$$9(4 + z) = 3(-3z - 4)$$

$$36 + 9z = -9z - 12$$

$$18z = -48$$

$$z = -\frac{8}{3}$$

Choice **(A)** is correct.

20. C

Difficulty: Easy

Category: Word Problems

Getting to the Answer: When writing a linear equation, a flat rate is a constant while a unit rate is always multiplied by the independent variable. For one day of work, Sandy is paid $70, which is a flat rate and should be the constant in the equation. You can identify the unit rate by looking for words like *per* or *for each*. The clue "for each" tells you to multiply $14 by the number of tires she sells, so the equation is *pay* = 14 × *number of tires* + 70, or $y = 14x + 70$. This matches **(C)**.

21. A

Difficulty: Easy

Category: Linear Graphs

Getting to the Answer: Read the axis labels carefully. The y-intercept is the point at which $x = 0$, which means the number of rides is 0. The y-intercept is $(0, 8)$. This means the cost is $8 before riding any rides, and therefore 8 most likely represents a flat entrance fee, **(A)**.

22. C

Difficulty: Easy

Category: Word Problems

Getting to the Answer: Because the car's value is always declining from the time it is purchased, its greatest value is its purchase price when new. The car's price at any time can be represented as the purchase price minus some value that depends on the car's age. In the given formula, $0.15x$ is subtracted from 27,000, suggesting that $0.15x$ represents the decline in value over time and 27,000 represents the car's original purchase price, choice **(C)**.

23. C

Difficulty: Medium

Category: Solving Equations

Getting to the Answer: Look for a way to make the math easier, such as clearing the fractions first. To do this, multiply both sides of the equation by 6, then solve for h using inverse operations:

$$6\left[\frac{2}{3}(3h)\right] - 6\left[\frac{5}{2}(h - 1)\right] = 6\left[-\frac{1}{3}\left(\frac{3}{2}h\right)\right] + 6[8]$$

$$4(3h) - 15(h - 1) = -2\left(\frac{3}{2}h\right) + 48$$

$$12h - 15h + 15 = -3h + 48$$

$$-3h + 15 = -3h + 48$$

$$15 \neq 48$$

Because the variable terms in the equation cancel out, and 15 does not equal 48, the equation has no solution. In other words, there is no value of h that satisfies the equation, so **(C)** is correct.

24. 14

Difficulty: Easy

Category: Solving Equations

Getting to the Answer: Eliminate the fractions to simplify the math. Multiply both sides of the equation by 4, then solve for y using inverse operations:

$$4\left[\frac{9}{4}(y-8)\right] = 4\left[\frac{27}{2}\right]$$
$$9(y-8) = 54$$
$$9y - 72 = 54$$
$$9y = 126$$
$$y = 14$$

Grid in **14**.

25. C

Difficulty: Easy

Category: Word Problems

Getting to the Answer: When a question involves several rates, break the situation into separate, manageable pieces and deal with each in turn. Visitors must pay the cyber cafe a flat $25 fee to join regardless of the number of visits. The first 50 visits cost $0.30 each, or $50(\$0.30) = \$15$. The remaining $72 - 50 = 22$ visits cost $0.10 each, or $22(\$0.10) = \$2.20$. The total cost for 72 visits is therefore $\$25.00 + \$15.00 + \$2.20 = \$42.20$, which is **(C)**.

26. D

Difficulty: Hard

Category: Word Problems

Getting to the Answer: Let h be the number of hours Jared spent using the Internet during the month. The first hour costs k dollars and the remaining hours $(h - 1)$ are charged at the rate of m dollars per hour. Therefore, the total charge for a month is $k + (h - 1)m$. Set this equal to the amount Jared paid and solve for h. Note that you're not going to get a numeric answer because the question doesn't give you the actual rates:

$$k + (h-1)m = 65.50$$
$$k + hm - m = 65.50$$
$$mh = 65.50 + m - k$$
$$h = \frac{65.50 + m - k}{m}$$

This expression matches **(D)**. Note that you could also use Picking Numbers to answer this question.

CHAPTER 5

Systems of Linear Equations

LEARNING OBJECTIVES

After completing this chapter, you will be able to:

- Solve systems of linear equations by substitution
- Solve systems of linear equations by combination
- Determine the number of possible solutions for a system of linear equations, if any

---

45/600 SmartPoints® (Medium Yield)

How Much Do You Know?

Directions: Try the questions that follow. Show your work so that you can compare your solutions to the ones found in the Check Your Work section immediately after this question set. The "Category" heading in the explanation for each question gives the title of the lesson that covers how to solve it. If you answered the question(s) for a given lesson correctly, and if your scratchwork looks like ours, you may be able to move quickly through that lesson. If you answered incorrectly or used a different approach, you may want to take your time on that lesson.

$$\begin{cases} -6x + 3y = 27 \\ x + y = 0 \end{cases}$$

1. What is the value of x for the given equations above?

   A) -3

   B) 0

   C) 3

   D) 5

2. A television set costs $25 less than twice the cost of a radio. If the television and radio together cost $200, how much more does the television cost than the radio?

   A) $50

   B) $75

   C) $100

   D) $125

3. At a snack stand, hot dogs cost $3.50 and hamburgers cost $5.00. If the snack stand sold 27 snacks and made $118.50 in revenue, how many hot dogs and how many hamburgers were sold?

   A) 16 hot dogs; 11 hamburgers

   B) 16 hot dogs; 16 hamburgers

   C) 11 hot dogs; 14 hamburgers

   D) 11 hot dogs; 16 hamburgers

4. A certain student cell phone plan charges $0.10 per text and $0.15 per picture, with no additional monthly fee. If a student sends a total of 75 texts and pictures in one month and is billed $8.90 for that month, how many more texts did he send than pictures?

   A) 19

   B) 28

   C) 36

   D) 47

$$\begin{cases} \frac{1}{8}q + \frac{1}{5}s = 40 \\ zq + 8s = 1,600 \end{cases}$$

5. In the system of linear equations shown, z represents a constant. If the system of equations has infinitely many solutions, what is the value of z?

   A) $\dfrac{1}{8}$

   B) 5

   C) 8

   D) 40

Answers and explanations are on the next page. ▶ ▶ ▶

Check Your Work

1. A

Difficulty: Easy

Category: Substitution

Getting to the Answer: Solve the second equation for y in terms of x (which yields $y = -x$), then substitute into the first equation and solve:

$$-6x - 3x = 27$$
$$-9x = 27$$
$$x = -3$$

Choice **(A)** is correct.

2. A

Difficulty: Medium

Category: Substitution

Getting to the Answer: Translate English into math to write a system of equations with r as the cost of the radio in dollars and t as the cost of the television in dollars. A television costs $25 less than twice the cost of the radio, or $t = 2r - 25$. Together, a radio and a television cost $200, so $r + t = 200$.

The system of equations is:

$$\begin{cases} t = 2r - 25 \\ r + t = 200 \end{cases}$$

The top equation is already solved for t, so substitute $2r - 25$ into the second equation for t:

$$r + 2r - 25 = 200$$
$$3r - 25 = 200$$
$$3r = 225$$
$$r = 75$$

The radio costs $75, so the television costs $2(75) - 25 = 150 - 25 = \$125$. This means the television costs $\$125 - \$75 = \$50$ more than the radio, which is **(A)**.

3. D

Difficulty: Medium

Category: Combination

Getting to the Answer: Begin by translating English into math. Define the variables logically: d for hot dogs, b for hamburgers. You're given the cost of each, as well as the number of snacks sold and the total revenue generated. Next, write the system of equations that represents the information given:

$$\begin{cases} d + b = 27 \\ 3.5d + 5b = 118.5 \end{cases}$$

Multiplying the top equation by -5 allows you to solve for d using combination:

$$-5d - 5b = -135$$
$$\underline{+3.5d + 5b = 118.5}$$
$$-1.5d + 0b = -16.5$$

Dividing both sides by -1.5 gives $d = 11$, which eliminates (A) and (B). Plugging 11 in for d in the first equation in the system gives you $11 + b = 27$. Subtract 11 from both sides to find that $b = 16$. **(D)** is correct.

4. A

Difficulty: Medium

Category: Combination

Getting to the Answer: Translate English into math to make sense of the situation. First, define your variables: t for texts and p for pictures are good choices. You know that this student sent a total of 75 texts and pictures. You're also told each text costs $0.10 and each picture is $0.15, and that the bill is $8.90. You'll have two equations: one relating the numbers of texts and pictures and a second relating the costs associated with each:

$$\begin{cases} t + p = 75 \\ 0.1t + 0.15p = 8.9 \end{cases}$$

Multiplying the second equation by 10 allows you to solve for p using combination:

$$t + p = 75$$
$$-(t + 1.5p = 89)$$

Subtract the second equation from the first to find that $-0.5p = -14$ and $p = 28$. But you're not done yet; you're asked for the difference between the text and picture count. Substitute 28 for p in the first equation and then solve for t to get $t = 47$. Subtracting 28 from 47 yields 19, which is **(A)**.

5. B

Difficulty: Medium

Category: Number of Possible Solutions

Getting to the Answer: A system of equations that has infinitely many solutions results when you can algebraically manipulate one equation to arrive at the other. Examining the right sides of the equations, you see that $40 \times 40 = 1{,}600$; therefore, multiplying the first equation by 40 will give 1,600 on the right: $5q + 8s = 1{,}600$. The first equation is now identical to the second equation, meaning z must be 5, which is **(B)**.

Substitution

To answer a question like this:

What is the value of y if $5x + 3y = 20$ and $x + y = 20$?

A) −40

B) −20

C)   20

D)   40

You need to know this:

A **system** of two linear equations simply refers to the equations of two lines. "Solving" a system of two linear equations usually means finding the point where the two lines intersect. (However, see the lesson titled "Number of Possible Solutions" later in this chapter for exceptions.)

There are two ways to solve a system of linear equations: substitution and combination. For some PSAT questions, substitution is faster; for others, combination is faster. We'll cover combination in the next lesson.

You need to do this:

To solve a system of two linear equations by substitution, do the following:

- Isolate a variable (ideally, one whose coefficient is 1) in one of the equations.
- Substitute the result into the other equation.

Explanation:

Isolate x in the second equation, then substitute the result into the first equation:

$$x = 20 - y$$
$$5(20 - y) + 3y = 20$$
$$100 - 5y + 3y = 20$$
$$-2y = -80$$
$$y = 40$$

Thus, **(D)** is correct. If you needed to know the value of x as well, you could now substitute 40 for y into either equation to find that $x = -20$.

Try on Your Own

Directions: Solve these questions using substitution. Take as much time as you need on these questions. Work carefully and methodically. There will be an opportunity for timed practice at the end of the chapter.

1. Clarice had twice as many nickels as dimes in her piggy bank. When she adds 4 more nickels, she has three times as many nickels as dimes. What was the total number of nickels and dimes in Clarice's piggy bank before she added the additional nickels?

   A)   4

   B)   8

   C)   12

   D)   16

HINT: Ask yourself: Which variable in Q2 is the easier one to isolate?

---

2. What is the value of b that satisfies $5c + 5b = 20$ and $5b - c = 4$?

$$\begin{cases} 5x - 4y = 10 + y \\ x - 3y = 4 \end{cases}$$

3. What is the value of $x - y$ from the solution of the above system of equations?

   A) -5

   B)   0

   C)   2

   D)   5

HINT: Since the correct answer to Q4 requires you to know the value for r, solve for and substitute s in terms of r.

---

4. If $3r + 2s = 24$ and $r + s = 12$, what is the value of $r + 6$?

   A)   0

   B)   4

   C)   6

   D)   12

5. At a certain restaurant, there are 25 tables and each table has either 2 or 4 chairs. If a total of 86 chairs accompany the 25 tables, how many tables have exactly 4 chairs?

   A)   7

   B)   12

   C)   15

   D)   18

Combination

> **LEARNING OBJECTIVE**
>
> After this lesson, you will be able to:
>
> - Solve systems of linear equations by combination

To answer a question like this:

$$\begin{cases} 6x - 5y = 21 \\ 3x + 3y = -6 \end{cases}$$

If the lines represented by the equations above intersect at the point (x, y), then what is the value of y?

A) -3

B) -2

C) 2

D) 3

You need to know this:

Combining two equations means adding or subtracting them, usually with the goal of either eliminating one of the variables or solving for a combination of variables (e.g., $5n + 5m$).

You need to do this:

To solve a system of two linear equations by combination, do the following:

- Make sure that the coefficients for one variable have the same absolute value. (If they don't, multiply one equation by an appropriate constant. Sometimes, you'll have to multiply both equations by constants.)
- Either add or subtract the equations to eliminate one variable.
- Solve for the remaining variable, then substitute its value into either equation to solve for the remaining variable.

Explanation:

Both variables have different coefficients in the two equations, but you can convert the $3x$ in the second equation to $6x$ by multiplying the entire second equation by 2:

$$2(3x + 3y = -6)$$
$$6x + 6y = -12$$

Now that the coefficients for one variable are the same, subtract the second equation from the first to eliminate the x variable. (Note that if the x-coefficients were 6 and -6, you would add the equations instead of subtracting.)

$$\begin{array}{r} 6x - 5y = 21 \\ -(6x + 6y = -12) \\ \hline 0x - 11y = 33 \end{array}$$

Solve this equation for y:

$$-11y = 33$$
$$y = -3$$

(A) is the correct answer. If the question asked for x instead of y, you would now substitute -3 into either of the original equations and solve for x. (For the record, $x = 1$.)

Try on Your Own

Directions: Solve these questions using combination. Take as much time as you need on these questions. Work carefully and methodically. There will be an opportunity for timed practice at the end of the chapter.

$$\begin{cases} 2x - 4y = 14 \\ 5x + 4y = 21 \end{cases}$$

6. What is the y-coordinate of the solution to the system of equations shown?

   A) -1

   B) 0

   C) $\dfrac{7}{3}$

   D) 5

HINT: There's no need to solve for b and c separately in Q7.

---

7. If $-8c - 3b = 11$ and $6b + 6c = 4$, what is the value of $3b - 2c$?

   A) -27

   B) -3

   C) 8

   D) 15

8. If $6a + 6b = 30$ and $3a + 2b = 14$, then what are the values of a and b?

   A) $a = 2; b = 2$

   B) $a = 4; b = 1$

   C) $a = 1; b = 4$

   D) $a = 3; b = 1$

9. Given $2x + 5y = 49$ and $5x + 3y = 94$, what is the product of x and y?

10. Sixty people attended a concert. Children's tickets sold for $8 each and adult tickets sold for $12 each. If $624 was collected in ticket money, how many more adults than children attended the concert?

    A)   0

    B)   12

    C)   24

    D)   60

Number of Possible Solutions

To answer a question like this:

$$\begin{cases} 10x - 4y = 8 \\ \quad\quad 8y = kx - 30 \end{cases}$$

In the system of linear equations above, k represents a constant. What is the value of $3k$ if the system of linear equations has no solution?

A) 20

B) 30

C) 60

D) 80

You need to know this:

The solution to a system of linear equations consists of the values of the variables that make both equations true.

A system of linear equations may have one solution, infinitely many solutions, or no solution.

If a system of equations represents two lines that intersect, then the system will have exactly **one solution** (in which the x- and y-values correspond to the point of intersection).

If a system of equations has **infinitely many solutions,** the two equations actually represent the same line. For example, $2x + y = 15$ and $4x + 2y = 30$ represent the same line. If you divide the second equation by 2, you arrive at the first equation. Every point along this line is a solution.

If a system of equations has **no solution,** as in the question above, the lines are parallel: there is no point of intersection.

No Solution

One Solution

Infinitely Many Solutions

You need to do this:

- If the question states that the system has no solution, set both x-coefficients equal to each other and both y-coefficients equal to each other to make the lines parallel, but be sure that the y-intercepts (or constant terms, if the equations are in $ax + by + c$ form) are different.
- If the question states that the system has infinitely many solutions, make the x-coefficients equal, the y-coefficients equal, and the y-intercepts (or constant terms) equal.
- If the question states that the system has one solution and provides the point of intersection, substitute the values at that point of intersection for x and y in the equations.

Explanation:

Start by recognizing that for two lines to be parallel, both the x-coefficients must be equal and the y-coefficients must be equal. Manipulate the second equation so that it is in the same format as the first one:

$$kx - 8y = 30$$

The y-coefficient in the first equation, $10x - 4y = 8$, is 4. Divide the second equation by 2 in order to make the y-coefficients in both equations equal:

$$\frac{k}{2}x - 4y = 15$$

Now, set the x-coefficient equal to that in the first equation:

$$\frac{k}{2} = 10$$
$$k = 20$$

Note that the question asks for the value of $3k$, so the correct answer is **(C)**, 60.

Try on Your Own

Directions: Take as much time as you need on these questions. Work carefully and methodically. There will be an opportunity for timed practice at the end of the chapter.

HINT: How can the x- and y-values you are given as the solution to the system in Q11 help you find h and k?

$$\begin{cases} hx - 5y = -15 \\ kx + 2y = -20 \end{cases}$$

11. What is the value of $\dfrac{k}{h}$ if the (x, y) solution of the above system of equations is $(-5, 2)$?

    A) $\dfrac{1}{3}$

    B) 2

    C) $\dfrac{24}{5}$

    D) 6

HINT: For Q12, if a system of equations has infinitely many solutions, what do you know about the two equations?

$$\begin{cases} 9x + 4y = 24 \\ qx - \dfrac{y}{3} = -2 \end{cases}$$

12. If q is a constant and the above system of equations has infinitely many solutions, what is the value of q ?

    A) -9

    B) $-\dfrac{3}{4}$

    C) $\dfrac{2}{3}$

    D) 9

HINT: For Q13, what does it mean, graphically, when a system has no solution?

$$\begin{cases} 8x + 4y = 17 \\ \dfrac{1}{5}x + zy = \dfrac{1}{2} \end{cases}$$

13. In the system of linear equations shown above, z is a constant. If the system has no solution, what is the value of z ?

    A) $\dfrac{1}{10}$

    B) $\dfrac{1}{4}$

    C) 8

    D) 10

$$\begin{cases} 3x - 4y = 10 \\ 6x + wy = 16 \end{cases}$$

14. For which of the following values of w will the system of equations above have no solution?

    A) -8

    B) -4

    C) 4

    D) 8

$$\begin{cases} \dfrac{1}{2}x - \dfrac{2}{3}y = c \\ 6x - 8y = -1 \end{cases}$$

15. If the system of linear equations shown above has infinitely many solutions, and c is a constant, what is the value of c ?

    A) $-\dfrac{1}{2}$

    B) $-\dfrac{1}{12}$

    C) 2

    D) 12

On Test Day

Many PSAT Math questions can be solved in more than one way. A little efficiency goes a long way in helping you get through the Math sections on time, so it's useful to try solving problems more than one way to learn which way is fastest.

Try this question using two approaches: substitution and combination. Time yourself on each attempt. Which approach allowed you to get to the answer faster?

16. What is the value of x if $25x - 7y = 28$ and $10x + 7y + 18 = 60$?

   A) $-\dfrac{14}{15}$

   B) $\dfrac{1}{2}$

   C) 2

   D) $3\dfrac{1}{7}$

The answer and both ways of solving can be found at the end of this chapter.

How Much Have You Learned?

Directions: For testlike practice, give yourself 15 minutes to complete this question set. Be sure to study the explanations, even for questions you answered correctly. They can be found at the end of this chapter.

17. What is the value of $y - x$, if $6x - 4y = 8$ and $5y - 7x = 12$?

   A) -8

   B)   4

   C)   12

   D)   20

18. A bed costs \$40 less than three times the cost of a couch. If the bed and couch together cost \$700, how much more does the bed cost than the couch?

   A)   \$185

   B)   \$225

   C)   \$330

   D)   \$515

$$\begin{cases} -32 = 9y + 4x \\ k = \dfrac{9}{16}y + \dfrac{1}{4}x \end{cases}$$

19. If k is a constant and the above system of linear equations has infinitely many solutions, what is the value of k?

   A) -8

   B) -4

   C) -2

   D) -1

$$\begin{cases} -13 = ay + 36x \\ 9 + 6bx = 7y \end{cases}$$

20. What is the value of $|a - b|$ if a and b are constants and the above system of equations has no solution?

   A) -13

   B) -8

   C)   8

   D)   13

21. If $\dfrac{1}{8}x + 4y = \dfrac{11}{2}$ and $-4y - x = 12$, what is $\dfrac{1}{4}$ of y?

22. A local airport has separate fees for commercial airliners and private planes. Commercial flights are charged a landing fee of $281 per flight and private planes are charged a landing fee of $31 per flight. On a given day, a total of 312 planes landed at the airport and $47,848 in landing fees was collected. Solving which of the following systems of equations yields the number of commercial airliners, c, and the number of private planes, p, that landed at the airport on the day in question?

A) $\begin{cases} c + p = 47{,}848 \\ 281c + 31p = 312 \end{cases}$

B) $\begin{cases} c + p = 312 \\ 31c + 281p = 47{,}848 \end{cases}$

C) $\begin{cases} c + p = 312 \\ 281c + 31p = 47{,}848 \end{cases}$

D) $\begin{cases} c + p = 47{,}848 \\ 31c + 281p = 312 \end{cases}$

23. At a certain coffee store, the small bag of beans costs $2.50 and the large bag of beans costs $15. If the store sold 27 small and large bags of beans and had $155 in revenue in one week, how many small bags and large bags of beans were sold?

A) 20 small bags, 7 large bags
B) 7 small bags, 20 large bags
C) 8 small bags, 19 large bags
D) 20 small bags, 9 large bags

$$\begin{cases} 2x + 3y = 8 - y \\ x - 6y = 10 \end{cases}$$

24. If (x, y) is a solution to the system of equations shown above, then what is the value of $x - y$?

A) $-\dfrac{3}{4}$

B) $\dfrac{19}{4}$

C) $\dfrac{11}{2}$

D) $\dfrac{25}{4}$

25. Guests at a wedding had two meal choices, chicken and vegetarian. The catering company charges $12.75 for each chicken dish and $9.50 for each vegetarian dish. If 62 people attended the wedding and the catering bill was $725.25, which of the following systems of equations could be used to find the number of people who ordered chicken, c, and the number of people who ordered vegetarian, v, assuming everyone ordered a meal?

A) $\begin{cases} c + v = 725.25 \\ 12.75c + 9.5v = 62 \end{cases}$

B) $\begin{cases} c + v = 62 \\ 12.75c + 9.5v = \dfrac{725.25}{2} \end{cases}$

C) $\begin{cases} c + v = 62 \\ 12.75c + 9.5v = 725.25 \end{cases}$

D) $\begin{cases} c + v = 62 \\ 12.75c + 9.5v = 725.25 \times 2 \end{cases}$

26. Two turkey burgers and a bottle of water cost $3.25. If three turkey burgers and a bottle of water cost $4.50, what is the cost of two bottles of water?

A) $0.75
B) $1.25
C) $1.50
D) $3.00

Reflect

Directions: Take a few minutes to recall what you've learned and what you've been practicing in this chapter. Consider the following questions, jot down your best answer for each one, and then compare your reflections to the expert responses on the following page. Use your level of confidence to determine what to do next.

When is substitution a good choice for solving a system of equations?

_____

_____

_____

When is combination a good choice for solving a system of equations?

_____

_____

_____

What does it mean if a system of equations has no solution? Infinitely many solutions?

_____

_____

_____

Expert Responses

When is substitution a good choice for solving a system of equations?

Substitution works best when at least one of the variables has a coefficient of 1, making the variable easy to isolate. This system, for example, is well suited for substitution:

$$a + 3b = 5$$
$$4a - 6b = 21$$

That's because in the first equation, you can easily isolate the a as a = 5 − 3b and plug that in for a in the other equation. By contrast, substitution would not be a great choice for solving this system:

$$2a + 3b = 5$$
$$4a - 6b = 21$$

If you used substitution now, you'd have to work with fractions, which is messy.

When is combination a good choice for solving a system of equations?

Combination is always a good choice. It is at its most difficult in systems such as this one:

$$2a + 3b = 5$$
$$3a + 5b = 7$$

Neither a-coefficient is a multiple of the other, and neither b-coefficient is a multiple of the other, so to solve this system with combination you'd have to multiply both equations by a constant (e.g., multiply the first equation by 3 and the second equation by 2 to create a 6a term in both equations). But substitution wouldn't be stellar in this situation, either.

Note that combination may be particularly effective when the PSAT asks for a variable expression. For example, if a question based on the previous system of equations asked for the value of 5a + 8b, then you could find the answer instantly by adding the equations together.

What does it mean if a system of equations has no solution? Infinitely many solutions?

A system of equations with no solution represents two parallel lines, which never cross. The coefficient of a variable in one equation will match the coefficient of the same variable in the other equation, but the constants will be different. For example, this system has no solution:

$$2x + 3y = 4$$
$$2x + 3y = 5$$

Subtracting one equation from the other yields the equation 0 = −1, which makes no sense.

If a system of equations has infinitely many solutions, then the two equations represent the same line. For example, this system has infinitely many solutions:

$$2x + 3y = 4$$
$$4x + 6y = 8$$

Dividing the second equation by 2 yields 2x + 3y = 4, so while the two equations look different, they are actually the same.

Next Steps

If you answered most questions correctly in the "How Much Have You Learned?" section, and if your responses to the Reflect questions were similar to those of the PSAT expert, then consider Systems of Linear Equations an area of strength and move on to the next chapter. Come back to this topic periodically to prevent yourself from getting rusty.

If you don't yet feel confident, review those parts of this chapter that you have not yet mastered. In particular, review the mechanics for solving a system of equations by substitution and by combination. Then, try the questions you missed again. As always, be sure to review the explanations closely.

Math

Answers and Explanations

1.   C

Difficulty: Easy

Getting to the Answer: Translate the words in the question into equations. Let n be the original number of nickels and d be the number of dimes. That there were "twice as many nickels as dimes" means that $n = 2d$. When 4 nickels are added, the number of nickels is 3 times the number of dimes. Thus, $n + 4 = 3d$. Substitute $2d$ for n in the second equation: $2d + 4 = 3d$. Subtract $2d$ from each side to get $4 = d$. The question asks for the original number of coins. The original number of nickels is $n = 2d = 8$ and the total number of coins is $4 + 8 = 12$, which is **(C)**.

2.   4/3 or 1.33

Difficulty: Medium

Getting to the Answer: Start by isolating c in the second equation: $c = 5b - 4$. Then, substitute into the first equation and solve:

$$5(5b - 4) + 5b = 20$$
$$5b - 4 + b = 4$$
$$6b = 8$$
$$3b = 4$$
$$b = \frac{4}{3}$$

Grid in **4/3** or **1.33** and move on.

3.   C

Difficulty: Medium

Getting to the Answer: Because x has a coefficient of 1 in the second equation, solve the system using substitution. Before you select your answer, make sure you found the right quantity (the difference between x and y).

First, solve the second equation for x and substitute:

$$x - 3y = 4 \rightarrow x = 4 + 3y$$
$$5(4 + 3y) - 4y = 10 + y$$
$$20 + 15y - 4y = 10 + y$$
$$20 + 11y = 10 + y$$
$$10y = -10$$
$$y = -1$$

Next, substitute this value back into $x = 4 + 3y$ and simplify:

$$x = 4 + 3(-1)$$
$$x = 4 - 3$$
$$x = 1$$

Finally, subtract $x - y$ to find the difference:

$$1 - (-1) = 2$$

Hence, **(C)** is correct. While substitution is a valid way to solve this because the second equation readily gives you x in terms of y, you could have just restated the first equation as $5x - 5y = 10$ and, therefore, $x - y = 2$.

4.   C

Difficulty: Medium

Getting to the Answer: Since the question asks for $r + 6$, substitute by solving for s using the second equation, $r + s = 12$, so $s = 12 - r$. Substitute $12 - r$ into the first equation to get $3r + 2(12 - r) = 24$. Distribute the 2 to get $3r + 24 - 2r = 24$. Next, combine like terms: $3r - 2r = 24 - 24$, which yields $r = 0$. Remember that the question asks for $r + 6$, not r by itself!

Choice **(C)** is correct.

5.   D

Difficulty: Hard

Getting to the Answer: Create a system of two linear equations where t represents tables with 2 chairs and f represents tables with 4 chairs. The first equation should represent the total number of *tables*, each with 2 or 4 chairs, or $t + f = 25$. The second equation should represent the total number of *chairs*. Because t represents tables with 2 chairs and f represents tables with 4 chairs, the second equation should be $2t + 4f = 86$. Now, solve the system using substitution. Solve the first equation for t in terms of f so that when you substitute the result into the second equation, you can solve directly for f:

$$t + f = 25 \rightarrow t = 25 - f$$
$$2(25 - f) + 4f = 86$$
$$50 - 2f + 4f = 86$$
$$2f = 36$$
$$f = 18$$

There are 18 tables with 4 chairs each, **(D)**. This is all the question asks for, so you don't need to find the value of t.

6. A

Difficulty: Easy

Getting to the Answer: Quickly compare the two equations. The system is already set up perfectly to solve using combination, so add the two equations to cancel $-4y$ and $4y$. Then, solve the resulting equation for x. Remember, the question asks for the y-coordinate of the solution, so you will need to substitute x back into one of the original equations and solve for y:

$$
\begin{aligned}
2x - 4y &= 14 & 2(5) - 4y &= 14 \\
5x + 4y &= 21 & 10 - 4y &= 14 \\
\hline
7x &= 35 & -4y &= 4 \\
x &= 5 & y &= -1
\end{aligned}
$$

Thus, **(A)** is correct.

7. D

Difficulty: Easy

Getting to the Answer: If you're not asked to find the value of an individual variable, the question may lend itself to combination. This question asks for $3b - 2c$, so don't waste your time finding the variables individually if you can avoid it. After rearranging the equations so that variables and constants are aligned, you can add the equations together:

$$
\begin{aligned}
+6b + 6c &= 4 \\
-3b - 8c &= 11 \\
\hline
3b - 2c &= 15
\end{aligned}
$$

This matches **(D)**.

8. B

Difficulty: Easy

Getting to the Answer: Looking at the coefficients of the two equations, you'll notice that multiplying the second equation by -3 will allow you to eliminate the b terms:

$$
\begin{aligned}
6a + 6b &= 30 \\
+\,-9a - 6b &= -42 \\
\hline
-3a + 0b &= -12
\end{aligned}
$$

Solving the resulting equation gives $a = 4$. Choice **(B)** is the only choice that contains this value for a, so it must be correct.

9. 51

Difficulty: Medium

Getting to the Answer: Rather than multiplying just one equation by a factor, you'll need to multiply both by a factor to use combination. Suppose you want to eliminate x. The coefficients of the x terms are 2 and 5, so you need to multiply the equations by numbers that will give you -10 and 10 as your new x term coefficients. To do this, multiply the first equation by -5 and the second equation by 2:

$$
\begin{aligned}
-5(2x + 5y &= 49) \\
2(5x + 3y &= 94)
\end{aligned}
$$

Add the resulting equations:

$$
\begin{aligned}
&-10x - 25y = -245 \\
+\;&10x + 6y = 188 \\
\hline
&0x - 19y = -57
\end{aligned}
$$

Solving for y gives you 3. Next, plug 3 back in for y in either equation and solve for x, which equals 17. Multiplying x and y together yields **51**. Grid in **51**.

10. B

Difficulty: Medium

Getting to the Answer: Translate English into math to extract what you need. First, define the variables using letters that make sense. Use c for children and a for adults. Now, break the word problem into shorter phrases: children's tickets sold for $8 each; adult tickets sold for $12 each; 60 people attended the concert; $624 was collected in ticket money. Translating each phrase into a math expression will produce the components needed:

Children's tickets (c) cost $8 each $\rightarrow 8c$

Adult tickets (a) cost $12 each $\rightarrow 12a$

60 people attended the concert $\rightarrow c + a = 60$

$624 was collected in ticket money $\rightarrow$ Total $\$ = 624$

Now, put the expressions together in a system:

$$
\begin{cases}
c + a = 60 \\
8c + 12a = 624
\end{cases}
$$

You can solve for the variables using combination by multiplying the first equation by 8 and subtracting it from the second equation:

$$8c + 12a = 624$$
$$\underline{-(8c + 8a = 480)}$$
$$0c + 4a = 144$$
$$a = 36$$

Plug this value into $c + a = 60$ to find that $c = 24$. Remember, the question asks for the difference between the number of adults and the number of children, so the correct answer is $36 - 24 = 12$, which corresponds to **(B)**.

11. C

Difficulty: Medium

Getting to the Answer: You are told that the solution to the system is $x = -5$ and $y = 2$. Substitute these values into both equations to find h and k:

$$hx - 5y = -15 \qquad\qquad kx + 2y = -20$$
$$h(-5) - 5(2) = -15 \qquad k(-5) + 2(2) = -20$$
$$-5h - 10 = -15 \qquad\qquad -5k + 4 = -20$$
$$-5h = -5 \qquad\qquad\quad -5k = -24$$
$$h = 1 \qquad\qquad\qquad k = \frac{24}{5}$$

So, $\dfrac{k}{h} = \dfrac{\frac{24}{5}}{1}$, making **(C)** correct.

12. B

Difficulty: Hard

Getting to the Answer: A system of equations that has infinitely many solutions describes a single line. Therefore, manipulation of one equation will yield the other. Look at the constant terms: to turn the 24 into -2, divide the first equation by -12:

$$\frac{(9x + 4y = 24)}{-12} \rightarrow -\frac{9}{12}x - \frac{4}{12}y = -2$$
$$\rightarrow -\frac{3}{4}x - \frac{1}{3}y = -2$$

The y term and the constant in the first equation now match those in the second. All that's left is to set the coefficients of x equal to each other: $q = -\frac{3}{4}$. Choice **(B)** is correct.

Note that you could also write each equation in slope-intercept form and set the slopes equal to each other to solve for q.

13. A

Difficulty: Hard

Getting to the Answer: A system of linear equations that has no solution should describe two parallel lines. This means the coefficients of the variables should be the same (so the slopes of the lines are the same). Only the constant should be different (so the y-intercepts are not the same). The easiest way to make the coefficients the same is to manipulate the second equation. Multiplying the second equation by 40 would make the coefficients of x the same in both equations: $8x + 40zy = 20$. Now, equate the coefficients of y to get $4y = 40zy$. Solve for z to reveal that $z = \frac{1}{10}$, which is **(A)**. Alternatively, you could write each equation in slope-intercept form and set the slopes equal to each other to solve for z.

14. A

Difficulty: Hard

Getting to the Answer: One way to answer the question is to think about the graphs of the equations. Graphically, a system of linear equations that has no solution indicates two parallel lines or, in other words, two lines that have the same slope. Write each of the equations in slope-intercept form, $y = mx + b$, and set their slopes, m, equal to each other to solve for w.

First equation:

$$3x - 4y = 10$$
$$-4y = -3x + 10$$
$$y = \frac{3}{4}x - \frac{5}{2}$$

Second equation:

$$6x + wy = 16$$
$$wy = -6x + 16$$
$$y = -\frac{6}{w}x + \frac{16}{w}$$

Set the slopes equal:

$$\frac{3}{4} = -\frac{6}{w}$$
$$3w = -24$$
$$w = -8$$

This matches **(A)**. Alternatively, you could manipulate the first equation to make the x-coefficients the same and then equate the coefficients of y to solve for w.

15. B

Difficulty: Hard

Getting to the Answer: A system of linear equations has infinitely many solutions if both lines in the system have the same slope and the same y-intercept (in other words, they are the same line). Write each of the equations in slope-intercept form, $y = mx + b$. Their slopes should be the same. To find c, set the y-intercepts, b, equal to each other and solve. Before rewriting the equations, multiply the first equation by 6 to make it easier to manipulate.

First equation:

$$6\left(\frac{1}{2}x - \frac{2}{3}y\right) = 6(c)$$
$$3x - 4y = 6c$$
$$-4y = -3x + 6c$$
$$y = \frac{3}{4}x - \frac{3}{2}c$$

Second equation:

$$6x - 8y = -1$$
$$-8y = -6x - 1$$
$$y = \frac{3}{4}x + \frac{1}{8}$$

Set the y-intercepts equal:

$$-\frac{3}{2}c = \frac{1}{8}$$
$$-24c = 2$$
$$c = -\frac{1}{12}$$

Hence, **(B)** is correct.

16. C

Difficulty: Medium

Category: Combination

Strategic Advice: The numbers here are fairly large, so substitution is not likely to be convenient. Moreover, the y-coefficients have the same absolute value, so combination will likely be the faster way to solve.

Getting to the Answer: Start by writing the second equation in the same form as the first, then use combination to solve for x:

$$\begin{aligned} 25x - 7y &= 28 \\ +10x + 7y &= 42 \\ \hline 35x &= 70 \\ x &= 2 \end{aligned}$$

Thus, **(C)** is correct.

If you feel more comfortable using substitution, you can maximize efficiency by solving one equation for $7y$ and substituting that value into the other equation:

$$10x + 7y = 42 \rightarrow 7y = 42 - 10x$$
$$25x - (42 - 10x) = 28$$
$$35x - 42 = 28$$
$$35x = 70$$
$$x = 2$$

Note that the arithmetic is fundamentally the same, but the setup using combination is quicker and visually easier to follow.

17. D

Difficulty: Medium

Category: Combination

Strategic Advice: When a question asks for a sum or difference of variables, consider solving by combination.

Getting to the Answer: Rearrange the equations to be in the same form, with the y terms before the x terms, and then add:

$$\begin{aligned} -4y + 6x &= 8 \\ +(5y - 7x &= 12) \\ \hline y - x &= 20 \end{aligned}$$

The correct answer is **(D)**.

18. C

Difficulty: Medium

Category: Substitution

Getting to the Answer: Write a system of equations where c is the cost of the couch in dollars and b is the cost of the bed in dollars. A bed costs $40 less than three times the cost of the couch, or $b = 3c - 40$. Together, a bed and a couch cost $700, so $b + c = 700$.

The system of equations is:

$$\begin{cases} b = 3c - 40 \\ b + c = 700 \end{cases}$$

The top equation is already solved for b, so substitute $3c - 40$ into the bottom equation for b and solve for c:

$$3c - 40 + c = 700$$
$$4c - 40 = 700$$
$$4c = 740$$
$$c = 185$$

Remember to check if you solved for the right thing! The couch costs \$185, so the bed costs $3(\$185) - \$40 = \$555 - \$40 = \$515$. This means the bed costs $\$515 - \$185 = \$330$ more than the couch. Therefore, **(C)** is correct.

19. C

Difficulty: Hard

Category: Number of Possible Solutions

Getting to the Answer: The system has infinitely many solutions, so both equations must describe the same line. Notice that if you multiply the x- and y-coefficients in the second equation by 16, you arrive at the x- and y-coefficients in the first equation. The constant k times 16 must then equal the constant in the first equation, or -32:

$$16k = -32$$
$$k = -2$$

Therefore, **(C)** is correct.

20. D

Difficulty: Hard

Category: Number of Possible Solutions

Getting to the Answer: Rearrange the equations and write them on top of each other so that the x- and y-terms line up:

$$\begin{cases} 36x + ay = -13 \\ 6bx - 7y = -9 \end{cases}$$

In a system of equations that has no solution, the x-coefficients must equal each other and the y-coefficients must equal each other, but the constant on the right needs to be different. Thus, for the x-coefficients, $36 = 6b$ and $b = 6$. For the y-coefficients, $a = -7$. The question asks for the value of $|a - b|$, which is $|-7 - 6| = |-13| = 13$, choice **(D)**.

21. 1/2 or .5

Difficulty: Medium

Category: Combination

Getting to the Answer: Start by clearing the fractions from the first equation (by multiplying by 8) to make the numbers easier to work with. Then, use combination to solve for y:

$$\begin{aligned} x + 32y &= 44 \\ + - x - 4y &= 12 \\ \hline 28y &= 56 \\ y &= 2 \end{aligned}$$

Take one-fourth of 2 to get $\frac{1}{2}$, then grid in **1/2** or **.5**.

22. C

Difficulty: Medium

Category: Word Problems

Getting to the Answer: Because the variables are defined in the question stem and because the answer choices contain the variables, the only thing left for you to do is to figure out how they relate to one another. There will be two equations: one involving the total number of aircraft that landed and one involving the total amount of landing fees collected. Add together both types of aircraft to get the total number of aircraft that landed: $p + c = 312$. Think carefully about which type of plane should be associated with which fee to get the latter. Commercial airliners are much more expensive; hence, your second equation should be $281c + 31p = 47{,}848$. Only **(C)** contains both of those equations.

23. A

Difficulty: Medium

Category: Combination

Getting to the Answer: Choose intuitive letters for the variables: s for the small bags, L for the large bags. You're given the cost of each, as well as the number of each sold and the total revenue generated. Next, write the system of equations that represents the information given:

$$\begin{cases} s + L = 27 \\ 2.5s + 15L = 155 \end{cases}$$

Multiplying the top equation by -15 allows you to solve for s using combination:

$$\begin{array}{r} -15s - 15L = -405 \\ + \quad 2.5s + 15L = 155 \\ \hline -12.5s = -250 \\ s = 20 \end{array}$$

Solving for s gives 20, which eliminates (B) and (C). Plugging this value back into the first equation allows you to find L, which is 7. Choice **(A)** is correct.

24. D

Difficulty: Medium

Category: Substitution

Getting to the Answer: Because x has a coefficient of 1 in the second equation, solve the system using substitution. First, solve the second equation for x to get $x = 6y + 10$. Then, substitute the resulting expression for x into the first equation and solve for y:

$$\begin{array}{r} 2(6y + 10) + 3y = 8 - y \\ 12y + 20 + 3y = 8 - y \\ 15y + 20 = 8 - y \\ 16y = -12 \\ y = -\dfrac{3}{4} \end{array}$$

Next, substitute this value back into $x = 6y + 10$ and simplify:

$$\begin{aligned} x &= 6\left(-\dfrac{3}{4}\right) + 10 \\ &= -\dfrac{9}{2} + \dfrac{20}{2} \\ &= \dfrac{11}{2} \end{aligned}$$

Finally, subtract $x - y$ to find that **(D)** is correct:

$$\dfrac{11}{2} - \left(-\dfrac{3}{4}\right) = \dfrac{22}{4} + \dfrac{3}{4} = \dfrac{25}{4}$$

25. C

Difficulty: Easy

Category: Word Problems

Getting to the Answer: Translate English into math. One equation should represent the total *number* of meals ordered, while the other equation should represent the *cost* of the meals.

The number of people who ordered chicken plus the number who ordered vegetarian equals the total number of people, 62, so one equation is $c + v = 62$. This means you can eliminate (A). Now, write the cost equation: the cost per chicken dish, \$12.75, times the number of dishes, c, plus the cost per vegetarian dish, \$9.50, times number of dishes, v, equals the total bill, \$725.25. The cost equation should be $12.75c + 9.5v = 725.25$. Together, these two equations form the system in **(C)**.

26. C

Difficulty: Medium

Category: Combination

Getting to the Answer: Translate English into math to write a system of equations with t being the cost of a turkey burger and w equaling the cost of a bottle of water. The first statement is translated as $2t + w = \$3.25$ and the second as $3t + w = \$4.50$. Now, set up a system:

$$\begin{cases} 2t + w = 3.25 \\ 3t + w = 4.50 \end{cases}$$

You could solve the system using substitution, but combination is quicker in this question because subtracting the first equation from the second eliminates w and you can solve for t:

$$\begin{array}{r} 3t + w = 4.50 \\ -(2t + w = 3.25) \\ \hline t = 1.25 \end{array}$$

Substitute this value for t in the first equation and solve for w:

$$\begin{aligned} 2(1.25) + w &= 3.25 \\ 2.5 + w &= 3.25 \\ w &= 0.75 \end{aligned}$$

Two bottles of water would cost $2 \times \$0.75 = \$1.50$, which is **(C)**.

Data
Analysis

CHAPTER 6

Ratios, Proportions, and Percents

LEARNING OBJECTIVES

After completing this chapter, you will be able to:

- Set up and solve a proportion for a missing value
- Use ratios to perform unit conversions
- Calculate percents and percent change

80/600 SmartPoints® (High Yield)

How Much Do You Know?

Directions: Try the questions that follow. Show your work so that you can compare your solutions to the ones found in the Check Your Work section immediately after this question set. The "Category" heading in the explanation for each question gives the title of the lesson that covers how to solve it. If you answered the question(s) for a given lesson correctly, and if your scratchwork looks like ours, you may be able to move quickly through that lesson. If you answered incorrectly or used a different approach, you may want to take your time on that lesson.

1. Seven out of every 250 students at a certain university who take a test are expected to score at least 90 percent. If the university gives this test to 12,000 students, how many would be expected to score at least 90 percent?

    A) 176

    B) 224

    C) 300

    D) 336

2. A homeowner wants to buy 81 square feet of grass for his yard, but the vendor he uses sells grass only by the square yard. How many square yards of grass does the homeowner need? (1 yard = 3 feet)

    A) 9

    B) 27

    C) 243

    D) 729

3. Ethanol can be mixed with gasoline to reduce automobile emissions. Much automotive gasoline is 15 percent ethanol by volume. An oil company tries decreasing the ethanol content to 6 percent to lower the cost. If a car with a 14-gallon tank is filled with the 15 percent blend and a second car with a 10-gallon tank is filled with the 6 percent blend, how many times more ethanol is in the first car than in the second car?

    A) 1.5

    B) 2.5

    C) 3.5

    D) 4.0

4. Kelania owns a bakery, and she adjusts the number of pounds of flour she orders each week based on the number she used the previous week. After the first week of the month, she decreased the number of pounds of flour she ordered by 25 percent, then increased the number by 10 percent the following week, then increased the number by an additional 50 percent in the last week of the month. What is the approximate total percent increase in the number of pounds of flour Kelania ordered from the start of the month until the end of the month?

    A) 20%

    B) 24%

    C) 30%

    D) 35%

5. The cost of tuition at a private nonprofit four-year college in 1988 was approximately $15,800. In 2013, the cost of tuition at the same type of college was approximately $30,100. If tuition experiences the same total percent increase over the next 25 years, approximately how much will tuition at a private nonprofit four-year college cost?

   A) $44,400

   B) $45,800

   C) $57,300

   D) $66,200

Check Your Work

1.   D

Difficulty: Easy

Category: Ratios and Proportions

Getting to the Answer: Assign a variable, say n, to the number of students expected to score at least 90 percent when 12,000 students take the test. Then, set up a proportion and solve for n:

$$\frac{7}{250} = \frac{n}{12,000}$$
$$250n = (7)(12,000)$$
$$250n = 84,000$$
$$n = 336$$

The correct answer is **(D)**.

2.   A

Difficulty: Easy

Category: Unit Conversion

Getting to the Answer: Map out your route from starting units to end units, being mindful of the fact that the question deals with units of area (square units). The starting quantity is in square feet, and the desired quantity is in square yards. The only conversion factor you need is 3 feet (ft) = 1 yard (yd). Setting up your route to square yards, you get:

$$\frac{81 \text{ ft}^2}{1} \times \frac{1 \text{ yd}}{3 \text{ ft}} \times \frac{1 \text{ yd}}{3 \text{ ft}} = \frac{81}{9} \text{ yd}^2 = 9 \text{ yd}^2$$

This matches **(A)**.

3.   C

Difficulty: Medium

Category: Percents

Getting to the Answer: Starting with the 14-gallon tank, plug the known values into the three-part formula: $15\% \times 14 = ? \rightarrow 0.15 \times 14 = 2.1$ gallons of ethanol. Repeat for the smaller tank: $6\% \times 10 = ? \rightarrow 0.06 \times 10 = 0.6$ gallons of ethanol. The question asks how many times more ethanol is in the larger tank, so divide the quantities to get $\frac{2.1}{0.6} = 3.5$. This matches **(C)**.

4.   B

Difficulty: Medium

Category: Percent Change

Getting to the Answer: Remember to avoid merely adding the percentages together. Find each change individually. You're not given a definite number of pounds of flour in the question, so assume Kelania starts with 100. To save a step with each change, calculate the total amount instead of the weekly increase or decrease. The first change is -25%; so the number of pounds of flour ordered the next week is $75\% \times 100 = 0.75 \times 100 = 75$. The second change is $+10\%$, which corresponds to $110\% \times 75 = 1.1 \times 75 = 82.5$ pounds. The final change is $+50\%$, which means there are now $150\% \times 82.5 = 1.5 \times 82.5 = 123.75$ pounds. The percent change is $\frac{123.75 - 100}{100} = \frac{23.75}{100} \times 100\% = 23.75\%$. Now, round to the nearest percent and you get 24%, which is **(B)**.

5.   C

Difficulty: Medium

Category: Percent Change

Getting to the Answer: Find the percent increase using the formula: percent change $= \frac{\text{actual change}}{\text{original value}}$. Then, apply the same percent increase to the amount for 2013. The amount of increase is $30,100 - 15,800 = 14,300$, so the percent increase is $\frac{14,300}{15,800} = 0.905 = 90.5\%$ over 25 years. If the total percent increase over the next 25 years is the same, the average cost of tuition will be $30,100 \times 1.905 = 57,340.50$, or about $57,300, which is **(C)**.

Ratios and Proportions

LEARNING OBJECTIVE

After this lesson, you will be able to:

- Set up and solve a proportion for a missing value

To answer a question like this:

 A property is projected to be built with dimensions of 1,245 feet long by 274 feet wide. The contractor wishes to build an exact replica scale model of the property that is 6 feet long. Approximately how many inches wide will the scale model's width be? (1 foot = 12 inches)

- A) 12
- B) 16
- C) 25
- D) 107

You need to know this:

A **ratio** is a comparison of one quantity to another. When writing ratios, you can compare one part of a group to another part of that group or you can compare a part of the group to the whole group. Suppose you have a bowl of apples and oranges: you can write ratios that compare apples to oranges (part to part), apples to total fruit (part to whole), and oranges to total fruit (part to whole).

Keep in mind that ratios convey *relative* amounts, not necessarily actual amounts, and that they are typically expressed in lowest terms. For example, if there are 10 apples and 6 oranges in a bowl, the ratio of apples to oranges would likely be expressed as $\frac{5}{3}$ on the PSAT rather than as $\frac{10}{6}$. However, if you know the ratio of apples to oranges and either the actual number of apples or the total number of pieces of fruit, you can find the actual number of oranges by setting up a proportion (see below).

Note that the PSAT may occasionally use the word "proportion" to mean "ratio."

A **proportion** is simply two ratios set equal to each other, for example, $\frac{a}{b} = \frac{c}{d}$. Proportions are an efficient way to solve certain problems, but you must exercise caution when setting them up. Noting the units of each piece of the proportion will help you put each piece of the proportion in the right place. Sometimes, the PSAT may ask you to determine whether certain proportions are equivalent—check this by cross-multiplying. You'll get results that are much easier to compare.

$$\text{If } \frac{a}{b} = \frac{c}{d}, \text{then: } ad = bc, \frac{a}{c} = \frac{b}{d}, \frac{d}{b} = \frac{c}{a}, \frac{b}{a} = \frac{d}{c}, \text{ BUT } \frac{a}{d} \neq \frac{c}{b}$$

Each derived ratio shown above except the last one is simply a manipulation of the first, so all except the last are correct. You can verify this via cross-multiplication ($ad = bc$ in each case except the last).

Alternatively, you can pick equivalent fractions $\frac{2}{3}$ and $\frac{6}{9}$ ($a = 2$, $b = 3$, $c = 6$, $d = 9$). Cross-multiplication gives $2 \times 9 = 3 \times 6$, which is a true statement. Dividing 2 and 3 by 6 and 9 gives $\frac{2}{6} = \frac{3}{9}$, which is also true, and so on. However, attempting to equate $\frac{2}{9}$ and $\frac{3}{6}$ will not work.

If you know any three numerical values in a proportion, you can solve for the fourth. For example, say a fruit stand sells 3 peaches for every 5 apricots and you are supposed to calculate the number of peaches sold on a day when 20 apricots were sold. You would use the given information to set up a proportion and solve for the unknown:

$$\frac{3}{5} = \frac{p}{20}$$

You can now solve for the number of peaches sold, *p*, by cross-multiplying:

$$60 = 5p$$
$$p = 12$$

Alternatively, you could use the common multiplier to solve for *p*: the numerator and denominator in the original ratio must be multiplied by the same value to arrive at their respective terms in the new ratio. To get from 5 to 20 in the denominator, you multiply by 4, so you also have to multiply the 3 in the numerator by 4 to arrive at the actual number of peaches sold: $4(3) = 12$.

You need to do this:

- Set up a proportion and solve for the unknown, either by cross-multiplying or by using the common multiplier.

Explanation:

The ratio of the length of the real property to that of the scale model is $\frac{1{,}245 \text{ feet}}{6 \text{ feet}}$. You know the actual width (274 feet), so set up a proportion and solve for the scale model's width:

$$\frac{1245 \text{ feet}}{6 \text{ feet}} = \frac{274 \text{ feet}}{x \text{ feet}}$$
$$1{,}245x = 1644$$
$$x \approx 1.320 \text{ feet}$$

The question asks for the answer in inches, not feet, so multiply by 12 inches per foot:

$1.320 \text{ feet} \times \dfrac{12 \text{ inches}}{1 \text{ foot}} = 15.840$ inches. Hence, **(B)** is correct.

Try on Your Own

Directions: Take as much time as you need on these questions. Work carefully and methodically. There will be an opportunity for timed practice at the end of the chapter.

HINT: You can save time by making the numbers in Q1 more manageable before you attempt to solve. Try making the number 4,000 easier to work with. (But don't forget to simplify both numerator and denominator!)

---

1. For every 4,000 snowblowers produced by a snow-blower factory, exactly 8 are defective. At this rate, how many snowblowers were produced during a period in which exactly 18 snowblowers were defective?

    A) 6,000

    B) 9,000

    C) 12,000

    D) 18,000

2. An engineer is monitoring construction of a 75-foot-long escalator. The difference in height between the two floors being connected was originally supposed to be 40 feet, but due to a calculation error, this figure must be reduced by 25 percent. The angle between the escalator and the floor must not change in order to comply with the building code. What is the change in length in feet between the original escalator measurement and its corrected value?

    A) 18.75

    B) 25

    C) 56.25

    D) 100

3. The number of cars that can safely pass through a stoplight is directly proportional to the length of time in seconds that the light is green. If 9 cars can safely pass through a light that stays green for 36 seconds, how many cars can safely pass through a light that stays green for 24 seconds?

    A) 4

    B) 6

    C) 7

    D) 8

4. If the total weight of 31 identical medieval coins is approximately 16 ounces, which of the following is closest to the weight, in ounces, of 97 of these coins?

    A) 5

    B) 19

    C) 50

    D) 188

HINT: For Q5, assign a variable as the common multiplier in the proportion of the pyramid's length:width:height, then express the volume in terms of that common multiplier.

5. For a school project, a student wants to build a replica of the Great Pyramid of Giza out of modeling clay. The real Great Pyramid has a square base with side length 750 feet and a height of 500 feet. If the student has 162 cubic inches of clay for her model, what height will her pyramid be in inches?

    (The formula for the volume of a pyramid is $V = \frac{1}{3}\, lwh$ and is provided in your test booklet.)

Unit Conversion

LEARNING OBJECTIVE

After this lesson, you will be able to:

● Set up equivalent ratios to make units cancel

To answer a question like this:

City A and city B are 2,000 miles apart, while city C is twice as far from city A as city A is from city B. What is the approximate distance, in inches, between city A and city C? (1 mile = 5,280 feet and 1 foot = 12 inches)

A) 4.3 million

B) 52 million

C) 127 million

D) 253 million

You need to know this:

You can use ratios to perform unit conversions. This is especially useful when there are multiple conversions or when the units are unfamiliar.

For example, though these units of measurement are no longer commonly used, there are 8 furlongs in a mile and 3 miles in a league. Say you're asked to convert 4 leagues to furlongs. A convenient way to do this is to set up the conversion ratios so that equivalent units cancel:

$$4 \text{ leagues} \times \frac{3 \text{ miles}}{1 \text{ league}} \times \frac{8 \text{ furlongs}}{1 \text{ mile}} = 4 \times 3 \times 8 = 96 \text{ furlongs}$$

Notice that all the units cancel out except the furlongs, which is the one you want.

You need to do this:

Set up a series of ratios to make equivalent units cancel. (Keep track of the units by writing them down next to the numbers in the ratios.) You should be left with the units you're converting into.

Explanation:

City C is twice as far from city A as city A is from city B, so city C is 2(2,000) = 4,000 miles away from city A. Set up a series of ratios to convert to inches (in):

$$4,000 \text{ mi} \times \frac{5,280 \text{ ft}}{1 \text{ mi}} \times \frac{12 \text{ in}}{1 \text{ ft}} = 4,000 \times 5,280 \times 12 \text{ in}$$
$$= 253,440,000 \text{ in} = 253.44 \text{ million inches}$$

Therefore, **(D)** is correct.

Try on Your Own

Directions: Take as much time as you need on these questions. Work carefully and methodically. There will be an opportunity for timed practice at the end of the chapter.

6. Jack is taking a road trip. If he travels 180 miles while his car uses gasoline at a rate of 40 miles per gallon and then travels another 105 miles while his car uses gasoline at a rate of 35 miles per gallon, how many gallons of fuel has his car consumed?

    A) 1.5

    B) 3.0

    C) 4.5

    D) 7.5

HINT: Begin Q7 by figuring out the cost per ounce of each can of pineapple.

---

7. If an 8-ounce can of pineapple sells for $0.72 and a 20-ounce can costs $1.10, how many more cents does the 8-ounce can cost per ounce than the 20-ounce can? (100 cents = 1 dollar)

8. An artist is creating a rectangular tile mosaic. Her desired pattern uses 5 green tiles and 3 blue tiles per square foot of mosaic. If the artist's entire mosaic is 12 feet by 18 feet, how many more green tiles than blue tiles will she need?

HINT: Be careful to use the correct units in Q9! What units are used in the question and what units appear in the answer choices?

---

9. The average college student reads at a rate of about 5 words per second. If the pages of Jorge's textbook contain an average of 500 words per page, how long will it take him to read a 45-page chapter?

    A) 50 minutes

    B) 1 hour, 15 minutes

    C) 1 hour, 25 minutes

    D) 1 hour, 40 minutes

10. Each MRI scan given at a hospital produces about 3.6 gigabits of data. Every night, for 8 hours, the hospital backs up the files of the scans. The hospital computers can upload the MRI scans at a rate of 2 megabits per second. What is the maximum number of MRI scans that the hospital can upload each night? (1 gigabit = 1,024 megabits)

    A) 15

    B) 16

    C) 56

    D) 202

Percents

To answer a question like this:

 Teachers surveyed their students at two different schools about their favorite classes to find out how many students favored math class. At the first school, they asked 512 students and of those, 12.5 percent responded favorably. At the second school, 24.8 percent of 625 students responded favorably. What percent of all the students surveyed responded favorably?

A) 15.4%

B) 19.3%

C) 25.4%

D) 31.9%

You need to know this:

To calculate percents, use this basic equation:

$$\text{Percent} = \frac{\text{part}}{\text{whole}} \times 100\%$$

Alternatively, use this statement: [blank] percent of [blank] is [blank]. Translating from English into math, you get [blank]% × [blank] = [blank].

You need to do this:

- Plug in the values for any two parts of the formula and solve for the third.
- In some calculations, you may find it convenient to express percents as decimals. To do this, use the formula above but stop before you multiply by 100 percent at the end.

Explanation:

Use a variation of the three-part percent formula to answer this question: whole $\times$ percent = part, where the percent is expressed as a decimal.

First, find the number of students at each school who responded favorably using the formula. For the first school: $512 \times 0.125 = 64$. For the second school: $625 \times 0.248 = 155$. Next, find the total number of students who were surveyed at both schools, which was $512 + 625 = 1{,}137$, and the total number who responded favorably, $64 + 155 = 219$. Finally, find the percent of people who responded favorably by using the formula one more time:

$$1{,}137 \times \text{percent} = 219 \times 100\%$$
$$\text{percent} = \frac{219}{1{,}137} \times 100\%$$
$$= 0.1926 \times 100\%$$
$$= 19.3\%$$

Of all the students surveyed, about 19.3% responded favorably, making **(B)** the correct answer.

Try on Your Own

Directions: Take as much time as you need on these questions. Work carefully and methodically. There will be an opportunity for timed practice at the end of the chapter.

11. A company sells dolls for $20 each. It decides to offer a discount of 20 percent for a month to see how many new customers it can attract. How much will each doll sell for during the month of the discount?

   A) $12

   B) $14

   C) $16

   D) $18

HINT: For Q12, begin by figuring out what percent of the budget actually goes to lunch.

---

12. A high school's Environment Club receives a certain amount of money from the school to host an all-day event. The club budgets 40 percent of the money for a guest speaker, 25 percent for educational materials, 20 percent to rent a hotel conference room, and the remainder for lunch. If the club plans to spend $225 on lunch for the participants, how much does it plan to spend on the guest speaker?

   A) $375

   B) $450

   C) $525

   D) $600

13. A bag of marbles contains 60 marbles that are either red, blue, or yellow. If there are 12 blue marbles, what percent of the bag is made of red and yellow marbles?

   A) 50%

   B) 60%

   C) 70%

   D) 80%

Questions 14 and 15 refer to the following information.

The following table shows the chemical makeup of one mole (a unit of measure commonly used in chemistry) of acetone and the approximate mass of a mole of each component element.

Chemical Makeup of One Mole of Acetone		
Element	Number of Moles	Mass per Mole (grams)
Oxygen	1	16
Carbon	3	12
Hydrogen	6	1

HINT: For Q14, use the percent formula. Which is the part and which is the whole?

14. Oxygen makes up what percent of the mass of 1 mole of acetone? Round your answer to the nearest whole percent.

15. If a chemist starts with 1,800 grams of acetone and uses up 930 grams, approximately how many moles of carbon are left? Round your answer to the nearest whole mole.

Percent Change

LEARNING OBJECTIVE

After this lesson, you will be able to:

● Calculate percent change

To answer a question like this:

For three days in a row, Bonnie changes the amount of lemonade made for her lemonade stand. First, she increases the amount made by 25 percent. Then, she decreases it by 10 percent. Finally, she increases it by 35 percent. What is the net percent increase in the amount of lemonade Bonnie made on the third day compared to original amount before the three days of changes, to the nearest whole percent? (The percent sign is understood after your answer. For example, if the answer is 15.1 percent, grid in 15.)

You need to know this:

You can determine the **percent change** in a given situation by applying this formula:

$$\text{Percent increase or decrease} = \frac{\text{amount of increase or decrease}}{\text{original amount}} \times 100\%$$

Sometimes, more than one change will occur. Be careful here, as it can be tempting to take a "shortcut" by just adding two percent changes together (which will almost always lead to an incorrect answer). Instead, you'll need to find the total amount of the increase or decrease and then apply the formula.

You need to do this:

● Calculate the actual increase or decrease.
● Divide by the *original* amount (not the new amount!).
● Multiply by 100 percent.

Explanation:

There isn't any starting number given, so pick 100 and then calculate the actual change. An increase of 25% brings the amount of lemonade made to 125. A 10% decrease from 125 brings the amount of lemonade made to $125 - 12.5 = 112.5$. Lastly, an increase of 35% puts the final amount of lemonade made at $112.5 + 0.35(112.5) = 112.5 + 39.375 = 151.875$. The actual increase, then, is $151.875 - 100 = 51.875$.

Now, plug this increase into the percent change formula, using your starting value of 100 as the denominator:

$$\text{Percent change} = \frac{51.875}{100} \times 100\% = 51.875\%$$

Round up and grid in **52**.

Try on Your Own

Directions: Take as much time as you need on these questions. Work carefully and methodically. There will be an opportunity for timed practice at the end of the chapter.

16. A used car dealership initially prices a car at $12,000. When the car fails to sell, the dealership reduces the price to $10,500. During a holiday sale, the dealership drops the price of the car an additional 5 percent below the reduced price. To the nearest tenth of a percent, what is the total percent discount from the car's initial price to the holiday sale price?

    A) 15.5%

    B) 16.9%

    C) 17.5%

    D) 20%

HINT: The first thing you'll want to do for Q17 is figure out how much sand and gravel was sold this year.

---

17. Last year, a sand and gravel company sold 280 tons of gravel and 220 tons of sand. This year, the company sold 20 percent more gravel by weight and 25 percent more sand by weight than it sold last year. By approximately what percent did the total weight of sand and gravel sold increase this year over last year?

    A) 22

    B) 45

    C) 56

    D) 111

HINT: Remember that when picking numbers for Q18, you don't have to pick realistic values. Pick numbers that are easy to work with in the given situation. For percent questions, the number is usually 100.

---

18. Over the past decade, the population of a certain town increased by 20 percent. If the population of the town increases 15 percent over the next decade, by what percent will the population have increased over the entire two-decade period?

    A) 33%

    B) 35%

    C) 38%

    D) 43%

19. Malik purchased a mutual fund to help save for his daughter's college costs. During the first year, the price of the fund increased by 15 percent. The following year, the price increased by an additional 12 percent. To the nearest percent, what is the percent increase in the price of the stock for the two years?

    A) 24

    B) 27

    C) 28

    D) 29

HINT: What information do you need to determine in order to answer Q20 correctly?

---

20. There are currently 6,210 fish in a lake. If the number of fish in the lake increased by 15 percent during the last year and 20 percent during the year before that, how many more fish are in the lake currently than in the lake two years ago?

On Test Day

When a question features multiple percentages, you have to make a key strategic decision: can I do the arithmetic on the percentages themselves and get the answer right away or do I have to calculate each percentage individually and do the arithmetic on the actual values?

For example, suppose a car traveling 50 miles per hour increases its speed by 20 percent and then decreases its speed by 20 percent. Can you just say that its final speed is 50 miles per hour since $+20\% - 20\% = 0$? No, because after a 20% increase, the car's speed becomes 120% of the original: $1.2(50) = 60$. When the car "decreases its speed by 20 percent," that 20 percent is calculated based on the new speed, 60, not the original speed, and 20 percent of 60 is greater than 20 percent of 50. Thus, the car's final speed is lower than its starting speed: $50(1.2)(0.8) = 48$ miles per hour.

By contrast, suppose you have to find how many more meat eaters than vegans live in a certain region where there are 13,450 residents, given that 62 percent of them eat meat and 8 percent of them are vegan. It may be tempting to find 62 percent of 13,450 ($0.62 \times 13,450 = 8,339$), then find 8 percent of 13,450 ($0.08 \times 13,450 = 1,076$), and finally subtract those two numbers to get the answer ($8,339 - 1,076 = 7,263$). This is a waste of time, though. Instead, you can quickly find the difference between the two percentages ($62 - 8 = 54$) and take 54 percent of the total to get the answer in one step: $13,450 \times 0.54 = 7,263$, the same answer.

If you *can* do arithmetic using the percentages but choose to do arithmetic on the raw numbers instead, you'll waste time doing unnecessary work. But if you *can't* do arithmetic on the percentages (as in the first example) but do anyway, then you'll get an incorrect answer. So, being able to tell whether you can or can't do the arithmetic on the percentages is a useful skill.

Luckily, the fundamental principle is simple: you can always do arithmetic on the percentages as long as the percentages are out of the same total. If the totals are different, then you must convert the percentages into actual values. Practice applying this principle on the following question.

21. There are 400 seniors and 420 juniors in a certain high school. Of the seniors, 65% are eligible for an advanced placement world history course. Among the juniors, 75% are not eligible to enroll in that course. How many more seniors than juniors could enroll in the course?

The answer and explanation can be found at the end of this chapter.

Math

How Much Have You Learned?

Directions: For testlike practice, give yourself 15 minutes to complete this question set. Be sure to study the explanations, even for questions you answered correctly. They can be found at the end of this chapter.

22. A certain city has 2,625 businesses and has a ratio of 5:2 of businesses that do not require safety inspections to those that do require safety inspections. Of the businesses that were required to have inspections, 12 percent had safety violations. How many businesses that required inspections did NOT have any safety violations?

    A)   90

    B)   315

    C)   660

    D)   2,310

23. An average consumer car can travel 120 miles per hour under controlled conditions. An average race car can travel 210 miles per hour. How many more miles can the race car travel in 30 seconds than the consumer car?

    A) $\frac{3}{4}$

    B)   1

    C) $\frac{3}{2}$

    D)   45

24. Engine oil often contains zinc, which reduces engine wear. Company A's oil contains 4 percent zinc and company B's oil contains 9 percent. Suppose a car uses 8 pints of company B's oil and a truck uses 6 quarts of company A's oil. How many times more zinc is in the car's oil than in the truck's? (1 quart = 2 pints)

    A)   0.34

    B)   0.67

    C)   1.5

    D)   3

25. When a consignment store gets a used piece of furniture to sell, it researches the original price and then reduces that price by 40 percent to determine the price of the used piece. Every 30 days after that, the price of the used piece is marked down an additional 20 percent until it is sold. The store gets a piece of used furniture on July 15. If the original price of the furniture was $1,050 and it is sold on September 5, what is the final selling price?

    A) $258.05

    B) $322.56

    C) $504.00

    D) $630.00

26. An amusement park is building a scale model of an airplane for a three-dimensional ride. The real airplane measures 220 feet from nose to tail. The amusement park plans to make the model airplane 36 feet long. If the wingspan of the real plane is 174 feet, approximately how many feet long should the wingspan on the ride's model airplane be?

    A)   17

    B)   28

    C)   35

    D)   45

27. Luca is from a country that uses the metric system and is visiting his cousin Drew in the United States, which uses the standard, or English, system. He gives Drew a family recipe for bread. The recipe is for one loaf and calls for 180 milliliters of milk. Drew wants to make five loaves. If 1 U.S. cup equals 236.588 milliliters, approximately how many cups of milk will Drew need?

    A) $\frac{3}{4}$

    B) $1\frac{1}{3}$

    C) $3\frac{4}{5}$

    D) $6\frac{1}{2}$

28. There are about 3 feet per meter and 1,000 meters per kilometer. Two cities are 1,800,000 feet apart; about how many kilometers apart are the two cities?

29. A professional speedway for Motorsport events wishes to build two new racetracks with the same proportions but different sizes, one for adult races and one for teen races. The racetracks will each have two straightaways, one shorter and one longer.

    If the adult track has straightaways that are 100 meters long and 150 meters long, then what is the length of the longer teen track straightaway if the shorter teen track straightaway is 50 meters long?

    A)   25
    B)   50
    C)   75
    D)   100

30. Last year, a farmer had 350 acres planted in corn and 160 acres planted in soybeans. This year, the farmer reduced the acreage planted in corn by 20 percent and reduced the acreage planted in soybeans by 15 percent. By approximately what percent did the farmer reduce the total acreage planted in corn and soybeans?

    A)   16.4%
    B)   16.9%
    C)   17.5%
    D)   18.4%

31. A store starts a sale to attract more customers. Mandy notices in the newspaper that the store has comforters on sale for 40 percent less than the original price. If Mandy pays $89.10 after the discount and a 10 percent sales tax on the discounted price, what is the original price of the comforter?

    A) $133
    B) $135
    C) $139
    D) $141

Reflect

Directions: Take a few minutes to recall what you've learned and what you've been practicing in this chapter. Consider the following questions, jot down your best answer for each one, and then compare your reflections to the expert responses on the following page. Use your level of confidence to determine what to do next.

What is a ratio and how is it different from a proportion?

_____

_____

_____

If you're given a ratio of one quantity to another, what can you say about the total number of quantities?

_____

_____

_____

When doing unit conversions, how can you make sure you're doing them correctly?

_____

_____

_____

Suppose the value of something increases by 20 percent. How can you calculate the final value in the fewest number of steps? What if the value decreases by 20 percent?

_____

_____

_____

What is the percent change formula and what is the biggest pitfall to avoid when using it?

_____

_____

_____

Expert Responses

What is a ratio and how is it different from a proportion?

A ratio is the relative comparison of one quantity to another. For example, if the ratio of dogs to cats in an animal shelter is 3 to 5, then there are 3 dogs for every 5 cats. A proportion is two ratios set equal to each other.

If you're given a ratio of one quantity to another, what can you say about the total number of quantities?

Given a ratio, you know that the total must be a multiple of the sum of the ratio's parts. For example, if the ratio of dogs to cats is 3 to 5, then the total number of dogs and cats must be a multiple of 3 + 5, or 8. This means that when the PSAT gives you one ratio, it's actually giving you several. If you're told that dogs:cats = 3:5, then you also know that dogs:total = 3:8 and cats:total = 5:8. You can use this "hidden" knowledge to your advantage.

When doing unit conversions, how can you make sure you're doing them correctly?

To do unit conversions correctly, set up the conversion in whichever way makes units cancel. For example, to convert 3 feet into inches, you multiply 3 feet by 12 inches per foot, because it cancels out the feet unit. If instead you multiplied 3 feet by 1 foot per 12 inches, then the resulting units would be "feet squared per inch," which makes no sense.

Suppose the value of something increases by 20 percent. How can you calculate the final value in the fewest number of steps? What if the value decreases by 20 percent?

The fastest way to increase a value by 20 percent is to multiply it by 1.2, which is 100% + 20% = 120%. Similarly, to decrease something by 20 percent, you multiply it by 0.8, which is 100% − 20% = 80%.

What is the percent change formula and what is the biggest pitfall to avoid when using it?

The percent change formula is as follows:

$$\text{Percent change} = \frac{\text{amount of increase or decrease}}{\text{original amount}} \times 100\%$$

A common mistake is to put the new amount on the bottom of the fraction rather than the original amount.

Next Steps

If you answered most questions correctly in the "How Much Have You Learned?" section, and if your responses to the Reflect questions were similar to those of the PSAT expert, then consider Ratios, Proportions, and Percents an area of strength and move on to the next chapter. Come back to this topic periodically to prevent yourself from getting rusty.

If you don't yet feel confident, review those parts of this chapter that you have not yet mastered and try the questions you missed again. As always, be sure to review the explanations closely.

Math

Answers and Explanations

1. B

Difficulty: Easy

Strategic Advice: When ratios involve large numbers, simplify if possible to make the calculations easier.

Getting to the Answer: Let b equal the number of snow-blowers produced. Set up a proportion and solve for b. Be sure to match the units in the numerators and in the denominators on both sides:

$$\frac{8 \text{ defective}}{4{,}000 \text{ produced}} = \frac{18 \text{ defective}}{b \text{ produced}}$$
$$\frac{1}{500} = \frac{18}{b}$$
$$1(b) = 500(18)$$
$$b = 9{,}000$$

This matches **(B)**.

2. A

Difficulty: Medium

Getting to the Answer: Draw a diagram to make sense of the given situation. Your diagram should look similar to what's shown:

The two triangles are similar, which means you can use a proportion to answer the question. First, find the correct height by taking 25% of 40, which is 10, and deducting that from 40 to get 30. Keeping the heights on the left of your proportion and the hypotenuses on the right, you have $\frac{30}{40} = \frac{x}{75}$. Reduce the left side to get $\frac{3}{4} = \frac{x}{75}$, then cross-multiply to eliminate the fractions: $225 = 4x$. Solving for x yields 56.25. But don't stop yet: the question asks for the difference in escalator length, not the new length. Subtract 56.25 from 75 to get 18.75, which matches **(A)**.

3. B

Difficulty: Easy

Getting to the Answer: To answer a question that says "directly proportional," set two ratios equal to each other and solve for the missing amount. Don't forget—match the units in the numerators and in the denominators on both sides.

Let c equal the number of cars that can safely pass through a light that lasts 24 seconds. Set up the proportion and solve:

$$\frac{9 \text{ cars}}{36 \text{ seconds}} = \frac{c \text{ cars}}{24 \text{ seconds}}$$
$$\frac{1 \text{ cars}}{4 \text{ seconds}} = \frac{c \text{ cars}}{24 \text{ seconds}}$$
$$24 = 4c$$
$$6 = c$$

Therefore, **(B)** is correct.

4. C

Difficulty: Easy

Getting to the Answer: Set up a proportion and cross-multiply to solve:

$$\frac{31}{16} = \frac{97}{x}$$
$$(16)(97) = 31x$$
$$x \approx 50.06$$

Choice **(C)** is correct. Given that the choices are spaced far apart, you could have used estimating to answer this question. Since 97 is about 3 times 31, look for the choice that is about 3 times 16, which is 48. Only **(C)** is close.

5. 6

Difficulty: Hard

Getting to the Answer: The formula for the volume of a pyramid is $V = \frac{1}{3} lwh$. The pyramid has a square base, so the length and width are equal. The proportion of the length:width:height is 750:750:500, which reduces to 3:3:2. Expressed with a common multiplier, this is $3x{:}3x{:}2x$.

Putting these proportions into the volume equation gives you:

$$V = \frac{1}{3}(3x)(3x)(2x) = \frac{1}{3}\left(18x^3\right) = 6x^3$$

The question states that the student has 162 cubic inches of modeling clay, so this value can be input for V to solve for x as follows:

$$V = 6x^3 = 162$$
$$x^3 = 27$$
$$\sqrt[3]{x^3} = \sqrt[3]{27}$$
$$x = 3$$

The last piece to remember is that height in the equation was replaced with $2x$, so the height of the student's model will be **6** inches. Grid in **6**.

6.   D

Difficulty: Easy

Getting to the Answer: To determine the equations to find the gallons of fuel used during each leg of Jack's trip, set up the units to cancel out. Plugging in values for the first leg, you get:

$$180 \ \text{miles} \times \frac{1 \ \text{gallon}}{40 \ \text{miles}} = 4.5 \ \text{gallons}$$

For the second leg:

$$105 \ \text{miles} \times \frac{1 \ \text{gallon}}{35 \ \text{miles}} = 3 \ \text{gallons}$$

Added together, there are $4.5 + 3 = 7.5$ gallons of fuel used, which matches **(D)**.

7.   3.5

Difficulty: Easy

Getting to the Answer: Whenever you're asked for the cost of something per a set measurement, think unit rates. First, determine the price per ounce (i.e., the unit rate) for the smaller can:

$$\frac{\$0.72}{8 \ \text{ounces}} = \$0.09/\text{ounce}$$

Next, do the same for the larger can:

$$\frac{\$1.10}{20 \ \text{ounces}} = \$0.055/\text{ounce}$$

Take the difference to get $\$0.035$, which is **3.5** cents. Pay careful attention to the way the question is worded—grid in **3.5**, not .035, because the question asks how many more cents, not dollars.

8.   432

Difficulty: Medium

Getting to the Answer: Determine the number of times the pattern repeats and then find the corresponding number of green tiles. The question states that the ratio of green to blue tiles is 5:3 and that the pattern appears once per square foot. There are $12 \times 18 = 216$ square feet in the mosaic, meaning there are $5 \times 216 = 1{,}080$ green tiles and $3 \times 216 = 648$ blue tiles. Taking the difference gives $1{,}080 - 648 = \mathbf{432}$ more green tiles than blue. Grid in **432**.

9.   B

Difficulty: Medium

Getting to the Answer: Pay careful attention to the units. As you read the question, decide how and when you will need to convert units. The answer choices are given in hours and minutes, but it's easier to solve for m in minutes by setting up one large conversion:

$$m = 45 \ \text{pages} \times \frac{500 \ \text{words}}{1 \ \text{page}} \times \frac{1 \ \text{second}}{5 \ \text{words}} \times \frac{1 \ \text{minute}}{60 \ \text{seconds}}$$
$$= 75 \ \text{minutes}$$

Because 75 minutes is not an answer choice, convert it to hours and minutes: 75 minutes = 1 hour, 15 minutes, **(B)**.

10. A

Difficulty: Hard

Getting to the Answer: Don't let all the technical words in this question overwhelm you. Solve it step-by-step, examining the units as you go. First, use the factor-label method to determine the number of *megabits* the computer can upload in one night (8 hours):

$$\frac{2 \text{ megabits}}{1 \text{ second}} \times \frac{60 \text{ seconds}}{1 \text{ minute}} \times \frac{60 \text{ minutes}}{1 \text{ hour}} \times \frac{8 \text{ hours}}{1 \text{ night}}$$
$$= \frac{57,600 \text{ megabits}}{1 \text{ night}}$$

Next, convert this amount to gigabits (because the information about the scans is given in gigabits, not megabits):

$$57,600 \text{ megabits} \times \frac{1 \text{ gigabit}}{1,024 \text{ megabits}} = 56.25 \text{ gigabits}$$

Finally, each scan produces about 3.6 gigabits of data, so divide this number by 3.6 to determine how many scans the computer can upload to the remote server: $\frac{56.25}{3.6} = 15.625$ scans. You should round this number down to 15, **(A)**, because the computer cannot complete the 16th scan in the time allowed.

11. C

Difficulty: Easy

Getting to the Answer: For discount problems, multiply the complement of the discount instead of subtracting the discount. The complement is 100% − discount (20%) = 80%. This will give the price of the doll after the discount. Use d as the variable for the price of the discounted doll:

$$d = 0.80(\$20)$$
$$d = \$16$$

(C) is correct.

12. D

Difficulty: Medium

Getting to the Answer: The total budget can be represented by 100%, so start there. The percent of the budget spent on lunch is 100% − 40% − 25% − 20% = 15%. You're told that the club plans to spend $225 on lunch. Let x be the total amount of the budget in dollars. Then

15% of x is 225, so $0.15x = 225$. Solving this equation for x yields $x = 1,500$. The total budget is $1,500. Of this amount, 40% was budgeted for a guest speaker, or $0.4 \times \$1,500 = \$600$. Choice **(D)** is correct.

13. D

Difficulty: Medium

Getting to the Answer: The question asks about the percent that is NOT blue marbles, so calculate the percent of blue marbles and subtract that from 100%.

$$\frac{12}{60} = \frac{1}{5} = 20\%$$
$$100\% - 20\% = 80\%$$

Choice **(D)** is correct.

14. 28

Difficulty: Medium

Getting to the Answer: Use the formula:

$$\text{Percent} = \frac{\text{part}}{\text{whole}} \times 100\%$$

To use the formula, find the part of the mass represented by oxygen: there is 1 mole of oxygen and it has a mass of 16 grams. Next, find the whole mass of 1 mole of acetone: 1 mole oxygen (16 g) + 3 moles carbon ($3 \times 12 = 36$ g) + 6 moles hydrogen ($6 \times 1 = 6$ g) = $16 + 36 + 6 = 58$. Now, use the percent formula:

$$\text{Percent} = \frac{16}{58} \times 100\%$$
$$= 0.2759 \times 100\%$$
$$= 27.59\%$$

Before you grid in your answer, make sure you follow the directions—round to the nearest whole percent. Grid in **28**.

15. 45

Difficulty: Hard

Strategic Advice: The question contains several steps. Think about the units given in the question and how you can use what you know to find what you need.

Getting to the Answer: Start with grams of acetone: the chemist starts with 1,800 and uses up 930, so there are $1{,}800 - 930 = 870$ grams left. From the previous question, you know that 1 mole of acetone has a mass of 58 grams, so there are $\frac{870}{58} = 15$ moles of acetone left. Don't grid in this amount because you're not finished yet! The question asks for the number of moles of *carbon*, not acetone. According to the table, each mole of acetone contains 3 moles of carbon, so there are $15 \times 3 = 45$ moles of carbon left. Grid in **45**.

16. B
Difficulty: Medium

Getting to the Answer: To find the total percent discount, you'll first need to determine the total discount in actual price. The first change is given: $\$12{,}000 - \$10{,}500 = \$1{,}500$. The second change is a 5% discount, which can be calculated using the price after the first reduction: $(.05)\$10{,}500 = \$525$. Therefore, the total drop in price is $\$1{,}500 + \$525 = \$2{,}025$. Now, apply the percent change formula:

$$\frac{\text{actual change}}{\text{original amount}} \times 100\% = \text{percent change}$$

$$\frac{2{,}025}{12{,}000} \times 100\% = 16.875\%$$

Since the question asks for the percent change to the nearest tenth of a percent, round the answer to 16.9%. That's choice **(B)**.

17. A
Difficulty: Medium

Getting to the Answer: To find the total percent increase in weight of sand and gravel sold, first find the total actual change in weight. The total weight sold this year for gravel is $280 + (0.20 \times 280) = 336$. The total weight sold for sand is $220 + (0.25 \times 220) = 275$. Therefore, this year's total weight is $336 + 275 = 611$. Last year's total weight was $280 + 220 = 500$. Thus, the change from last year to this year is $611 - 500 = 111$. Now, apply the percent change formula:

$$\frac{\text{actual change}}{\text{original amount}} \times 100\% = \text{percent change}$$

$$\frac{111}{500} \times 100\% = 22.2\%$$

Choice **(A)** is correct.

18. C
Difficulty: Medium

Getting to the Answer: One key piece of information not given is the initial population of the town. Since this is a percent change question, pick 100 for the initial population. (Your number doesn't have to be realistic, only easy to work with.) Over the last decade, the population increased by 20%, so that is an increase from 100 to 120. Over the next decade, if the population increases by 15%, the total population would become $120 + (0.15)120 = 120 + 18 = 138$. Therefore, the total increase in actual population over the two decades is $138 - 100 = 38$. Now, apply the percent change formula:

$$\frac{\text{actual change}}{\text{original amount}} \times 100\% = \text{percent change}$$

$$\frac{38}{100} \times 100\% = 38\%$$

Choice **(C)** is correct.

19. D
Difficulty: Medium

Getting to the Answer: Since the price of the mutual fund is not given and this is a percentage change question, plug in $100 for the initial price and then calculate the changes in sequence. After the first year, the price would have been $\$100 \times (1 + 0.15) = \$115$. Then, the price at the end of the second year would have been $\$115 \times (1 + 0.12) = \$128.80$. This is a 28.8% increase from the original $100 price. The question asks for the answer to the nearest percent, which is 29%, so **(D)** is correct.

20. 1710
Difficulty: Hard

Getting to the Answer: Work backward using the known information to find the actual number of fish in the lake for each of the past two years. You know the increase in the number of fish over the last year was 15%, so you can set up the following equation, where x represents the actual number of fish last year:

$$1.15x = 6{,}210$$
$$x = \frac{6{,}210}{1.15}$$
$$x = 5{,}400$$

Now, do the same process for the previous year. You know that 5,400 represents the number of fish after an increase of 20%, so you can call the original number of fish at the beginning of the first year y and use the following equation to find y:

$$1.20y = 5,400$$
$$y = \frac{5,400}{1.2}$$
$$y = 4,500$$

Now you have the starting number of fish from two years ago, so you can subtract this from the current number to find the actual change in the number of fish over the entire two years: $6,210 - 4,500 = 1,710$.

Grid in **1710**.

21. 155

Difficulty: Medium

Category: Percents

Strategic Advice: The total numbers of seniors and juniors are different, so you'll have to apply the given percentages to the number of students in each class to determine the numbers of students eligible for the course in each class, then subtract the results to find the difference. Be careful: the percentage for juniors is stated as those who are NOT eligible.

Getting to the Answer: The number of seniors eligible is $\frac{65\%}{100\%} \times 400 = 260$. The percentage of juniors who are not eligible is 75%, so the percentage who are eligible is $100\% - 75\% = 25\%$. Thus, the number of eligible juniors is $\frac{25\%}{100\%} \times 420 = 105$. The difference is $260 - 105 = 155$. Grid in **155**.

22. C

Difficulty: Medium

Category: Percents

Getting to the Answer: Break the actual question into short steps. First, find the number of businesses that were required to have inspections. There are 2,625 businesses. The part-to-part ratio of businesses that require inspections to those that do not is 2:5, so the ratio of those business that require inspections to the total number of businesses is $\frac{2}{2+5} = \frac{2}{7}$. So, the total number of businesses that need inspections is

$\frac{2}{7} \times 2625 = 750$. This is the number of businesses that had violations; 12% of the those is $0.12 \times 750 = 90$.

Finally, find the number of businesses that did NOT have violations by subtracting 90 from 750 to get $750 - 90 = 660$ businesses that did not have any safety issues. Choice **(C)** is correct.

23. A

Difficulty: Medium

Category: Unit Conversion

Getting to the Answer: Let the units in this question guide you to the solution. The speeds of the cars are given in miles per hour, but the question asks about the number of miles each car can travel in 30 seconds, so convert miles per hour to miles per second and then multiply by 30 seconds. The difference in speeds between the two vehicles is $210 - 120 = 90$ miles per hour. Now, set up a conversion:

$$\frac{90 \text{ mile(s)}}{\text{hour}} \times \frac{1 \text{ hour}}{60 \text{ minute(s)}} \times \frac{1 \text{ minute(s)}}{60 \text{ seconds}} \times 30 \text{ seconds}$$
$$= \frac{3}{4} \text{ mile(s)}$$

The race car can travel $\frac{3}{4}$ miles farther in 30 seconds, so **(A)** is correct.

24. C

Difficulty: Hard

Category: Unit Conversion

Getting to the Answer: It's easiest to compare two amounts when they are written in the same units, so start by converting the car's pints to quarts and then go from there. The conversion from pints to quarts is straightforward:

$$8 \text{ pints} \times \frac{1 \text{ quart(s)}}{2 \text{ pints}} = 4 \text{ quart(s)}$$

Next, find the amount of zinc in each car using the percent formula: Percent $\times$ whole = part. Write the percents as decimals and multiply:

Car: 0.09×4 quarts $= 0.36$ quarts of zinc

Truck: 0.04×6 quarts $= 0.24$ quarts of zinc

Finally, compare the amount in the car to the amount in the truck: $\frac{0.36}{0.24} = 1.5$. The car has 1.5 times as much zinc in its oil as the truck, which is **(C)**.

25. C

Difficulty: Hard

Category: Percent Change

Getting to the Answer: Draw a chart or diagram with the various price reductions for each 30 days. Determine the percent change and new price for each date.

Date	Percent of Most Recent Price	Resulting Price
Jul 15	$100 - 40\% = 60\%$	$\$1,050 \times 0.6 = \$630$
Aug 15	$100 - 20\% = 80\%$	$\$630 \times 0.8 = \$504$

You can stop here because the item was sold on September 5, which is not 30 days after August 15. The final selling price is $504, **(C)**.

26. B

Difficulty: Medium

Category: Ratios and Proportions

Getting to the Answer: Set up a proportion. Try writing the proportion in words first, then fill in the values:

$$\frac{\text{real wingspan}}{\text{real length}} = \frac{\text{model wingspan}}{\text{model length}}$$

$$\frac{174}{220} = \frac{x}{36}$$

$$36(174) = 220(x)$$

$$6,264 = 220x$$

$$28.473 = x$$

The ride's model airplane wingspan is approximately 28 feet, **(B)**.

27. C

Difficulty: Easy

Category: Unit Conversion

Getting to the Answer: Break the question into short steps and solve each step, checking units as you go. First, find the total number of *milliliters* (mL) of milk Drew will need for 5 loaves:

$$\frac{180 \text{ mL}}{1 \text{ loaf}} \times 5 \text{ loaves} = 900 \text{ mL}$$

Second, convert the total number of milliliters needed to *cups*:

$$900 \text{ mL} \times \frac{1 \text{ cup}}{236.588 \text{ mL}} = \frac{900}{236.588} \text{ cups} \approx 3.804 \text{ cups}$$

Drew will need about 3.8 or $3\frac{8}{10} = 3\frac{4}{5}$ cups of milk, **(C)**. Note that estimating 900 divided by 236 as a little less than 4 is sufficient for answering this question without the use of a calculator, based on the answer choices.

28. 600

Difficulty: Easy

Category: Unit Conversion

Getting to the Answer: For unit conversions, start by deciding whether to multiply or divide. The question asks you to convert from feet to kilometers, so you should divide because a foot is a smaller measurement than a kilometer is. In other words, there will be fewer kilometers than feet. Convert feet into meters, and then meters into kilometers:

$$\frac{1,800,000 \text{ feet}}{1} \times \frac{1 \text{ meter(s)}}{3 \text{ feet}} \times \frac{1 \text{ kilometer(s)}}{1,000 \text{ meter(s)}}$$
$$= 600 \text{ kilometer(s)}$$

Grid in **600**.

29. C

Difficulty: Easy

Category: Ratios and Proportions

Getting to the Answer: Set up a proportion and cross-multiply to solve for the unknown:

$$\frac{100}{150} = \frac{50}{x}$$

$$100x = 150(50)$$

$$x = \frac{7500}{100}$$

$$x = 75$$

Thus, **(C)** is correct.

30. D

Difficulty: Medium

Category: Percent Change

Getting to the Answer: To find the total percent reduction in total acreage, first find the total actual reduction in acreage. For corn, that's $(0.20 \times 350) = 70$ acres; for soybeans, it's $0.15(160) = 24$ acres. Therefore, the total change in acreage planted in corn and soybeans is $70 + 24 = 94$ acres. The total number of acres planted in corn and soybeans was $350 + 160 = 510$ acres. Use this information to apply the percent change formula:

$$\frac{\text{actual change}}{\text{original amount}} \times 100\% = \text{percent change}$$

$$\frac{94}{510} \times 100\% \approx 18.4\%$$

(D) is correct.

31. B

Difficulty: Hard

Category: Percent Change

Getting to the Answer: Set up an equation with the original price having the variable C. Instead of subtracting the 40% discount, use the complement and multiply by that: $100\% - 40\% = 60\% = 0.6$, so the discounted price is $0.60C$. The sales tax is a percentage of this discounted price, so multiply by $100\% + \text{tax}\,(10\%) = 110\% = 1.1$, which gives $1.1(0.60C)$. This amount should equal what Mandy actually paid: $1.1(0.60C) = 89.10$. Solve for C:

$$1.1(0.60C) = 89.10$$
$$0.66C = 89.10$$
$$C = \frac{89.10}{0.66}$$
$$C = 135$$

Thus, **(B)** is correct. You could also solve this question using Backsolving.

CHAPTER 7

Tables, Statistics, and Probability

LEARNING OBJECTIVES

After completing this chapter, you will be able to:

- Draw inferences about data presented in a variety of graphical formats
- Find an unknown value given the average
- Calculate mean, median, mode, and range
- Describe standard deviation and margin of error
- Determine whether a survey is valid or biased
- Draw inferences about surveys and data samples
- Calculate probabilities based on data sets

60/600 SmartPoints® (High Yield)

How Much Do You Know?

Directions: Try the questions that follow. Show your work so that you can compare your solutions to the ones found in the Check Your Work section immediately after this question set. The "Category" heading in the explanation for each question gives the title of the lesson that covers how to solve it. If you answered the question(s) for a given lesson correctly, and if your scratchwork looks like ours, you may be able to move quickly through that lesson. If you answered incorrectly or used a different approach, you may want to take your time on that lesson.

Questions 1 and 2 refer to the following information.

	French	German	Italian	Japanese	Total
Freshmen	342	261	489	103	1,195
Sophomores	276	199	324	54	853
Juniors	190	108	252	29	579
Seniors	158	97	219	24	498
Total	966	665	1,284	210	3,125

1. Assuming that all students are required to take exactly one language, which student class contains the greatest percentage of students enrolled in a Romance (French or Italian) language?

    A) Freshmen

    B) Sophomores

    C) Juniors

    D) Seniors

2. A group of 150 freshmen were randomly selected for a survey that asked whether they were excited to continue their foreign language studies in the next school year. Of this group, 93 said they were excited to continue, 37 said they were not excited to continue, and 20 said they did not know yet whether they were excited to continue. Using the data from this survey and the table, which of the following is most likely a valid conclusion?

    A) About 130 freshman students do not know yet whether they are excited to continue foreign language studies next year.

    B) About 240 freshman students are not excited to continue foreign language studies next year.

    C) About 440 freshman students are not excited to continue foreign language studies next year.

    D) About 740 freshman students are excited to continue foreign language studies next year.

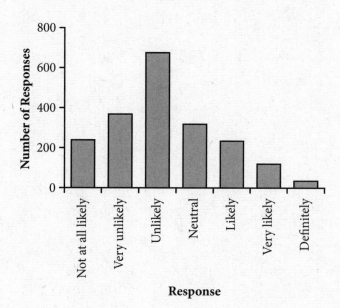

4. The average (arithmetic mean) of the data list $\{2, 4, 5, 8, 9, x, 3\}$ is 5. What is the value of x ?

3. Liam is conducting a market research study to determine the effectiveness of advertisements on social networking sites. He surveyed a randomly selected group of 2,000 young adults on how likely they are to purchase from a company based on its advertisements on social networking sites. Respondents rated their likelihood to purchase on a scale from 1 to 7, with 1 being "Not at all likely" and 7 being "Definitely." The results are summarized in the bar graph above. Which of the following statements is NOT true based on the survey results?

A) mode $= 3$

B) median $= 3$

C) mean $<$ median

D) $2 <$ mean < 5

Questions 5 and 6 refer to the following information.

The table below summarizes the results of a survey about the favorite sports of a group of high school students. Assume that every student has a favorite sport and that students could select only one favorite.

	Freshmen	Sophomores	Juniors	Seniors	Total
Football	441	414	388	450	1,693
Baseball	317	343	249	283	1,192
Soccer	222	284	347	316	1,169
Basketball	370	314	365	291	1,340
Total	1,350	1,355	1,349	1,340	5,394

5. The research group that conducted the survey wants to select one participant at random for a follow-up survey. Given that the selected participant is not a freshman, what is the probability of the research group randomly selecting someone who chose baseball as his or her favorite sport?

    A) 0.1622

    B) 0.2164

    C) 0.2399

    D) 0.2948

6. Based on the table provided, which of the following is NOT a true statement?

    A) About 27% of the entrants in the freshman prize drawing voted for basketball as their favorite sport.

    B) About 23% of the entrants in the sophomore prize drawing voted for basketball as their favorite sport.

    C) About 27% of the entrants in the junior prize drawing voted for basketball as their favorite sport.

    D) About 30% of the entrants in the senior prize drawing voted for basketball as their favorite sport.

Check Your Work

1. C

Difficulty: Medium

Category: Tables and Graphs

Getting to the Answer: Focus on the columns of the table that you need and block out the rest. Start by identifying how many students in each class are enrolled in either French or Italian (freshmen: 342 French, 489 Italian; sophomores: 276 French, 324 Italian; juniors: 190 French, 252 Italian; seniors: 158 French, 219 Italian). Next, extract the total foreign language enrollment of each class from the table (freshmen: 1,195; sophomores: 853; juniors: 579; seniors: 498). To find the percentages, divide the Romance language part by the language total, then multiply by 100% to convert to a percent:

$$\text{Freshmen: } \frac{342 + 489}{1195} \times 100\% = 69.54\%$$

$$\text{Sophomores: } \frac{276 + 324}{853} \times 100\% = 70.34\%$$

$$\text{Juniors: } \frac{190 + 252}{579} \times 100\% = 76.34\%$$

$$\text{Seniors: } \frac{158 + 219}{498} \times 100\% = 75.70\%$$

The junior class has the highest percent enrollment in Romance languages, so **(C)** is correct.

2. D

Difficulty: Medium

Category: Surveys and Data Samples

Strategic Advice: Find what you need about the group from the follow-up survey. Then, extrapolate to see which answer choice matches your calculations.

Getting to the Answer: First, determine the number of freshmen who fall into each of the three groups of the follow-up survey:

Percent excited to continue: $\frac{93}{150} \times 100 = 62\%$

Percent not excited to continue: $\frac{37}{150} \times 100 = 24.67\%$

Percent who do not know yet whether they are excited to continue: $\frac{20}{150} \times 100 = 13.33\%$

There are 1,195 freshmen in the original survey, making the number excited to continue $0.62 \times 1{,}195 = 740.9 \approx 741$; the number not excited to continue $0.2467 \times 1{,}195 = 294.8 \approx 295$; and the number who do not know yet whether they are excited to continue $0.1333 \times 1{,}195 = 159.3 \approx 159$. Choice (D) states that about 740 freshmen are excited to continue their foreign language studies, which matches these findings. Choice **(D)** is therefore correct.

3. C

Difficulty: Medium

Category: Statistics

Getting to the Answer: Examine the bar chart to evaluate the choices.

(A): The bar for "Unlikely" (which is 3 on the scale given in the question) is clearly the tallest, so this is the mode. Eliminate (A).

(B): There are 2,000 responses, so the median is the average of responses 1,000 and 1,001. The total of the first two bars is about 600. Since the third bar is about 700, that means that the median response is indeed within this bar. Eliminate (B).

(C): The data is skewed to the right, meaning that the extreme values on the right will weight the mean calculation to make the mean greater than the median. Thus, **(C)** is not true and is the correct choice.

(D): If you were not certain that (C) was the correct choice, you could see that the substantial majority of values are between 2 and 5 inclusive, so the mean has to be somewhere within that wide range. Eliminating (D) confirms **(C)** as correct.

4. 4

Difficulty: Medium

Category: Statistics

Strategic Advice: When the goal is to find a missing value in a set of data and the average is given, consider using the balance approach. We'll demonstrate both approaches starting with the average formula.

Getting to the Answer: The question requires finding the value of x in the given data set using the average of the data set. The values given in the data, besides x, are: 2, 4, 5, 8, 9, and 3. The average is given as 5. To find the missing value x, plug the known values into the average formula and solve for x:

$$\frac{2+4+5+8+9+x+3}{7} = 5$$

$$\frac{31+x}{7} = 5$$

$$31+x = 35$$

$$x = 4$$

Grid in **4** as the correct answer.

Alternatively, to use the balance approach, write down how much each value is above or below the average of 5. For example, the first value of 2 is 3 below the average: $2 - 5 = -3$.

Now, observe that, excluding the variable, the values are $-3 + (-1) + 0 + 3 + 4 + (-2) = 1$. Without the variable, the total is 1 more than what you'd expect based on the average. So for the values to balance out to the average, the variable value must be one less than the average of 5, or $5 - 1 = 4$. Grid in **4**.

5. B

Difficulty: Medium

Category: Probability

Getting to the Answer: The question says that the selected candidate is not a freshman, so focus on the sophomore, junior, and senior columns. This makes the total possible outcomes for this drawing $1{,}355 + 1{,}349 + 1{,}340 = 4{,}044$. The total number of upperclassmen who voted for baseball as their favorite sport (number of desired outcomes) is $343 + 249 + 283 = 875$. Divide this by the total to find the probability: $\frac{875}{4044} \approx 0.2164$, which makes **(B)** correct.

6. D

Difficulty: Easy

Category: Tables and Graphs

Getting to the Answer: The question asks for the answer choice that is NOT a true statement, so test each one. Use the table to determine the correct percents for each choice. Notice that all choices are about the estimated percent of students in each class who voted for basketball as their favorite sport, so use the percent formula, $\text{percent} = \frac{\text{part}}{\text{whole}} \times 100\%$. In each case, the part is the number of students in each class who voted for basketball, while the whole is the total number of students in that class:

(A): $\frac{370}{1350} \times 100\% = 0.274 \approx 27\%$

(B): $\frac{314}{1355} \times 100\% = 0.231 \approx 23\%$

(C): $\frac{365}{1349} \times 100\% = 0.270 \approx 27\%$

(D): $\frac{291}{1340} \times 100\% = 0.217 \approx 22\%$

Hence, **(D)** must be correct since the statement was about 30% and NOT about 22%.

Tables and Graphs

LEARNING OBJECTIVE

After this lesson, you will be able to:

● Draw inferences about data presented in a variety of graphical formats

To answer a question like this:

A restaurant owner wants the restaurant's grand opening to go well and sets a goal of selling an average of 90 pounds of steak per day for the first three weeks. The dot plot shows the number of pounds sold in the first 20 days. What is the minimum number of pounds the restaurant would need to sell on the last day to meet the goal?

A) 60

B) 80

C) 100

D) 140

You need to know this:

The PSAT uses some straightforward methods of representing data sets that you are certainly already familiar with. You likely don't need to review, for example, how to look up information in a table or read a bar chart. There are, however, some less common types of plots that show up from time to time that can be confusing at first glance.

● **Tables, bar charts, and line graphs** show up all the time in the Math sections (and in the Reading and Writing & Language sections, too). They shouldn't be difficult to interpret, but it's helpful to keep in mind that the test maker often includes more information than you actually need. It's important to consider what the question asks for so that you find only the information that you need.

- **Frequency tables and dot plots** are ways of representing how many times a data point appears within a data set. Here is a data set (the number of appliances sold by a single sales person over some time frame) presented as a dot plot:

Appliance Sales

Number Sold

Each "X" represents one instance in the data set of each "number sold." So, for example, there were two different days on which this person sold 3 appliances, three different days on which this person sold 4 appliances, and so on. The data could just as easily be written as a data set {3, 3, 4, 4, 4, 5, 6, 6, 6, 7, 8, 10, 10}, or placed in a frequency table:

Number Sold	Frequency
1	0
2	0
3	2
4	3
5	1
6	3
7	1
8	1
9	0
10	2

- **Histograms** look a lot like bar charts and can be read in the same way, but they are similar to frequency tables and dot plots in that they show how many times a certain value shows up in a data set for a variable. The histogram for the appliances data set would look like this:

Notice that the histogram is basically the same as the dot plot for this data set. Histograms are better for representing larger data sets for which individual dots would be difficult to count.

You need to do this:

- When presented with a question that uses a graph or table to present information, first inspect the format of the graph or table. What kind of graph or table is it? What information is presented on each axis? What information do you need to find in order to answer the question?
- Find the information you need from the table or graph and then use the information for any calculation the question might require, such as taking the average, finding the median, or thinking about standard deviation.
- Use the average formula, $\text{average} = \dfrac{\text{sum}}{\text{number of items}}$, to find unknowns. For example, if you know that the average of five terms is 7, and you know that four of the terms are 3, 6, 8, and 9, you can call the last term x and plug into the equation, then solve for x:

$$7 = \frac{3+6+8+9+x}{5}$$
$$35 = 26 + x$$
$$x = 9$$

Explanation:

This question gives you an average and asks for a missing value. First, set up a general equation for the average:

$$\text{average} = \frac{\text{sum}}{\text{number of items}}$$

The event takes place over three weeks, which is 21 days, and the average is given as 90 pounds per day. Use the dot plot to calculate how many pounds were sold in the first 20 days by adding all the numbers given, which is 1,750 pounds. Let p represent the missing number of pounds sold:

$$90 = \frac{1,750 + p}{21}$$

Multiply both sides by 21 to get rid of the fraction and then subtract 1,750 from both sides to isolate p:

$$1,890 = 1,750 + p$$
$$p = 140$$

The correct answer is **(D)**.

Try on Your Own

Directions: Take as much time as you need on these questions. Work carefully and methodically. There will be an opportunity for timed practice at the end of the chapter.

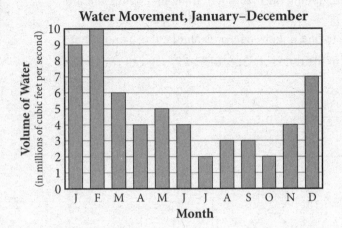

Water Movement, January–December

1. A researcher placed a fluid motion sensor in the Atlantic Ocean along the North Carolina coast to study the movement of the water. Every morning at 6:00 a.m., the movement of the water past the sensor was recorded. The figure above shows the results. Based on the data, which of the following would be a valid conclusion? (Assume that the summer months are June, July, and August and the winter months are December, January, and February.)

   A) In general, a greater volume of water moves per month in the Atlantic Ocean during the winter months than during the summer months.

   B) In general, a greater volume of water moves per month in the Atlantic Ocean during the summer months than during the winter months.

   C) In general, a greater volume of water moves per month in the oceans around the world during the winter months than during the summer months.

   D) In general, a greater volume of water moves per month in the oceans around the world during the summer months than during the winter months.

HINT: Focus on the parts of the table that are required to answer Q2 and ignore the rest.

	Cars	Trucks	SUVs	Total
No Service	39	20	13	72
Rotate	48	36	60	144
Replace	7	8	17	32
Total	94	64	90	248

2. When a consumer gets an oil change for a vehicle, the service technician typically checks the tread depth and wear condition of the tires. The technician then recommends one of the following: no service needed, rotate tires, or replace one or more tires. The table above shows one technician's recommendations for the month of June. For what fraction of cars and trucks did this technician recommend a tire rotation?

   A) $\dfrac{21}{62}$

   B) $\dfrac{42}{79}$

   C) $\dfrac{18}{31}$

   D) $\dfrac{7}{12}$

Questions 3 and 4 refer to the following information.

Group	Proportion
A: inert, mild or no side effects	34.5%
B: inert, moderate side effects	9.2%
C: inert, severe side effects	6.2%
D: drug, mild or no side effects	9.5%
E: drug, moderate side effects	12.8%
F: drug, severe side effects	27.8%

Dr. Hunter is overseeing a treatment-resistant influenza Phase I trial with 400 healthy participants: half are given the drug and half are given an inert pill. The table shows a distribution of the severity of gastrointestinal side effects.

3. How many trial participants did not have severe side effects?

HINT: Use the calculation you did for Q3 to answer Q4.

4. Of those who had severe side effects, what percent were administered the drug? (Round to the nearest whole number and omit the percent sign when gridding in your answer.)

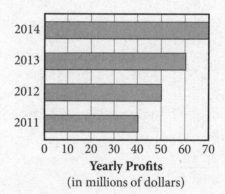

Yearly Profits
(in millions of dollars)

5. The graph above shows the yearly profits of an organic produce company. If the company's profits continue to grow at the same rate, in which year will it have a yearly profit that is 100% greater than its profit in 2013 ?

A) 2019

B) 2020

C) 2021

D) 2022

	TV Owners	Thursday Viewing Audience (all channels)
Under age 35	4,100	1,900
Age 35 or older	3,400	1,600

6. The table above displays data that show the number of TV owners in the town of Jonesville and how many of these owners had their televisions on during a particular Thursday evening. On that evening, 20 percent of TV owners in Jonesville tuned in to a certain channel. If a channel's nightly rating is reported as a fraction and is defined as $\dfrac{\text{Number of channel's viewers}}{\text{Total viewing audience that night}}$, then what was the channel's nightly rating?

Statistics

LEARNING OBJECTIVES

After this lesson, you will be able to:

- Calculate mean, median, mode, and range
- Define standard deviation and margin of error

To answer a question like this:

Two different schools record how many meters their running teams can run. Each school has 21 members on its team, and the distances in meters run by each member are recorded above. If M_A and S_A are the median and standard deviation, respectively, of team A, and M_B and S_B are the median and standard deviation, respectively, of team B, then which of the following statements is true?

A) $M_A < M_B$ and $S_A < S_B$

B) $M_A > M_B$ and $S_A < S_B$

C) $M_A > M_B$ and $S_A > S_B$

D) $M_A < M_B$ and $S_A > S_B$

You need to know this:

Suppose a nurse took a patient's pulse at different times of day and found it to be 75, 78, 71, 71, and 68. Here are six fundamental statistics figures you can determine for this data set:

- **Mean (also called arithmetic mean or average):** The sum of the values divided by the number of values. For this data set, the mean pulse is $\frac{75 + 78 + 71 + 71 + 68}{5} = \frac{363}{5} = 72.6$.

- **Median:** The value that is in the middle of the set *when the values are arranged in ascending order*. The pulse values in ascending order are 68, 71, 71, 75, and 78. The middle term is the third term, making the median 71. (If the list consists of an even number of values, the median is the average of the middle two values.)

- **Mode:** The value that occurs most frequently. The value that appears more than any other is 71, which appears twice (while all other numbers appear only once), so it is the mode. If more than one value appears the most often, that's okay; a set of data can have multiple modes. For example, if the nurse took the patient's pulse a sixth time and it was 68, then both 71 and 68 would be modes for this data set.

- **Range:** The difference between the highest and lowest values. In this data set, the lowest and highest values are 68 and 78, respectively, so the range is $78 - 68 = 10$.

- **Standard deviation:** A measure of how far a typical data point is from the mean. A low standard deviation means most values in the set are fairly close to the mean; a high standard deviation means there is much more spread in the data set. On the PSAT, *you will need to know what standard deviation is and what it tells you about a set of data, but you won't have to calculate it.*

- **Margin of error:** A description of the maximum expected difference between a true statistics measure (e.g., the mean or median) for a data pool and that same statistics measure for a random sample from the data pool. A lower margin of error is achieved by increasing the size of the random sample. As with standard deviation, *you will need to know what a margin of error is on the PSAT, but you won't be asked to calculate one.*

You need to do this:

- To compare two standard deviations, look at how spread out the data set is. The more clustered the data, the lower the standard deviation.

- To find the median, arrange *all* values in order. In a dot plot or frequency distribution table, that means finding the group with the middle value.

Explanation:

Start with the standard deviation. The scores in team B are more clustered around the mean, so the standard deviation for team B will be smaller than that for team A, where the scores are more spread out. Eliminate (A) and (B).

To calculate the medians of the two classes, you need to find the middle value in each data set. Each class has 21 students, so the middle score will be the 11th term. Count from the left of each dot plot to find that the 11th score for team A is 4,500 and for team B is 4,000. So the median for team B is smaller, which makes **(C)** correct.

Try on Your Own

Directions: Take as much time as you need on these questions. Work carefully and methodically. There will be an opportunity for timed practice at the end of the chapter.

HINT: For Q7, think about what standard deviation means.

	Huiping	Deanna	Katya
Dive 1	8.2	9.0	7.7
Dive 2	7.3	7.1	8.4
Dive 3	8.6	6.5	7.5
Dive 4	8.0	8.6	8.1
Dive 5	9.1	6.1	8.1
Dive 6	8.4	8.9	7.2
Mean Score	8.27	7.70	7.83
Standard Deviation	0.61	1.29	0.45

7.   Huiping, Deanna, and Katya are three varsity divers who recently competed in an exhibition diving meet. Their diving scores for each of their six dives are shown in the above table. According to the data, which of the following is a valid conclusion?

   A)   Huiping dived the most consistently because her mean score is the highest.

   B)   Katya dived the most consistently because her standard deviation is the lowest.

   C)   Katya dived the least consistently because her mean score is the lowest.

   D)   Deanna dived the most consistently because her standard deviation is the highest.

Fuel Efficiency Ratings

8.   The bar graph above shows the number of convertibles made by several manufacturers with various fuel efficiency ratings. What is the mean fuel efficiency rating for these convertibles?

   A)   25

   B)   27

   C)   30

   D)   32

HINT: For Q9, start by determining the sum of the number of miles for all 10 days.

Marathon Training

Distance (miles)

9.   A runner is training for a marathon. His goal is to run an average of 5 miles per day for the first 10 days of his training. The dot plot above shows the number of miles he ran each day during the first 9 days. How many miles must he run on the 10th day to reach his goal?

   A)   5

   B)   5.5

   C)   6

   D)   6.5

Year	Number of Eligible Employees
2010	*n*
2011	874
2012	795
2013	732
2014	821

10. The table above shows the number of employees at a certain company who were eligible for group health insurance each year from 2010 to 2014. If the median number of eligible employees for the five years was 821, and no two years had the same number of eligible employees, what is the least possible value for *n* ?

    A) 733
    B) 796
    C) 822
    D) 875

11. In a local rock climbing group, the mean novice member age is 22 years and the mean experienced member age is 26 years. Which of the following can be concluded about the average age, *a*, of the experienced and novice members of this rock climbing group?

    A) $22 < a < 26$
    B) $a = 24$
    C) $a > 24$
    D) $a < 24$

HINT: Arrange the values in Q12 in ascending order to find the median and quickly identify the mode.

12. Data set K consists of the values 11, 4, 0, 7, 14, 1, 3, 7, and 13. Which of the following has the least value?

    A) The mode of data set K
    B) The median of data set K
    C) The mean of data set K
    D) One-half the range of data set K

Surveys and Data Samples

LEARNING OBJECTIVES

After this lesson, you will be able to:

- Determine whether a survey is valid or biased
- Draw inferences about surveys and data samples

To answer a question like this:

A county commerce department conducted a survey of 200 customers of one of the county's pizzerias. The purpose of the survey was to estimate the average number of take-out pizzas purchased each year by residents of the county. The average number of pizzas purchased per year by these 200 customers was 43. Which of the following statements must be true based on this information?

A) The survey is representative, so 43 is a reasonable estimate of the average number of pizzas purchased annually by the county's residents.

B) The survey is not representative of the target population due to a bias inherent in the sampling method.

C) The average number of pizzas purchased by the county's residents is fewer than one per week.

D) The average number of pizzas purchased per county resident per year cannot be determined from such a small sample.

You need to know this:

You will see occasional questions on the PSAT Math sections that do not require any calculations or even test your ability to interpret numerical data. Instead, these questions test your ability to draw logical conclusions about surveys and data sampling methods.

Answering these questions correctly hinges on your ability to tell whether a data sample is **representative** of the larger population. A representative sample is a small group that shares key characteristics with a larger group you are trying to draw conclusions about.

A sample that is selected truly at random is generally representative of the larger group. For example, a scientist who wants to learn the average height of the penguins in a colony of 200 might measure the heights of a random sample of only 20 penguins. As long as the 20 penguins are selected at random, their average height will approximate the average height of the birds in the entire colony.

On the other hand, a sample that is not selected at random may not be representative and may lead to a biased conclusion. For instance, imagine that a small town uses volunteer firefighters and that a stipulation for becoming a volunteer firefighter is living within a mile of the fire station. If you wanted to know what percent of households in the town include at least one volunteer firefighter, you would need to survey a random sample of households from the entire town, not just a sample of households within a mile of the fire station. A sample of households within a mile of the fire station would be a biased sample and would lead to an erroneous conclusion (namely, that the percent of households in the town that include at least one volunteer firefighter is higher than it actually is).

Math

You need to do this:

- Check whether the data sample represents the larger population. If it doesn't, the survey is biased.
- In questions that ask you to draw a conclusion from a random (unbiased) sample, look for the answer choice for which the representative sample accurately reflects the larger population. For example, in a question asking for a conclusion based on a sample of librarians, the correct answer will match the sample to a larger population of librarians, not to a population of, say, accountants.

Explanation:

The sample in this question consists of the 200 customers of a pizzeria. This is not a randomly selected sample. It is likely that frequent purchasers of pizza will be overrepresented at a pizzeria. Thus, the survey is biased, so **(B)** is correct.

Try on Your Own

Directions: Take as much time as you need on these questions. Work carefully and methodically. There will be an opportunity for timed practice at the end of the chapter.

13. A polling company wanted to determine whether American voters would support a constitutional amendment that requires a person running for the U.S. Senate to have a minimum of a bachelor's degree. To do this, the company conducted a survey by sending 20,000 text messages across the entire United States to randomly selected phones with text-messaging capabilities. For every text that the company sent, it received a response to the survey. Which of the following best explains why this random sample is unlikely to be a representative sample of the American population's opinion in an actual election?

A) The survey was biased because most Americans who own a cell phone have a bachelor's degree.

B) Most Americans don't care about this issue, which is likely to skew the results.

C) Surveys conducted via text messaging are illegal and as such are not considered reliable.

D) There is no way to verify whether the respondents to the survey were U.S. citizens who were registered to vote.

14. A medical testing company conducted an experimental study to determine which of three antihistamines is most effective for alleviating allergy symptoms. If the only allergies treated in the course of the study were pollen allergies, which of the following is true?

A) The antihistamine that is found to be the most effective will work for all allergies.

B) The antihistamine that is found to be the most effective will work only for pollen allergies.

C) The study will be able to produce results concerning the effects of the antihistamines only on pollen allergies.

D) The study is clearly biased and, therefore, not relevant to determining which antihistamine is most effective.

HINT: For Q15, first find the percent of the 200 students polled who want to see movies.

15. The PTA is planning to sponsor a cultural arts day at school. It asked 200 randomly selected students what the focus of the day should be. Of those students asked, 42 recommended having a speaker, 48 asked for an art display, 60 wanted to taste foods from around the world, and the rest said they would like to watch cultural movies. If there are 1,260 students in the school, about how many would you expect to want to watch cultural movies?

HINT: For Q16, make sure you're answering the question
you're actually being asked.

16. SoFast Internet is hoping to expand its services to three new counties in rural Virginia. According to its research, a total of approximately 86,400 homes in the three counties currently have Internet service. SoFast surveys a sample of 500 randomly selected households with Internet service and finds that 225 are not satisfied with their current provider. SoFast would be the only other Internet service provider in the area, and it is confident that it will be able to acquire 80% of the dissatisfied households. Based on this information and the results of the sample survey, about how many new customers should SoFast be able to acquire?

A)   31,104

B)   38,880

C)   41,608

D)   69,120

17. A psychology professor at a large university is conducting a research project on pre-law students' study habits for courses required for their majors versus their study habits for strictly elective courses. His original plan was to randomly select 250 third-year pre-law students and 250 fourth-year pre-law students and ask them to estimate the amount of time they spend studying for the two course types. Due to a printing error, only 200 survey copies were made; 50 of these went to third-years and 150 went to fourth-years. Assuming 100% of the surveys are returned, what effect(s) will the printing error have on the data collected?

A)   The mean study times will be skewed toward third-year students and the margins of error will increase.

B)   The mean study times will be skewed toward fourth-year students and the margins of error will increase.

C)   The mean study times will be skewed toward third-year students and the margins of error will decrease.

D)   The mean study times will be skewed toward fourth-year students and the margins of error will decrease.

Probability

To answer a question like this:

Levels Passed in Video Game

Name	Levels Passed
Imani	3
Micah	7
Corentin	5
Marco	4
Dikembe	1
Rachel	10

 The above table shows how many levels each player passed in the same video game. If these players represent a random sample, what is the probability that a given player will pass at least four levels in this game?

A) 25%

B) 33%

C) 50%

D) 67%

You need to know this:

Probability is a fraction or decimal between 0 and 1 comparing the number of desired outcomes to the number of total possible outcomes. A probability of 0 means that an event will not occur; a probability of 1 means that it definitely will occur. The formula is as follows:

$$\text{probability} = \frac{\text{number of desired outcomes}}{\text{number of total possible outcomes}}$$

For instance, if you roll a six-sided die, each side showing a different number from 1 to 6, the probability of rolling a number higher than 4 is $\frac{2}{6} = \frac{1}{3}$, because there are two numbers higher than 4 (5 and 6) and six numbers total (1, 2, 3, 4, 5, and 6).

To find the probability that an event will *not* happen, subtract the probability that the event will happen from 1. Continuing the previous example, the probability of *not* rolling a number higher than 4 would be:

$$1 - \frac{1}{3} = \frac{2}{3}$$

The PSAT tends to test probability in the context of data tables. Using a table, you can find the probability that a randomly selected data value (be it a person, object, etc.) will fit a certain profile. For example, the following table summarizing a survey on water preference might be followed by a question asking for the probability that a person randomly selected for a follow-up survey falls into a given category.

	Tap	Carbonated	Bottled	Total
Urban	325	267	295	887
Rural	304	210	289	803
Total	629	477	584	1,690

If the question asked for the probability of randomly selecting an urbanite who prefers tap water from all the participants of the original survey, you would calculate it using the same general formula as before:

$$\frac{\text{\# urban, tap}}{\text{\# total}} = \frac{325}{1,690} = \frac{5}{26} \approx 0.192$$

If the question asked for the probability of randomly selecting an urbanite for the follow-up survey, given that the chosen participant prefers tap water, the setup is a little different. This time, the number of possible outcomes is the total participants *who prefer tap water*, which is 629, not the grand total of 1,690. The calculation is now:

$$\frac{\text{\# urban, tap}}{\text{\# total, tap}} = \frac{325}{629} \approx 0.517$$

Conversely, if you needed to find the probability of selecting someone who prefers tap water for the follow-up survey, given that the chosen participant is from an urban area, the new number of possible outcomes would be the urban participant total (887). The calculation becomes:

$$\frac{\text{\# urban, tap}}{\text{\# total, urban}} = \frac{325}{887} \approx 0.366$$

You need to do this:

- Determine the number of desired and total possible outcomes by looking at the table.
- Read the question carefully when determining the number of possible outcomes: do you need the entire set or a subset?

Explanation:

Use the probability formula: $\text{probability} = \frac{\text{number of desired outcomes}}{\text{number of total outcomes}}$. The numerator is the number of people who can pass at least four levels, which is 4. The total number of people in the data table are 6. So, $\text{probability} = \frac{4}{6} = \frac{2}{3} \approx 0.667$. The closest answer to this is **(D)**.

Try on Your Own

Directions: Take as much time as you need on these questions. Work carefully and methodically. There will be an opportunity for timed practice at the end of the chapter.

	Apples	Berries	Pears	Oranges	Exotics	Total
Frankie	30	32	22	18	13	115
Bao	18	28	27	24	15	112
Craig	37	31	18	31	22	139
Ekanta	28	35	32	15	24	134
Total	113	126	99	88	74	500

18. Frankie, Bao, Craig, and Ekanta are selling boxes of fruit to raise money for a senior class trip. The summary of their sales is provided in the table above. The students decide to give away a free box of fruit to someone who purchased from them. Assuming no buyers purchased more than one box of fruit, what is the probability that the randomly selected buyer had previously purchased a box of berries or exotic fruit?

	Winter	Spring	Summer	Fall	Total
Apples	38	40	52	85	215
Bananas	47	53	50	30	180
Oranges	43	66	82	44	235
Pineapples	22	41	46	11	120
Total	150	200	230	170	750

The table above shows the number of apples, bananas, oranges, and pineapples sold at Freddie's Fruit Stand during each of the four seasons in 2018.

19. Of the following, which is closest to the percentage of all the pieces of fruit sold that were bananas?

    A) 15

    B) 20

    C) 24

    D) 30

HINT: See if you can answer Q20 without actually calculating exactly what percentage of fruit sold is pineapples.

---

20. For which season did pineapples make up the largest percentage of the total pieces of fruit sold?

    A) Winter

    B) Spring

    C) Summer

    D) Fall

	Strongly Disagree	Disagree	Agree	Strongly Agree	Total
Freshmen	35	40	24	36	135
Sophomores	37	28	12	23	100
Juniors	24	22	36	38	120
Seniors	30	40	21	24	115
Total	126	130	93	121	470

21. Students at Fairview High School were asked to rate their level of agreement with the school's decision to change the school colors from blue and white to maroon and orange. The results are shown in the table above, by level of agreement and class of student. If underclassmen are defined as freshmen and sophomores, what percentage of underclassmen agree or strongly agree with the new policy? Round your answer to the nearest whole number and ignore the percent sign when gridding your response.

HINT: Take the time to make sure you're pulling the correct information from the table and graph for Q22.

Table 1

Age of Orange Trees	Percent Distribution
Less than 3 years old	15%
3–5 years old	20%
6–10 years old	25%
Older than 10 years	40%

A large fruit orchard has 2,500 orange trees. Table 1 above shows the distribution of ages of the orange trees in the orchard. A county inspector has been notified that a highly contagious bacterial disease called citrus canker has infected some of the orange trees. The inspector randomly tests 4% of each age group of the trees. Her findings are shown in Table 2 below.

Table 2

Age of Orange Trees	Number with Citrus Cankers
Less than 3 years old	8
3–5 years old	6
6–10 years old	8
Older than 10 years	3

22. What is the probability that an orange tree selected at random from the tested trees less than 3 years old will have citrus canker?

A) 0.03

B) 0.12

C) 0.15

D) 0.53

On Test Day

The PSAT tests the concept of average (arithmetic mean) fairly heavily. The average formula will serve you well on questions that ask about a sum of values or the average of a set of values, but for questions that give you the average and ask for a missing value in the data set, there is an alternative that can be faster: the balance approach.

The balance approach is based on the idea that if you know what the average is, you can find the totals on both sides of the average and then add the missing value that makes both sides balance out. This approach is especially helpful if the values are large and closely spaced. Imagine that a question gives you the set $\{976, 980, 964, 987, x\}$ and tells you that the average is 970. You would reason as follows: 976 is 6 over the average, 980 is 10 over, 964 is 6 under, and 987 is 17 over. That's a total of $6 + 10 - 6 + 17 = 27$ over, so x needs to be 27 under the average, or $970 - 27 = 943$.

Try solving the question below both ways, using first the average formula and then the balance approach. If you find the latter to be fast and intuitive, add it to your test day arsenal.

	Jerseys	Shorts	T-Shirts	Tank Tops	Sweatshirts	Sweatpants
Red	6	3	4	7	8	8
Green	2	7	5	3	5	4
Blue	8	9	7	5		4

23. The table above shows the types and colors of sportswear in stock at a sporting goods store. If the mean number of blue articles of clothing in stock is 7, then what is the number of blue sweatshirts the store has in stock?

The correct answer and both ways of solving can be found at the end of the chapter.

How Much Have You Learned?

Directions: For testlike practice, give yourself 15 minutes to complete this question set. Be sure to study the explanations, even for questions you got right. They can be found at the end of this chapter.

Questions 24 and 25 refer to the following information.

The table below shows the distribution of applicants by age and level of education for a management trainee program offered at a retail store.

Age Group	High School Diploma Only	2-Year Degree	4-Year Degree	Total
18–25	23	12	3	38
26–35	16	19	9	44
36–45	11	13	2	26
Older than 45	2	2	0	4
Total	52	46	14	112

24. According to the data, which age group had the smallest percentage of people with a high school diploma only?

   A) 18–25

   B) 26–35

   C) 36–45

   D) Older than 45

25. Based on the table, if a single applicant is selected at random from all the applicants, what is the probability that he or she will have a 2-year degree and be at least 26 years old?

   A) $\dfrac{19}{112}$

   B) $\dfrac{17}{56}$

   C) $\dfrac{19}{46}$

   D) $\dfrac{23}{56}$

Questions 26 and 27 refer to the following information.

The Kp Index measures the energy added to Earth's magnetic field from the Sun on a scale of 0–9, with 1 representing a solar calm and 5 or more indicating a magnetic storm, or solar flare. The magnetic fluctuations are measured in three-hour intervals (12 a.m.–3 a.m., 3 a.m.–6 a.m., and so on). The bar graph below shows the measurements for a five-day period in September.

Solar Flare Occurrences

Each bar = 3 hours

26. Based on the graph, a solar flare lasted for how many hours on September 11 ?

27. If a single 3-hour time period between September 9 and September 13 (including the start and end dates) is chosen at random, what is the probability that a solar flare occurred during that time?

Questions 28 and 29 refer to the following information.

Most cinemas have multiple movie theaters, each running a variety of movies all day. The following table shows the daily costs associated with keeping each theater open.

Expense per Theater	Amount
Electricity	$150/day
Trash Disposal and Cleaning	$80/day
Operational Staff	$11/hour

28. Cinema XV has 15 movie theaters, each of which averages 600 customers per day. If the cinema closes 6 of the theaters during the winter months but total theater attendance stays the same, what is the average daily attendance per theater among the remaining theaters?

29. If each theater requires one operational staff member for 14 hours, how much money does Cinema XV save per day during the winter months by closing six theaters?

Questions 30 and 31 refer to the following information.

The following table shows the number of babies born in a certain hospital in October 2018. The table categorizes the births by whether the mother participated in a new prenatal program and whether the baby was below, above, or within the healthy weight range as defined by the World Health Organization.

	Below Range	Within Range	Above Range	Total
Participant	1	55	10	66
Not a Participant	8	49	5	62
Total	9	104	15	128

30. The at-risk group is defined as all babies above or below the healthy weight range. What percent of the babies born at this hospital in October 2018 were considered at-risk? Round your answer to the nearest whole number and ignore the percent sign when gridding your response.

31. The hospital decides to focus its study on the two at-risk groups with the highest number of babies: Not a Participant/Below Range and Participant/Above Range. If a baby is randomly selected from all those born at this hospital in October 2018, what is the probability that the baby belongs to one of those two groups?

Questions 32 and 33 refer to the following information.

A team of researchers studied the effect of sleep masks on rapid eye movement (REM) sleep. Study participants were divided into three groups: the first group did not wear sleep masks, the second group wore regular sleep masks, and the third group wore sleep masks that were contoured away from the eyes and lashes. The results of the study are shown in the following table.

	No Mask	Regular Mask	Contoured Mask	Total
Experienced REM Sleep	14	33	78	125
Did Not Experience REM Sleep	34	29	22	85
Total	48	62	100	210

32. What percent of the participants who experienced REM sleep during the study wore a contoured mask?

    A) 37.1%

    B) 47.6%

    C) 59.5%

    D) 62.4%

33. Based on the results of this study, if a company sold 12,000 of the contoured sleep masks, about how many of the consumers should experience REM sleep using the mask, assuming the participants in the study were a good representative sample?

    A) 4,457

    B) 5,714

    C) 7,488

    D) 9,360

Reflect

Directions: Take a few minutes to recall what you've learned and what you've been practicing in this chapter. Consider the following questions, jot down your best answer for each one, and then compare your reflections to the expert responses on the following page. Use your level of confidence to determine what to do next.

What are some common ways the PSAT may present data?

_____

_____

_____

What is the difference between median, mode, and range?

_____

_____

_____

What does the standard deviation of a data set tell you?

_____

_____

_____

When can you generalize the results of a survey of a small group to a larger group?

_____

_____

_____

What are two ways to calculate the probability of a single event?

_____

_____

_____

Expert Responses

What are some common ways the PSAT may present data?

The PSAT may present data in tables, bar charts, line graphs, dot plots, and histograms.

What is the difference between median, mode, and range?

The median of a set is the middle value, whereas the mode is the most common value. The range of a set is the distance between the smallest value and the largest one.

What does the standard deviation of a data set tell you?

A data set's standard deviation reflects how far apart the numbers are from each other. The standard deviation of a set whose numbers are all the same—for example, $\{5, 5, 5, 5\}$—is 0. The greater the distance between the numbers, the greater the standard deviation.

When can you generalize the results of a survey of a small group to a larger group?

A survey can be generalized to a larger population if the data sample is representative. To be representative, the data sample needs to be drawn at random from the larger population.

What are two ways to calculate the probability of a single event?

One way is to use the basic probability formula:

$$probability = \frac{number\ of\ desired\ outcomes}{number\ of\ total\ outcomes}$$

Alternatively, the probability that an event happens is 1 minus the probability that it doesn't happen.

Next Steps

If you answered most questions correctly in the "How Much Have You Learned?" section, and if your responses to the Reflect questions were similar to those of the PSAT expert, then consider Tables, Statistics, and Probability an area of strength and move on to the next chapter. Come back to this topic periodically to prevent yourself from getting rusty.

If you don't yet feel confident, review those parts of this chapter that you have not yet mastered, then try the questions you missed again. In particular, make sure that you understand the six terms explained in the Statistics lesson and the probability formulas explained in the Probability lesson. As always, be sure to review the explanations closely.

Answers and Explanations

1. A

Difficulty: Easy

Getting to the Answer: The question states that the data were collected in the Atlantic Ocean, so any conclusion drawn can be generalized only to that particular geographic region. Eliminate (C) and (D). The question defines the winter months as December, January, and February. According to the data, a greater volume of water moved during those months than during the summer months of June, July, and August, so **(A)** is correct.

2. B

Difficulty: Easy

Getting to the Answer: The question asks only about cars and trucks, so ignore the column for SUVs. The technician recommended a tire rotation for 48 cars and 36 trucks (a total of 84) out of the $94 + 64 = 158$ cars and trucks that he serviced. This represents $\frac{84}{158} = \frac{42}{79}$ of the cars and trucks, making **(B)** correct.

3. 264

Difficulty: Easy

Getting to the Answer: You know from the table that 27.8% of participants who were administered the drug experienced severe side effects. Add this to the 6.2% who had severe side effects while given the inert pill to get 34.0% total with severe side effects, meaning $100\% - 34.0\% = 66.0\%$ did not have them. Using the three-part percent formula, you find $0.66 \times 400 = 264$ participants did not sustain severe side effects. Grid in **264**.

4. 82

Difficulty: Medium

Getting to the Answer: From the previous question, you know that 264 trial participants did not have severe side effects; therefore, $400 - 264 = 136$ participants did. The table indicates that 27.8% of the 400 participants were given the drug and sustained severe side effects, which equates to $0.278 \times 400 \approx 111$ participants. So, 111 out of the 136 participants who had severe side effects were given the drug:

$$\frac{111}{136} \times 100\% = 81.6\%$$

Be sure to round this up to the nearest whole percent, as indicated in the question. Grid in **82**.

5. A

Difficulty: Medium

Getting to the Answer: According to the bar graph, the company's yearly profits have been growing by about $10 million annually. To reach yearly profits that are 100% greater than (or double) its profits in 2013, the company would need yearly profits of $2 \times \$60$ million $= \$120$ million. This is $50 million more than in 2014. At $10 million more per year, reaching this target would take 5 more years. Thus, the company should double its 2013 profits in $2014 + 5 = 2019$, which is **(A)**.

6. 3/7 or .428

Difficulty: Medium

Getting to the Answer: According to the expression provided, you need the number of viewers and the total viewing audience:

Channel's viewers = 20% of TV owners

$= 0.20(4{,}100 + 3{,}400) = 0.2(7{,}500) = 1{,}500$

Total viewing audience $= 1{,}900 + 1{,}600 = 3{,}500$

Nightly rating $= \frac{1{,}500}{3{,}500} = \frac{3}{7}$

Grid in **3/7** or **.428**.

7. B

Difficulty: Easy

Getting to the Answer: Consider the difference between mean and standard deviation: mean is a measure of center, while standard deviation is a measure of spread. The four answers all involve diving consistency, which means the explanation should involve standard deviation. Eliminate (A) and (C). Higher diving consistency means lower standard deviation (and vice versa); the only choice that reflects this—and correctly represents the data in the table—is **(B)**.

8.   B

Difficulty: Easy

Getting to the Answer: The mean of a set of numbers is the same as the average, which is the sum of the values divided by the number of values. Use the graph to find the sum of the fuel efficiency ratings and then calculate the mean. To save time, multiply the frequency in each category by the rating and then divide by the total number of convertibles: $(6 \times 15) + (18 \times 25) + (9 \times 35) + (2 \times 45) = 945$, and there are $6 + 18 + 9 + 2 = 35$ total convertibles, so $\frac{945}{35} = 27$. Choice **(B)** is correct.

9.   C

Difficulty: Medium

Getting to the Answer: Understanding how averages and sums are connected is the key to answering a question like this. If the average of 10 numbers is 5, then the sum of the 10 numbers must be 50 (because $\frac{50}{10} = 5$). Use the dot plot to find the total number of miles the runner has already run. Then, subtract this number from 50. The runner has already run $3.5 + 2(4) + 2(4.5) + 5 + 2(6) + 6.5 = 44$ miles, so he needs to run $50 - 44 = 6$ miles on the 10th day. Choice **(C)** is correct.

10.   C

Difficulty: Hard

Getting to the Answer: The median is the middle number in a series of numbers. Arrange the number of employees from least to greatest, making sure that 821 is in the middle. Use n to balance out the number of eligible employees on either side of 821:

$$732, 795, 821, 874, n$$

or

$$732, 795, 821, n, 874$$

Because there are two numbers below the median (732 and 795), there must be two numbers above the median, 874 and n. Be careful—n could be on either side of 874. Since no two years had the same number, n could be anything greater than 821. Its least possible value is 822. Choice **(C)** is correct.

11.   A

Difficulty: Hard

Getting to the Answer: To answer this question, you need to understand the assumptions each inequality makes to identify the correct one. Start with (A). This is a reasonable conclusion to draw because the question does not specify anything about the relative quantity of experienced and novice club members, so keep (A) as a possible correct answer for the moment. Choice (B) assumes there are equal numbers of experienced and novice members. Choice (C) assumes there are more experienced than novice members, while (D) assumes there are more novice than experienced members. Because no information on the relative numbers of each is given, (B), (C), and (D) are all incorrect, leaving **(A)** as the only option.

12.   C

Difficulty: Medium

Getting to the Answer: First arrange the elements of data set K in increasing order: 0, 1, 3, 4, 7, 7, 11, 13, 14. The mode is 7 because that is the only value that appears twice. There are nine values, so the median is the fifth number, which is also 7. The mean is
$$\frac{0 + 1 + 3 + 4 + 7 + 7 + 11 + 13 + 14}{9} = \frac{60}{9} = 6\frac{2}{3}.$$
Finally, the range is $14 - 0 = 14$. One-half of that is 7. The mean has the least value, so **(C)** is correct.

13.   D

Difficulty: Medium

Getting to the Answer: A good representative sample is not only random but also a good representation of the population in question. Here, the population in question is American voters. Choice (A) could be tempting because it might be true that cell phone owners are more educated, and more educated voters may prefer more educated senators, but not everyone with a cell phone is a registered voter. For example, minors, noncitizens, and citizens who aren't registered to vote are likely to make up at least a portion of the recipients of random texts sent out by the polling company. Since the survey is intended to sample voters, that is an important distinction. Thus, the inability to verify if the respondents were even registered to vote means that despite being randomly selected, the sample is unlikely to be a good representative sample. Choice **(D)** is correct.

14. C

Difficulty: Medium

Getting to the Answer: The study only looked at pollen allergies, so the sample was limited. You can eliminate (A) because not all allergies were included in the sample—you can't say anything about them one way or the other. You can eliminate (B) by similar reasoning: the antihistamine found to be most effective for pollen allergies may or may not be the most effective one for other types of allergies as well; there is just no way to tell. You can eliminate (D) because the question doesn't tell you anything about the data collection methods, so you can't determine whether the study was biased. This means that **(C)** is correct—the study will be able to produce results concerning the effects of the antihistamines only on pollen allergies.

15. 315

Difficulty: Medium

Getting to the Answer: When making inferences about populations based on data from a random, representative sample, find the percent of the sample data that matches the given criterion and multiply by the total population. Of the 200 students in the sample, $200 - 42 - 48 - 60 = 50$ students said they would like to watch cultural movies. This represents $\frac{50}{200} = \frac{1}{4}$, or 25%. Multiply $0.25 \times 1,260$ to arrive at 315 students. Grid in **315**.

16. A

Difficulty: Hard

Getting to the Answer: The sample of households was randomly selected, so if $\frac{225}{500} = 0.45$ (or 45%) of the surveyed households are not satisfied with their current providers, you can infer that 45% of the total households in the three counties are not satisfied with their providers. Multiply by the total number of customers in the population to find that $86,400 \times 0.45 = 38,880$ customers are not satisfied. Be careful—this is not the correct answer, so don't choose (B). The company is confident that it can acquire 80% of these customers, or $38,880 \times 0.80 = 31,104$ customers. Choice **(A)** is correct.

17. B

Difficulty: Hard

Getting to the Answer: Fewer surveys than planned means a larger margin of error, so eliminate (C) and (D). And surveying significantly more fourth-year students than third-year students means the data will be skewed toward fourth-year students. Choice **(B)** is the only choice that specifies both effects.

18. 2/5 or .4

Difficulty: Easy

Getting to the Answer: According to the table, the students sold 126 boxes of berries and 74 boxes of exotic fruits. Add these together and divide by the total boxes sold to get $\frac{126 + 74}{500} = \frac{200}{500} = \frac{2}{5} = 0.4$. Grid in **2/5** or **.4**.

19. C

Difficulty: Easy

Getting to the Answer: To calculate the percentage of all fruits that were bananas, simply find the total number of bananas sold, divide by the total pieces of fruit sold, and multiply by 100%:

$$\frac{180}{750} \times 100\% = 24\%$$

Choice **(C)** is correct.

20. B

Difficulty: Medium

Getting to the Answer: You are asked about the percentage of sales of pineapples for each season. Thus, you will want to refer to the Pineapples row of the table. Use estimation strategies to determine percentages for each season:

Winter: 22 of 150 pieces of fruit sold in the winter were pineapples. Recognize that $\frac{25}{150} = \frac{1}{6}$, so slightly less than $\frac{1}{6}$ (or ~17%) of the fruit sold in the winter were pineapples.

Spring: 41 of 200 pieces of fruit sold in the spring were pineapples. You should recognize that $\frac{40}{200} = \frac{1}{5}$, so the percentage of pieces of fruit sold that were pineapples is slightly *above* 20% in the spring.

Summer: 46 of 230 pieces of fruit sold in the summer were pineapples. The fraction $\frac{46}{230}$ actually reduces to exactly $\frac{1}{5}$, so exactly 20% of the pieces of fruit sold in the summer were pineapples.

Fall: Only 11 of 170 pieces of fruit sold in the fall were pineapples. This ratio is very similar to $\frac{10}{170} = \frac{1}{17}$, which is going to be much smaller than the percentages in the other three seasons.

Thus, **(B)** is the correct answer.

21. 40

Difficulty: Medium

Getting to the Answer: Read the question carefully to determine which rows and columns of the tables you will need. First, you are told that you are looking only at underclassmen, which are defined as freshmen and sophomores. Thus, you only need to consider the first two rows of the table. There are $100 + 135 = 235$ under-classmen at the school. Next, you need to determine how many underclassmen either agreed or strongly agreed with the change of colors: $24 + 36 = 60$ freshmen and $12 + 23 = 35$ sophomores either agreed or strongly agreed with the change. Thus, the percentage of under-classmen who either agreed or strongly agreed with the new policy can be expressed as $\frac{95}{235} \times 100\% \approx 40.43\%$. Round down and grid in **40**.

22. D

Difficulty: Hard

Getting to the Answer: The probability that one tree less than 3 years old randomly selected from those that were tested would have cankers is equal to the number of trees less than 3 years old that had cankers divided by the total number of trees less than 3 years old that were tested. This means you need only two numbers to answer the question. One of those numbers is in the second table—8 trees less than 3 years old had cankers. Finding the other number is the tricky part. Use information from the question stem and Table 1. The inspector tested 4% of the total number of trees less than 3 years old, or 4% of 15% of 2,500 trees. Multiply to find that $0.04 \times 0.15 \times 2,500 = 15$ trees less than 3 years old were tested. This means the probability is $\frac{8}{15} \approx 0.533$, which matches choice **(D)**.

23. 9

Difficulty: Medium

Category: Statistics

Strategic Advice: When the goal is to find a missing value in a set of data and the average is given, consider using the balance approach. We'll demonstrate both approaches starting with the average formula.

Getting to the Answer: The question is about blue sportswear, so ignore the data for the other colors. The given numbers for blue sportswear are 8, 9, 7, 5, and 4. The average is given as 7. If you call the missing value x, plugging the known values into the average formula results in the following:

$$\frac{8+9+7+5+x+4}{6} = 7$$
$$\frac{33+x}{6} = 7$$
$$33 + x = 42$$
$$x = 9$$

Grid in **9** as the correct answer.

Alternatively, to use the balance approach, write down how much each value is above or below the average of 7. For example, the value for jerseys is 1 above the average: $8 - 7 = 1$.

Jerseys	Shorts	T-Shirts	Tank Tops	Sweatshirts	Sweatpants
8: +1	9: +2	7: 0	5: −2		4: −3

Now, observe that, excluding sweatshirts, the values are $+1 + 2 + 0 - 2 - 3 = -2$. Without the value for sweatshirts, the total is 2 less than what you'd expect based on the average. So for the values to balance out to the average, the sweatshirts' value must be 2 more than the average of 7, or $7 + 2 = 9$. Grid in **9**.

24. B

Difficulty: Medium

Category: Tables and Graphs

Getting to the Answer: To calculate the percentage of people in each age group who had a high school diploma only, divide the number of people in *that* age group with only a high school diploma by the total number of appli-cants in *that* age group. Choice **(B)** is correct because $\frac{16}{44} \approx 0.364 = 36.4\%$, which is a lower percentage than that of the other age groups (18 to 25 $\approx$ 60.5%, 36 to 45 $\approx$ 42.3%, and Older than 45 = 50%).

25. B

Difficulty: Hard

Category: Probability

Getting to the Answer: The first criterion is fairly straightforward—the applicant must have a 2-year degree, so focus on that column in the table. The second criterion is a bit trickier—*at least 26 years old* means 26 years old or older, so you'll need to use the values in the rows for 26–35, 36–45, and Older than 45. There were 19 in the 26–35 age group who had a 2-year degree, 13 in the 36–45 age group, and 2 in the Older than 45 age group, resulting in a total of $19 + 13 + 2 = 34$ out of 112 applicants. The probability of randomly selecting one applicant from any of these three groups is $\frac{34}{112}$, which reduces to $\frac{17}{56}$, so **(B)** is correct.

26. 15

Difficulty: Easy

Category: Tables and Graphs

Getting to the Answer: Read the graph carefully, including the key at the bottom that tells you that each bar represents a 3-hour period. The question tells you that a Kp Index of 5 or more indicates a solar flare. On September 11, the graph shows 4 bars at a Kp Index of 5 and 1 bar at a Kp Index of 6, for a total of five 3-hour periods during which a solar flare occurred. This represents a total of $5 \times 3 = \mathbf{15}$ hours. Grid in **15**.

27. 5/40 or 1/8 or .125

Difficulty: Medium

Category: Probability

Getting to the Answer: Probability compares the number of desired outcomes (number of 3-hour periods with a Kp index greater than or equal to 5) to the total number of possible outcomes (total number of 3-hour periods between September 9 and September 13).

Count the number of bars in the graph that have a height of 5 or more—there are 5. Count the total number of bars—there are 8 for each of the 5 days, for a total of 40. This means there were five 3-hour periods out of 40 during which a solar flare occurred, so the probability of randomly selecting one of those periods is $\frac{5}{40} = \frac{1}{8}$. You could also grid in the answer as **.125**.

28. 1000

Difficulty: Hard

Category: Statistics

Getting to the Answer: Originally there were 15 theaters and they averaged 600 customers each per day for a total attendance of $15 \times 600 = 9,000$ per day. Even after the 6 theaters closed, the total attendance remained the same. Then, however, the number of theaters was $15 - 6 = 9$, so recalculate the average as follows:

$$\text{new average attendance} = \frac{\text{total attendance}}{\text{new number of theatres}}$$
$$= \frac{9,000}{9}$$
$$= 1,000$$

Grid in **1000**.

29. 2304

Difficulty: Medium

Category: Tables and Graphs

Getting to the Answer: Use the information in the table to calculate how much it costs to run each theater—this will tell you how much the cinema saves by not running the theater. Then multiply by 6.

Electricity $= \$150$

End-of-Day Cleaning $= \$80$

Operational Staff $= 1$ at $\$11$/hour $\times 14$ hours $= \$154$

Total $= \$150 + \$80 + \$154 = \$384$ per theater

The total savings is $6 \times \$384 = \$2,304$. Grid in **2304**.

30. 19

Difficulty: Easy

Category: Tables and Graphs

Getting to the Answer: There are 9 babies below the healthy range and 15 babies above, so there are $9 + 15 = 24$ total babies who fall above or below the range. There are 128 babies total, which means that $\frac{24}{128} = 0.1875 \approx 19\%$ of all the babies born at this hospital in 2018 were considered at-risk. Grid in **19**.

31. 9/64 or .141

Difficulty: Medium

Category: Probability

Getting to the Answer: From the table, the numbers for Not a Participant/Below Range and Participant/Above Range are 8 and 10, respectively, with a total of $8 + 10 = 18$. There were 128 babies born in the hospital in October 2018, so the probability of randomly selecting one from the two specified groups is $\frac{18}{128} = \frac{9}{64}$. You could also grid this as **.141**.

32. D

Difficulty: Easy

Category: Tables and Graphs

Getting to the Answer: The question asks only about participants who experienced REM sleep, so focus on this row. Of the 125 participants who experienced REM sleep, 78 of them wore a contoured mask. This represents $\frac{78}{125} = 0.624$, or 62.4%, which is **(D)**.

33. D

Difficulty: Easy

Category: Surveys and Data Samples

Getting to the Answer: The question asks about consumers who purchase a contoured mask, so focus on that column in the table. Assuming the participants in the study were a good representative sample, 78 out of 100, or 78%, of the 12,000 consumers should experience REM sleep. Multiply $0.78 \times 12,000$ to arrive at 9,360, which is **(D)**.

Passport to Advanced Math

CHAPTER 8

Functions

LEARNING OBJECTIVES

After completing this chapter, you will be able to:

- Apply function notation
- Define the domain and range of a function
- Evaluate the output of a function for a given input
- Interpret the graph of a function
- Write a function to describe a rule or data set

105/600 SmartPoints® (Very High Yield)

How Much Do You Know?

Directions: Try the questions that follow. Show your work so that you can compare your solutions to the ones found in the Check Your Work section immediately after this question set. The "Category" heading in the explanation for each question gives the title of the lesson that covers how to solve it. If you answered the question(s) for a given lesson correctly, and if your scratch-work looks like ours, you may be able to move quickly through that lesson. If you answered incorrectly or used a different approach, you may want to take your time on that lesson.

1. Given that $f(x) = 2x + 1$ and $g(x) = \dfrac{x+2}{3}$, what is the product of $f(-5)$ and $g(-5)$?

   A) -6

   B) -2

   C) 3

   D) 9

2. For the two functions $f(x)$ and $g(x)$, tables of values follow. What is the value of $f(g(1))$?

x	$f(x)$
-2	8
-1	6
0	4
1	2

x	$g(x)$
-1	-4
1	0
2	2
4	6

   A) 0

   B) 2

   C) 4

   D) 6

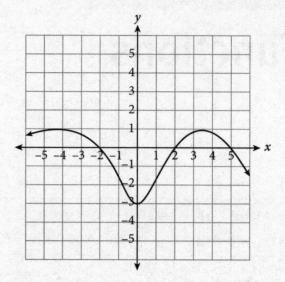

3. The figure shows the graph of $r(x)$. What is one value of x for which $r(x) = 0$?

Game	Number of Students
1	5
2	11
3	21
4	35
5	53
6	75
7	101
8	131

4. West Valley High School is encouraging students to wear school colors when they attend the home football games by giving a prize to one of the students who does so. The school finds that, as the prizes get more exciting, participation begins to increase. If j represents the game number and $f(j)$ represents the number of students in school colors at game j, which of the following functions best describes the information in the table?

A) $f(j) = j + 4$

B) $f(j) = 2j + 5$

C) $f(j) = \frac{1}{2}j^2 + 7$

D) $f(j) = 2j^2 + 3$

5. Scientists are modeling population trends and have noticed that when a certain bacterial population changes, the change is based on a linear function of the amount of time elapsed in hours. When $t = 21$ hours, the population is 8 colonies, and when $t = 35$ hours, the population is 10 colonies. Which of the following best describes $f(t)$?

A) $f(t) = \frac{1}{3}t + 1$

B) $f(t) = \frac{1}{5}t + 3$

C) $f(t) = \frac{1}{7}t + 5$

D) $f(t) = 7(t - 5)$

Check Your Work

1. D

Difficulty: Easy

Category: Function Notation

Getting to the Answer: Read carefully to see what the question is asking. You need to find the product (fg) of the results when you evaluate each function at $x = -5$. You could multiply the two functions together and then evaluate the result, but it's quicker to evaluate each function and then multiply:

$$f(-5) = 2(-5) + 1 = -10 + 1 = -9$$

$$g(-5) = \frac{-5+2}{3} = \frac{-3}{3} = -1$$

Now, multiply to get $(-9)(-1) = 9$, which is **(D)**.

2. C

Difficulty: Easy

Category: Function Notation

Getting to the Answer: This is a composition of functions, so start with the innermost set of parentheses, which is $g(1)$. According to the $g(x)$ table, when $x = 1$, $g(x) = 0$. Then, $x = 0$ becomes the input for f. Now, find $f(0)$; the $f(x)$ table shows this is equal to 4, which is **(C)**.

3. 2 or 5

Difficulty: Easy

Category: Graphs of Functions

Getting to the Answer: The notation $r(x) = 0$ means that the function is crossing the x-axis (has a y-value of 0), so look for the x-intercepts. The function $r(x)$ intersects the x-axis at $x = -2$, 2, and 5. Only positive values are allowed in Grid-in questions, so use **2** or **5**.

4. D

Difficulty: Easy

Category: Describing Real-Life Situations with Functions

Getting to the Answer: You're given two variables, j and f, which represent the game number and the number of students wearing school colors, respectively. From the data, you can see the rate of change in the number of students is not constant (not linear), so eliminate (A) and (B). Next, try plugging a point toward the bottom of the table into (C) and (D):

$$(C): 131 = \frac{1}{2} \times 8^2 + 7$$

$$131 = \frac{1}{2} \times 64 + 7$$

$$131 = 32 + 7$$

$$131 \neq 39$$

Only **(D)** is left and is correct. For the record:

$$(D): 131 = 2 \times 8^2 + 3$$

$$131 = 2 \times 64 + 3$$

$$131 = 128 + 3$$

$$131 = 131$$

5. C

Difficulty: Medium

Category: Describing Real-Life Situations with Functions

Getting to the Answer: Because the slopes of all the answer choices are different, you can use the slope formula to determine which choice is correct. The number of colonies *depends* on the time elapsed, so start by writing the information given as ordered pairs in the form (time, number of colonies). Using the ordered pairs (21, 8) and (35, 10), the slope is

$$m = \frac{y_2 - y_1}{x_2 - x_1} = \frac{10-8}{35-21} = \frac{2}{14} = \frac{1}{7}.$$

The only choice with this slope is **(C)**.

Function Notation

To answer a question like this:

$$h(x) = \frac{5x + 5}{3x - 6}$$

The function $h(x)$ is defined above. Out of the statements below, which must be true about $h(x)$?

  I. $h(8) = 2.5$

 II. The domain of $h(x)$ is all real numbers.

 III. $h(x)$ may be positive or negative.

A) I and II only

B) I and III only

C) II and III only

D) I, II, and III

You need to know this:

A **function** is a rule that generates one unique output for a given input. In function notation, the x-value is the input and the y-value, designated by $f(x)$, is the output. (Note that other letters besides x and f may be used.)

For example, a linear function has the same form as the slope-intercept form of a line; $f(x)$ is equivalent to y:

$$f(x) = mx + b$$

In questions that describe real-life situations, the y-intercept will often be the starting point for the function. You can think of it as $f(0)$, or that value of the function where $x = 0$.

The set of all possible x-values is called the **domain** of the function, while the set of all possible y-values is called the **range**.

You need to do this:

- To find $f(x)$ for some value of x, substitute the concrete value in for the variable and do the arithmetic.
- For questions that ask about the domain of a function, check whether any inputs are not allowed, for example, because they cause division by zero.
- For questions that ask about a function of a function, such as $g(f(x))$, start on the inside and work your way out.

Explanation:

Check each statement. For the first statement, plug in 8 for x:

$$\frac{5(8) + 5}{3(8) - 6} = \frac{40 + 5}{24 - 6} = \frac{45}{18} = 2.5$$

So the first statement is true. Eliminate choice (C).

For the second statement, you need to determine the set of all permitted x-values for this function. Note that the function will be undefined at $x = 2$ (because at $x = 2$, the denominator would be zero). Thus, 2 is not a permitted x-value, and the domain is not all real numbers. The second statement is false. Eliminate (A) and (D).

By process of elimination, the answer is **(B)**, and on test day, you would stop here. For the record, here's why the third statement is true: you've already established that $h(8) = 2.5$, so $h(x)$ can be positive. Try a smaller value for x, such as zero, to get a negative value for $h(x)$: $h(0) = \dfrac{2(0) + 5}{3(0) - 6} = \dfrac{5}{-6} = -\dfrac{5}{6}$, so $h(x)$ can be negative as well, which means statement III is true.

Try on Your Own

Directions: Take as much time as you need on these questions. Work carefully and methodically. There will be an opportunity for timed practice at the end of the chapter.

x	$g(x)$
-4	0
-3	2
-2	4
-1	6
0	8
1	10

x	$h(x)$
-2	-4
-1	2
0	0
1	-2
2	-4

HINT: Are there any answer choices in Q1 you can eliminate right away?

---

1. If $f(x) = x^2 - x$ for all $x \leq -1$ and $f(x) = 0$ for all $x > -1$, which of the following could NOT be a value of $f(x)$?

    A) -4

    B) 0

    C) $\dfrac{7}{13}$

    D) 2

4. Several values for the functions $g(x)$ and $h(x)$ are shown in the tables above. What is the value of $g(h(-2))$?

    A) -2

    B) 0

    C) 4

    D) 10

HINT: For Q2, remember that when dealing with nested functions, you should work from the inside out.

---

2. If $f(x) = x^2 + 17$ and $g(x) = \dfrac{3x}{x+1}$, where $x \neq -1$, what is $g(f(3))$?

    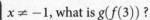

    A) $\dfrac{26}{9}$

    B) $\dfrac{299}{16}$

    C) 26

    D) $\dfrac{113}{4}$

5. If $f(x) = -4x + 1$ and $g(x) = \sqrt{x} + 2.5$, what is the value of $f\left(g\left(\dfrac{1}{4}\right)\right)$?

    A) -11

    B) 0

    C) 2.5

    D) 3

HINT: Begin Q3 by solving for $h(5)$ and $h(2)$: plug in 5 for x, then plug in 2 for x.

---

3. If $h(x) = 3x - 1$, what is the value of $h(5) - h(2)$?

    A) 3

    B) 8

    C) 9

    D) 14

Graphs of Functions

LEARNING OBJECTIVE

After this lesson, you will be able to:

- Identify the correct graph of a function

To answer a question like this:

x	$h(x)$
-3	-7
-2	-5
-1	0
0	3
1	11
2	23
3	40

The minimum value of function g, whose graph is shown above, is m. Values for the function h are shown in the table above. What is the value of $h(m)$?

A) -7

B) -5

C) 0

D) 3

You need to know this:

Interpreting graphs of functions is similar to interpreting graphs of equations. For example:

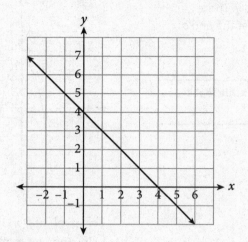

Say the graph above represents the function $f(x)$, and you're asked to find the value of x for which $f(x) = 6$. Because $f(x)$ represents the output value, or range, you can translate this to, "When does the y-value equal 6?" To answer the question, find 6 on the y-axis, then trace over to the function (the line). Read the corresponding x-value: it's -2, so when $f(x) = 6$, x must be -2.

The PSAT may sometimes ask about a function's **maximum** or **minimum**. These terms mean the greatest and least value of the function, respectively. This graph of $f(x)$ does not have a maximum or minimum because the arrows on the line indicate that it continues infinitely in both directions. The preceding question, however, does show a function with a maximum.

You need to do this:

- Treat $f(x)$ as the y-coordinate on a graph.
- The maximum and minimum refer to a function's greatest and least y-coordinates, respectively.

Explanation:

Start by identifying m, which occurs at the lowest point of the function at $(0, -3)$. The "minimum value of function g" means the least y-value, so $m = -3$. Next, use the table to find $h(-3)$, which is the y-value for the x-value of -3. According to the table, when $x = -3$, $h(x) = -7$. Hence, **(A)** is correct.

Try on Your Own

Directions: Take as much time as you need on these questions. Work carefully and methodically. There will be an opportunity for timed practice at the end of the chapter.

HINT: For Q6, remember that $f(x)$ and $g(x)$ are found on the y-axis on the graphs.

---

6. In the figure shown above, what is the value of $f(0) + g\left(\frac{1}{2}\right)$?

A)   −4

B)   6

C)   10

D)   14

HINT: For Q7, the x-values determine the domain, while the y-values determine the range.

---

7. The graph of $f(x)$ is shown above. Which of the following represents the domain and range of the function?

A)   Domain: $f(x) \geq 5$
     Range: all real numbers

B)   Domain: $f(x) \leq 5$
     Range: all real numbers

C)   Domain: all real numbers
     Range: $f(x) \geq 5$

D)   Domain: all real numbers
     Range: $f(x) \leq 5$

8. The figure shown above represents the function $q(x) = \sqrt{x}$. Which statement about the function is NOT true?

    A) $q(0) = 0$

    B) $q(2) = 4$

    C) The range of $q(x)$ is $y \geq 0$.

    D) The domain of $q(x)$ is $x \geq 0$.

10. The function $f(x)$ is graphed in the *xy*-plane above. If the maximum value of $f(x) = z$, what is the value of $-f(z)$?

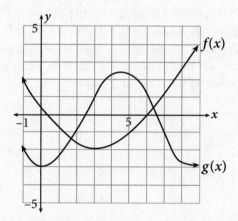

9. In the figure shown above, what is the value of $f(3) - g(3)$?

    A) -3

    B) 0

    C) 3

    D) 6

Describing Real-Life Situations with Functions

LEARNING OBJECTIVE

After this lesson, you will be able to:

- Write a function to describe a rule or data set

To answer a question like this:

Type of Meat	Pounds of Meat per Package	Profit per Pound, in Dollars
Sausage	42	1.10
Ground Beef	30	0.38
Salami	36	0.74
Bacon	32	0.50
Ham	40	0.98
Chicken	34	0.62

 A certain meat distribution company sells several varieties of meat. The company sells the different varieties in differently sized packages. The number of pounds per package and the profit per pound for the different varieties is shown in the table above. The relationship between the number of pounds per package (m) and the profit, in dollars, that the company makes per pound (p) can be represented by a linear function. Which of the following functions correctly represents the relationship?

A) $p(m) = 0.09m - 0.41$

B) $p(m) = 0.08m - 0.82$

C) $p(m) = 0.07m - 1.11$

D) $p(m) = 0.06m - 1.42$

You need to know this:

Modeling real-life situations using functions is the same as modeling them using equations; the only difference is the function notation and the rule that each input has only one output.

For example, suppose a homeowner wants to determine the cost of installing a certain amount of carpet in her living room. Say that the carpet costs $0.86 per square foot, the installer charges a $29 installation fee, and sales tax on the total cost is 7%. Using your algebra and function knowledge, you can describe this situation in which the cost, c, is a function of square footage, f. The equation would be $c = 1.07(0.86f + 29)$. In function notation, this becomes $c(f) = 1.07(0.86f + 29)$, where $c(f)$ is shorthand for "cost as a function of square footage." The following table summarizes what each piece of the function represents in the scenario.

English	Overall cost	Square footage	Material cost	Installation fee	Sales tax
Math	c	f	$0.86f$	29	1.07

You need to do this:

In word problems involving function notation, translate the math equations exactly as you learned in chapter 4 in the Word Problems lesson, but substitute $f(x)$ for y.

Explanation:

Note that the question asks for the relationship between the pounds of meat per package, m, and the profit per pound, p, and that the answer choices all start with $p(m)$. Given the context, this must mean, "profit as a function of the pounds of meat." All the choices express a linear relationship, so you can't rule out any of them on that basis.

There are several approaches you could take to find the correct answer. One would be to recognize that all the choices are in the form $p(m) = km + b$ (a variation of the slope-intercept form $y = mx + b$) and that you can set up a system of linear equations using the data from any two rows of the table to solve for k and b. That approach would look like this:

$$1.10 = 42k + b$$
$$- \quad (0.50 = 32k + b)$$
$$0.60 = 10k$$
$$0.60 = k$$

$$0.50 = 0.06(32) + b$$
$$0.50 = 1.92 + b$$
$$b = -1.42$$

If $k = 0.06$ and $b = -1.42$, the correct function is $p(m) = 0.06k - 1.42$, so **(D)** is correct.

Another approach would be to use two of the pairs of data points from the table to calculate a slope; for example, using the "sausage" and "bacon" rows would yield $\frac{1.10 - 0.5}{42 - 32} = \frac{0.60}{10} = 0.06$. Because only one answer has a slope of 0.06, you can pick **(D)**.

One last approach: you could backsolve. Plug any one of the rows of data from the table into all four answer choices. The fourth row, "Bacon," has the easiest numbers to work with, so use those. You are checking which equation will produce a profit of $0.50 per pound given 32 pounds per package:

(A): $0.09(32) - 0.41 = 2.47 \neq 0.50$, eliminate.
(B): $0.08(32) - 0.82 = 1.74 \neq 0.50$, eliminate.
(C): $0.07(32) - 1.11 = 1.13 \neq 0.50$, eliminate.
(D): $0.06(32) - 1.42 = 0.50$

Again, **(D)** is correct.

Math

Try on Your Own

Directions: Take as much time as you need on these questions. Work carefully and methodically. There will be an opportunity for timed practice at the end of the chapter.

HINT: Are there any answer choices in Q11 that you can immediately eliminate?
---

11. A biologist studying the birth rate of a certain fish uses the function $b(n)$ to analyze the fish's effect on other parts of the ecosystem, where n is the number of eggs laid by the fish over a given period of time. Which of the following lists could represent the domain for the biologist's function?

    A) $\{\ldots -1,500, -1,000, -500, 0, 500, 1,000, \\ 1,500 \ldots \}$

    B) $\{-1,500, -1,000, -500, 0, 500, 1,000, 1,500\}$

    C) $\{0, 0.25, 0.5, 0.75, 1, 1.25, 1.5 \ldots \}$

    D) $\{0, 500, 1,000, 1,500, 2,000 \ldots \}$

12. A book publisher pays writers a base fee of $2,500 for each book that it publishes, plus 5 cents per word. If one of its writers earned $8,000 on her book last year, how many words, w, did she write for the publisher?

    A) 11,000

    B) 110,000

    C) 155,000

    D) 250,000

HINT: How does knowing the starting height of the solution help you construct the function in Q13?
---

13. Tyree is dropping old pennies into a jar that contains a cleaning solution. As he adds more pennies, the height of the solution in the jar changes based on the number of pennies he adds. The figure shows this relationship after 50 pennies have been dropped in the jar. If the height of the solution in the jar was 5 inches (in) before any pennies were added, which of the following linear functions represents the relationship between the number of pennies, p, and the height in inches, $h(p)$, of the solution in the jar?

    A) $h(p) = 0.7p + 5$

    B) $h(p) = 0.7p + 8.5$

    C) $h(p) = 0.07p + 5$

    D) $h(p) = 0.07p + 8.5$

HINT: Begin Q14 by calculating the parts per million at both 10 and 20 hours.

$$c(t) = -0.05t^2 + 2t + 2$$

14. Doctors use the function shown above to calculate the concentration, in parts per million, of a certain drug in a patient's bloodstream after t hours. How many more parts per million of the drug are in the bloodstream after 20 hours than after 10 hours?

15. A teacher is buying supplies for the upcoming school year. Every year, basic classroom supplies such as chalk and paper cost her $500, and she spends an additional $25 per child in her class. The school reimburses her $10 per child for half the children in her class. Which function best describes the amount, in dollars, that the teacher spends per school year on supplies, given that s represents the number of students in the class?

A) $f(s) = 500 + 20s$

B) $f(s) = 495 + 25s$

C) $f(s) = 500 + 30s$

D) $f(s) = 505 + 25s$

On Test Day

The PSAT likes to test the modeling of real-life situations. Get comfortable with function notation in these questions. Remember that you can write the equation of a line as $y = mx + b$ or as $f(x) = mx + b$, where m is the slope and b is the y-intercept. Both mean the same thing. In the formula using function notation, the slope indicates rate of change. Often, in questions asking about real-life situations, the x variable indicates time. In that case, the y-intercept (i.e., the value of the function at $x = 0$, or $f(0)$) indicates the starting point.

16. An environmental agency is working to reduce the amount of toxic waste that a company discards in the ocean. Currently, the company discards 10.8 million pounds of toxic waste annually, and the agency's goal is to eliminate that amount by collecting the toxic waste and putting it through a process that makes the substance nontoxic. If the agency increases its processing capacity at a constant rate and meets its goal at the end of the 14th year, which of the following linear functions f could the agency use to model the amount of toxic waste (in millions of pounds) being added to the ocean t years into the program?

    A) $f(t) = -\dfrac{108}{35}t + 10.8$

    B) $f(t) = -\dfrac{27}{35}t + 10.8$

    C) $f(t) = \dfrac{27}{35}t + 10.8$

    D) $f(t) = \dfrac{108}{35}t + 10.8$

The answer and explanation can be found at the end of this chapter.

How Much Have You Learned?

Directions: For testlike practice, give yourself 15 minutes to complete this question set. Be sure to study the explanations, even for questions you got right. They can be found at the end of this chapter.

17. A function is defined by the equation
     $f(x) = \frac{2}{5}x - 7$. For what value of x does $f(x) = 5$?

    A) -5

    B) 2

    C) 9

    D) 30

18. If $f(x) = -x + 5$ and $g(x) = x^2$, which of the fol-
     lowing is NOT in the range of $f(g(x))$?

    A) -11

    B) 0

    C) 1

    D) 9

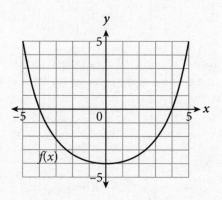

19. The graph of the function $f(x)$ is shown above. What is the domain of the function?

    A) $y \geq -4$

    B) All real numbers

    C) $y > -4$

    D) The domain is undefined.

20. Jayesh is a 150-pound, 5-foot-10-inch, 18-year-old male, and he requires 2,048 calories per day to maintain his weight when he doesn't exercise. When he plays basketball, he burns 231 additional calories per hour. Assuming he wants to maintain his current weight, how many more calories per day does he require if he plays basketball for four hours instead of two hours?

21. Two functions are defined as follows:
    $f(x) = \dfrac{2x^2 + 4}{x}$ and $g(x) = x^2 - 2$. What is the value of $g(f(x))$ when $x = 2$?

    A) 6

    B) 12

    C) 34

    D) 36

22. The point $(3, 6)$ lies on the graph of function f in the xy-plane. If $f(x) = \dfrac{k}{x^3} + x$, then what is the value of k?

24. If $f(x) = \dfrac{2x + 6}{4}$ and $g(x) = 2x - 1$, what is $f(g(x))$?

A) $x + 1$

B) $2x + 2$

C) $4x + 1$

D) $4x + 4$

23. A scientist is studying the average annual growth of trees in a newly planted forest. The average height of the trees was 3.6 feet when they were planted, and they have grown an average of 2.4 feet per year since then. The scientist has been studying the growth of the trees for five years. If she uses the function $g(y) = h + 2.4(y)$, where h is the height (in feet) of the trees five years after they were planted and y is the number of years after the fifth year, to determine the expected further growth of these trees from the sixth year onward, which of the following would be included in the range of the scientist's results?

A) 6

B) 10.8

C) 15.4

D) 18

25. The functions $f(x)$ and $g(x)$ are graphed in the xy-plane above. What is the value of $f(-2) - g(2)$?

A) -30

B) -20

C) -15

D) 20

26. To install fencing, a builder charges $15 per foot for the first 100 feet plus an additional $12 per foot thereafter. If c represents the total cost of a fence installation, in dollars, and x represents the length of the fence in feet, then which of the following functions best describes the cost of a fence that is more than 100 feet long?

A) $c(x) = 150 - 12(100 - x)$

B) $c(x) = 150 + 12(x - 100)$

C) $c(x) = 12(100 - x) - 150$

D) $c(x) = 12(x - 100) - 150$

27. The complete graph of the function $f(x)$ in the xy-plane is shown above. What is the domain of $f(x)$?

A) All real numbers greater than -5

B) All real numbers between and including -5 and 3

C) All real numbers between and including -3 and 3

D) All real numbers

Reflect

Directions: Take a few minutes to recall what you've learned and what you've been practicing in this chapter. Consider the following questions, jot down your best answer for each one, and then compare your reflections to the expert responses on the following page. Use your level of confidence to determine what to do next.

What are the domain and range of a function?

_____

_____

_____

What is another way to write the function $f(x) = x + 4$?

_____

_____

_____

In the function above, what does x represent? What does $f(x)$ represent?

_____

_____

_____

What will the above function look like when graphed?

_____

_____

_____

In a function whose x-value represents time, what does the y-intercept represent?

_____

_____

_____

Expert Responses

What are the domain and range of a function?

The domain of a function indicates the possible x-values, and the range of a function indicates the possible y-values. For example, in the function f(x) = x², the domain is all real numbers because any number can be squared, and the range is any number greater than or equal to 0, because x² can't be negative.

What is another way to write the function $f(x) = x + 4$?

When you graph the function on the xy-coordinate plane, you can replace f(x) with y. This function is equivalent to y = x + 4.

In the function above, what does *x* represent? What does $f(x)$ represent?

In this function, x is the input and f(x) is the output.

What will the above function look like when graphed?

The slope of the line is 1 and its y-intercept is 4, so it will move from the lower left to the upper right and cross the y-axis at y = 4.

In a function whose *x*-value represents time, what does the *y*-intercept represent?

The y-intercept represents the initial quantity when t = 0. Say a function represents the progress of a machine manufacturing widgets at a rate of 6 widgets per hour. The machine adds the widgets it makes to a growing pile that consisted of 12 widgets when the machine started working. If this function were graphed as a function of time, the y-intercept would be 12—the pile of 12 widgets that were there when the machine started its task.

Next Steps

If you answered most questions correctly in the "How Much Have You Learned?" section, and if your responses to the Reflect questions were similar to those of the PSAT expert, then consider Functions an area of strength and move on to the next chapter. Come back to this topic periodically to prevent yourself from getting rusty.

If you don't yet feel confident, review those parts of this chapter that you have not yet mastered. All three lessons in this chapter cover question types that are fairly common on the PSAT, and it is to your advantage to have a firm grasp on this material, so go back over it until you feel more confident. Then, try the questions you missed again. As always, be sure to review the explanations closely.

Answers and Explanations

1.   A

Difficulty: Easy

Getting to the Answer: You're looking for a value that is NOT possible for $f(x)$. You're told $f(x) = 0$ for all $x > -1$, so you can eliminate (B) right away. The other part of the function gives $f(x) = x^2 - x$ for all $x \leq -1$. Plugging any negative number less than or equal to -1 into this part of the function gives a negative number squared minus the original negative number, which will always be positive. For example, $f(-3) = (-3)^2 - (-3) = 9 + 3 = 12$. Therefore, the range of $f(x)$ will always be greater than or equal to 0. This eliminates (C) and (D), leaving **(A)** as the correct answer.

2.   A

Difficulty: Easy

Getting to the Answer: Make sure you compute the functions in this composition in the correct order. Start with the innermost set of parentheses as you would with any composition of functions. Substitute 3 for x in $f(x)$: $f(3) = x^2 + 17 = 3^2 + 17 = 26$. Next, take the output of $f(3)$ and use it as the input for $g(x)$: $g(26) = \frac{3 \times 26}{26 + 1} = \frac{78}{27} = \frac{26}{9}$. This matches **(A)**.

3.   C

Difficulty: Easy

Getting to the Answer: Substitute 5 and then 2 for x in the function and find the difference in the results:

$$h(x) = 3x - 1$$
$$h(5) = 3(5) - 1 = 15 - 1 = 14$$
$$h(2) = 3(2) = 6 - 1 = 5$$
$$h(5) - h(2) = 14 - 5 = 9$$

Choice **(C)** is correct. Caution—this is not the same as subtracting $5 - 2$ and then substituting 3 into the function.

4.   B

Difficulty: Medium

Strategic Advice: The notation $(g(h(x))$ can be read "g of h of x." It means that when x is substituted into $h(x)$, the output becomes the input for $g(x)$.

Getting to the Answer: Start with the innermost function. Use the $h(x)$ table to find $h(-2)$; when $x = -2$, the output $h(x) = -4$. Use -4 as the input for $g(x)$ to find $g(-4)$ from the $g(x)$ table. When $x = -4$, the output $g(x) = 0$. Choice **(B)** is correct.

5.   A

Difficulty: Hard

Getting to the Answer: The notation $f(g(x))$ means: find $g(x)$, then substitute the result into $f(x)$. Substitute $\frac{1}{4}$ for x in $g(x)$ and simplify:

$$g\left(\frac{1}{4}\right) = \sqrt{\frac{1}{4}} + 2.5 = \frac{1}{2} + 2.5 = 3$$

Next, substitute the result into $f(x)$:

$$f(3) = -4(3) + 1 = -12 + 1 = -11$$

Therefore, $f\left(g\left(\frac{1}{4}\right)\right) = -11$, so **(A)** is correct.

6.   D

Difficulty: Easy

Getting to the Answer: Begin by finding $f(0)$. When $x = 0$ on the graph of function f, $y = 4$. Therefore, $f(0) = 4$. Now, repeat for $g\left(\frac{1}{2}\right)$. When $x = \frac{1}{2}$ on function g, $y = 10$; thus, $g\left(\frac{1}{2}\right) = 10$. You're asked for the sum of $f(0)$ and $g\left(\frac{1}{2}\right)$, so substitute the appropriate numbers to get $4 + 10 = 14$, which is **(D)**.

7.   D

Difficulty: Easy

Getting to the Answer: To determine the domain, look at the x-values. To determine the range, look at the y-values. For the domain, the graph is continuous and has arrows on both sides, so the domain is all real numbers. This means you can eliminate choices (A) and (B). For the range, the function's maximum is located at $(0, 5)$, which means the highest possible value of $f(x)$ is 5. The graph is continuous and opens downward, so the range of the function is $f(x) \leq 5$, making **(D)** correct.

8. B

Difficulty: Medium

Getting to the Answer: Compare each answer choice, one at a time, to the graph. Be careful—you're looking for the statement that is NOT true, so cross out true statements as you go. The statement in (A) is true (and therefore not correct) because at $x = 0$, y is also 0. For (B), when $x = 2$, $q(x)$, or y, is somewhere between 1 and 2, not equal to 4, so this statement is NOT true, making **(B)** the correct answer. For the record, the statements in (C) and (D) are both true because the x-values (domain) and y-values (range) are all greater than or equal to 0.

9. A

Difficulty: Medium

Getting to the Answer: Graphically, the notation $f(3)$ means the y-value when $x = 3$. It may help to draw dots on the graph. Find $x = 3$ on the x-axis, then mark each function at this x-value on the graph as shown here:

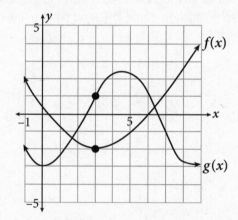

Now, read the y-coordinates from the graph, paying close attention to which function is which, and subtract: $f(3) = -2$ and $g(3) = 1$, so $f(3) - g(3) = -2 - 1 = -3$. **(A)** is correct.

10. 2

Difficulty: Hard

Getting to the Answer: First, find the maximum value, which means the highest y-value. The maximum value occurs at the point $(0, 3)$ so 3 is the maximum value. Find $f(3)$ by locating the y-value when $x = 3$. The point $(3, -2)$ means that $f(3) = -2$. Remember that the question asks for the value of $-f(z) = -f(3) = -(-2) = 2$. Grid in **2**.

11. D

Difficulty: Easy

Getting to the Answer: The domain of a function represents the possible input values. In this function, the input values are represented by n, which is the number of eggs laid by the fish over a given period of time. Because there cannot be a negative number of eggs laid or a fraction of an egg laid, the list in **(D)** is the only one that could represent the function's domain.

12. B

Difficulty: Easy

Getting to the Answer: First, figure out the function that will show you how the magazine publisher pays its writers. The writers earn $2,500 plus $0.05 per word. So the function for earnings, E, is: $E(w) = \$2,500 + \$0.05(w)$.

Plug in what you know and solve for what you don't. The writer made $8,000 for writing one book, so $8,000 = \$2,500 + .05(w)$. Solve for w:

$$\$8,000 = \$2,500 + \$0.05(w)$$
$$\$5,500 = \$0.05(w)$$
$$w = 110,000$$

So to earn $8,000, the writer wrote 110,000 words for the publishing company. That matches **(B)**.

13. C

Difficulty: Medium

Strategic Advice: The question tells you that the function is linear, which means you need to know the slope (rate of change in the height of the solution) and the y-intercept (height of the solution when there are 0 pennies) to pick the correct function.

Getting to the Answer: You already know the height of the solution when there are 0 pennies—it's 5 inches. This means you can eliminate (B) and (D). To determine the rate of change in the height of the solution, write what you know as ordered pairs, and then use the slope formula:

At 0 pennies, the height is 5 inches → $(0, 5)$.

At 50 pennies, the height is 8.5 inches → $(50, 8.5)$.

The rate of change in the height of the solution is $\frac{8.5 - 5}{50 - 0} = \frac{3.5}{50} = 0.07$. This means the correct function is $h(p) = 0.07p + 5$, which is **(C)**.

14. 5

Difficulty: Medium

Getting to the Answer: Evaluate the function at $t = 20$ and at $t = 10$, then subtract the results. Make sure you follow the correct order of operations as you simplify:

$$c(20) = -0.05(20)^2 + 2(20) + 2$$
$$= -0.05(400) + 40 + 2$$
$$= -20 + 40 + 2$$
$$= 22$$

$$c(10) = -0.05(10)^2 + 2(10) + 2$$
$$= -0.05(100) + 20 + 2$$
$$= -5 + 20 + 2$$
$$= 17$$

The question asks how many more parts per million are in a patient's bloodstream after 20 hours than after 10 hours, so subtract $22 - 17 = 5$. Grid in **5**.

15. A

Difficulty: Medium

Getting to the Answer: The teacher spends $500 plus $25 per child, or $500 + 25s$. But she is reimbursed $10 for half of the children in the class, so subtract $10(0.5)(s)$ to give $500 + 25s - 5s = 500 + 20s$. The correct function is $f(s) = 500 + 20s$, which matches **(A)**.

16. B

Difficulty: Medium

Category: Describing Real-Life Situations with Functions

Strategic Advice: When modeling a real-life situation with a linear function, the starting point in the description is the y-intercept of the equation and the rate of change is the slope. Eliminate choices as you go; you may find that you are able to answer the question after only one or two steps. Never do more math than necessary to answer the question.

Getting to the Answer: In this question, the agency is reducing the amount of toxic waste disposed annually, so the slope must be negative. Eliminate (C) and (D) because their positive slopes indicate an *increasing* function.

The starting point, or y-intercept, is the amount of toxic waste the company is now discarding, or 10.8 million

pounds. Unfortunately, this value is the same in (A) and (B), so you'll need to calculate the value of the slope more precisely.

The agency wants to eliminate all toxic waste produced in a year by the end of 14 years, so to find the amount of reduction per year, divide 10.8 by 14.

The value $-\frac{10.8}{14}$ does not appear in the choices, and the slopes in the choices do not have decimal points, so multiply the fraction by 1 in the form of $\frac{10}{10}$ and reduce until you see a value that matches an answer choice. So, $-\frac{10.8}{14} \times \frac{10}{10} = -\frac{108}{140} = -\frac{27}{35}$, so **(B)** is correct.

17. D

Difficulty: Medium

Category: Function Notation

Getting to the Answer: The question says that the value of $f(x) = 5$ and asks for the value of x that produces this result. This means you are solving for x, not substituting for x. Set the function equal to 5, and solve using inverse operations:

$$5 = \frac{2}{5}x - 7$$
$$12 = \frac{2}{5}x$$
$$12(5) = 2x$$
$$60 = 2x$$
$$30 = x$$

Thus, **(D)** is correct.

18. D

Difficulty: Hard

Category: Function Notation

Getting to the Answer: When dealing with a composition (or nested functions), the range of the inner function becomes the domain of the outer function, which in turn produces the range of the composition. In the composition $f(g(x))$, the function $g(x) = x^2$ is the inner function. Every value of x, when substituted into this function, will result in a nonnegative value (because the value of x is squared). This means the smallest possible range value of $g(x)$ is 0. Now, look at $f(x)$: substituting large positive values of x in the function will result in large negative numbers. Consequently, substituting the smallest value from the range of g, which is 0, results in the largest range value for the composition, which is $-0 + 5 = 5$. Therefore, the range of $f(g(x))$ is ≤ 5. The only answer choice that does not fall within this range is **(D)**.

19. B

Difficulty: Easy

Category: Graphs of Functions

Getting to the Answer: The domain of a function is all possible x-values. In this case, the arrows indicate the graph is going to continue infinitely in both directions, so every x-value is possible, meaning the domain of the function is all real numbers. **(B)** is correct.

Note that if you forgot whether it is the x- or y-value that gives you the domain, (A) would have been a tempting choice. (A) actually gives the correct *range* of the function, which is determined by all possible y-values.

20. 462

Difficulty: Medium

Category: Describing Real-Life Situations with Functions

Getting to the Answer: Questions sometimes include extra information that you don't need to get the answer. For this question, all you need to consider is the difference in calories between playing basketball for 4 hours and playing basketball for 2 hours. Since that activity burns 231 calories per hour, the difference is $2 \times 231 = 462$. Grid in **462**.

21. C

Difficulty: Easy

Category: Function Notation

Getting to the Answer: The trick to questions like this one is to make sure you're careful with the order of the nested functions. Work from the inside out. In this case, you're asked for g of f, so start with $f(x)$, plugging in the given value for x:

$f(2) = \dfrac{2(2)^2 + 4}{2} = \dfrac{2(4) + 4}{2} = \dfrac{8 + 4}{2} = \dfrac{12}{2} = 6$.

Now, move to the outer function:

$g(6) = 6^2 - 2 = 36 - 2 = 34$. This matches **(C)**.

Note that if you had worked your nested functions in the wrong order—as you would if you'd been asked for $f(g(x))$—your final result would have been 6, which matches (A). Always double-check that you're working your way through nested functions in the correct order, from the inside to the outside.

22. 81

Difficulty: Easy

Category: Function Notation

Getting to the Answer: Remember that $f(x)$ means y. Substitute 3 for x and 6 for $f(x)$ to find k:

$$6 = \frac{k}{3^3} + 3$$
$$6 = \frac{k}{27} + 3$$
$$3 = \frac{k}{27}$$
$$81 = k$$

Grid in **81**.

23. D

Difficulty: Medium

Category: Describing Real-Life Situations with Functions

Getting to the Answer: The range of the function is all of the possible $g(y)$ values. So this question asks you to determine which numbers are too small to be part of the range of the scientist's data.

First, calculate how tall the trees would be when the scientist begins to use her function: $h = 3.6 + 2.4(5) = 15.6$ feet. Having solved for h, the function can now be written as $g(y) = 15.6 + 2.4y$, where y is greater than or equal to 0, and the range will be any value greater than or equal to 15.6. Only **(D)** is larger than 15.6, so it is correct.

24. A

Difficulty: Hard

Category: Function Notation

Getting to the Answer: To find $f(g(x))$, replace the variable in $f(x)$ with $g(x)$, or $2x - 1$:

$$f(x) = \frac{2x + 6}{4}$$
$$f(g(x)) = \frac{2(g(x)) + 6}{4} = \frac{2(2x - 1) + 6}{4}$$
$$f(g(x)) = \frac{4x - 2 + 6}{4} = \frac{4x + 4}{4} = x + 1$$

Thus, **(A)** is correct.

25. B

Difficulty: Medium

Category: Graphs of Functions

Getting to the Answer: Start by figuring out the y-values needed. On the graph, $f(-2)$ has a value of 5, while $g(2)$ has a value of 25. Therefore, $f(-2) - g(2) = 5 - 25 = -20$. This matches **(B)**.

26. B

Difficulty: Medium

Category: Describing Real-Life Situations with Functions

Getting to the Answer: The cost for the first 100 feet will be $15(100) = \$150$. This number will be added to the cost for the remainder of the fence. Eliminate (C) and (D), which subtract the 150 instead of adding it.

Now, consider what happens after the first 100 feet. The remaining length of fencing is the total length, x, minus the first 100 feet, or $x - 100$. Multiply by 12 to find the cost for this section of the fence: $12(x - 100)$. The complete function, then, is $c(x) = 150 + 12(x - 100)$. This matches **(B)**.

27. C

Difficulty: Medium

Category: Graphs of Functions

Getting to the Answer: The domain is all the x-values that will yield a value for $f(x)$. From left to right, notice that the graph goes from -3 to 3 and includes the endpoints. Thus, **(C)** is correct.

CHAPTER 9

Quadratics

LEARNING OBJECTIVES

After completing this chapter, you will be able to:

- Solve a quadratic equation by factoring
- Recognize the classic quadratics
- Solve a quadratic equation by completing the square
- Solve a quadratic equation by applying the quadratic formula
- Relate properties of a quadratic function to its graph and vice versa
- Solve a system of one quadratic and one linear equation

60/600 SmartPoints® (High Yield)

How Much Do You Know?

Directions: Try the questions that follow. Show your work so that you can compare your solutions to the ones found in the Check Your Work section immediately after this question set. The "Category" heading in the explanation for each question gives the title of the lesson that covers how to solve it. If you answered the question(s) for a given lesson correctly, and if your scratchwork looks like ours, you may be able to move quickly through that lesson. If you answered incorrectly or used a different approach, you may want to take your time on that lesson.

1. If $x^2 + 8x = 48$ and $x > 0$, what is the value of $x - 5$?

    A) -9

    B) -1

    C) 4

    D) 7

2. What is the absolute value of the difference between the roots of $4x^2 - 36 = 0$?

    A) -6

    B) 0

    C) 3

    D) 6

3. Which of the following is equivalent to $x^2 - 6x + 10 = 0$?

    A) $(x - 3)^2 = -1$

    B) $(x + 3)^2 = -1$

    C) $(x - 6)^2 = 26$

    D) $(x + 6)^2 = 26$

$$y = 2x^2 - 8x + c$$

4. The quadratic above has only one distinct, real root. What is the value of c?

    A) -8

    B) -4

    C) 4

    D) 8

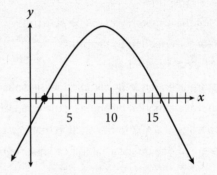

5. Which of the following equations could represent the above graph?

    A) $y = -x^2 + 18x - 32$

    B) $y = -x^2 + 14x - 32$

    C) $y = x^2 - 14x - 32$

    D) $y = x^2 + 18x + 32$

$$\begin{cases} y = x + 1 \\ y = \dfrac{1}{2}x^2 - x - \dfrac{3}{2} \end{cases}$$

6. If (a, b) is a solution to the system of equations shown, what is the value of a, given that $a > 0$?

Check Your Work

1. B

Difficulty: Medium

Category: Solving Quadratics by Factoring

Strategic Advice: When finding solutions to a quadratic equation, always start by rewriting the equation to make it equal to 0 (unless both sides of the equation are already perfect squares). Then, take a peek at the answer choices—if they are all integers that are easy to work with, then factoring is probably the quickest method for solving the equation. If the answers include messy fractions or square roots, then using the quadratic formula may be a better choice.

Getting to the Answer: To make the equation equal to 0, subtract 48 from both sides to get $x^2 + 8x - 48 = 0$. The answer choices are all integers, so factor the equation. Look for two numbers whose product is -48 and whose sum is 8. The two numbers are -4 and 12, so the factors are $(x - 4)$ and $(x + 12)$. Set each factor equal to 0 and solve to find that $x = 4$ and $x = -12$. The question states that $x > 0$, so x must equal 4. Before selecting an answer, don't forget to check that you answered the right question—the question asks for the value of $x - 5$, not just x, so the correct answer is $4 - 5 = -1$. **(B)** is correct.

2. D

Difficulty: Hard

Category: Classic Quadratics

Getting to the Answer: Notice that this is a difference of squares, so use the formula $a^2 - b^2 = (a + b)(a - b)$ with $a^2 = 4x^2$. This means that $a = 2x$ and $b^2 = 36$, so $b = 6$. Therefore, $(2x + 6)(2x - 6) = 0$. Set both equal to 0 and solve:

$$
\begin{aligned}
2x + 6 &= 0 & 2x - 6 &= 0 \\
2x &= -6 & 2x &= 6 \\
x &= -3 & x &= 3
\end{aligned}
$$

Remember that the question asks for the absolute difference of the roots. Think of a number line and count from -3 to 3. The difference is 6. Alternatively, just take the absolute value of the difference between the roots:

$$\left| 3 - (-3) \right| = 6$$

Thus, **(D)** is correct.

3. A

Difficulty: Medium

Category: Completing the Square

Getting to the Answer: The format of the answer choices makes completing the square the best approach for this problem. Since the first term has a constant of 1, that makes completing the square more straightforward. Make sure to move the constant term to the right side of the equation before dividing the x term constant by 2 and squaring. Also, make sure that the squared term contains a negative constant since the x term in the original quadratic is negative:

$$
\begin{aligned}
x^2 - 6x + 10 &= 0 \\
x^2 - 6x + \underline{} &= -10 + \underline{} \\
\left(\frac{b}{2}\right)^2 = \left(-\frac{6}{2}\right)^2 &= (-3)^2 = 9 \\
x^2 - 6x + 9 &= -10 + 9 \\
(x - 3)^2 &= -1
\end{aligned}
$$

Therefore, **(A)** is correct. Note that (C) is the result if you forgot to divide b by 2.

4. D

Difficulty: Medium

Category: The Quadratic Formula

Getting to the Answer: In order for the quadratic to have only one root, the discriminant must be equal to 0. Plug the numbers given into the discriminant, set it equal to 0, and solve for c:

$$
\begin{aligned}
b^2 - 4ac &= 0 \\
(-8)^2 - 4(2)(c) &= 0 \\
64 - 8c &= 0 \\
64 &= 8c \\
8 &= c
\end{aligned}
$$

Therefore, **(D)** is correct.

5. A

Difficulty: Hard

Category: Graphs of Quadratics

Strategic Advice: Use the visual information in the graph to eliminate answers quickly. A negative coefficient of the squared term means that the graph opens downward. The roots of a quadratic are where the graph crosses the x-axis.

Getting to the Answer: Because the quadratic opens downward, the x^2-coefficient must be negative, so you can eliminate (C) and (D). According to the graph, the roots are $x = 2$ and $x = 16$. That means that the factored form of the quadratic will be either $(-x + 2)(x - 16)$ or $(x - 2)(-x + 16)$. These factored forms are actually equivalent because $(-x + 2) = (-1)(x - 2)$ and $(x - 16) = (-1)(-x + 16)$, which means:

$$(-x + 2)(x - 16) = (-1 \times -1)(x - 2)(-x + 16)$$

$$(-x + 2)(x - 16) = (x - 2)(-x + 16)$$

Use FOIL on one of them to see if it matches the expanded form of the quadratic in (A) or (B):

$$(-x + 2)(x - 16) = -x^2 + 16x + 2x - 32$$

$$= -x^2 + 18x - 32$$

Thus, **(A)** is correct.

Another approach would be to use Picking Numbers. After eliminating (C) and (D) for having upward parabolas and calculating the roots, simply pick the more manageable of the two x-intercepts, $x = 2$, and plug it into the equations in (A) and (B) to see which one results in $y = 0$:

(A): $y = -(2)^2 + 18(2) - 32$

$y = -(4) + 36 - 32 = 0$, keep.

(B): $y = -(2)^2 + 14(2) - 32$

$y = -(4) + 28 - 32 = -8 \neq 0$, eliminate.

(A) is indeed correct.

6. 5

Difficulty: Hard

Category: Systems of Quadratic and Linear Equations

Getting to the Answer: Unfortunately, this is a non-calculator question, so you'll need to solve the system using substitution, rather than by graphing it on your calculator. Substitute the first equation for y into the second. Before you solve for x, multiply the whole equation by 2 to remove the fractions. Then, set the whole equation equal to 0 and factor:

$$x + 1 = \frac{1}{2}x^2 - x - \frac{3}{2}$$

$$2(x + 1) = 2\left(\frac{1}{2}x^2 - x - \frac{3}{2}\right)$$

$$2x + 2 = x^2 - 2x - 3$$

$$0 = x^2 - 4x - 5$$

$$0 = (x + 1)(x - 5)$$

Now, set each factor equal to 0 and solve to find that $x = -1$ and $x = 5$. The question asks only for a, which is the x-coordinate of the solution, so you do not need to substitute x back into an equation and solve for y. The two possible values of a are -1 and 5. Because the question specifies that $a > 0$, the answer must be **5**. Grid in **5**.

Math

Solving Quadratics by Factoring

LEARNING OBJECTIVE

After this lesson, you will be able to:

● Solve a quadratic equation by factoring

To answer a question like this:

If $x^2 + x = 20$ and $x < 0$, what is the value of $x - 7$?

A) −12

B) −5

C) 5

D) 12

You need to know this:

A quadratic expression is a second-degree polynomial—that is, a polynomial containing a squared variable. You can write a quadratic expression as $ax^2 + bx + c$.

The **FOIL** acronym (which stands for First, Outer, Inner, Last) will help you remember how to multiply two binomials: multiply the first terms together (ac), then the outer terms (ad), then the inner terms (bc), and finally the last terms (bd):

$$(a + b)(c + d) = ac + ad + bc + bd$$

FOIL can also be done in reverse if you need to go from a quadratic to its factors.

To solve a quadratic equation by factoring, the quadratic must be set equal to zero. For example:

$$x^2 + x - 56 = 0$$
$$(x + 8)(x - 7) = 0$$

From the binomial factors, you can find the **solutions**, also called **roots** or **zeros**, of the equation. For two factors to be multiplied together and produce zero as the result, one or both those factors must be zero. In the example above, either $x + 8 = 0$ or $x - 7 = 0$, which means that $x = -8$ or $x = 7$.

You need to do this:

To solve a quadratic equation by factoring:

- Set the quadratic equal to zero, so it looks like this: $ax^2 + bx + c = 0$.
- Factor the squared term. (For factoring, it's easiest when a, the coefficient in front of x^2, is equal to 1.)
- Make a list of the factors of c. Remember to include negatives.
- Find the factor pair that, when added, equals b, the coefficient in front of x.
- Write the quadratic as the product of two binomials.
- Set each binomial equal to zero and solve.

Explanation:

Set the equation equal to zero and factor the first term:

$$x^2 + x = 20$$
$$x^2 + x - 20 = 0$$
$$(x \pm ?)(x \pm ?) = 0$$

Next, consider factors of -20, keeping in mind that they must sum to 1, so *the factor with the greater absolute value must be positive*. The possibilities are 20×-1, 10×-2 and 5×-4. The factor pair that sums to 1 is 5×-4. Write that factor pair into your binomials:

$$(x - 4)(x + 5) = 0$$

Set each factor equal to zero and solve:

$$(x - 4) = 0 \qquad (x + 5) = 0$$
$$x = 4 \qquad\qquad x = -5$$

The question says that $x < 0$, so $x = -5$. However, you are *not* done. The question asks for $x - 7$, which is -12. Therefore, **(A)** is correct.

Try on Your Own

Directions: Take as much time as you need on these questions. Work carefully and methodically. There will be an opportunity for timed practice at the end of the chapter.

1. Which of the following is an equivalent form of the expression $(x-4)(x+2)$?

   A) $x^2 - 8x - 2$

   B) $x^2 - 2x - 8$

   C) $x^2 + 2x - 8$

   D) $x^2 - 2x + 8$

2. What is the positive difference between the zeros of $g(x) = -2x^2 + 16x - 32$?

3. What positive value(s) of z satisfy the equation $4z^2 + 32z - 81 = -1$?

   A) 2

   B) 2 and -10

   C) 4 and 2

   D) None of the above

HINT: For Q4, is there anything you can factor out of the numerator or the denominator?

---

4. Which of the following is equivalent to $\dfrac{x^2 - 4x + 4}{2x^2 + 4x - 16}$?

   A) $\dfrac{1}{2}$

   B) $\dfrac{x}{x+4}$

   C) $-\dfrac{2-x}{2(x+4)}$

   D) $\dfrac{x^2 - 4x + 4}{x^2 + 2x - 8}$

HINT: Begin Q5 by solving for the zeros of each answer choice.

---

5. If a quadratic function $f(x)$ has solutions a and b such that $a < 0$, $b > 0$, and $|b| > |a|$, which of the following could be equal to $f(x)$?

   A) $4x^2 + 4x - 24$

   B) $-x^2 + x + 6$

   C) $-x^2 - x + 6$

   D) $3x^2 - 6x$

Classic Quadratics

LEARNING OBJECTIVE

After this lesson, you will be able to:

- Recognize the classic quadratics

To answer a question like this:

Which of the following expressions is equivalent to $36x^4y^6 - 4$?

A) $6(x^4y^6 - 2)$

B) $-6(x^2y^3 + 2)$

C) $(6x^2y^2 - 2)(6x^2y^2 + 2)$

D) $(6x^2y^3 - 2)(6x^2y^3 + 2)$

You need to know this:

Memorizing the following classic quadratics will save you time on test day:

- $x^2 - y^2 = (x + y)(x - y)$

  - This is known as a "difference of squares" because it takes the form of one perfect square minus another perfect square.

- $x^2 + 2xy + y^2 = (x + y)^2$
- $x^2 - 2xy + y^2 = (x - y)^2$

You need to do this:

When you see a pattern that matches either the left or the right side of one of the above equations, simplify by substituting its equivalent form. For example, say you need to simplify the following:

$$\frac{a^2 - 2ab + b^2}{a - b}$$

You would substitute $(a - b)(a - b)$ for the numerator and cancel to find that the expression simplifies to $a - b$:

$$\frac{a^2 - 2ab + b^2}{a - b} = \frac{(a - b)(a - b)}{a - b} = \frac{a - b}{1} = a - b$$

Explanation:

The expression $36x^4y^6 - 4$ is a difference of perfect squares. The square root of $36x^4y^6$ is $6x^2y^3$ and the square root of 4 is 2, so the correct factors are $\left(6x^2y^3 - 2\right)\left(6x^2y^3 + 2\right)$. Hence, **(D)** is correct.

Try on Your Own

Directions: Take as much time as you need on these questions. Work carefully and methodically. There will be an opportunity for timed practice at the end of the chapter.

HINT: What can you do to make $(a - b)^2$ in Q6 easier to work with?

---

6. For all a and b, what is the product of $(a - b)^2$ and $(a + b)$?

    A) $a^2 - b^2$

    B) $a^3 - b^3$

    C) $a^3 - ab^2 + a^2b - b^3$

    D) $a^3 - ab^2 - a^2b + b^3$

7. Which equation does NOT have a solution at $x = -4$?

    A) $y = x^2 - 8x + 16$

    B) $y = x^2 + 8x + 16$

    C) $y = x^2 - 16$

    D) $y = 4x^2 + 32x + 64$

HINT: One of the given equations in Q8 is a classic quadratic.

---

8. A rectangle has an area of $A = x^4 - 196$. If the width of the rectangle is $w = x^2 - 14$, what is the length?

    A) $x + 14$

    B) $x^2 + 14$

    C) $x^2 - 14$

    D) $x - 14$

9. A rectangular prism has a height of x, a width of 7 less than the height, and a length 14 more than the width. What is the volume of the prism?

    A) $V = x^2 - 14x + 49$

    B) $V = x^2 + 14x + 49$

    C) $V = x^3 - 49$

    D) $V = x(x^2 - 49)$

HINT: For Q10, is there any variable you can factor out from each term?

$$16m^2 p^2 + 72mzp^2 + 81z^2 p^2$$

10. Which of the following expressions is equivalent to the expression above?

    A) $p^2(16m^2 + 9z)(8m + 9z)$

    B) $p^2(4m + 9z)^2$

    C) $2p^2m(8m + 36z + 40z^2) + z^2$

    D) $p^2(16m^2 + 72mz + 27z^2)$

Completing the Square

LEARNING OBJECTIVE

After this lesson, you will be able to:

- Solve a quadratic equation by completing the square

To answer a question like this:

Which of the following has the same roots as $30 - 8x = x^2 - y$?

A) $y = (x - 4)^2 - 30$
B) $y = (x - 4)^2 + 30$
C) $y = (x + 4)^2 - 46$
D) $y = (x + 4)^2 + 46$

You need to know this:

For quadratics that do not factor easily, you'll need one of two strategies: completing the square or the quadratic formula (taught in the next lesson). To complete the square, you'll create an equation in the form $(x + h)^2 = k$, where h and k are constants.

As with factoring, completing the square is most convenient when the coefficient in front of the x^2 term is 1.

You need to do this:

Here are the steps for completing the square, demonstrated with a simple example.

Step	Scratchwork
Starting point:	$x^2 + 8x - 8 = 0$
1. Move the constant to the opposite side.	$x^2 + 8x = 8$
2. Divide b, the x-coefficient, by 2, and square the quotient.	$b = 8; \left(\frac{b}{2}\right)^2 = \left(\frac{8}{2}\right)^2 = (4)^2 = 16$
3. Add the number from the previous step to both sides of the equation and factor.	$x^2 + 8x + 16 = 8 + 16$ $(x + 4)(x + 4) = 24$ $(x + 4)^2 = 24$
4. Take the square root of both sides.	$\sqrt{(x + 4)^2} = \pm\sqrt{24} \rightarrow x + 4 = \pm\sqrt{24} = \pm\sqrt{4}\sqrt{6}$ $x + 4 = \pm 2\sqrt{6}$
5. Split the result into two equations and solve each one.	$x + 4 = 2\sqrt{6} \rightarrow x = 2\sqrt{6} - 4$ $x + 4 = -2\sqrt{6} \rightarrow x = -2\sqrt{6} - 4$

Explanation:

First, write the equation in standard form: $y = x^2 + 8x - 30$. Move the 30 to the other side to temporarily get it out of the way. Then, complete the square on the right-hand side, by finding $\left(\frac{b}{2}\right)^2 = \left(\frac{8}{2}\right)^2 = 4^2 = 16$ and adding the result to both sides of the equation:

$$y = x^2 + 8x - 30$$
$$y + 30 = x^2 + 8x$$
$$y + 30 + 16 = x^2 + 8x + 16$$
$$y + 46 = x^2 + 8x + 16$$

The answer choices are all written in factored form. The right side of the equation is a classic quadratic that factors as follows:

$$y + 46 = (x + 4)(x + 4)$$
$$y + 46 = (x + 4)^2$$

Finally, solve for y to get $y = (x + 4)^2 - 46$, which makes **(C)** correct.

Try on Your Own

Directions: Take as much time as you need on these questions. Work carefully and methodically. There will be an opportunity for timed practice at the end of the chapter.

11. Which of the following equations has the same solutions as $x^2 + 6x + 17 = y$?

    A) $y = (x - 3)^2 - 26$

    B) $y = (x - 3)^2 + 8$

    C) $y = (x + 3)^2 + 8$

    D) $y = (x + 3)^2 + 17$

12. Which of the following are roots for $x^2 + 10x - 8 = 0$?

    A) $x = \pm\sqrt{108} - 10$

    B) $x = \pm\sqrt{33} - 5$

    C) $x = \pm\sqrt{33} - 25$

    D) $x = \pm\sqrt{33} + 25$

13. Which of the following is equivalent to $x^2 + 4x + 16 = 0$?

    A) $(x + 4)^2 = -12$

    B) $(x + 4)^2 = 0$

    C) $(x - 2)^2 = 0$

    D) $(x + 2)^2 = -12$

HINT: What can you divide each term by to make the equation in Q14 easier to work with?

---

14. What value of x satisfies the equation $4x^2 + 24x = -8$?

    A) $-3 - \sqrt{7}$

    B) $3 - \sqrt{7}$

    C) 3

    D) $3 + \sqrt{7}$

The Quadratic Formula

LEARNING OBJECTIVE

After this lesson, you will be able to:

- Solve a quadratic equation by applying the quadratic formula

To answer a question like this:

$$4x^2 - 7x - 4 = 0$$

Which of the following values of x satisfy the equation above?

A) 1 and 4

B) $-\dfrac{7}{8} + \dfrac{\sqrt{113}}{8}$ and $-\dfrac{7}{8} - \dfrac{\sqrt{113}}{8}$

C) $\dfrac{7}{8} + \dfrac{\sqrt{113}}{8}$ and $\dfrac{7}{8} - \dfrac{\sqrt{113}}{8}$

D) No real solutions

You need to know this:

The quadratic formula can be used to solve any quadratic equation. It yields solutions to a quadratic equation that is written in standard form, $ax^2 + bx + c = 0$:

$$x = \frac{-b \pm \sqrt{b^2 - 4ac}}{2a}$$

The $\pm$ sign that follows $-b$ indicates that you will have two solutions, so remember to find both.

The expression under the radical ($b^2 - 4ac$) is called the **discriminant**, and its value determines the *number* of real solutions. If the discriminant is positive, the equation has two distinct real solutions. If the discriminant is equal to 0, there is only one distinct real solution. If the discriminant is negative, there are no real solutions because you cannot take the square root of a negative number.

The arithmetic can get complicated, so reserve the quadratic formula for equations that cannot be solved by factoring and those in which completing the square is difficult because $a \neq 1$.

You need to do this:

Get the quadratic equation into the form $ax^2 + bx + c = 0$. Then, substitute a, b, and c into the quadratic formula and simplify.

Explanation:

In the given equation, $a = 4$, $b = -7$, and $c = -4$. Plug these values into the quadratic formula and simplify:

$$x = \frac{-b \pm \sqrt{b^2 - 4ac}}{2a}$$

$$x = \frac{-(-7) \pm \sqrt{(-7)^2 - 4(4)(-4)}}{2(4)}$$

$$x = \frac{7 \pm \sqrt{49 - (-64)}}{8}$$

$$x = \frac{7 \pm \sqrt{113}}{8}$$

$$x = \frac{7}{8} + \frac{\sqrt{113}}{8} \quad \text{or} \quad x = \frac{7}{8} - \frac{\sqrt{113}}{8}$$

The correct answer is **(C)**.

Try on Your Own

Directions: Take as much time as you need on these questions. Work carefully and methodically. There will be an opportunity for timed practice at the end of the chapter.

HINT: For Q15, what does it mean if there are no zeros on the graph of a quadratic equation?

---

15. Which of the quadratic functions shown has no zeros?

A)

B)

C)

D)

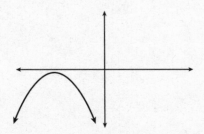

HINT: For Q16, what does the expression under the square root sign in the quadratic formula indicate?

---

16. Which of the following are the real values of x that satisfy the equation $3x^2 + 2x + 4 = 5x$?

A) 3 and -2

B) $\frac{3}{5}$ and $-\frac{2}{5}$

C) 0

D) The equation has no real solutions.

17. Which of the following are the roots of the equation $x^2 + 8x - 3 = 0$?

A) $-4 \pm \sqrt{19}$

B) $-4 \pm \sqrt{3}$

C) $4 \pm \sqrt{3}$

D) $4 \pm \sqrt{19}$

HINT: For Q18, remember that for a parabola to have two real solutions, the discriminant $b^2 - 4ac$ must be greater than zero.

---

18. Which quadratic equation has two real solutions?

A) $y = 2x^2 + 4x + 2$

B) $y = 5x^2 + 5x - 5$

C) $y = 5x^2 - 5x + 5$

D) $y = 2x^2 - 4x + 2$

$$y = 8a^2 + 4a - 1$$

19. What are the roots of the above equation?

A) $\frac{-1 \pm \sqrt{3}}{4}$

B) $\frac{-1 \pm \sqrt{3}}{2}$

C) $\frac{1 \pm \sqrt{3}}{4}$

D) $\frac{1 \pm \sqrt{3}}{2}$

Graphs of Quadratics

LEARNING OBJECTIVE

After this lesson, you will be able to:

- Relate properties of a quadratic function to its graph and vice versa

To answer a question like this:

Which of the following statements is NOT true, given the equation $y = (4x - 3)^2 + 6$?

A) The vertex is (3, 6).

B) The y-intercept is (0, 15).

C) The parabola opens upward.

D) The graph does not cross the x-axis.

You need to know this:

A quadratic function is a quadratic equation set equal to y or $f(x)$ instead of 0. Remember that the solutions (also called "roots" or "zeros") of any polynomial function are the same as the x-intercepts. To solve a quadratic function, substitute 0 for y, or $f(x)$, then solve algebraically. Alternatively, you can plug the equation into your graphing calculator and read the x-intercepts from the graph.

The graph of every quadratic equation (or function) is a **parabola**, which is a symmetric U-shaped graph that opens either upward or downward. To determine which way a parabola will open, examine the value of a in the equation. If a is positive, the parabola will open upward. If a is negative, it will open downward. Take a look at the examples above to see this graphically.

Like quadratic equations, quadratic functions will have zero, one, or two distinct real solutions, corresponding to the number of times the parabola crosses (or touches) the x-axis, as shown in the illustrations below. Graphing is a powerful way to determine the number of solutions a quadratic function has.

There are three algebraic forms that a quadratic equation can take: standard, factored, and vertex. Each is provided in the following table along with the graphical features that are revealed by writing the equation in that particular form.

Standard	Factored	Vertex
$y = ax^2 + bx + c$	$y = a(x - m)(x - n)$	$y = a(x - h)^2 + k$
The y-intercept is c.	Solutions are m and n.	The vertex is (h, k).
In real-world contexts, the starting quantity is c.	The x-intercepts are m and n.	The minimum/maximum of the function is k.
This is the format used to solve via quadratic formula.	The vertex is halfway between m and n.	The axis of symmetry is given by $x = h$.

You've already seen standard and factored forms earlier in this chapter, but vertex form might be new to you. In vertex form, a is the same as the a in standard form, and h and k are the coordinates of the **vertex** (h, k). If a quadratic function is not in vertex form, you can still find the x-coordinate of the vertex by plugging the appropriate values into the equation $h = \frac{-b}{2a}$, which is also the equation for the axis of symmetry (see graph that follows). Once you determine h, plug this value into the quadratic function and solve for y to determine k, the y-coordinate of the vertex.

The equation of the **axis of symmetry** of a parabola is $x = h$, where h is the x-coordinate of the vertex.

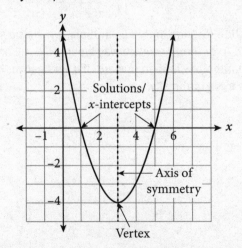

You need to do this:

- To find the vertex of a parabola, get the function into vertex form, $y = a(x - h)^2 + k$, or use the formula $h = \frac{-b}{2a}$.

- To find the y-intercept of a quadratic function, plug in 0 for x.

- To determine whether a parabola opens upward or downward, look at the coefficient of a. If a is positive, the parabola opens upward. If negative, it opens downward.

- To determine the number of x-intercepts, set the quadratic function equal to 0 and solve or examine its graph. (Quadratic function questions show up on both the no-calculator and calculator sections of the PSAT.)

Explanation:

Be careful: the equation looks like vertex form, $y = a(x - h)^2 + k$, but it's not quite there because the x has a coefficient of 4 inside the parentheses. You could rewrite the equation in vertex form, but this would involve squaring the quantity in parentheses and then completing the square, which would take quite a bit of time. Alternatively, you could notice that the smallest possible value for y in this function is 6, which happens when the squared term, $(4x - 3)^2$, equals zero. To check (A), find the x-value when $y = 6$:

$$4x - 3 = 0$$
$$4x = 3$$
$$x = \frac{3}{4}$$

So the vertex is $\left(\frac{3}{4}, 6\right)$, not (3, 6). It follows that **(A)** is false and is the correct answer.

For the record:

Choice (B): Substitute 0 for x and simplify to find that the y-intercept is indeed (0, 15). Eliminate.

Choice (C): The squared term is positive, so the parabola *does* open upward. Eliminate.

Choice (D): Because the parabola opens upward and the vertex is at $y = 6$, above the x-axis, the parabola cannot cross the x-axis. This statement is true as well, so it can also be eliminated, which confirms that **(A)** is correct.

Try on Your Own

Directions: Take as much time as you need on these questions. Work carefully and methodically. There will be an opportunity for timed practice at the end of the chapter.

HINT: For Q20, which form of a quadratic would you use to find its solutions?

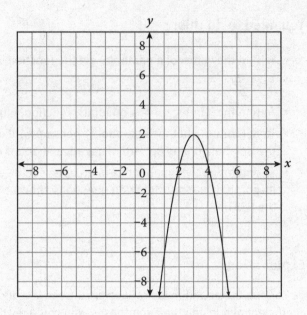

20. The following quadratic equations are all representations of the graph shown. Which equation enables the easiest calculation of the x-intercepts of the graph?

    A) $y = \frac{3}{4}x^2 - \frac{1}{2}x - 2$

    B) $y + \frac{25}{12} = \frac{1}{12}(3x - 1)^2$

    C) $y = \frac{1}{12}(3x - 1)^2 - \frac{25}{12}$

    D) $y = \frac{1}{4}(3x + 4)(x - 2)$

21. Which of the following represents the function shown in the graph?

    A) $f(x) = -(x - 3)^2 + 2$

    B) $f(x) = -2(x - 3)^2 + 2$

    C) $f(x) = -2(x + 3)^2 + 2$

    D) $f(x) = -(x + 3)^2 + 2$

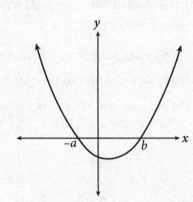

22. If the distance from $-a$ to b in the figure shown is 10, which of the following could be the factored form of the graph's equation?

    A) $y = (x - 7)(x - 3)$

    B) $y = (x - 7)(x + 3)$

    C) $y = (x - 8)(x - 2)$

    D) $y = (x - 1)(x + 10)$

Distance (in yards)

23. If $y = ax^2 + bx + c$ represents the equation of the graph shown in the figure, which of the following statements is NOT true?

A) The value of a is a negative number.

B) The value of c is a negative number.

C) The y-value is increasing for $x < 3$ and decreasing for $x > 3$.

D) The zeros of the equation are $x = -2$ and $x = 8$.

25. The figure above shows the partial trajectory of a cannonball shot into the air. Assuming that the cannonball lands at a point where the height is 0, approximately how many feet farther did the cannonball travel horizontally than vertically upward? (1 yard = 3 feet)

A) 335

B) 425

C) 935

D) 1,390

HINT: Begin Q24 by considering what the x-intercepts would represent in terms of the ball's trajectory.

24. If a catapult is used to throw a lead ball from ground level, the path of the ball can be modeled by a quadratic equation, $y = ax^2 + bx + c$, where x is the horizontal distance that the ball travels and y is the height of the ball. If one of these catapult-launched lead balls travels 150 feet before hitting the ground and reaches a maximum height of 45 feet, which of the following equations represents its path?

A) $y = -0.008x^2 + 1.2x$

B) $y = -0.008x^2 - 150x$

C) $y = 45x^2 + 150x$

D) $y = 125x^2 + 25x$

Math

Systems of Quadratic and Linear Equations

LEARNING OBJECTIVE

After this lesson, you will be able to:

- Solve a system of one quadratic and one linear equation

To answer a question like this:

In the xy-plane, two equations, $y + 2x = -4x^2 + 5$ and $y - 5 = -6x$, intersect at points $(0, 5)$ and (a, b). What is the value of $-b$?

You need to know this:

You can solve a system of one quadratic and one linear equation by substitution, exactly as you would for a system of two linear equations. Alternatively, if the question appears on the calculator section, you can plug the system into your graphing calculator.

You need to do this:

- Isolate y in both equations.
- Set the equations equal to each other.
- Put the resulting equation into the form $ax^2 + bx + c = 0$.
- Solve this quadratic by factoring, completing the square, or using the quadratic formula. (You are solving for the x-values at the points of intersection of the original two equations.)
- Plug the x-values you get as solutions into one of the original equations to generate the y-values at the points of intersection. (Usually, the linear equation is easier to work with than the quadratic.)

Explanation:

Start by isolating y in both equations to get $y = -6x + 5$ and $y = -4x^2 - 2x + 5$. Now, set the right sides of the equations equal and solve for x:

$$-6x + 5 = -4x^2 - 2x + 5$$
$$4x^2 - 4x = 0$$
$$4x(x - 1) = 0$$
$$x = 0 \text{ or } 1$$

The question says that $(0, 5)$ is one point of intersection for the two equations and asks for the y-value at the other point of intersection, so plug $x = 1$ into either of the original equations and solve for y. Using the linear equation will be faster:

$$y = -6(1) + 5$$
$$y = -1$$

So $(a, b) = (1, -1)$. The question asks for $-b$, so grid in **1**.

Try on Your Own

Directions: Take as much time as you need on these questions. Work carefully and methodically. There will be an opportunity for timed practice at the end of the chapter.

HINT: You can take a shortcut in Q26. There's no need to isolate y in the second equation.

$$\begin{cases} y = 3x \\ x^2 - y^2 = -288 \end{cases}$$

26. If (x, y) is a solution to the system of equations shown here, what is the value of x^2?

   A)   6
   B)   36
   C)   144
   D)   1,296

HINT: Don't try to find solutions to all the systems in the answer choices of Q27. Backsolve instead.

---

27. One of the x-coordinates of the solutions to a system of equations is -8. Which of the following could be the system?

   A) $\begin{cases} y = -x - 1 \\ y = (x - 8)^2 - 3 \end{cases}$

   B) $\begin{cases} y = x + 8 \\ y = (x + 3)^2 - 8 \end{cases}$

   C) $\begin{cases} y = x + 8 \\ y = (x + 3)^2 - 2 \end{cases}$

   D) $\begin{cases} y = -x - 1 \\ y = (x + 5)^2 - 2 \end{cases}$

HINT: For Q28, what does it mean when a system of equations has only one solution?

---

28. Which system of equations has only one solution?

   A) $g(x) = -2(x + 3)^2 - 5$
      $f(x) = x - 5$

   B) $g(x) = -2(x + 3)^2 - 5$
      $f(x) = 5$

   C) $g(x) = -2(x + 3)^2 - 5$
      $f(x) = x + 5$

   D) $g(x) = -2(x + 3)^2 - 5$
      $f(x) = -5$

29. Will the graph of $f(x) = \dfrac{5}{2}x - 2$ intersect the graph of $f(x) = \dfrac{1}{2}x^2 + 2x - 3$?

   A) Yes, only at the vertex of the parabola
   B) Yes, once on each side of the vertex
   C) Yes, twice to the right of the vertex
   D) No, the graphs will not intersect.

On Test Day

Remember that the PSAT doesn't ask you to show your work. If you find the algebra in a question challenging, there is often another way to get to the answer.

Try to answer this question first by setting the two functions equal to each other and then by plugging the values of one of the intersection points into one of the functions. Which approach do you find easier? There's no right or wrong answer— just remember your preferred approach and try it first if you see a question like this on test day.

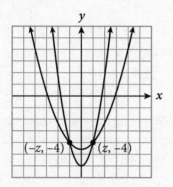

30. The functions $f(x) = 2x^2 - 5$ and $g(x) = 6x^2 - 7$ are graphed in the xy-plane above. The points where the two functions intersect are $(z, -4)$ and $(-z, -4)$. What is the value of z ?

A) $\dfrac{1}{2}$

B) $\dfrac{\sqrt{2}}{2}$

C) 0.8

D) 1.2

The correct answer and both ways of solving can be found at the end of this chapter.

How Much Have You Learned?

Directions: For testlike practice, give yourself 15 minutes to complete this question set. Be sure to study the explanations, even for questions you answered correctly. They can be found at the end of this chapter.

31. A car's fuel economy generally increases as its speed increases, but past a certain speed, it starts to drop, as depicted for a particular car in the graph above. What is the best estimate of this car's fuel economy, in miles per gallon, at 100 miles per hour?

    A) 0

    B) 10

    C) 17

    D) 41

32. The x-intercepts of the equation $y = x^2 - 9x + 20$ are m and n, where $m > n$. What is the value of m?

33. Shawna throws a baseball into the air. The equation $h = -5(t^2 - 4t + 4) + 22$ represents the height of the ball in meters t seconds after it is thrown. Which of the following equations could represent the height of a second ball that was thrown by Meagan, if Meagan's ball did not go as high as Shawna's ball?

    A) $h = -10(t - 4)^2 + 27$

    B) $h = -10(t - 2)^2 + 25$

    C) $h = -8(2t - 1)^2 + 23$

    D) $h = -5(t - 2)^2 + 21$

34. Which of the following equations could represent a parabola that has a minimum value of -3 and whose axis of symmetry is the line $x = 2$?

    A) $y = (x - 3)^2 + 2$

    B) $y = (x + 3)^2 + 2$

    C) $y = (x - 2)^2 - 3$

    D) $y = (x + 2)^2 - 3$

35. Which of the following is a solution to the equation $x^2 + 24 = 14x - x^2$?

    A) -3

    B) $\dfrac{12}{7}$

    C) 4

    D) 7

36. Which of the following is an equivalent form of
$4x^2 - 8x + 64 = 0$?

    A) $(x - 2)^2 = -12$

    B) $(x + 2)^2 = 12$

    C) $(x - 1)^2 = -15$

    D) $(x + 1)^2 = 15$

37. Which of the following is equivalent to $64x^2 - 81y^2$?

    A) $(8x + 9y)(8x - 9y)$

    B) $(9x + 8y)(9x - 8y)$

    C) $(8x + 9y)^2$

    D) $(8x - 9y)^2$

38. Which of the following quadratics has only one real solution?

    A) $4x^2 = 3x - 8$

    B) $10x = 2 - x^2$

    C) $7x^2 + 2x - 5 = 0$

    D) $3x^2 - 6x + 3 = 0$

$$\begin{cases} y - 3x = x^2 - 10 \\ y - 4 = -2x \end{cases}$$

39. What is the absolute difference of the values of x for the solutions to the system of equations above?

40. Which of the following coordinates is the vertex of the parabola $y = x^2 - 14x + 3$?

    A) $(7, -46)$

    B) $(-7, -46)$

    C) $(14, -193)$

    D) $(-14, -193)$

Math

Reflect

Directions: Take a few minutes to recall what you've learned and what you've been practicing in this chapter. Consider the following questions, jot down your best answer for each one, and then compare your reflections to the expert responses on the following page. Use your level of confidence to determine what to do next.

What features in a quadratic equation should you look for to decide whether to factor, complete the square, or apply the quadratic formula?

_____

_____

_____

Which constant in the vertex form of a quadratic function gives its maximum or minimum?

_____

_____

Which form of a quadratic equation gives its y-intercept?

_____

_____

Which form of a quadratic equation gives its x-intercepts, assuming the equation has two real roots?

_____

_____

_____

How do you solve a system of one linear and one quadratic equation?

_____

_____

_____

Expert Responses

What features in a quadratic equation should you look for to decide whether to factor, complete the square, or apply the quadratic formula?

Get the equation into standard form. If the coefficient in front of the squared term is 1, try factoring, but don't spend longer than about 15 seconds on the attempt. If you can't get the quadratic factored quickly, look at the coefficient on the middle term: if it is even, completing the square will be an efficient approach. Finally, the quadratic formula will work for any quadratic, no matter what the coefficients are.

Which constant in the vertex form of a quadratic function gives its maximum or minimum?

The vertex form is $y = a(x - h)^2 + k$. The constant k is the y-value at the vertex, which occurs at the maximum or minimum.

Which form of a quadratic equation gives its y-intercept?

The standard form, $y = ax^2 + bx + c$. The y-intercept is given by c.

Which form of a quadratic equation gives its x-intercepts, assuming the equation has two real roots?

The factored form, $y = a(x - m)(x - n)$. The x-intercepts are at $x = m$ and $x = n$.

How do you solve a system of one linear and one quadratic equation?

Put the linear equation in the form $y = mx + b$ and the quadratic in the form $y = ax^2 + bx + c$. Set the right sides of the equations equal to each other and solve.

Next Steps

If you answered most questions correctly in the "How Much Have You Learned?" section, and if your responses to the Reflect questions were similar to those of the PSAT expert, then consider Quadratics an area of strength and move on to the next chapter. Come back to this topic periodically to prevent yourself from getting rusty.

If you don't yet feel confident, review those parts of this chapter that you have not yet mastered. In particular, study the table describing the different forms of quadratics in the Graphs of Quadratics lesson. Then, try the questions you missed again. As always, be sure to review the explanations closely.

Answers and Explanations

1. B

Difficulty: Easy

Getting to the Answer: FOIL the binomials $(x - 4)(x + 2)$: First: $(x)(x) = x^2$. Outer: $(2)(x)$. Inner: $(-4)(x)$. Last: $(2)(-4) = -8$. Add all the terms together and combine like terms: $x^2 - 4x + 2x - 8 = x^2 - 2x - 8$. The correct answer is **(B)**.

2. 0

Difficulty: Easy

Getting to the Answer: All the question is really asking you to do is solve for the zeros and subtract them:

$$g(x) = -2x^2 + 16x - 32$$
$$0 = -2x^2 + 16x - 32$$
$$0 = -2\left(x^2 - 8x + 16\right)$$
$$0 = x^2 - 8x + 16$$
$$0 = (x - 4)(x - 4)$$

The quadratic has only one unique solution, 4, so the positive difference between the zeros of the function is 0. Grid in **0**.

3. A

Difficulty: Easy

Getting to the Answer: Rearrange the equation first so you can factor 4 out. From there, divide by 4, then factor as usual:

$$4z^2 + 32z - 81 = -1$$
$$4z^2 + 32z - 80 = 0$$
$$4\left(z^2 + 8z - 20\right) = 0$$
$$z^2 + 8z - 20 = 0$$
$$(z + 10)(z - 2) = 0$$

Keep in mind that while z is equal to -10 or 2, the problem asks only for the positive value, which is **(A)**. Reading carefully, you could have eliminated (B) before doing any calculations because it includes a negative value.

4. C

Difficulty: Medium

Strategic Advice: None of the choices has a remainder, suggesting that you probably will not need polynomial division for this question. Try factoring the numerator and denominator to see if something will cancel out.

Getting to the Answer: Start by factoring out a 2 in the denominator to make that quadratic a bit simpler. Once there, factor to reveal an $(x - 2)$ term that will cancel out:

$$\frac{x^2 - 4x + 4}{2\left(x^2 + 2x - 8\right)} = \frac{(x - 2)\,\cancel{(x - 2)}}{2(x + 4)\,\cancel{(x - 2)}} = \frac{(x - 2)}{2(x + 4)}$$

Unfortunately, none of the answer choices match. Try factoring -1 out of the numerator:

$$\frac{(x - 2)}{2(x + 4)} = \frac{(-1)(-x + 2)}{2(x + 4)} = \frac{(-1)(2 - x)}{2(x + 4)} = -\frac{(2 - x)}{2(x + 4)}$$

The correct answer is **(C)**.

5. B

Difficulty: Hard

Getting to the Answer: Set each answer choice equal to zero and factor to determine which one meets the criteria posed in the question: the solutions must have different signs and the positive solution must have a greater absolute value than the negative solution.

(A): $4x^2 + 4x - 24 = 4\left(x^2 + x - 6\right) = 4(x - 2)(x + 3) = 0$

The solutions are 2 and -3. They have different signs, but the negative solution has the greater absolute value. Eliminate (A).

(B): $-x^2 + x + 6 = (-1)\left(x^2 - x - 6\right) = (-1)(x - 3)(x + 2) = 0$

This time, the solutions are -2 and 3, so the criteria are met. **(B)** is correct.

For the record:

(C): $-x^2 - x + 6 = (-1)\left(x^2 + x - 6\right) = (-1)(x + 3)(x - 2) = 0$

This has the same solutions as (A). Eliminate (C).

(D): $3x^2 - 6x = 3x(x - 2) = 0$

The solutions are 0 and 2. Eliminate (D) and confirm that **(B)** is correct.

6. D

Difficulty: Medium

Getting to the Answer: Expand the first factor to take advantage of the difference of squares, and then use FOIL to multiply the two factors that remain:

$$(a-b)^2(a+b) = [(a-b)(a-b)](a+b)$$
$$= (a-b)[(a-b)(a+b)]$$
$$= (a-b)(a^2-b^2)$$
$$= a^3 - ab^2 - a^2b + b^3$$

This matches **(D)**.

7. A

Difficulty: Medium

Getting to the Answer: This question can be solved two ways. One is to factor each choice and solve for the solutions, and whichever does not have a solution of $x = -4$ is correct. Another way is to plug in $x = -4$ for each choice; if the equation does not equal 0, then that choice is correct. Luckily, plugging $x = -4$ into the first choice results in 64 and not 0. Choice (A) factored would be $(x-4)^2$, so its only unique root is $x = 4$. Hence, **(A)** is correct.

8. B

Difficulty: Medium

Getting to the Answer: Start by noticing that the area equation is a difference of perfect squares. Use the difference of squares formula $(a^2 - b^2) = (a+b)(a-b)$ where $(x^4 - 196) = (x^2 + 14)(x^2 - 14)$. Because area is length times width ($A = lw$) and the width is $x^2 - 14$, the length must be $x^2 + 14$, so **(B)** is correct.

9. D

Difficulty: Medium

Getting to the Answer: The volume equation for a rectangular prism is $V = lwh$, so work with one variable at a time and then plug all of the dimensions in. The height will just be x, so $h = x$. The width is 7 less than the height, so subtract 7 from the height, or x, which gives $w = x - 7$. The length is 14 more than the width, so $l = (x - 7) + 14 = x + 7$. Plug all of these values into the volume formula and recognize a difference of squares to get $x(x - 7)(x + 7) = x(x^2 - 49)$. Thus, **(D)** is correct.

10. B

Difficulty: Medium

Getting to the Answer: Factor out the common term p^2 to get $p^2(16m^2 + 72mz + 81z^2)$. Eliminate (D), which is equivalent until the final term. Notice that $16m^2 + 72mz + 81z^2$ is a classic quadratic:

$$16m^2 + 72mz + 81z^2 = (4m + 9z)^2$$

So the original expression is equal to $p^2(4m + 9z)^2$. Thus, **(B)** is correct. Another way to solve would have been to FOIL, or distribute, each choice and see which one results in the given expression.

11. C

Difficulty: Medium

Strategic Advice: Equations that are equivalent have the same solutions, so you are looking for the equation that is simply written in a different form. You could expand each of the equations in the answer choices, but unless you get lucky, this strategy will use up quite a bit of time. The answer choices are written in vertex form, so use the method of completing the square to rewrite the equation given in the question stem.

Getting to the Answer: First, subtract the constant, 17, from both sides of the equation. To complete the square on the right-hand side, find $\left(\dfrac{b}{2}\right)^2 = \left(\dfrac{6}{2}\right)^2 = 3^2 = 9$, and add the result to both sides of the equation:

$$y = x^2 + 6x + 17$$
$$y - 17 = x^2 + 6x$$
$$y - 17 + 9 = x^2 + 6x + 9$$
$$y - 8 = x^2 + 6x + 9$$

Next, factor the right-hand side of the equation (which should be a perfect square trinomial), and rewrite it as a square. Finally, solve for y:

$$y - 8 = (x + 3)(x + 3)$$
$$y - 8 = (x + 3)^2$$
$$y = (x + 3)^2 + 8$$

This matches **(C)**.

Math

12. B

Difficulty: Medium

Getting to the Answer: Since the first term has a constant of 1, completing the square can be used right away. Make sure to move the constant term to the right side of the equation before dividing the x term by 2 and squaring:

$$x^2 + 10x - 8 = 0$$
$$x^2 + 10x + \_\_ = 8 + \_\_$$
$$\left(\frac{b}{2}\right)^2 = (5)^2 = 25$$
$$x^2 + 10x + 25 = 8 + 25$$
$$(x + 5)^2 = 33$$
$$\sqrt{(x + 5)^2} = \sqrt{33}$$
$$(x + 5) = \pm\sqrt{33}$$
$$x = \pm\sqrt{33} - 5$$

Therefore, **(B)** is correct.

13. D

Difficulty: Medium

Getting to the Answer: Since the first term has a constant of 1, completing the square can be used right away. Make sure to move the constant term to the right side of the equation before dividing the x term constant by 2 and squaring:

$$x^2 + 4x + 16 = 0$$
$$x^2 + 4x + \_\_ = -16 + \_\_$$
$$\left(\frac{b}{2}\right)^2 = (2)^2 = 4$$
$$x^2 + 4x + 4 = -16 + 4$$
$$(x + 2)^2 = -12$$

Therefore, **(D)** is correct.

14. A

Difficulty: Hard

Getting to the Answer: When something doesn't factor cleanly, consider completing the square or using the quadratic formula. Start by dividing the entire equation by 4 so that the x^2-coefficient is 1:

$$4x^2 + 24x + 8 = 0 \rightarrow x^2 + 6x + 2 = 0$$

Factoring won't work here. The coefficient b is even, so try completing the square:

$$\left(\frac{b}{2}\right)^2 = \left(\frac{6}{2}\right)^2 = (3)^2 = 9$$
$$x^2 + 6x + 2 = 0$$
$$x^2 + 6x = -2$$
$$x^2 + 6x + ⑨ = -2 + ⑨$$
$$x^2 + 6x + 9 = 7$$
$$(x + 3)^2 = 7$$
$$(x + 3) = \pm\sqrt{7}$$
$$x = -3 \pm \sqrt{7}$$

The question asks for just one solution, so **(A)** is the correct answer.

15. D

Difficulty: Easy

Getting to the Answer: There are no zeros for choice **(D)** because the parabola never intersects or touches the x-axis. The discriminant of the quadratic formula for choice **(D)** will be negative because there are no real zeros.

There is a pair of zeros for choices (A) and (B). There is one zero for choice (C).

16. D

Difficulty: Medium

Strategic Advice: When factoring isn't easy, try a different approach. If you were able to use a calculator, the fastest method might be to graph the function. Because this is a no-calculator question, use the quadratic formula.

Getting to the Answer: The first step in answering the question is to manipulate the equation so that it's equal to 0:

$$3x^2 + 2x + 4 = 5x$$
$$3x^2 - 3x + 4 = 0$$

Now, solve using the quadratic formula:

$$x = \frac{-b \pm \sqrt{b^2 - 4ac}}{2a}$$
$$x = \frac{3 \pm \sqrt{(-3)^2 - 4(3)(4)}}{2(3)}$$
$$x = \frac{3 \pm \sqrt{9 - 48}}{6}$$
$$x = \frac{3 \pm \sqrt{-39}}{6}$$

When you solve using the quadratic formula, you get a negative number under the square root, which means there are no real solutions. The correct answer is **(D)**.

Although you couldn't use a graphing calculator for this question, for the record, if you could graph the function, you'd see that the graph does not cross the *x*-axis, which means no real solutions:

$$y = 3x^2 - 3x + 4$$

(D) is indeed correct.

17. A

Difficulty: Hard

Strategic Advice: The roots of an equation are the same as its solutions. The equation doesn't factor using reverse FOIL, so you'll have to use a different method to find the solutions. The equation is already written in the form $y = ax^2 + bx + c$, and the coefficients are fairly small, so using the quadratic formula is probably the quickest method.

Getting to the Answer: Note the values that you'll need: $a = 1$, $b = 8$, and $c = -3$. Then, substitute these values into the quadratic formula and simplify:

$$x = \frac{-b \pm \sqrt{b^2 - 4ac}}{2a}$$
$$= \frac{-(8) \pm \sqrt{(8)^2 - 4(1)(-3)}}{2(1)}$$
$$= \frac{-8 \pm \sqrt{64 + 12}}{2}$$
$$= \frac{-8 \pm \sqrt{76}}{2}$$

This is not one of the answer choices, which tells you that you'll need to simplify the radical, but before you do, you can eliminate (C) and (D) because the non-radical part of the solutions is $\frac{-8}{2} = -4$, not 4. To simplify the radical, look for a perfect square that divides into 76 and take its square root:

$$x = \frac{-8 \pm \sqrt{4 \times 19}}{2}$$
$$= \frac{-8 \pm 2\sqrt{19}}{2}$$
$$= -4 \pm \sqrt{19}$$

This matches **(A)**.

18. B

Difficulty: Medium

Getting to the Answer: The discriminant is part of the quadratic formula. When the discriminant is negative, there are no real solutions to the equation because the square root of a negative number is not a real number. When the discriminant is 0, there is only one solution. For there to be two real solutions, the discriminant, $b^2 - 4ac$, must be greater than 0.

(A): $a = 2, b = 4, c = 2$. The discriminant is $4^2 - 4(2)(2) = 16 - 16 = 0$, so this has one real solution. Eliminate (A).

(B): $a = 5, b = 5, c = -5$. The discriminant is $5^2 - (4)(5)(-5) = 25 + 100 = 125$, so choice **(B)** must have two real solutions and is correct.

For the record, the discriminant of (C) is -75 and the discriminant of (D) is 0.

19. A

Difficulty: Medium

Getting to the Answer: Since the answer choices have radicals, factoring the equation would be extremely difficult. Use the quadratic formula to find the roots of the equation:

$$x = \frac{-b \pm \sqrt{b^2 - 4ac}}{2a}$$

$$x = \frac{-4 \pm \sqrt{4^2 - 4(8)(-1)}}{2(8)}$$

$$x = \frac{-4 \pm \sqrt{48}}{16}$$

$$x = \frac{-4 \pm \sqrt{16 \times 3}}{16}$$

$$x = \frac{-4 \pm 4\sqrt{3}}{16}$$

$$x = \frac{-1 \pm \sqrt{3}}{4}$$

This matches **(A)**.

20. D

Difficulty: Medium

Strategic Advice: Quadratic equations can be written in several forms, each of which reveals something important about the graph. For example, the vertex form of a quadratic equation, $y = a(x - h)^2 + k$, gives the minimum or maximum y-value of the function, k, while the standard form, $y = ax^2 + bx + c$, shows the y-intercept, c.

Getting to the Answer: The factored form of a quadratic equation makes it easiest to calculate the solutions to the equation, which graphically represent the x-intercepts. Choice **(D)** is the only equation written in factored form and therefore must be correct. You can set each factor equal to 0 and quickly solve to find that

the x-intercepts of the graph are $x = -\frac{4}{3}$ and $x = 2$, which agree with the graph. (Note that each unit on the graph is 0.5.)

21. B

Difficulty: Medium

Getting to the Answer: The parabola opens downward, so the a term should be negative. Unfortunately, all the choices have a negative a term, so you're not able to eliminate any of them. All of the choices appear to be in vertex form, so take a look at the graph: the vertex appears to be at $(3, 2)$; only (A) and (B) match this. To decide between them, plug in some values from points on the graph, such as the two x-intercepts, $(2, 0)$ and $(4, 0)$. Check if $f(2) = 0$ for (A): $-((2) - 3)^2 + 2 = -(-1)^2 + 2 = -(1) + 2 = 1$. Eliminate (A) because $f(2) \neq 0$. Only **(B)** is left and is correct. For this equation, both $x = 2$ and $x = 4$ produce a result of $f(x) = 0$.

22. B

Difficulty: Medium

Getting to the Answer: According to the graph, one x-intercept is to the left of the y-axis and the other is to the right. This tells you that one x-intercept has a positive x-value and the other x-intercept has a negative x-value, so you can immediately eliminate choices (A) and (C) because both factors have the same sign. To choose between choices (B) and (D), find the x-intercepts by setting each factor equal to 0 and solving for x. In choice (B), the x-intercepts are 7 and -3. In choice (D), the x-intercepts are 1 and -10. Choice **(B)** is correct because the x-intercepts are exactly 10 units apart, while the x-intercepts in choice (D) are 11 units apart. Alternatively, given that the distance between the two intercepts is 10 units, you could have just found the choice with the two factors for which the positive difference between the numerical terms is 10: $3 - (-7) = 10$.

23. B

Difficulty: Medium

Strategic Advice: The coefficients are given as unknowns, so you'll need to think about how their values affect the graph. You'll need to recall certain vocabulary. Recall that *increasing* means rising from left to right, while *decreasing* means falling from left to right, and *zero* is another way of saying *x*-intercept. Compare each statement to the graph to determine whether it is true, eliminating choices as you go. Remember, you are looking for the statement that is NOT true.

Getting to the Answer: The parabola opens downward, so *a* must be negative, which means you can eliminate (A). When a quadratic equation is written in standard form, *c* is the *y*-intercept of the parabola. According to the graph, the *y*-intercept is above the *x*-axis and is therefore positive, so the statement in **(B)** is false, making it the correct answer.

For the record, (C) is true because the graph rises from left to right until you get to $x = 3$, and then it falls. Choice (D) is true because the zeros are the same as the *x*-intercepts, and the graph does intersect the *x*-axis at -2 and 8.

24. A

Difficulty: Hard

Getting to the Answer: Begin by considering the shape of the parabola formed by the path of the ball: because the ball starts and ends at ground level ($y = 0$) and travels a horizontal distance of 150 feet ($x = 150$), it must have *x*-intercepts of $(0, 0)$ and $(150, 0)$. In addition, the question tells you that it reaches a maximum height of 45 feet ($y = 45$) and, because the vertex is halfway between the two *x*-intercepts, the vertex must be at $(75, 45)$. The vertex is above the *x*-intercepts, so this is a downward parabola. You can immediately eliminate choices (C) and (D), which have positive *a* values, making them upward parabolas. To decide between (A) and (B), try plugging in the coordinates of the vertex or an *x*-intercept to see which equation holds. For example, here are the calculations if you use $(150, 0)$:

(A): $0 = -0.008(150)^2 + 1.2(150) = -180 + 180 = 0$, keep.

(B): $0 = -0.008(150)^2 - 150(150) = -180 - 22,500$
$= -22,680 \neq 0$, eliminate.

Thus, **(A)** is correct.

If you have time, you could also graph each equation in your graphing calculator and find the one that has a maximum value of 45, which would show again that **(A)** is the only equation for which this is true.

25. D

Difficulty: Hard

Getting to the Answer: Make sure you read the axis labels, the question, and the answer choices carefully. The vertical axis is labeled in feet, while the horizontal axis is labeled in yards. The answer choices are given in feet, so you'll need to convert the yards to feet.

The question asks for the difference between the horizontal and vertical distances the cannonball travels. You have a parabola-shaped graph, so sketch in a quadratic model, making sure to extend it past the last point all the way back to the *x*-axis.

Horizontally, the cannonball starts at 0 yards and travels to about 485 yards, or $485 \times 3 = 1,455$ feet. Determining vertical travel is a bit more involved. According to the graph, the cannonball's peak height is about 75 feet, but it started at 10 vertical feet (*not* 0), making the net upward distance traveled 65 feet. Subtract to find the difference, $1,455 - 65 = 1,390$ feet, which is **(D)**.

Note: Don't worry if you didn't draw the model exactly right or if you didn't get the exact same answer. The choices should be far enough apart that you'll still know which one is correct.

26. B

Difficulty: Medium

Getting to the Answer: Even though one of the equations in this system is not linear, you can still solve the system using substitution. You already know that y is equal to $3x$, so substitute $3x$ for y in the second equation. Don't forget that when you square $3x$, you must square both the coefficient and the variable:

$$x^2 - y^2 = -288$$
$$x^2 - (3x)^2 = -288$$
$$x^2 - 9x^2 = -288$$
$$-8x^2 = -288$$
$$x^2 = 36$$

The question asks for the value of x^2, not x, so there is no need to take the square root of 36 to find the value of x. Choice **(B)** is correct.

27. D

Difficulty: Hard

Strategic Advice: Solving each system would be absurdly time-consuming. Backsolving will be faster.

Getting to the Answer: Substitute $x = -8$, the x-value at one of the points of intersection, into each equation. The correct system will have both equations equaling the same number, which is the y-value at that point of intersection. Look at each answer choice:

(A): $y = -x - 1 = -(-8) - 1 = 8 - 1 = 7$
$$y = (x - 8)^2 - 3 = ((-8) - 8)^2 - 3$$
$$= (-16)^2 - 3 = 256 - 3 = 253$$

$7 \neq 253$, so eliminate (A).

(B): $y = x + 8 = (-8) + 8 = 0$
$$y = (x + 3)^2 - 8 = ((-8) + 3)^2 - 8$$
$$= (-5)^2 - 8 = 25 - 8 = 17$$

$0 \neq 17$, so eliminate (B).

(C): $y = x + 8 = (-8) + 8 = 0$
$$y = (x + 3)^2 - 2 = ((-8) + 3)^2 - 2$$
$$= (-5)^2 - 2 = 25 - 2 = 23$$

$0 \neq 23$, so eliminate (C).

(D): $y = -x - 1 = -(-8) - 1 = 8 - 1 = 7$
$$y = (x + 5)^2 - 2 = ((-8) + 5)^2 - 2$$
$$= (-3)^2 - 2 = 9 - 2 = 7$$

$7 = 7$, so the two equations in (D) intersect at the point $(-8, 7)$. Thus, **(D)** is correct.

28. D

Difficulty: Hard

Strategic Advice: All of the choices present a system of equations that includes a parabola and a line. For a system of equations to have only one solution, the graphs must have only one point of intersection.

Getting to the Answer: Notice that all of the choices have the same parabola with a vertex of $(-3, -5)$. Choices (B) and (D) have horizontal lines, which are easy to check. Choice (B) has a horizontal line at $y = 5$, but with the parabola facing downward, the parabola will never intersect it. Choice (D) has a horizontal line at $y = -5$, which is where the parabola's vertex lies. This means the line is tangent to the parabola and will touch the parabola only once to create only one solution. Thus, **(D)** is correct. For the record, (A) has two points of intersection and (C) has none.

29. C

Difficulty: Hard

Category: Systems of Quadratic and Linear Equations

Getting to the Answer: If this question is in the calculator section, you can graph the two functions simultaneously and observe that they intersect each other twice. If you are not visually sold on what the correct answer is, you can do a little investigating by using your calculator to tell you the values of the vertex (the minimum) and the points of intersection.

If this is in the non-calculator section, you'll instead need to solve this by hand by setting the two equations equal to each other to see whether they intersect and, if so, how many times:

$$\frac{5}{2}x - 2 = \frac{1}{2}x^2 + 2x - 3$$

$$0 = \frac{1}{2}x^2 - \frac{1}{2}x - 1$$

$$0 = \frac{1}{2}\left(x^2 - x - 2\right)$$

$$0 = x^2 - x - 2$$

$$0 = (x + 1)(x - 2)$$

You'll see that the functions do intersect each other at two locations, $x = -1$ and $x = 2$. You now need to determine the location of the vertex to compare. Using the formula given for the x-coordinate of the vertex (h), you can do this quite easily:

$$h = \frac{-b}{2a} = \frac{-2}{2\left(\frac{1}{2}\right)} = \frac{-2}{1} = -2$$

You need not calculate the y-coordinate (k) because you already have the answer. Both of the points of intersection, -1 and 2, occur to the right of the vertex. The answer is **(C)**.

30. B

Difficulty: Medium

Category: Graphs of Quadratics

Getting to the Answer: Set $f(x)$ equal to $g(x)$:
$2x^2 - 5 = 6x^2 - 7$. Isolate the x^2 terms on one side to get $2 = 4x^2$, so $x^2 = \frac{1}{2}$. Take the square root of both sides to see that $x = \pm\sqrt{\frac{1}{2}} = \pm\frac{1}{\sqrt{2}}$, which means that the two intersections of the functions occur when $x = -\frac{1}{\sqrt{2}}$ and $x = \frac{1}{\sqrt{2}}$. None of the choices match, so multiply the numerator and denominator by $\sqrt{2}$ to convert these to $\pm\frac{\sqrt{2}}{2}$. From the graph, you can see that these are the values of $\pm z$, so $z = \frac{\sqrt{2}}{2}$. **(B)** is correct.

Alternatively, you could plug in the coordinates of one of the intersections into either function. Using $f(x)$, the y-coordinate is -4 and the x-coordinate is z. So, $-4 = 2z^2 - 5$. The math works out exactly the same as for the first approach: $z^2 = \frac{1}{2}$, so $z = \pm\frac{\sqrt{2}}{2}$, and, from the graph, you can determine that $z = \frac{\sqrt{2}}{2}$. Again, **(B)** is correct.

31. B

Difficulty: Easy

Category: Graphs of Quadratics

Getting to the Answer: Sketch a regression line on the graph. You'll notice it has a slight curve. Extending the regression line to the x-axis allows you to reasonably estimate what your fuel economy at 100 miles per hour (mph) will be. Notice that the miles per gallon (mpg) drop from 80 mph to 90 mph is slightly less than 10, so it is reasonable to expect a drop of another full 10 mpg as the curve steepens from 90 mph to 100 mph. Therefore, the mpg at 100 mph would be about 10, so **(B)** is correct.

32. 5

Difficulty: Easy

Category: Solving Quadratics by Factoring

Getting to the Answer: Factor the given quadratic by finding factors of 20 that add, or subtract, to get the middle constant 9. Notice that -4 and -5 will multiply to get 20 and add to get -9. So, $x^2 - 9x + 20 = (x - 4)(x - 5)$. Set both equal to 0 and solve for x to get $x = 4$ and $x = 5$. Remember that the question asks for m, where $m > n$, or in other words for the larger of the two roots, so grid in **5**.

33. D

Difficulty: Hard

Category: Graphs of Quadratics

Getting to the Answer: Look for an equation among the choices that has a maximum value that is less than the maximum height of Shawna's toss. To determine the peak height of Shawna's throw, convert the given equation to vertex form, $y = a(x - h)^2 + k$, where the maximum value is given by k. Notice that the polynomial within the parentheses factors to $(t - 2)^2$. Thus, you can restate the given equation as $-5(t - 2)^2 + 22$. So the vertex of the equation for Shawna's throw is $(2, 22)$, which means that the maximum height was 22 meters.

Conveniently, the choices are all stated in vertex form. The only one with the k term less than 22 is **(D)**, which makes that the correct choice. (Notice that this equation differs from the restated version of the given equation only by the k term.)

34. C

Difficulty: Medium

Category: Graphs of Quadratics

Getting to the Answer: When a quadratic equation is written in vertex form, $y = a(x - h)^2 + k$, the minimum value (or the maximum value if $a < 0$) is given by k, and the axis of symmetry is given by the equation $x = h$. The question states that the minimum of the parabola is -3, so look for an equation where $k = -3$. You can eliminate choices (A) and (B) because $k = 2$ in both equations. The question also states that the axis of symmetry is $x = 2$, so h must be 2. Be careful: this can be tricky. The equation in choice (D) is not correct because the vertex form of a parabola includes the term $(x - h)$ not $(x + h)$, so $(x + 2)$ should be interpreted as $(x - (-2))$, with axis of symmetry at $x = -2$. This means **(C)** is correct.

35. C

Difficulty: Medium

Category: Solving Quadratics by Factoring

Getting to the Answer: Rearrange the equation into the standard quadratic form by subtracting everything from the right side of the equal sign: $2x^2 - 14x + 24 = 0$. Next, divide the equation by 2 to make factoring easier: $x^2 - 7x + 12 = 0$. Now, use reverse FOIL to determine the factors. You need factors of 12 that sum to -7. Those are -3 and -4, so your equation factors to $(x - 3)(x - 4) = 0$. That means the solutions to the equation are $x = 3$ and $x = 4$. Since only one of these is among the answers, **(C)** is correct.

36. C

Difficulty: Hard

Category: Completing the Square

Getting to the Answer: First divide both sides by 4, so that $4x^2 - 8x + 64 = 0$ becomes $x^2 - 2x + 16 = 0$. Notice that this cannot be solved by factoring, so use the completing the square method:

$$x^2 - 2x + 16 = 0$$
$$x^2 - 2x + \underline{} = -16 + \underline{}$$
$$\left(\frac{b}{2}\right)^2 = (-1)^2 = 1$$
$$x^2 - 2x + 1 = -16 + 1$$
$$(x - 1)^2 = -15$$

Therefore, **(C)** is correct.

37. A

Difficulty: Medium

Category: Classic Quadratics

Getting to the Answer: Notice that this quadratic is a difference of squares, so use the formula $a^2 - b^2 = (a + b)(a - b)$. Set a^2 equal to $64x^2$ and take the square root of both sides to find that $a = 8x$. Do the same thing with b^2 and $81y^2$ to find that $b = 9y$. Fill in $(a + b)(a - b)$ with the values you found for a and b to get $(8x + 9y)(8x - 9y)$. Therefore, **(A)** is correct.

38. D

Difficulty: Hard

Category: Quadratic Formula

Strategic Advice: The discriminant is the part of the quadratic formula that determines whether a quadratic equation has 1 or 2 distinct real solutions or only imaginary solutions. Note that a quadratic will have only one distinct real solution when the discriminant equals 0.

Getting to the Answer: Convert the equations to standard quadratic form, if necessary, and calculate the discriminant for each choice to see which one equals 0:

(A) converts to $4x^2 - 3x + 8 = 0$. The discriminant is $(-3)^2 - 4(4)(8) = 9 - 128 = -119$. This is not equal to 0, so eliminate (A).

(B) converts to $x^2 + 10x - 2 = 0$. The discriminant is $(10)^2 - 4(1)(-2) = 100 + 8 = 108$. Eliminate (B).

(C) is already in the proper form. The discriminant is $(2)^2 - 4(7)(-5) = 4 + 140 = 144$. Eliminate (C).

Only **(D)** is left, so it is correct. For the record, the discriminant for **(D)** does, in fact, equal 0. Divide through by the common factor of 3 to get $x^2 - 2x + 1 = 0$, so the discriminant is $(-2)^2 - 4(1)(1) = 0$.

39. 9

Difficulty: Hard

Category: Systems of Quadratic and Linear Equations

Getting to the Answer: Rearrange both equations to isolate y in terms of x:

$$y - 3x = x^2 - 10 \rightarrow y = x^2 + 3x - 10$$
$$y - 4 = -2x \rightarrow y = -2x + 4$$

Set both equations equal to each other to find where they intersect. Combine like terms on one side of the equation:

$$x^2 + 3x - 10 = -2x + 4$$
$$x^2 + 3x + 2x - 10 - 4 = 0$$
$$x^2 + 5x - 14 = 0$$

This quadratic equation can be solved by factoring since two factors of -14, 7 and -2, add to 5. Hence, $(x + 7)(x - 2) = 0$ and $x = -7$ and $x = 2$. The question asks for the absolute difference, so subtract the roots and evaluate as an absolute value:

$$\left|2 - (-7)\right| = 9$$

Grid in **9**.

40. A

Difficulty: Hard

Category: Completing the Square

Strategic Advice: Vertex form is usually a good option when questions ask for coordinates of the vertex. One of the best methods to convert quadratic equations into vertex form is completing the square.

Getting to the Answer: The x^2 term has a coefficient of 1, so no manipulation of the equation is necessary before completing the square. Move the constant term to the right side of the equation before dividing the x term's coefficient by 2 and squaring:

$$x^2 - 14x + 3 = 0$$
$$x^2 - 14x + \underline{} = -3 + \underline{}$$
$$\left(\frac{b}{2}\right)^2 = (-7)^2 = 49$$
$$x^2 - 14x + 49 = -3 + 49$$
$$(x - 7)^2 = 46$$
$$(x - 7)^2 - 46 = 0$$

Now the equation $y = (x - 7)^2 - 46$ is in vertex form, $y = a(x - h)^2 + k$, where the vertex is (h, k). To find the x-coordinate of the vertex, or h, be aware of the negative sign before h in vertex form. In this case, $-h = -7$, so $h = 7$. Only **(A)** has an x-coordinate of 7, so it must be correct.

For the record, the y-coordinate, or k, of the vertex is -46. The vertex therefore is $(h, k) = (7, -46)$, so **(A)** is indeed correct.

PART 3

PSAT Reading

CHAPTER 10

The Method for PSAT Reading Questions

LEARNING OBJECTIVES

After completing this chapter, you will be able to:

- Read PSAT Reading passages strategically
- Apply the Method for PSAT Reading Questions efficiently and effectively to PSAT Reading questions

How to Do PSAT Reading

The PSAT Reading section is made up of four passages and one set of paired passages, each approximately 500–750 words long and accompanied by 9 or 10 questions for a total of 47 questions in the section. To tackle all of this effectively in 60 minutes, the most successful test takers:

- Read the passages strategically to zero in on the text that leads to points
- Approach the questions with a method that minimizes rereading and leads directly to correct answers

The key to maximizing correct answers is learning in advance the kinds of questions that the test asks. PSAT Reading questions focus more on the author's purpose (*why* she wrote this passage) and the passage's structure (*how* the author makes and supports her points) than on the details or facts of the subject matter (*what* this passage is about).

Knowing that the PSAT rewards your attention to *how* and *why* the author wrote the passage or chose to include certain words or examples puts you in the driver's seat. You can read more effectively and answer the questions more quickly and confidently.

In this chapter, we'll give you an overview of how to tackle Reading passages and questions. The other chapters in this unit will help you become a stronger reader and introduce the six PSAT Reading question types, as well as provide tips for improving your approach to paired passages, primary sources passages, and literature passages (see online appendices).

Try the passage and questions that follow on your own. Then, compare your approach to our recommendations for how to approach PSAT Reading and reflect on how you can become a more efficient test taker.

Questions 1–10 refer to the following passage.

The following passage, adapted from an article in an encyclopedia of U.S. culture, addresses some of the influences of the automobile on life in the United States during the twentieth century.

Few developments have so greatly affected American life as the automobile. Indeed, it would be hard to overestimate its impact. Since mass

5 production of the automobile became feasible in the early twentieth century, the car has had a significant effect on nearly every facet of American life, including how we work, where we live,

10 and what we believe.

Interestingly, it was the process of building cars rather than the cars themselves that first brought a sea change to the American workplace.

15 In 1914, a Ford plant in Highland Park, Michigan, used the first electric conveyor belt, greatly increasing the efficiency of automobile manufacturing. Assembly lines for the production of

20 automobiles were quickly adopted and became highly mechanized, providing a new model for industrial business. In contrast to European manufacturers, which employed a higher percentage

25 of skilled laborers to produce fewer and costlier cars, American companies focused on turning out a large quantity of affordable cars utilizing less-skilled laborers. Assembly-line production was

30 a mixed blessing, as it enabled higher productivity and more affordable cars but resulted in less-satisfied workers with less-interesting jobs. The value of efficiency was emphasized over

35 personal pride and investment in the work.

As cars became more popular, their effect on population distribution was likewise profound. Unlike railroads,

40 which helped concentrate the population in cities, the automobile contributed to urban sprawl and, eventually, to the rise of suburbs. People no longer needed to live near railroad

45 lines or within walking distance of their jobs, and so were drawn to outlying areas with less congestion and lower property taxes. Business districts became less centralized for

50 similar reasons. Sadly, this movement toward suburbs exacerbated social stratification. Since cars were initially affordable only to wealthier people, the upper and middle classes moved out

55 of cities. Many businesses followed, attracted by the educated, well-trained workforce. As good jobs also moved out of cities, the people who remained were further disadvantaged and

60 even less able to leave. Though few anticipated it in the heady early days of suburban growth, by the century's end, cars had helped to further entrench social divisions in America by making

65 possible great physical distances between rich and poor.

Automobile ownership has also transformed our individual lives and values. Historian James Flink

70 has observed that automobiles particularly altered the work patterns and recreational opportunities of farmers and other rural inhabitants by reducing the isolation that had been

75 characteristic of life in the country. Of course, there were also profound changes in the recreational activities of suburban and urban dwellers. For example, the 1950s saw a huge increase

80 in drive-in movie theaters, fast-food
establishments, supermarkets, and
shopping centers—most facets of how
we ate, shopped, and played changed
to accommodate the car. Family life
85 was also affected: cars changed dating
behavior by allowing teenagers more
independence from parental supervision
and control, and they provided women
with more freedom to leave the home.
90 This personal mobility and autonomy
afforded by the car has become an
integral part of American culture.

1. The primary purpose of the passage is to

   A) defend the use of assembly lines in automobile
   manufacturing.

   B) draw a contrast between U.S. population
   distribution before and after the advent of the
   automobile.

   C) explain certain changes in recreational
   activities in cities, suburbs, and the country.

   D) describe the wide-ranging impact of the
   automobile on American society.

2. The author refers to European and American manufacturing practices in lines 22–29 primarily to

   A) demonstrate the quality difference between
   European and American cars.

   B) argue for a return to a less mechanized but less
   efficient factory system.

   C) highlight the positive and negative effects of
   the automobile on the American workplace.

   D) suggest that greater efficiency and more skilled
   laborers can improve the American workplace.

3. As used in line 39, "profound" most nearly means

   A) absolute.

   B) unintelligible.

   C) far-reaching.

   D) thoughtful.

4. In lines 39–43 ("Unlike … suburbs"), what distinction does the author draw between the two types of transportation?

    A) Railroads are a more efficient mode of transportation than automobiles.

    B) Automobiles allow greater flexibility, while railroads operate on a fixed schedule.

    C) Railroads promote clustered populations, while automobiles promote dispersed populations.

    D) Automobiles replaced railroads as the preferred American mode of transportation.

5. It can be inferred that the author believes social stratification in the United States to be

    A) a positive development caused by less centralized business districts.

    B) an unfortunate result of ready but expensive transportation.

    C) an outgrowth of the rise of supermarkets and shopping centers.

    D) a collective choice resulting from personal mobility and autonomy.

6. Which choice provides the best evidence for the answer to the previous question?

    A) Lines 48–50 ("Business … reasons")

    B) Lines 50–52 ("Sadly … stratification")

    C) Lines 78–84 ("For example … car")

    D) Lines 90–92 ("This personal … culture")

7. The author regards the conclusions of historian James Flink as

    A) insufficiently supported and unconvincing.

    B) tangential to more important issues.

    C) unimportant though persuasive.

    D) accurate but incomplete.

8. Which choice provides the best evidence for the answer to the previous question?

    A) Lines 67–69 ("Automobile … values")

    B) Lines 69–78 ("Historian … dwellers")

    C) Lines 78–84 ("For example … car")

    D) Lines 84–89 ("Family … home")

9. As used in line 82, "facets" most nearly means

    A) aspects.

    B) faces.

    C) surfaces.

    D) viewpoints.

10. The author mentions dating behavior in lines 85–86 in order to

    A) show why teenagers had more independence from parental supervision.

    B) tie drive-in movie theaters to strained relationships between parents and their teenage children.

    C) illustrate one way in which the automobile changed American family life.

    D) challenge James Flink's thesis that the effects of the automobile on recreational opportunities were limited to rural populations.

Strategic Reading

The PSAT Reading Test is an open-book test; the passage is right there for you to reference. Moreover, the PSAT actively tests your skill in looking up details; there are Command of Evidence questions that actually ask you to cite the line numbers for the evidence you used to answer a question. Because of the way the test is constructed, it is in your best interest to read fairly quickly, noting the outline of the passage as you go, marking up the page with margin notes as you read, getting a solid understanding of the main idea, but not taking the time to memorize details.

Be sure to read the pre-passage blurb, the short introduction that comes before the passage. Identify any information that helps you to understand the topic of the passage or to anticipate what the author will discuss. For the previous passage, the blurb states the topic (the automobile) and announces that the passage will discuss some of its influences on American life. That's an invitation to keep your eye out for multiple effects of the automobile as you read.

You'll learn all the skills you need to read strategically in the next chapter, but for now, here's an example of an expert's passage map. Don't worry if yours doesn't look exactly like this (or even anything like this) yet. Follow the expert's thought process in the discussion that follows the passage to see what he was thinking and asking as he read the passage.

Reading

Reading

Automobile Passage Map

The following passage, adapted from an article in an encyclopedia of U.S. culture, addresses some of the influences of the automobile on life in the United States during the twentieth century.

Few developments have so greatly affected American life as the automobile. Indeed, it would be hard to overestimate its impact. Since mass

5 production of the automobile became feasible in the early twentieth century, the car has had a significant effect on nearly every facet of American life, including how we work, where we live,

10 and what we believe.

Interestingly, it was the process of building cars rather than the cars themselves that first brought a sea change to the American workplace.

15 In 1914, a Ford plant in Highland Park, Michigan, used the first electric conveyor belt, greatly increasing the efficiency of automobile manufacturing. Assembly lines for the production of

20 automobiles were quickly adopted and became highly mechanized, providing a new model for industrial business. In contrast to European manufacturers, which employed a higher percentage

25 of skilled laborers to produce fewer and costlier cars, American companies focused on turning out a large quantity of affordable cars utilizing less-skilled laborers. Assembly-line production was

30 a mixed blessing, as it enabled higher productivity and more affordable cars but resulted in less-satisfied workers with less-interesting jobs. The value of efficiency was emphasized over

35 personal pride and investment in the work.

As cars became more popular, their effect on population distribution was likewise profound. Unlike railroads,

40 which helped concentrate the

Margin notes:

influence of cars in U.S.

manufac-
turing
process was
key

assembly
lines

Euro./skilled
vs.
U.S./unskilled

author: ↑
production
but unhappy
labor

ANALYSIS

Pre-passage blurb: The source is an encyclopedia, so the passage will be neutral and factual. The topic is automobiles and American life.

¶1: The author emphasizes the depth and breadth of the automobile's influences. The last sentence tells you to expect later paragraphs on American work patterns, demographics, and beliefs.

¶2: How Americans work: the author explains how the popularity of assembly lines in the U.S. led to increased productivity and lower prices for cars but led to a less satisfied, less skilled workforce.

¶3: Where Americans live: the author explains that cars allowed wealthier people to move out of the cities. The author has a strong negative opinion of this trend, arguing that it deepened the wealth gap.

population in cities, the automobile
contributed to urban sprawl and,
eventually, to the rise of suburbs. People
no longer needed to live near railroad

45 lines or within walking distance of
their jobs, and so were drawn to
outlying areas with less congestion
and lower property taxes. Business
districts became less centralized for

50 similar reasons. Sadly, this movement
toward suburbs exacerbated social
stratification. Since cars were initially
affordable only to wealthier people, the
upper and middle classes moved out

55 of cities. Many businesses followed,
attracted by the educated, well-trained
workforce. As good jobs also moved
out of cities, the people who remained
were further disadvantaged and

60 even less able to leave. Though few
anticipated it in the heady early days of
suburban growth, by the century's end,
cars had helped to further entrench
social divisions in America by making

65 possible great physical distances
between rich and poor.

Automobile ownership has also
transformed our individual lives
and values. Historian James Flink

70 has observed that automobiles
particularly altered the work patterns
and recreational opportunities of
farmers and other rural inhabitants by
reducing the isolation that had been

75 characteristic of life in the country.
Of course, there were also profound
changes in the recreational activities
of suburban and urban dwellers. For
example, the 1950s saw a huge increase

80 in drive-in movie theaters, fast-food
establishments, supermarkets, and
shopping centers—most facets of how
we ate, shopped, and played changed
to accommodate the car. Family life

85 was also affected: cars changed dating

Margin notes:

cars led to
suburbs (no
need for
trains)

author: bad
effect—
divided rich
and poor
more

personal
lives
changed

¶4: What Americans believe: the author
outlines changes cars brought to Americans'
personal lives: rural people less isolated, more
recreation for everyone, and even changes to
family life and dating.

examples

family life
changes

behavior by allowing teenagers more
independence from parental supervision
and control, and they provided women
with more freedom to leave the home.
90 This personal mobility and autonomy
afforded by the car has become an
integral part of American culture.

BIG PICTURE

Main Idea: The growth of the automobile profoundly changed how Americans work, where they live, and how they spend their personal and family time.

Author's Purpose: To outline the impact of the car's popularity on three aspects of American life and culture

---

> PSAT READING STRATEGY
>
> A good rule of thumb for summarizing a passage's main idea is to boil down the author's take-away to the reader to a single sentence. If the author had only a few seconds to make his point, what would he like the reader to remember?

Notice that the PSAT expert reads actively, consistently summing up and paraphrasing what the author has said, asking what must come next, and never getting too caught up in details. The expert reader is not thrown off by encountering a new or unfamiliar term. He uses context to understand what it must mean and remembers that he can always consult the passage if he needs to remember a name or a definition. Finally, before turning to the questions, the expert takes a few seconds to summarize the "big picture." This will help him answer questions about the passage's main idea and the author's purpose or point of view.

The Method for PSAT Reading Questions

The best-prepared PSAT test takers know that time is one of the PSAT Reading section's biggest challenges. They also know that trying to speed up and cut corners can lead to sloppy mistakes, or worse, to reading a paragraph over and over because it just isn't sinking in. So, after setting themselves up for success with helpful passage notes and a clear big picture summary, PSAT experts use a simple four-step method to tackle each question quickly and confidently.

For example, take a look at this question from the set above:

In lines 39–43 ("Unlike … suburbs"), what distinction does the author draw between the two types of transportation?

A) Railroads are a more efficient mode of transportation than automobiles.

B) Automobiles allow greater flexibility, while railroads operate on a fixed schedule.

C) Railroads promote clustered populations, while automobiles promote dispersed populations.

D) Automobiles replaced railroads as the preferred American mode of transportation.

Because different question types require different strategies, start by *unpacking* the information in the question stem and identifying the question type. You'll learn to name and characterize the six PSAT Reading question types in chapter 12. This is a Detail question, which means that you should be able to find the correct answer in the passage almost verbatim.

Next, based on the type of question, *research* the passage or consult your passage map to get the information you need. This question provides specific line numbers to go to. Here's the sentence you need: "Unlike railroads, which helped concentrate the population in cities, the automobile contributed to urban sprawl and, eventually, to the rise of suburbs."

Now, with the relevant part of the passage in mind, *predict* what the correct answer will say. In this case, you're looking for an answer choice that says that railroads tend to keep people in cities or that cars promote urban sprawl or both.

Finally, use your prediction to evaluate the choices and *find* the one correct answer. Only choice **(C)** is a match for the prediction based on the research you did: railroads promote "clustered populations," that is, cities, while cars promote "dispersed populations," that is, suburbs.

Notice that experts don't merely read or look at the answers; they *evaluate* them, knowing that only one of them answers the question correctly and that the other three are demonstrably incorrect in some way. Because PSAT experts arm themselves with strong predictions in step 3, they can often zero in on the correct response without wasting time by rereading or hunting around in the passage to check each answer. You'll go over the strategies and tactics that experts use for steps 2–4 in chapter 13.

The steps are shown in the table below:

The Method for PSAT Reading Questions	
Step 1.	Unpack the question stem
Step 2.	Research the answer
Step 3.	Predict the answer
Step 4.	Find the one correct answer

Take a look at our expert's application of the Method for PSAT Reading Questions to the questions from the passage on automobiles. Look for questions on which your own approach could have been faster and more confident.

Question	Analysis
1. The primary purpose of the passage is to A) defend the use of assembly lines in automobile manufacturing. B) draw a contrast between U.S. population distribution before and after the advent of the automobile. C) explain certain changes in recreational activities in cities, suburbs, and the country. D) describe the wide-ranging impact of the automobile on American society.	**Step 1: Unpack the question stem.** Questions that ask for the main idea or primary purpose of a passage are Global questions. With a strong big picture summary, these can be answered quickly and confidently. **Step 2: Research the answer.** Your big picture summary would be the place to go to research this. If you struggled to come up with a good summary, the first and last paragraphs are often good places to research. **Step 3: Predict the correct answer.** A good big picture summary will say that the purpose of this passage is to outline three specific influences of the car on American life. **Step 4: Find the one correct answer.** Choice **(D)** is correct; it matches the scope of the passage without being too broad or too narrow. (A), (B), and (C) are all too narrow, referring to only portions of the passage. The correct answer to a Global question must take the entire passage into account.

Question	Analysis
2. The author refers to European and American manufacturing practices in lines 22–29 primarily to A) demonstrate the quality difference between European and American cars. B) argue for a return to a less mechanized but less efficient factory system. C) highlight the positive and negative effects of the automobile on the American workplace. D) suggest that greater efficiency and more skilled laborers can improve the American workplace.	**Step 1: Unpack the question stem.** Questions that provide a detail and ask about the role it plays in the text are Function questions. The correct answer will be found by returning to the indicated portion of the text and considering the context as well as the author's purpose. **Step 2: Research the answer.** Return to the lines indicated in the question stem. The sentence in lines 22–29 begins with the phrase "In contrast," and discusses how Europeans used skilled labor to create "fewer and costlier cars," while Americans used less-skilled laborers to produce a larger quantity of goods. This statement is followed by a discussion of the "mixed blessings" of assembly-line car production. **Step 3: Predict the correct answer.** The author used these lines to indicate a difference between the types of laborers and the quantity of products produced in each country, in addition to indicating the benefits and disadvantages of assembly-line production. **Step 4: Find the one correct answer.** The prediction matches correct answer **(C)**. Choice (A) is a faulty use of detail; the author never makes the claim that American and European cars differ in quality, only that the laborers producing them are more or less skilled. While the author does point out disadvantages of assembly-line production, at no point does the author indicate that a return to a less efficient factory system would be better, eliminating (B). The author never claimed that using more skilled laborers was necessarily good or bad, as stated in (D), instead only pointing out the variation in skill as a difference between European and American manufacturing.

Reading

Question	Analysis
3. As used in line 39, "profound" most nearly means A) absolute. B) unintelligible. C) far-reaching. D) thoughtful.	**Step 1: Unpack the question stem.** Questions that ask you to define how an author used a word in a passage are Vocabulary-in-Context questions. The correct answer is a word that could easily replace the indicated word without altering the sentence's meaning. **Step 2: Research the answer.** Return to the line indicated in the question stem and read the sentences around the indicated word to get context. Given the theme of the preceding paragraph, the word "likewise" in line 39 indicates that the author will discuss another important impact that cars had on American life. **Step 3: Predict the correct answer.** Since "profound" is used in reference to population distribution and the next sentence states that "the automobile contributed to urban sprawl," look for an answer choice that means "important" or "extensive." **Step 4: Find the one correct answer.** The prediction leads to the correct answer, **(C)**. Choice (A) is extreme; an "absolute" effect would imply that there were no other influences. (B) means impossible to understand, and it is clear from the rest of this paragraph that the profound effects on population distribution were both observable and understandable. (D) is a synonym of the word "profound" when it is used to describe an idea; however, the previous paragraph did not discuss a "thoughtful" impact of the automobile, but rather a "far-reaching" one.

Question	Analysis
4. In lines 39–43 ("Unlike ... suburbs"), what distinction does the author draw between the two types of transportation? A) Railroads are a more efficient mode of transportation than automobiles. B) Automobiles allow greater flexibility, while railroads operate on a fixed schedule. C) Railroads promote clustered populations, while automobiles promote dispersed populations. D) Automobiles replaced railroads as the preferred American mode of transportation.	**Step 1: Unpack the question stem.** A question asking what "distinction" the author draws in a specific portion of the passage is a Detail question. The correct answer must be stated explicitly in the passage. **Step 2: Research the answer.** Return to lines 39–43. The author states that while railroads concentrated people in cities, the automobile "contributed to urban sprawl" and the rise of suburbs. **Step 3: Predict the answer.** Look for an answer choice that indicates that railroads brought people together, while cars moved people apart. **Step 4: Find the one correct answer.** Choice **(C)** matches the prediction and is correct. While (A), (B), and (D) may be true statements, these comparisons are never discussed in the passage.
5. It can be inferred that the author believes social stratification in the United States to be A) a positive development caused by less centralized business districts. B) an unfortunate result of ready but expensive transportation. C) an outgrowth of the rise of supermarkets and shopping centers. D) a collective choice resulting from personal mobility and autonomy.	**Step 1: Unpack the question stem.** Questions that use the word "inferred" are almost always Inference questions. They require you to identify something that follows from the passage without having been directly stated. **Step 2: Research the answer.** Social stratification is mentioned in lines 51–52. In line 50, the author uses the word "Sadly" to introduce the topic. **Step 3: Predict the answer.** In most Inference questions, you won't be able to predict the correct answer word for word, but, in this case, you can characterize the tone of the correct answer choice as one of sadness or regret. **Step 4: Find the one correct answer.** Choice **(B)** is correct; it is the only choice that reflects the author's use of "Sadly." The author would not be saddened by a positive development, as in choice (A). While the increase in the number of supermarkets and shopping centers, (C), is mentioned, as is the increase in personal mobility and autonomy, (D), neither is cited as the cause of social stratification.

Question	Analysis
6. Which choice provides the best evidence for the answer to the previous question? A) Lines 48–50 ("Business … reasons") B) Lines 50–52 ("Sadly … stratification") C) Lines 78–84 ("For example … car") D) Lines 90–92 ("This personal … culture")	**Step 1: Unpack the question stem.** This is a Command of Evidence question that asks you to locate a piece of text stated in the passage that supports the correct answer to the preceding question. **Step 2: Research the answer.** In Command of Evidence questions, the answer choices all designate specific sentences or statements in the passage and indicate their precise locations by line numbers. After researching the answer to the previous question in the passage, leave your finger on the lines where you found the support for the correct answer. Then, see if those lines appear in the choices. **Step 3: Predict the answer.** Lines 50–52 are the only ones that directly address social stratification, and, as stated in the previous question, the author's use of the word "Sadly" supports the answer that social stratification was an unfortunate development. **Step 4: Find the one correct answer.** Choice **(B)** cites the evidence for the correct answer to the preceding question, making it the correct choice for this Command of Evidence question. None of the incorrect choices refer to "social stratification," much less the author's opinion of it.

Question	Analysis
7. The author regards the conclusions of historian James Flink as A) insufficiently supported and unconvincing. B) tangential to more important issues. C) unimportant though persuasive. D) accurate but incomplete.	**Step 1: Unpack the question stem.** Questions that ask for conclusions that can be drawn from information in the passage but are not explicitly stated are Inference questions. The correct answer may require you to combine two seemingly unrelated statements from the text. **Step 2: Research the answer.** James Flink is mentioned in line 69 as a historian who observed lifestyle changes for "farmers and other rural inhabitants" as a result of the increasingly widespread use of automobiles. To better gauge the author's opinion of Flink, read the lines prior to and after line 69. The keywords "Of course" in line 76 indicate the beginning of the author's point of view. The author uses the connection keyword "also" and the emphasis keyword "profound" to state that lifestyle changes were not solely limited to "farmers and other rural inhabitants." **Step 3: Predict the answer.** Predict that the author generally agrees with Flink but also adds another aspect to Flink's thesis. **Step 4: Find the one correct answer.** Choice **(D)** is correct. (A) is incorrect because, overall, the author does agree with Flink. Choices (B) and (C) are incorrect because the author does not view Flink's conclusions as "tangential" or "unimportant."

Question	Analysis
8. Which choice provides the best evidence for the answer to the previous question? A) Lines 67–69 ("Automobile … values") B) Lines 69–78 ("Historian … dwellers") C) Lines 78–84 ("For example … car") D) Lines 84–89 ("Family … home")	**Step 1: Unpack the question stem.** This is a Command of Evidence question that asks you to locate a piece of text stated in the passage that supports the correct answer to the preceding question. **Step 2: Research the answer.** As per the last question, after introducing historian James Flink, the author proceeds to first agree with his observation about the automobile's impact on rural communities and then extend that idea to other populations. The keywords "Of course" and "also" (line 76) indicate the author's opinion. **Step 3: Predict the answer.** The correct answer will include line 76. **Step 4: Find the one correct answer.** Choice **(B)** includes the relevant lines and is correct. (A) explains why the author included Flink's work, but does not provide the author's opinion of that work. (C) is an example cited to support the author's opinion, not Flink's opinion. (D) indicates another effect of the automobile on the personal lives of Americans, but does not provide the author's opinion of Flink's conclusion.
9. As used in line 82, "facets" most nearly means A) aspects. B) faces. C) surfaces. D) viewpoints.	**Step 1: Unpack the question stem.** Questions that ask you to define how an author used a word in a passage are Vocabulary-in-Context questions. The correct answer is a word that could easily replace the indicated word without altering the sentence's meaning. **Step 2: Research the answer.** Reread the sentence that includes line 82 and replace "facets" with a word or phrase that gives the sentence the same meaning. **Step 3: Predict the answer.** "Facets" can be replaced with *ways* or *characteristics* without changing the intended meaning. **Step 4: Find the one correct answer.** Choice **(A)** is a match for the prediction and the correct answer. Choices (B), (C), and (D) are all alternative definitions of "facets," but they do not fit the context.

Question	Analysis
10. The author mentions dating behavior in lines 85–86 in order to A) show why teenagers had more independence from parental supervision. B) tie drive-in movie theaters to strained relationships between parents and their teenage children. C) illustrate one way in which the automobile changed American family life. D) challenge James Flink's thesis that the effects of the automobile on recreational opportunities were limited to rural populations.	**Step 1: Unpack the question stem.** A question that asks why the author included something in the text is a Function question. The correct answer will explain the author's purpose for discussing dating behavior in paragraph 4. **Step 2: Research the answer.** This question stem leads you directly to lines 85–86, where the author discusses various ways that family life was affected by the automobile. The author provides dating behavior as an example of these changes. **Step 3: Predict the answer.** Predict that dating behavior was included as an example of how the automobile changed family life. **Step 4: Find the one correct answer.** This prediction matches **(C)**, the correct answer. (A) is a distortion of information in the passage. The passage mentions the increased independence of teenagers as further evidence of the changes to American family life. (B) is incorrect because the author does not attempt to make such a connection in this passage. (D) is incorrect because the passage never suggests that Flink has such a thesis. While Flink happened to limit his studies to rural populations, that does not imply that Flink believed other populations were unaffected by the automobile. The author is attempting to expand upon Flink's work, not challenge his ideas.

Putting It All Together

That's the expert's approach to PSAT Reading in action. Take a moment to go over the steps one more time. Imagine applying them to the next question set you'll try. As you use the Method for PSAT Reading Questions repeatedly, it will become second nature. You won't have to say "step 1, step 2, ..." in your head; you'll just be performing them, and you'll be improving your score in the PSAT Reading section as you do.

As you consider the purpose of strategic reading and the steps of the Method for PSAT Reading Questions, think back to what you saw the PSAT expert accomplish in each step as she tackled the Automobile passage and its questions.

PSAT READING PASSAGE STRATEGY

- Extract everything you can from the pre-passage blurb
- Read each paragraph actively
- Summarize the passage's big picture

- PSAT experts never skip the pre-passage blurb. They quickly process any information that it provides for the context of the passage or that helps them anticipate what the author will cover.

- Great test takers read *actively*, asking what the author's purpose is in writing each paragraph. They also anticipate where the passage will go. Experts *map* the passage by jotting down summaries for each paragraph. They might also circle or underline keywords or phrases that indicate the author's opinion, details he wishes to highlight or emphasize, and the comparisons and contrasts he makes in the text. You will focus on these active reading and mapping skills in chapter 11.

- Experts pause for a moment after actively reading the passage to summarize the big picture by noting the passage's main idea and the author's primary purpose in writing it.

Method for PSAT Reading Questions	
Step 1.	Unpack the question stem
Step 2.	Research the answer
Step 3.	Predict the answer
Step 4.	Find the one correct answer

- **Step 1.** Great test takers determine the kind of question being asked, which indicates the kind of thinking and research the question requires. They also look for clues in the question stem to tell them where in the passage to find the correct answer. In chapter 12, you'll learn the characteristics of six types of questions found in the PSAT Reading section, and you'll learn to spot the most common research clues.

- **Step 2.** PSAT experts never answer a question on a whim. Instead they turn to the passage text or to their summaries of it. Here's where a good passage map becomes invaluable. If you're unsure where in the passage a detail or opinion was mentioned, many PSAT Reading questions could lead you to reread all or most of the passage. That's a huge waste of time. With practice, you'll learn to use the research clues from the question stem to zero in on the relevant lines of text or paragraph summary.

- **Step 3.** Before reading the answer choices, top scorers predict (or at least characterize) what the correct answer will say. This allows them to evaluate each choice against the prediction. It's not always possible to predict the correct answer word for word, but you should be able to use your research to establish the criteria for the correct answer.

- **Step 4.** In a PSAT Reading question, there is *one* correct answer. The other choices are demonstrably incorrect. Test takers who start reading the answer choices before completing steps 2 (Research) and 3 (Predict) often find themselves rereading portions of the passage after each answer choice, or worse, comparing the answer choices to each other instead of testing them against a strong prediction. If you find yourself struggling with two or more answer choices, stop. Rephrase your prediction to establish what the correct answer must say and evaluate the choices against that prediction.

By reading strategically and using the Method for PSAT Reading Questions every time you practice, you'll internalize the steps. By test day, you'll be attacking this section efficiently and accurately without even thinking about it.

In the next section, you'll see another PSAT Reading passage accompanied by 10 questions. Map the passage and apply the Method for PSAT Reading Questions presented in this lesson to answer the questions as quickly and confidently as possible.

Reading

How Much Have You Learned?

Directions: Take 15 minutes to apply the PSAT Reading passage strategy and question method to the following passage and question set. Assess your work by comparing it to the expert responses at the end of the chapter.

Questions 1–10 refer to the following passage.

The following passage is adapted from a 2016 article about single-celled organisms that was published in a popular science magazine.

The vast majority of living things are single-celled organisms. Despite their great numbers, our understanding of these life forms on even a basic
5 biochemical and phylogenetic level is only a few decades old and continues to evolve.

For most of the twentieth century, it was believed that all life forms could
10 be broadly classified into two main groups, called domains: eukaryotes, or organisms possessing a cell nucleus; and prokaryotes, or organisms lacking such a nucleus. The terms "prokaryotes"
15 and "bacteria" were used more or less interchangeably. Only in the 1970s was it discovered that there are in fact two very distinct groups of prokaryotes, not any more related to each other
20 than they are related to the eukaryotes: bacteria and archaea. This discovery was made by Carl Woese, who in 1990 proposed a three-domain system based on phylogenetics, or the degree
25 of genetic relatedness among species. Woese proposed separating bacteria and archaea based on analysis of their ribosomal RNA, genetic material that plays an active role in the formation of
30 proteins. The phylogenetic branches of Bacteria, Archaea, and Eukarya form the basis of the three-domain system of classification still in use today.

When they were first discovered,
35 all archaea were believed to be extremophiles—that is, organisms living in extreme conditions such as very hot, cold, or chemically caustic environments. We now know that
40 these organisms exist in large numbers in virtually all habitats, including in the human digestive tract. We also know that most prokaryotes that cause disease are bacteria, not archaea.
45 And we have an ever-improving understanding of the biochemical pathways employed by these two groups of organisms.

Despite our growing understanding
50 of prokaryotes, the evolutionary relationships among the Bacteria, Archaea, and Eukarya are far from clear. A comparison of the genomes of species in these three domains done
55 in 1997 showed similarities between the Bacteria and Archaea in the genes coding for enzymes, and similarities between the Archaea and Eukarya in the genes coding for protein synthesis
60 machinery. Moreover, although the Archaea are prokaryotes, the proteins that give their chromosomes structure are similar to those within the nucleus of the Eukarya. In other words, the
65 Archaea seem to be related, in different ways, to both the Bacteria and the Eukarya. Because the Eukarya are the most recent domain to evolve, it has been hypothesized that the first
70 eukaryotic cell originally arose from a prokaryotic cell within the Archaea.

If this hypothesis is correct, there still remains a tantalizing mystery: the evolution of the eukaryotic nucleus. The
75 nucleus is a complex structure within a eukaryotic cell that is encased in a membrane and that contains the cell's genetic material. There are a number

of competing models for how this
80 structure might have evolved. Leaving
out the most controversial of these,
which involves viruses, there are three
that have found significant support
within the scientific community. The
85 first is the "syntrophic model," which
states that ancient archaea slipped
inside bacterial cells and eventually
became those cells' nuclei. The second
model is based on the observation
90 that certain prokaryotes have recently
been discovered to possess a primitive
nucleus. This model suggests that
archaea might, by degrees, have
evolved complex chromosomes and
95 eventually also the nuclear membrane
encasing those chromosomes. Finally,
the most recent model proposes that
ancient archaea could have developed
a second external cell membrane, with
100 the internal cell membrane eventually
becoming the nucleus. Whether any of
these models turns out to be correct,
the discovery of the Archaea as a
separate prokaryotic domain has given
105 rise to a fascinating field of research
into evolutionary relationships.

1. The main purpose of the passage is to

    A) describe the discovery of the Archaea domain
        and its implications.

    B) suggest that the three-domain system of
        classification should be more widely adopted.

    C) refute the idea that bacteria are the most
        ancient life forms.

    D) argue for the inclusion of eukaryotes in the
        Archaea domain.

2. Based on information in the passage, it can be rea-
    sonably inferred that ribosomal RNA

    A) has improved our biochemical understanding
        of single-celled organisms.

    B) determines whether or not a single-celled
        organism has a nucleus.

    C) serves as a marker of how closely different
        species are related to one another.

    D) exists only in archaea that prefer extreme
        environments.

3. Which choice provides the best evidence for the
    answer to the previous question?

    A) Lines 2–7 ("Despite … evolve")

    B) Lines 8–14 ("For most … a nucleus")

    C) Lines 21–25 ("This discovery … species")

    D) Lines 34–39 ("When … environments")

4. In line 30, "branches" most nearly means

    A) boughs.

    B) offices.

    C) chapters.

    D) groupings.

5. The author presents the idea that the Eukarya evolved from the Archaea as

   A) conclusively proven.

   B) plausible but not definitively established.

   C) unlikely at best.

   D) convincingly disproved.

6. Which choice provides the best evidence for the answer to the previous question?

   A) Lines 30–33 ("The phylogenetic ... today")

   B) Lines 45–48 ("And we ... organisms")

   C) Lines 49–53 ("Despite ... clear")

   D) Lines 92–96 ("This model ... chromosomes")

7. The third paragraph serves mainly to

   A) note a common misconception about the Archaea.

   B) present new information about extremophiles.

   C) draw a contrast between the Bacteria and the Archaea.

   D) provide examples of the improved understanding of prokaryotes.

8. According to the passage, the genetic similarities between the Archaea and the Eukarya are significant primarily because

   A) they imply extremophilic origins for the Archaea.

   B) they suggest an evolutionary origin for the Eukarya.

   C) they undermine the belief that the Bacteria are of more ancient origin than the Archaea.

   D) they make it impossible to consider more than three phylogenetic domains.

9. In line 79, "models" most nearly means

   A) ideals.

   B) hypotheses.

   C) examples.

   D) figurines.

10. According to the passage, the syntrophic model of the evolution of the eukaryotic nucleus posits that

    A) the first eukaryotes arose from a fusion of archaea and bacteria.

    B) viruses played a role in producing the first eukaryotic cells.

    C) the first eukaryotes developed directly from archaea.

    D) a second cell membrane was involved in its development.

Reflect

Directions: Take a few minutes to recall what you've learned and what you've been practicing in this chapter. Consider the following questions, jot down your best answer for each one, and then compare your reflections to the expert responses on the following page. Use your level of confidence to determine what to do next.

Describe active, or strategic, reading on PSAT passages.

_____

_____

_____

What do PSAT experts mean by summarizing the big picture of a passage?

_____

_____

_____

How can writing brief "margin notes" help you answer PSAT Reading questions more effectively?

_____

_____

_____

What does a PSAT expert look for in the question stem of a PSAT Reading question?

_____

_____

_____

Why do expert test takers predict or characterize the correct answer to each PSAT Reading question before assessing the answer choices?

_____

_____

_____

What will you do differently on future passages and their questions?

_____

_____

_____

Reading

Expert Responses

Describe active, or strategic, reading on PSAT passages.

Because the PSAT asks many questions about why *an author has written the passage or about* how *the author makes a point, expert test takers read for the author's purpose and main idea. Noting keywords that indicate a shift or contrast in points of view or that indicate opinions and emphases help keep PSAT experts on point as they anticipate where the passage will go.*

What do PSAT experts mean by summarizing the big picture of a passage?

To read for the big picture means being able to accurately summarize the main idea of a passage and to note the author's purpose for writing it. The big picture summary helps you answer Global questions and questions that ask about the author's opinion or point of view.

How can writing brief "margin notes" help you answer PSAT Reading questions more effectively?

Jotting down margin notes provides a reference "map" to the subject or purpose of each paragraph in the passage. It helps you locate specific subjects or opinions expressed in the passage when they are called out in the questions.

What does a PSAT expert look for in the question stem of a PSAT Reading question?

Each question stem indicates the type of question and contains clues as to whether the answer will come from researching the passage text or from your big picture summary. Many question stems have specific clues (e.g., line numbers or references to details from the passage) that tell you precisely where to research.

Why do expert test takers predict or characterize the correct answer to each PSAT Reading question before assessing the answer choices?

Predicting or characterizing the correct answer allows you to evaluate each answer choice one time and to avoid rereading for every answer choice. Wrong answers often distort what the passage said or misuse details from the passage, so it's best to research the passage once to know what the correct answer must say before diving into the choices.

What will you do differently on future passages and their questions?

There is no one-size-fits-all answer to this question. Each student has his or her own initial strengths and opportunities in the Reading section. What's important here is that you're honestly self-reflective. Take what you need from the expert's examples and strive to apply it to your own performance. Many test takers convince themselves that they'll never get faster or more confident in PSAT Reading, but the truth is, many test takers who now routinely ace the Reading section were much slower and more hesitant before they learned to approach this section systematically and strategically.

Next Steps

If you answered most questions correctly in the "How Much Have You Learned?" section, and if your responses to the Reflect questions were similar to those of the PSAT expert, then consider the Method for PSAT Reading Questions an area of strength and move on to the next chapter. Come back to this topic periodically to prevent yourself from getting rusty.

If you don't yet feel confident, review the material in "The Method for PSAT Reading Questions," then try the questions you missed again. As always, be sure to review the explanations closely.

Answers and Explanations

Bacteria Passage Map

The following passage is adapted from a 2016 article about single-celled organisms that was published in a popular science magazine.

1-cell organisms: lots of them, still learning

The vast majority of living things are single-celled organisms. Despite their great numbers, our understanding of these life forms on even a basic

5 biochemical and phylogenetic level is only a few decades old and continues to evolve.

For most of the twentieth century, it was believed that all life forms could

used to be 2 divisions: euk. and prok.

10 be broadly classified into two main groups, called domains: eukaryotes, or organisms possessing a cell nucleus; and prokaryotes, or organisms lacking such a nucleus. The terms "prokaryotes"

15 and "bacteria" were used more or less interchangeably. Only in the 1970s was it discovered that there are in fact two very distinct groups of prokaryotes, not any more related to each other

now 3—euk. and 2 kind of prok.: bact. & arch

20 than they are related to the eukaryotes: bacteria and archaea. This discovery was made by Carl Woese, who in 1990 proposed a three-domain system based on phylogenetics, or the degree

Woese discovered

25 of genetic relatedness among species. Woese proposed separating bacteria and archaea based on analysis of their ribosomal RNA, genetic material that plays an active role in the formation of

30 proteins. The phylogenetic branches of Bacteria, Archaea, and Eukarya form the basis of the three-domain system of classification still in use today.

When they were first discovered,

recent discoveries

35 all archaea were believed to be extremophiles—that is, organisms living in extreme conditions such as

ANALYSIS

Pre-passage blurb: The topic of the passage is single-celled organisms. Because the source is a popular science magazine, you'll likely see descriptions of recent information or discoveries.

¶1: As expected, the passage will focus on what scientists are *now* learning about single-celled organisms.

¶2: This paragraph provides some background. Prior to the 1970s, scientists thought all life could be divided into two categories: eukaryotes (having a cell nucleus) and prokaryotes (lacking a cell nucleus). Back then, scientists didn't make a distinction between prokaryotes and bacteria. But, in the 1970s, they realized there were two totally different kinds of prokaryotes: bacteria and archaea. Carl Woese, the scientist who discovered this, came up with the new three-domain system—Bacteria, Archaea, and Eukarya (encompassing the eukaryotes)—that scientists use now.

¶3: This paragraph gives three more recent discoveries. First, different species of archaea exist in all kinds of environments. Second, the prokaryotes that cause disease are almost all bacteria, not archaea. Third, scientists have learned more about the biochemical pathways used by archaea and bacteria.

very hot, cold, or chemically caustic
environments. We now know that
40 these organisms exist in large numbers
in virtually all habitats, including in
the human digestive tract. We also
know that most prokaryotes that
cause disease are bacteria, not archaea.
45 And we have an ever-improving
understanding of the biochemical
pathways employed by these two groups
of organisms.

Despite our growing understanding
50 of prokaryotes, the evolutionary
relationships among the Bacteria,
Archaea, and Eukarya are far from
clear. A comparison of the genomes of
species in these three domains done
55 in 1997 showed similarities between
the Bacteria and Archaea in the genes
coding for enzymes, and similarities
between the Archaea and Eukarya in
the genes coding for protein synthesis
60 machinery. Moreover, although the
Archaea are prokaryotes, the proteins
that give their chromosomes structure
are similar to those within the nucleus
of the Eukarya. In other words, the
65 Archaea seem to be related, in different
ways, to both the Bacteria and the
Eukarya. Because the Eukarya are
the most recent domain to evolve, it
has been hypothesized that the first
70 eukaryotic cell originally arose from a
prokaryotic cell within the Archaea.

If this hypothesis is correct, there
still remains a tantalizing mystery: the
evolution of the eukaryotic nucleus. The
75 nucleus is a complex structure within
a eukaryotic cell that is encased in a
membrane and that contains the cell's
genetic material. There are a number
of competing models for how this
80 structure might have evolved. Leaving
out the most controversial of these,
which involves viruses, there are three
that have found significant support
within the scientific community. The

*what we
don't know:
evol. rela-
tions*

*Arch. has
similarities
w/ both Euk.
and Bact.*

*theory to
explain*

*more we
don't know:
how euk.
nucleus
evolved*

3 theories:

¶4: Here, the author addresses what scientists *don't yet know* about the three domains. Studying genes, it turns out that archaea have some things in common with bacteria but have other things in common with eukaryotes. As a result, scientists hypothesize that eukaryotes evolved from archaea.

¶5: If eukaryotes did come from archaea (which have no cell nucleus), the author says, the question of how eukaryotes got their cell nucleus is a "tantalizing mystery." The author lays out three scientifically supported theories that might have the answer. The first says archaea slipped inside bacteria and became the nucleus. The second says archaea slowly developed nuclei. The third (and most recent) says archaea developed a second outer membrane and the internal membrane became the nucleus. The author sums up by saying that the discovery of the Archaea has led to the "fascinating" research into evolutionary relationships among the three domains.

85 (first) is the "syntrophic model," which
    states that ancient archaea slipped
    inside bacterial cells and eventually
    became those cells' nuclei. The (second)
    model is based on the observation
90 that certain prokaryotes have recently
    been discovered to possess a primitive
    nucleus. This model suggests that
    archaea might, by degrees, have
    evolved complex chromosomes and
95 eventually also the nuclear membrane
    encasing those chromosomes. (Finally),
    the (most recent) model proposes that
    ancient archaea could have developed
    a second external cell membrane, with
100 the internal cell membrane eventually
    becoming the nucleus. Whether any of
    these models turns out to be correct,
    the (discovery) of the Archaea as a
    separate prokaryotic domain (has given)
105 rise to a fascinating field of research
    into evolutionary relationships.

BIG PICTURE

Main Idea: The discovery of three domains of life has led to interesting research in the evolutionary relationships among the domains.

Author's Purpose: To explain the background of discoveries about archaea and bacteria and the current research in evolution to which those discoveries led

---

1. A

Difficulty: Easy

Category: Global

Strategic Advice: If all the choices begin with verbs, use the author's tone to quickly eliminate choices.

Getting to the Answer: The tone of this passage is descriptive, not persuasive, so you can immediately eliminate (B), (C), and (D). The passage discusses the discovery of a new domain of one-celled organisms, the Archaea, confirming that **(A)** is the correct answer.

2. C

Difficulty: Medium

Category: Inference

Getting to the Answer: A small detail like "ribosomal RNA" may not be in your passage map, but three capital letters like "RNA" should stand out if you have to skim over the passage. Once you find it, read carefully and match the information in the passage to the choices. "RNA" appears in line 28. Woese used analysis of ribosomal RNA to separate the Bacteria from the Archaea. The preceding sentence says that Woese proposed his three-domain system based on the "degree of genetic relatedness among species" (lines 24–25). So ribosomal RNA must be a way of determining how related species are to each other. This matches **(C)**.

(A), (B), and (D) are distortions of the information in the passage. Although ribosomal RNA did improve scientific understanding of the types of single-celled organisms, the text does not connect ribosomal RNA to the *biochemistry* of single-celled organisms, so (A) is incorrect. Ribosomal RNA is used to distinguish between the two types of one-celled organisms that do *not* have nuclei, not between those that have nuclei and those that do not, so (B) is incorrect. Although archaea were originally believed to be extremophiles, this view was discounted; moreover, it was never connected to ribosomal RNA. Eliminate (D).

3. C

Difficulty: Medium

Category: Command of Evidence

Getting to the Answer: The support to the previous question comes from the two sentences in lines 21–30. Choice **(C)** cites the first of these sentences and is thus the correct answer.

(A) and (B) have no connection to ribosomal RNA. (D) introduces the early thinking about archaea and again has no connection to ribosomal RNA.

4. D

Difficulty: Easy

Category: Vocab-in-Context

Getting to the Answer: Return to line 30, read the sentence it contains, and predict a word or phrase to replace "branches" that retains the original meaning of the sentence. That sentence says, "the ... branches ... form the basis of the ... system of classification," so "categories" would be a good prediction. This matches **(D)**, the correct answer.

(A), (B), and (C) are alternative definitions of "branches" that do not make sense in the context of the passage. The text is not discussing branches of trees ("boughs"), branches of a business ("offices"), or branches of a club ("chapters").

5. B

Difficulty: Hard

Category: Inference

Getting to the Answer: The evolutionary relationships among the three domains are discussed in paragraph 4, which begins with the sentence "Despite our growing understanding of prokaryotes, the evolutionary relationships among the Bacteria, Archaea, and Eukarya are far from clear" (lines 49–53). The paragraph ends with the hypothesis that the Eukarya evolved from the Archaea, but that first sentence announces the author's opinion of that hypothesis: it hasn't been conclusively established. Eliminate (A). The author does seem to think that the stated hypothesis has evidence to support it: the Archaea are related to the Eukarya, and the Eukarya evolved later. Eliminate (C) and (D). The correct answer is therefore **(B)**.

6. C

Difficulty: Hard

Category: Command of Evidence

Getting to the Answer: The evidence for the answer to the last question comes from several sentences in paragraph 4. The first sentence shows that the author thinks the hypothesis is not proven; that is found in lines 49–53, which corresponds to choice **(C)**, the correct answer.

(A) is concerned with the three-domain system. (B) is about biochemistry, not genetic relatedness. (D) might be tricky: these lines describe one of the models of the evolution of the eukaryotic nucleus, and according to that model, the Eukarya evolved from the Archaea. But the author states no opinion in that sentence.

7. D

Difficulty: Medium

Category: Function

Getting to the Answer: Review your passage map and determine how the third paragraph contributes to the author's overall purpose. A good map would note that the third paragraph provides information on the new domain of one-celled organisms, the Archaea. Archaea are defined in lines 16–21 as prokaryotes, so **(D)** is correct.

(A) is too narrow. Although the paragraph does note, and correct, the original thinking about archaea, it continues to provide other examples of new knowledge about prokaryotes. (B) is a subtle distortion of information in the passage. Although archaea were originally considered to be extremophiles, the text corrects that error. (C) is a faulty use of a detail from the passage. A contrast is drawn between bacteria and archaea, but this discussion is presented in the second paragraph, not the third.

8. B

Difficulty: Hard

Category: Detail

Getting to the Answer: This question contains two clues. First, the question refers to the similarities between the Archaea and Eukarya. Consult your passage notes to find that this clue sends you to the fourth paragraph. Second, the question asks why those similarities are important, so scan the fourth paragraph for the similarities between the Archaea and Eukarya and look for a word or phrase indicating a reason. The similarities are mentioned in lines 60–64, and the reason is introduced by the keyword "Because" (line 67). The similarities are important because they indicate there may be an evolutionary connection between Archaea and Eukarya. Therefore, **(B)** is correct.

(A) is a distortion of information presented in the passage. Although archaea were originally thought to be extremophiles, the passage does not connect extreme environments to the *origins* of archaea. (C) and (D) are not discussed in the passage at all. The similarities between archaea and eukaryotes are not connected to the origin of the Bacteria, as in (C), nor to any limitation of the number of domains, as in (D).

9. B

Difficulty: Medium

Category: Vocab-in-Context

Getting to the Answer: Lines 78–80 refer to "a number of competing models for how this structure might have evolved." Substitute a different word that would make sense and use that word as your prediction. *Ideas* or *theories* would be good predictions. Choice **(B)** is a match and the correct answer.

(A), (C), and (D) are alternative definitions of "models" that do not fit the context. (A) might be tricky. The word "ideals" indicates a high standard to be aimed at; it does not have the same meaning as "ideas."

10. A

Difficulty: Easy

Category: Detail

Getting to the Answer: The eukaryotic nucleus is discussed in the last paragraph. A quick skim shows that the "syntrophic model" is mentioned in line 85. The sentence states that according to this model, "archaea slipped inside bacterial cells and eventually became those cells' nuclei" (lines 86–88). So the eukaryotic cell arose from the two types of prokaryotic cells according to this model, making **(A)** correct.

(B) is incorrect because the theory that involves viruses is the controversial one that the author chooses not to describe. (C) refers to the second and third theories that are described, not the syntrophic model. Similarly, (D) refers to the third theory, not the syntrophic model.

CHAPTER 11

PSAT Reading Passage Strategies

LEARNING OBJECTIVES

After completing this chapter, you will be able to:

- Identify keywords that promote active reading and relate passage text to the questions
- Create short, accurate margin notes that help you research the text efficiently
- Summarize the big picture of the passage

How Much Do You Know?

Directions: In this chapter, you'll learn how PSAT experts actively read the passage, take notes, and summarize the main idea to prepare themselves to answer all of the passage's questions quickly and confidently. You saw this kind of reading modeled in the previous chapter. To get ready for the current chapter, take five minutes to actively read the following passage by 1) noting the keywords that indicate the author's point of view and the passage's structure, 2) jotting down a quick description next to each paragraph, and 3) summarizing the big picture (the passage's main idea and the author's purpose for writing it). When you're done, compare your work to the sample passage map that follows.

This passage is adapted from a 2018 article reviewing the benefits and shortcomings of a financial model called microcredit.

Until a few decades ago, it was virtually impossible for an impoverished person to obtain credit from an institutional source like a
5 bank. Lacking collateral or verifiable income, such people—often citizens of developing nations—simply could not qualify for even a small loan from a traditional financial institution. As a
10 result, these people were unable to start businesses that could free them from the trap of poverty.

Some financial experts put forth an intriguing theory: if impoverished
15 people had access to very small loans, called microloans, for the purpose of funding small businesses, they could lift themselves up from poverty to self-employment and perhaps even into
20 a position to employ others. In 1976, an economics professor in Bangladesh extended a microloan of 27 dollars to a group of impoverished village women for the purpose of buying supplies for
25 their business manufacturing bamboo stools. The loan allowed the women to make a modest profit and grow their business to a point of self-sufficiency.

Advocates of microlending built
30 on this initial success, maintaining that microcredit was an avenue to widespread entrepreneurship among the poor that could increase individual

wealth and, ultimately, reduce poverty.
35 Additionally, since microloans were frequently extended to women borrowers, supporters contended that microfinance was a way to empower women. A variety of microcredit
40 organizations sprang up to serve the needs of the poor in Asia, Latin America, Africa, and Eastern Europe.

A number of different microlending business models developed, and over
45 the ensuing decades, the number of customers of microcredit grew from a few hundred to tens of millions worldwide. Microlenders and microcredit advocates told stories of
50 desperately poor people who had lifted themselves out of poverty and into self-sufficiency, and of impoverished women who had become family breadwinners through the use of
55 microloans. Microfinance, it seemed, was a tremendous success.

Soon, however, another side of the story came to light. Anecdotes emerged about impoverished borrowers
60 who were unable to pay their interest from their business earnings, became imprisoned in debt, and were forced to sell off their meager possessions to meet their loan obligations. Other stories
65 described customers who used their loans for consumption spending rather than to finance businesses, and who were thus unable either to pay their interest or to return the original money
70 borrowed. A backlash developed against

microlending. Members of the media, politicians, and public administrators harshly criticized the industry and its advocates for promoting a process
75 that could harm rather than help the neediest and most vulnerable people.

Nevertheless, economists were more cautious. They recognized that anecdotes were not adequate to support
80 either side of the debate meaningfully. What was needed was solid scientific evidence that could quantify the real impacts of microlending. Academics focused on finance and
85 development performed a number of studies exploring various aspects of microfinance.

When researchers aggregated the findings of the best of these studies,
90 they concluded that microlending was not the panacea claimed by its advocates. Poverty had not been alleviated on a widescale, or even measurably reduced. Moreover, there
95 was little if any evidence that women had been substantially empowered by microcredit. Perhaps most tellingly, the average incomes of microloan customers had not risen above their
100 previous levels.

Critics jumped on these findings, claiming that they proved that microfinance as a whole was a failure.

Undeterred, advocates could still point
105 to a variety of less dramatic yet still worthwhile positive outcomes that resulted from microcredit. While borrowers had not increased their incomes on average, they often replaced
110 longer hours of grueling wage-work with more fulfilling and less onerous self-employment. In many cases, temptation spending—expenditures on things like tobacco, alcohol, and
115 gambling—had been reduced in favor of greater savings and expenditures on durable goods, better food, and healthcare. There is also evidence that borrowers' use of microcredit
120 extended beyond financing small businesses to "income smoothing," the use of microloans to ease the financial stresses of temporary or seasonal unemployment, crop failures, health
125 crises, and the like.

While the original lofty expectations for microfinance were overly optimistic, it would be unfair and inaccurate to classify the practice as a failure. Rather,
130 microfinance should be viewed as a useful tool to help impoverished people better their circumstances, even if only modestly.

Microcredit Passage Map

This passage is adapted from a 2018 article reviewing the benefits and shortcomings of a financial model called microcredit.

Until a few decades ago, it was virtually impossible for an impoverished person to obtain credit from an institutional source like a

5 bank. Lacking collateral or verifiable income, such people—often citizens of developing nations—simply could not qualify for even a small loan from a traditional financial institution. As a

10 result, these people were unable to start businesses that could free them from the trap of poverty.

Some financial experts put forth an intriguing theory: if impoverished

15 people had access to very small loans, called microloans, for the purpose of funding small businesses, they could lift themselves up from poverty to self-employment and perhaps even into

20 a position to employ others. In 1976, an economics professor in Bangladesh extended a microloan of 27 dollars to a group of impoverished village women for the purpose of buying supplies for

25 their business manufacturing bamboo stools. The loan allowed the women to make a modest profit and grow their business to a point of self-sufficiency.

Advocates of microlending built

30 on this initial success, maintaining that microcredit was an avenue to widespread entrepreneurship among the poor that could increase individual wealth and, ultimately, reduce poverty.

35 Additionally, since microloans were frequently extended to women borrowers, supporters contended that microfinance was a way to empower women. A variety of microcredit

40 organizations sprang up to serve

very poor could not get loans

theory: microloans could help

example

pro-microloan arguments

ANALYSIS

Pre-passage blurb: The passage will likely define "microcredit" and then analyze its advantages and disadvantages.

¶1: The author presents a problem: in the past, impoverished people could not get loans to help them get out of poverty.

¶2: The author defines microcredit—very small loans to people in poverty—and presents an example of its early success for women in a small Bangladeshi village.

¶3: This paragraph outlines the growth of microcredit. Lenders contended that micro-loans would build entrepreneurship, especially helping women.

the needs of the poor in Asia, Latin
America, Africa, and Eastern Europe.

A number of different microlending
business models developed, and over
45 the ensuing decades, the number of
customers of microcredit grew from
a few hundred to tens of millions
worldwide. Microlenders and
microcredit advocates told stories of
50 desperately poor people who had lifted
themselves out of poverty and into
self-sufficiency, and of impoverished
women who had become family
breadwinners through the use of
55 microloans. Microfinance, it seemed,
was a tremendous success.

Soon, however, another side of
the story came to light. Anecdotes
emerged about impoverished borrowers
60 who were unable to pay their interest
from their business earnings, became
imprisoned in debt, and were forced to
sell off their meager possessions to meet
their loan obligations. Other stories
65 described customers who used their
loans for consumption spending rather
than to finance businesses, and who
were thus unable either to pay their
interest or to return the original money
70 borrowed. A backlash developed against
microlending. Members of the media,
politicians, and public administrators
harshly criticized the industry and
its advocates for promoting a process
75 that could harm rather than help the
neediest and most vulnerable people.
Nevertheless, economists were
more cautious. They recognized that
anecdotes were not adequate to support
80 either side of the debate meaningfully.
What was needed was solid scientific
evidence that could quantify the
real impacts of microlending.
Academics focused on finance and
85 development performed a number of
studies exploring various aspects of
microfinance.

*microloan
successes*

*microloan
failure
stories*

*economists:
need real
data*

¶4: Microcredit lenders grew to the millions
and the practice *seemed* to be very successful.
The word "seemed" suggests that the next
paragraph will give a counterargument.

¶5: The contrast word, "however," and the
phrase "another side of the story" indicate
that this paragraph is about the downside of
microcredit. The author outlines several negative stories and says the result was a public
backlash.

¶6: Here's another contrast ("Nevertheless"):
economists didn't want good or bad stories;
they wanted real data and performed studies.

When researchers aggregated the findings of the best of these studies, they concluded that microlending was not the panacea claimed by its advocates. Poverty had not been alleviated on a widescale, or even measurably reduced. Moreover, there was little if any evidence that women had been substantially empowered by microcredit. Perhaps most tellingly, the average incomes of microloan customers had not risen above their previous levels.

research results

Critics jumped on these findings, claiming that they proved that microfinance as a whole was a failure. Undeterred, advocates could still point to a variety of less dramatic yet still worthwhile positive outcomes that resulted from microcredit. While borrowers had not increased their incomes on average, they often replaced longer hours of grueling wage-work with more fulfilling and less onerous self-employment. In many cases, temptation spending—expenditures on things like tobacco, alcohol, and gambling—had been reduced in favor of greater savings and expenditures on durable goods, better food, and healthcare. There is also evidence that borrowers' use of microcredit extended beyond financing small businesses to "income smoothing," the use of microloans to ease the financial stresses of temporary or seasonal unemployment, crop failures, health crises, and the like.

anti: microcredit a failure

VS.

pro: still good outcomes

While the original lofty expectations for microfinance were overly optimistic, it would be unfair and inaccurate to classify the practice as a failure. Rather, microfinance should be viewed as a useful tool to help impoverished people better their circumstances, even if only modestly.

author: microloans somewhat helpful

¶7: The studies gave three negative results: 1) poverty not alleviated, 2) women not helped, and 3) no increase in average income.

¶8: Because of the negative conclusions, critics of microcredit said the whole idea was a failure, but microcredit supporters pointed out several small, good outcomes: 1) reduced hard labor, 2) reduced temptation spending, and 3) better individual crisis management.

¶9: Author's conclusion: microcredit is *not* a total failure; it can give people in poverty some help.

BIG PICTURE

Main Idea: Microcredit provides some relief for impoverished people even if it is not the total success its supporters imagined.

Author's Purpose: To analyze the claims of microcredit advocates and critics in light of research on the subject

PSAT Reading Strategies—Keywords, Margin Notes, and the Big Picture Summary

LEARNING OBJECTIVES

After this lesson, you will be able to:

- Identify keywords that promote active reading and relate passage text to the questions
- Create short, accurate margin notes that help you research the text efficiently
- Summarize the big picture of the passage

To read and map a passage like this:

This passage is adapted from an article called "Nature's Tiny Farmers" that appeared in a popular biology magazine in 2018.

Leafcutter ants are among the most ecologically important animals in the American tropics. At least forty-seven species of leafcutter ants range from
5 as far south as Argentina to as far north as the southern United States. These ants, as their name implies, cut sections of vegetation—leaves, flowers, and grasses—from an array of plants,
10 taking the cut sections back into their underground nests. However, the ants don't feed on the vegetation they cut; in fact, they're unable to digest the material directly. Instead, they carry
15 the fragments into dedicated chambers within their nests, where they cultivate a particular species of nutritious fungus on the cut vegetation. It is this fungus that the ants eat and feed to their
20 larvae.

Remarkably, each species of leafcutter ant cultivates a different species of fungus, and each of these fungi grows nowhere but within the
25 nests of its own species of leafcutter ant. According to entomologist Ted Schultz of the Smithsonian National Museum of Natural History, "The fungi that [the ants] grow are never found in the
30 wild, they are now totally dependent on the ants." In other words, over millions of years, the ants have actually domesticated the fungi, much as we humans have domesticated the plants
35 we grow for crops.

The leafcutters' foraging trails extend hundreds of meters throughout the landscape. The ants harvest a wide range of vegetation but are selective,
40 preferring particular plant species and picking younger growth to cut. Research has also shown that the ants often limit how much they cut from a single plant, possibly in response to chemical
45 defenses the cut plant produces. In this way, the amount of damage they cause to individual plants is limited.

Leafcutters are probably the most important environmental engineers
50 in the areas they occupy. A single leafcutter nest can extend as far as 21 meters underground, have a central mound 30 meters in diameter with branches extending out to a radius of
55 80 meters, contain upwards of 1,000 individual chambers, and house up to eight million ants. Where they are present, leafcutters are responsible for up to 25 percent or more of the
60 total consumption of vegetation by all herbivores.

Alejandro G. Farji-Brener of Argentina's National Scientific and Technical Research Council and
65 Mariana Tadey of the National University of Comahue wanted to better understand how the activities of leafcutter ants influence soil conditions. To do so, they analyzed the data from
70 a large number of previous studies to determine how various environmental factors play into the ants' behavior and their effects on local ecology.

The researchers found that
75 overall soil quality and fertility are dramatically higher where leafcutters are present. The ants affect the soil in two ways: first, the physical shifting of the soil that occurs as a
80 consequence of nest construction improves soil porosity, drainage, and aeration; additionally, the ants' fungus-cultivating activities generate enormous amounts of plant waste,
85 which the ants carry away, either into specialized chambers within the nest or to dedicated refuse piles outside. In fact, this movement of organic matter may be the largest performed by any

90 animal in the environment. This transfer of huge volumes of organic material results in greatly enriched soil, with nutrient levels that are orders of magnitude higher than in areas where 95 the ants are not present.

The researchers also determined that seeds germinate more easily and at higher rates in these soils. Additionally, plants grow substantially better in soils 100 that have been modified by leafcutters. In effect, then, the ants create conditions that encourage the growth of plants, thereby greatly improving the conditions of the landscape in general. 105 Furthermore, in areas of disturbance or degradation, such as lands that have been overgrazed or deforested, or those suffering from the effects of fire or drought, leafcutters are major 110 contributors to the natural restoration of healthy plant communities and the overall recovery of the land. The study concludes that "in terms of conservation, ant-nest areas should be 115 especially protected…because they are hot spots of plant productivity and diversity."

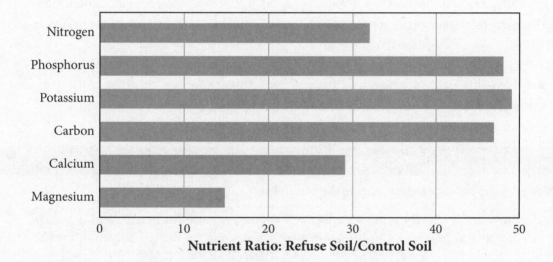

Nutrient Ratio: Refuse Soil/Control Soil

Relative Nutrient Content of Leafcutter Ant Soils—Ratios of Leafcutter Ant Soils to Control Soil		
Nutrient	**Nest Soil: Control Soil**	**Refuse Soil: Control Soil**
Nitrogen	1.4:1	33:1
Phosphorus	2.0:1	48:1
Potassium	1.4:1	49:1
Carbon	4.2:1	47:1
Calcium	1.9:1	29:1
Magnesium	2.2:1	15:1

You'll need to know this:

- PSAT Reading passages are preceded by short blurbs that tell you about the author and source of the passage.
- There are three categories of keywords that reveal an author's purpose and point of view and that unlock the passage's structure:
  - **Opinion and Emphasis**—words or phrases that signal that the author finds a detail noteworthy (e.g., *especially, crucial, important, above all*) or has an opinion about it (e.g., *fortunately, disappointing, I suggest, it seems likely*)
  - **Connection and Contrast**—words or phrases that suggest that a subsequent detail continues the same point (e.g., *moreover, in addition, also, further*) or that indicate a change in direction or point of difference (e.g., *but, yet, despite, on the other hand*)
    - In some passages, these keywords may show steps in a process or developments over time (e.g., *traditionally, in the past, recently, today, first, second, finally, earlier, since*).
  - **Evidence and Example**—words or phrases that indicate an argument (the use of evidence to support a conclusion), either the author's or someone else's (e.g., *thus, therefore, because*), or that introduce an example to clarify or support another point (e.g., *for example, such as, to illustrate*)
- PSAT experts read strategically, jotting down brief, accurate, and useful margin notes next to each paragraph.
- Expert test takers summarize the passage as a whole by paying attention to its big picture:
  - **Main Idea**—the author's primary conclusion or overall takeaway
  - **Author's Purpose**—the author's reason for writing the passage
    - Express this as a verb (e.g., *to explain, to evaluate, to argue, to refute*)

READING PASSAGE AND QUESTION STRATEGY

Why read the passage before reading the questions?

Each PSAT Reading passage is accompanied by 9 or 10 questions. One or two of the questions may ask about the passage as a whole. The others will ask about specific paragraphs, details, or arguments within the passage. PSAT experts use deliberate Reading strategies to answer all of the questions quickly and accurately, with a minimum of rereading.

You'll need to do this:

THE PSAT READING PASSAGE STRATEGY

- Extract everything you can from the pre-passage blurb
- Read each paragraph actively
- Summarize the passage's big picture

Extract everything you can from the pre-passage blurb:

- Quickly prepare for the passage by unpacking the pre-passage blurb.
  - What does the title and date of the original book or article tell you about the author and her purpose for writing?
  - What information can you glean from the source (nonfiction book, novel, academic journal, etc.)?
  - Is there any other information that provides context for the passage?

Read each paragraph actively:

- Note keywords (circling or underlining them may help) and use them to focus your reading on:
  - The author's purpose and point of view
  - The relationships between ideas
  - The illustrations or other support provided for passage claims

---

KEYWORDS

Why pay attention to keywords?

Keywords indicate opinions and signal structure that make the difference between correct and incorrect answers on PSAT questions. Consider this question:

> With which one of the following statements would the author most likely agree?
>
> 1. Coffee beans that grow at high altitudes typically produce dark, mellow coffee when brewed.
>
> 2. Coffee beans that grow at high altitudes typically produce light, acidic coffee when brewed.

To answer that based on a PSAT passage, you will need to know whether the author said:

> Type X coffee beans grow at very high altitudes *and so* produce a dark, mellow coffee when brewed.

That would make choice (1) correct. But if the author instead said:

> Type X coffee beans grow at very high altitudes *but* produce a *surprisingly* dark, mellow coffee when brewed.

Then choice (2) would be correct. The facts in the statements did not change at all, but the correct answer to the PSAT question would be different in each case because of the keywords the author chose to include.

- As you read, jot down brief, accurate margin notes that will help you research questions about specific details, examples, and paragraphs.
  - Paraphrase the text (put it into your own words) as you go.
  - Ask "What's the author's point and purpose?" for each paragraph.

MARGIN NOTES

Why jot down notes next to each paragraph?

PSAT Reading is an open-book test. The answer is always in the passage. Margin notes help you zero in on the details and opinions you need to answer questions like these:

As used in line 32, "erased" most nearly means

In the context of the passage as a whole, the question in lines 72–74 primarily functions to help the author

The passage most strongly implies which of the following statements about the Great Recession?

In the third paragraph (lines 52–74), the most likely purpose of the author's discussion of the "gig economy" is to

---

Summarize the passage's big picture:

- At the end of the passage, pause for a few seconds to summarize the passage's big picture to prepare for Global questions. Ask yourself:
  - "What is the main idea of the entire passage?"
  - "Why did the author write it?"

THE BIG PICTURE

Why summarize the passage's big picture?

Summarizing the big picture prepares you to answer Global questions such as the following:

Which one of the following most accurately expresses the main point of the passage?

The passage primarily serves to

Explanation:

Leafcutter Passage Map

This passage is adapted from an article called "Nature's Tiny Farmers" that appeared in a popular biology magazine in 2018.

Leafcutter ants are among the (most) (ecologically important) animals in the American tropics. At least forty-seven species of leafcutter ants range from

5 as far south as Argentina to as far north as the southern United States. These ants, (as their name implies,) cut sections of vegetation—leaves, flowers, and grasses—from an array of plants,

10 taking the cut sections back into their underground nests. (However,) the ants don't feed on the vegetation they cut; (in fact,) they're unable to digest the material directly. (Instead,) they carry

15 the fragments into dedicated chambers within their nests, where they cultivate a particular species of nutritious fungus on the cut vegetation. It is this fungus that the ants eat and feed to their

20 larvae.

leafcutter ants "farm" fungus using cut vegetation

(Remarkably,) each species of leafcutter ant cultivates a different species of fungus, and each of these fungi grows (nowhere but) within the

25 nests of its own species of leafcutter ant. According to entomologist Ted Schultz of the Smithsonian National Museum of Natural History, "The fungi that [the ants] grow are never found in the

30 wild, they are now totally dependent on the ants." (In other words,) over millions of years, the ants have (actually) domesticated the fungi, much as we humans have domesticated the plants

35 we grow for crops.

unique fungus for each ant species

ant domesticated fungus

The leafcutters' foraging trails extend hundreds of meters throughout the landscape. The ants harvest a (wide) (range) of vegetation but are selective,

40 preferring particular plant species and

ants' plant cutting explained

ANALYSIS

Pre-passage blurb: The passage was written for a popular biology magazine, so no expertise is expected. The title hints that these ants "cultivate" in some way.

PSAT Reading Strategy: On the actual PSAT, the pre-passage blurb will always give the author's name, the title of the book or article from which the passage was adapted, and the year it was published. When necessary, the blurb may also include a context-setting sentence with additional information. Train yourself to unpack the blurb to better anticipate what the passage will cover.

¶1: The author emphasizes the leafcutter ants' value for the environment and explains their name: they cut leaves and grasses and use them to grow the fungi they eat.

¶2: Using the opinion keyword "remarkably," the author writes that each species of leafcutter ant cultivates its own species of fungus, which grows only in that ant species' nest. Citing an entomologist who says that the fungi are dependent on the ants, the author makes the point that the ants have actually *domesticated* the fungi, as humans have domesticated crop plants.

¶3: The author describes the size of the ants' harvest areas. They cut a wide variety of vegetation, "but" (contrast keyword) they are selective about what they take and limit the damage they do to individual plants.

picking younger growth to cut. Research
has also shown that the ants often
limit how much they cut from a single
plant, possibly in response to chemical
45   defenses the cut plant produces. In this
way, the amount of damage they cause
to individual plants is limited.

Leafcutters are probably the most
important environmental engineers
50   in the areas they occupy. A single
leafcutter nest can extend as far as
21 meters underground, have a central
mound 30 meters in diameter with
branches extending out to a radius of
55   80 meters, contain upwards of 1,000
individual chambers, and house up
to eight million ants. Where they are
present, leafcutters are responsible
for up to 25 percent or more of the
60   total consumption of vegetation by all
herbivores.

Alejandro G. Farji-Brener of
Argentina's National Scientific and
Technical Research Council and
65   Mariana Tadey of the National
University of Comahue wanted to
better understand how the activities of
leafcutter ants influence soil conditions.
To do so, they analyzed the data from
70   a large number of previous studies to
determine how various environmental
factors play into the ants' behavior and
their effects on local ecology.

The researchers found that
75   overall soil quality and fertility are
dramatically higher where leafcutters
are present. The ants affect the
soil in two ways: first, the physical
shifting of the soil that occurs as a
80   consequence of nest construction
improves soil porosity, drainage,
and aeration; additionally, the ants'
fungus-cultivating activities generate
enormous amounts of plant waste,
85   which the ants carry away, either into
specialized chambers within the nest or
to dedicated refuse piles outside.

why ants so impt to environ-ment

2 scientists research LC ants

review prev studies

findings: soil better where LC ants are

reason 1

reason 2

¶4: The author highlights the ants' importance as "environmental engineers" by describing the size of their nests and the volume of vegetation they consume in their areas.

¶5: The author introduces two researchers who analyzed a large number of earlier studies to investigate how leafcutter ants affect the soil.

¶6: The researchers' findings: leafcutter ants improve soil quality. This occurs "two ways": 1) physically shifting the soil, and 2) creating plant waste with their fungus cultivation. The author emphasizes that leafcutter ants may be *the largest* mover of organic matter in their environment.

(In fact,) this movement of organic matter
may be the (largest) performed by any   HUGE
                                             impact
90 animal in the environment. This
    transfer of huge volumes of organic
    material results in greatly enriched soil,
    with nutrient levels that are (orders of)
    (magnitude higher) than in areas where
95 the ants are not present.

        The researchers (also determined)   more
    that seeds germinate more easily and at   findings:
    higher rates in these soils. (Additionally,) seeds and
    plants grow substantially better in soils plants grow
                                              better
100 that have been modified by leafcutters.
    In effect, then, the ants create
    conditions that encourage the growth
    of plants, (thereby) greatly improving the
    conditions of the landscape in general.
105 (Furthermore,) in areas of disturbance
    or degradation, such as lands that
    have been overgrazed or deforested,
    or those suffering from the effects of
    fire or drought, leafcutters are major
110 contributors to the natural restoration
    of healthy plant communities and
    the overall recovery of the land. The   recom-
    study (concludes) that "in terms of   mendation:
                                             protect LC
    conservation, ant-nest areas should be   ant areas
115 especially protected...because they
    are hot spots of plant productivity and
    diversity."

¶7: Another finding from the researchers: soils altered by the ants feature higher rates of seed germination and better-growing plants. The ants help to restore damaged landscapes. Because the ants are so important, the researchers recommend protecting the areas with leafcutter ant nests, noting that they are "hot spots" for plant diversity.

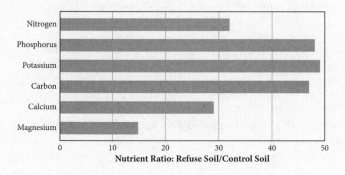

Nutrient Ratio: Refuse Soil/Control Soil

Graph: The caption indicates that this graph refers to "Nutrient Ratio: Refuse Soil/Control Soil." The bars of the graph represent various nutrients (nitrogen, phosphorus, etc). So, the longer a bar, the more that nutrient is present in refuse soil when compared to control soil.

Reading

Relative Nutrient Content of Leafcutter Ant Soils— Ratios of Leafcutter Ant Soils to Control Soil		
Nutrient	**Nest Soil: Control Soil**	**Refuse Soil: Control Soil**
Nitrogen	1.4:1	33:1
Phosphorus	2.0:1	48:1
Potassium	1.4:1	49:1
Carbon	4.2:1	47:1
Calcium	1.9:1	29:1
Magnesium	2.2:1	15:1

Table: The table compares "leafcutter ant" soils to "control" soils (soils that leafcutter ants did not impact). On the left are the ratios of nutrients in nest soil to control soil. All of the nutrients are present in greater amounts in the nest soil than in the control. On the right are the ratios of nutrients in refuse soil to control soil. The nutrients are present in even greater amounts in the refuse soil than in the nest soil. Leafcutter ants increase the amount of these nutrients in their nest soil, and increase it even more in their refuse soil. The rightmost column of the table includes the same data as depicted visually in the graph.

CHARTS AND GRAPHS IN PSAT READING

- What information does the graphic contain?
- Why has the author included the graphic?
- Which paragraph(s) does this information relate to?
- Does the graphic display any trends or relationships that support a point made in the passage?

In the Reading section, you will not be asked to perform calculations from the data in graphs. You will be asked how they relate to the passage and which claims or arguments they support or refute.

BIG PICTURE

Main Idea: Leafcutter ants are impressive environmental engineers with profound and positive effects on their environments.

Author's Purpose: To describe the range, nests, and fungus cultivation of the ants and to summarize the research on how they alter and improve their environments

---

Now, try another passage on your own. Use the PSAT Reading strategies and tactics you've been learning to read and map this passage as quickly and accurately as you can.

Try on Your Own

Directions: Actively read and map the following passage by 1) circling or underlining keywords (from the Emphasis and Opinion, Connection and Contrast, or Evidence and Example categories), 2) jotting down brief, accurate margin notes that reflect good paraphrases of each paragraph, and 3) summing up the big picture. When you're done, compare your work to that of a PSAT expert in the Answers and Explanations at the end of the chapter.

This passage, about the decline of the Norse colonies that once existed in Greenland, is from a comprehensive 2015 research report examining this anthropological mystery.

In 1721, the Norwegian missionary Hans Egede discovered that the two known Norse settlements on Greenland were completely deserted. Ever since,
5　the reasons behind the decline and eventual disappearance of these people have been greatly debated. Greenland, established by the charismatic outlaw Erik the Red in about 986 c.e., was
10　a colony of Norway by 1000 c.e., complete with a church hierarchy and trading community. After several relatively prosperous centuries, the colony had fallen on hard times and
15　was not heard from in Europe, but it wasn't until Egede's discovery that the complete downfall of the settlement was confirmed.

Throughout the nineteenth century,
20　researchers attributed the demise of the Norse colonies to war between the colonies and Inuit groups. This is based largely on evidence from the work *Description of Greenland*,
25　written by Norse settler Ivar Bardarson around 1364, which describes strained relationships between the Norse settlers and the Inuits who had recently come to Greenland. However, because there is
30　no archaeological evidence of a war or a massacre, and the extensive body of Inuit oral history tells of no such event, modern scholars give little credence to these theories.

35　New theories about the reason for the decline of the Norse colonies are being proposed partially because the amount of information available is rapidly increasing. Advances in
40　paleoclimatology, for example, have increased the breadth and clarity of our picture of the region. Most notably, recent analyses of the central Greenland ice core, coupled with data obtained
45　from plant material and sea sediments, have indicated severe climate changes in the region that some are now calling a "mini ice age." Such studies point toward a particularly warm period
50　for Greenland that occurred between the years 800 c.e. and 1300 c.e., which was then followed—unfortunately for those inhabiting even the most temperate portions of the island—by a
55　steady decline in overall temperatures that lasted for nearly 600 years. The rise and fall of the Norse colonies in Greenland, not surprisingly, roughly mirrors this climate-based chronology.

60　Researchers have also found useful data in a most surprising place—fly remains. The insect, not native to the island, was brought over inadvertently on Norse ships. Flies survived in the
65　warm and unsanitary conditions of the Norse dwellings and barns and died out when these were no longer inhabited. By carbon dating the fly remains, researchers have tracked the occupation
70　of the settlements and confirmed that the human population began to decline around 1350 c.e.

Changing economic conditions likely also conspired against the settlers. The colonies had founded a moderately successful trading economy based on exporting whale ivory, especially important given their need for the imported wood and iron that were in short supply on the island. Unfortunately, inexpensive and plentiful Asian and African elephant ivory flooded the European market during the fourteenth century, destroying Greenland's standing in the European economy. At the same time, the trading fleet of the German Hanseatic League supplanted the previously dominant Norwegian shipping fleets. Because the German merchants had little interest in the Norse colonists, Greenland soon found itself visited by fewer and fewer ships each year until its inhabitants were completely isolated by 1480 c.e.

Cultural and sociological factors may have also contributed to the demise of the Norse settlements. The Inuit tribes, while recent immigrants to Greenland, had come from nearby areas to the west and had time-tested strategies to cope with the severe environment. The Norse settlers, however, seem to have viewed themselves as fundamentally European and did not adopt Inuit techniques. Inuit apparel, for example, was far more appropriate for the cold, damp environment; the remains from even the last surviving Norse settlements indicate a costume that was undeniably European in design. Likewise, the Norse settlers failed to adopt Inuit hunting techniques and tools, such as the toggle harpoon, which made it possible to capture calorie-rich seal meat. Instead, the Norse relied on the farming styles that had been so successful for their European ancestors, albeit in a radically different climate. It seems likely that this stubborn cultural inflexibility prevented the Norse civilization in Greenland from adapting to increasingly severe environmental and economic conditions.

How Much Have You Learned?

Directions: Take five minutes to actively read the following passage by 1) noting the keywords, 2) jotting down margin notes next to each paragraph, and 3) summarizing the big picture. When you're done, compare your work to the Answers and Explanations at the end of the chapter.

This passage, about infant language acquisition, is adapted from a research paper written in 2017 that explored early childhood development.

Infants are born as scientists, constantly interacting with and questioning the world around them. However, as any good scientist
5 knows, simply making observations is not sufficient; a large part of learning is dependent on being able to communicate ideas, observations, and feelings with others. Though most
10 infants do not produce discernible words until around age one or one-and-a-half, they begin gaining proficiency in their native languages long before that. In fact, many linguists agree that a
15 newborn baby's brain is already pre-programmed for language acquisition, meaning that it's as natural for a baby to talk as it is for a dog to dig.

According to psycholinguist Anne
20 Cutler, an infant's language acquisition actually begins well before birth. At only one day old, newborns have demonstrated the ability to recognize the voices and rhythms heard
25 during their last trimester in the muffled confines of the womb. In general, infants are more likely to attend to a specific voice stream if they perceive it as more familiar than other
30 streams. Newborns tend to be especially partial to their mother's voice and her native language, as opposed to another woman or another language. For example, when an infant is presented
35 with a voice stream spoken by his mother and a background stream

delivered by an unfamiliar voice, he will effortlessly attend to his mother while ignoring the background stream.
40 Therefore, by using these simple yet important cues, and others like them, infants can easily learn the essential characteristics and rules of their native language.
45 However, it is important to note that an infant's ability to learn from the nuances of her mother's speech is predicated upon her ability to separate that speech from the sounds of the
50 dishwasher, the family dog, the bus stopping on the street outside, and, quite possibly, other streams of speech, like a newscaster on the television down the hall or siblings playing in
55 an adjacent room. Infants are better able to accomplish this task when the voice of interest is louder than any of the competing background noises. Conversely, when two voices are of
60 equal amplitude, infants typically demonstrate little preference for one stream over the other. Researchers have hypothesized that because an infant's ability to selectively pay attention to
65 one voice or sound, even in a mix of others, has not fully developed yet, the infant is actually interpreting competing voice streams that are equally loud as one single stream with unfamiliar
70 patterns and sounds.

During the first few months after birth, infants will subconsciously study the language being used around them, taking note of the rhythmic
75 patterns, the sequences of sounds, and the intonation of the language.

Newborns will also start to actively process how things like differences in pitch or accented syllables further
80 affect meaning. Interestingly, up until six months of age, they can still recognize and discriminate between the phonemes (single units of sound in a language like "ba" or "pa") of other
85 languages. Though infants do display a preference for the language they heard in utero, most infants are not biased towards the specific phonemes of that language.
90   This ability to recognize and discriminate between all phonemes comes to an end by the middle of their first year, at which point infants start displaying a preference for phonemes
95 in their native language, culminating at age one, when they stop responding to foreign phonemes altogether. This is part of what is known as the "critical period," which begins at birth and
100 lasts until puberty. During this period, as the brain continues to grow and change, language acquisition is instinctual, explaining why young children seem to pick up languages so
105 easily.

Reflect

Directions: Take a few minutes to recall what you've learned and what you've been practicing in this chapter. Consider the following questions, jot down your best answer for each one, and then compare your reflections to the expert responses on the following page. Use your level of confidence to determine what to do next.

Why do PSAT experts note keywords as they read?

_____

_____

_____

What are the three categories of keywords? Provide some examples from each category.

- _____
    - Examples: _____
- _____
    - Examples: _____
- _____
    - Examples: _____

Why do PSAT experts jot down margin notes next to the text?

_____

_____

_____

What are the elements of a strong big picture summary?

_____

_____

_____

Expert Responses

Why do PSAT experts note keywords as they read?

Keywords indicate what the author finds important, express his point of view about the subject and details of the passage, and signal key points in the passage structure. Keywords are the pieces of text that help test takers see which parts of the passage are likely to be mentioned in questions and help the test taker to distinguish between correct and incorrect answer choices about those parts of the passage.

What are the three categories of keywords? Provide some examples from each category.

1. *Opinion and Emphasis*
    - Examples: *indeed, quite, masterfully, inadequate*

2. *Connection and Contrast*
    - Examples: *furthermore, plus, however, on the contrary*

3. *Evidence and Example*
    - Examples: *consequently, since, for instance, such as*

Why do PSAT experts jot down margin notes next to the text?

Margin notes help the test taker research questions that ask about details, examples, and arguments mentioned in the passage by providing a "map" to their location in the text. Margin notes can also help students answer questions about the passage structure and the purpose of a specific paragraph.

What are the elements of a strong big picture summary?

A strong big picture summary prepares a test taker to answer any question about the main idea of the passage or the author's primary or overall purpose in writing it. After reading the passage, PSAT experts pause to ask, "What's the main point of the passage?" and "Why did the author write it?"

Next Steps

If you answered most questions correctly in the "How Much Have You Learned?" section, and if your responses to the Reflect questions were similar to those of the PSAT expert, then consider PSAT Reading Passage Strategies an area of strength and move on to the next chapter. Come back to this topic periodically to prevent yourself from getting rusty.

If you don't yet feel confident, review the material in "PSAT Reading Strategies—Keywords, Margin Notes, and the Big Picture Summary," then try the exercises you missed again. As always, be sure to review the explanations closely.

Answers and Explanations

Norse Passage Map

This passage, about the decline of the Norse colonies that once existed in Greenland, is from a comprehensive 2015 research report examining this anthropological mystery.

In 1721, the Norwegian missionary Hans Egede discovered that the two known Norse settlements on Greenland were completely deserted. (Ever since,)
5   the reasons behind the decline and eventual disappearance of these people have been (greatly debated.) Greenland, established by the charismatic outlaw Erik the Red in about 986 c.e., was
10   a colony of Norway by 1000 c.e., complete with a church hierarchy and trading community. After several relatively prosperous centuries, the colony had fallen on hard times and
15   was not heard from in Europe, but it wasn't until Egede's discovery that the (complete downfall) of the settlement was confirmed.

Throughout the (nineteenth century,)
20   researchers (attributed) the demise of the Norse colonies to war between the colonies and Inuit groups. This is (based) largely (on) evidence from the work *Description of Greenland*,
25   written by Norse settler Ivar Bardarson around 1364, which describes strained relationships between the Norse settlers and the Inuits who had recently come to Greenland. (However, because) there is
30   no archaeological evidence of a war or a massacre, and the extensive body of Inuit oral history tells of no such event, (modern scholars give little credence to) these theories.
35   (New theories) about the reason for the decline of the Norse colonies are being proposed (partially because) the amount of information available

GL colony gone by 1721— reasons debated

1800s research-ers said cause was war w/ Inuits

but no arch. evid.

much new info

ANALYSIS

Pre-passage blurb: The topic of the passage is the "anthropological mystery" of Norse colonies in Greenland that disappeared. The passage is based on a 2015 research report, so there are likely to be many factual details.

¶1: The writer provides background on the existence of the Norse settlements in Greenland. In the 1700s, a missionary discovered that settlements had been deserted. The settlements' decline is a matter of debate—and given the pre-passage blurb, it is reasonable to predict that the rest of the passage will address this debate.

¶2: Nineteenth-century researchers relied on an account by a Norse settler to conclude that the decline was caused by war between Norse and Inuit people. The writer's use of the contrast keyword "however" signals a problem with this theory: modern scholars reject it due to a lack of evidence from archaeology or Inuit oral history. Expect to learn more about the modern theories next.

is rapidly increasing. Advances in
40 paleoclimatology, for example, have
increased the breadth and clarity of
our picture of the region. Most notably,
recent analyses of the central Greenland
ice core, coupled with data obtained
45 from plant material and sea sediments,
have indicated severe climate changes
in the region that some are now calling
a "mini ice age." Such studies point
toward a particularly warm period
50 for Greenland that occurred between
the years 800 c.e. and 1300 c.e., which
was then followed—unfortunately
for those inhabiting even the most
temperate portions of the island—by a
55 steady decline in overall temperatures
that lasted for nearly 600 years. The
rise and fall of the Norse colonies in
Greenland, not surprisingly, roughly
mirrors this climate-based chronology.
60 Researchers have also found useful
data in a most surprising place—fly
remains. The insect, not native to the
island, was brought over inadvertently
on Norse ships. Flies survived in the
65 warm and unsanitary conditions of the
Norse dwellings and barns and died out
when these were no longer inhabited.
By carbon dating the fly remains,
researchers have tracked the occupation
70 of the settlements and confirmed that
the human population began to decline
around 1350 c.e.

Changing economic conditions
likely also conspired against the
75 settlers. The colonies had founded a
moderately successful trading economy
based on exporting whale ivory,
especially important given their need
for the imported wood and iron that
80 were in short supply on the island.
Unfortunately, inexpensive and plentiful
Asian and African elephant ivory
flooded the European market during
the fourteenth century, destroying

climate data

big climate change b/4 colony decline

fly remains

dating shows human decline ~1350

econ problems, too

ivory market ↓

¶3: New information is driving new theories. The writer uses example keywords ("for example") to introduce evidence from paleoclimatology, which indicates that a "mini ice age" corresponded with the fall of the Norse in Greenland. In addition, carbon dating of flies—which the Norse brought to Greenland—helps to confirm when the colonies began to decline.

¶4: The writer describes an additional theory: economic conditions hurt the settlers. Their trade in whale ivory became less profitable as elephant ivory reached European markets, and the rise of German merchants meant that fewer ships visited the Greenland colonies.

85 Greenland's standing in the European
economy. At the same time, the trading
fleet of the German Hanseatic League
supplanted the previously dominant
Norwegian shipping fleets. Because the

+ German traders didn't visit GL

90 German merchants had little interest
in the Norse colonists, Greenland soon
found itself visited by fewer and fewer
ships each year until its inhabitants
were completely isolated by 1480 c.e.

95   Cultural and sociological factors may
have also contributed to the demise of
the Norse settlements. The Inuit tribes,
while recent immigrants to Greenland,
had come from nearby areas to the

also cultural factors

100 west and had time-tested strategies to
cope with the severe environment. The
Norse settlers, however, seem to have
viewed themselves as fundamentally
European and did not adopt Inuit

105 techniques. Inuit apparel, for example,
was far more appropriate for the
cold, damp environment; the remains
from even the last surviving Norse
settlements indicate a costume that

Euro. clothes

110 was undeniably European in design.
Likewise, the Norse settlers failed to
adopt Inuit hunting techniques and
tools, such as the toggle harpoon, which
made it possible to capture calorie-rich

hunting vs. farming

115 seal meat. Instead, the Norse relied on
the farming styles that had been so
successful for their European ancestors,
albeit in a radically different climate. It
seems likely that this stubborn cultural

120 inflexibility prevented the Norse
civilization in Greenland from adapting
to increasingly severe environmental
and economic conditions.

¶5: One further theory is that Norse culture may not have adapted properly to Greenland. The writer compares the Inuit and the Norse, using the examples of clothing, hunting, and farming. While the Inuit (native to the Arctic) had tools and practices suited to the environment, the Norse (in the author's opinion, "stubborn[ly]") maintained European techniques inappropriate to Greenland.

BIG PICTURE

Main Idea: New information shows that factors such as climate, economy, and culture may have caused the collapse of the Norse colonies in Greenland.

Author's Purpose: To describe current theories (and evidence for them) of what happened to the Norse in Greenland

---

Reading

Infant Language Passage Map

This passage, about infant language acquisition, is adapted from a research paper written in 2017 that explored early childhood development.

Infants are born as scientists, ~~constantly interacting~~ with ~~and~~ ~~questioning~~ the world around them. ~~However,~~ as any good scientist
5 knows, simply making observations is not sufficient; a large part of learning is dependent on being able to communicate ideas, observations, and feelings with others. ~~Though~~ most
10 infants do not produce discernible words until around age one or one-and-a-half, they begin gaining proficiency in their native languages long before that. ~~In fact,~~ many linguists agree that a
15 newborn baby's brain is already pre-programmed for language acquisition, meaning that it's as natural for a baby to talk as it is for a dog to dig.
~~According to~~ psycholinguist Anne
20 Cutler, an infant's language acquisition actually begins well before birth. At ~~only one day old,~~ newborns have demonstrated the ability to recognize the voices and rhythms heard
25 during their last trimester in the muffled confines of the womb. ~~In general,~~ infants are more likely to attend to a specific voice stream ~~if~~ they perceive it as more familiar than other
30 streams. Newborns tend to be ~~especially~~ ~~partial~~ to their mother's voice and her native language, as opposed to another woman or another language. ~~For~~ ~~example,~~ when an infant is presented
35 with a voice stream spoken by his mother and a background stream delivered by an unfamiliar voice, he will effortlessly attend to his mother while ignoring the background stream.
40 ~~Therefore,~~ by using these simple yet

babies start learning lang. b/4 they can talk

"pre-pro-grammed"

Cutler: learn lang. b/4 birth

support

ANALYSIS

Pre-passage blurb: The passage is from a research text about "infant language acquisition." It will likely be a factual, academic review of ideas and theories.

¶1: Using a couple of similes to make her point, the author states a central thesis: infants begin learning their native language well before they can produce words. She states that linguists consider babies "pre-programmed for language acquisition." The following paragraphs will elaborate on and support this thesis.

¶2: The first elaboration comes from psycho-linguist Anne Culter: infants start acquiring language before birth. The rest of the para-graph supports this claim. Newborns imme-diately recognize familiar voices, preferring their mother's voice and easily attending to it instead of others. This helps the infant learn his or her native tongue.

important cues, and others like them, infants can easily learn the essential characteristics and rules of their native language.

45 (However) it is important to note that an infant's ability to learn from the nuances of her mother's speech is predicated upon her ability to separate that speech from the sounds of the

50 dishwasher, the family dog, the bus stopping on the street outside, and, quite possibly, other streams of speech, like a newscaster on the television down the hall or siblings playing in

55 an adjacent room. Infants are (better) able to accomplish this task (when) the voice of interest is louder than any of the competing background noises. (Conversely,) when two voices are of

60 equal amplitude, infants typically demonstrate little preference for one stream over the other. Researchers have (hypothesized) that (because) an infant's ability to selectively pay attention to

65 one voice or sound, even in a mix of others, has not fully developed yet, the infant is (actually interpreting) competing voice streams that are equally loud as one single stream with unfamiliar

70 patterns and sounds.

During the first few months after birth, infants (will subconsciously) study the language being used around them, taking note of the rhythmic

75 patterns, the sequences of sounds, and the intonation of the language. Newborns (will also) start to actively process how things like differences in pitch or accented syllables further

80 affect meaning. (Interestingly,) up until six months of age, they can still recognize and discriminate between the phonemes (single units of sound in a language like "ba" or "pa") of other

85 languages. (Though) infants do display a preference for the language they heard

need mom's voice sep. from bkgd

+ louder than other voices

newborns learn patterns

<6 mos.: "hear" other lang. too

¶3: The author explains some limiting factors (note the opening contrast keyword, "however") for infant language acquisition. Babies can learn from their mother's speech only if they can separate that speech from background noise. They are better at focusing on their mother's voice when the mother's voice is louder than other sounds. Research indicates that they cannot interpret different voices of equal volume separately.

¶4: The author explains how infants start learning their native language. They subconsciously study patterns, sounds, and intonation, and start to connect sound to meaning. The author emphasizes (with "[i]nterestingly") that, up to six months old, babies can distinguish between the sounds in *unfamiliar* languages, not only the language they were exposed to in the womb.

Reading

in utero, most infants are not biased
towards the specific phonemes of that
language.

90   This ability to recognize and
discriminate between all phonemes
comes to an end by the middle of their
first year, (at which point) infants start
displaying a preference for phonemes
95 in their native language, culminating
at age one, when they stop responding
to foreign phonemes altogether. This is
part of what is known as the "(critical)
(period,)" which begins at birth and
100 lasts until puberty. During this
period, as the brain continues to grow
and change, language acquisition is
instinctual, (explaining why) young
children seem to pick up languages so
105 easily.

*~1 yr.:
prefer
their own
lang.*

*crit. pd.:
still easier
to learn
other
lang.*

¶5: The author continues along the development timeline. By age one, infants prefer their
own language's sounds (and stop responding
to other languages' sounds). Still, it's easier to
learn foreign languages (it's still "instinctual,"
says the author) up through puberty because
the brain is still growing and changing.

BIG PICTURE

Main Idea: Infants listen to voices in their environments to acquire language instinctually, possibly starting
before they are even born.

Author's Purpose: To explain the abilities and limitations of infants in acquiring language

---

CHAPTER 12

PSAT Reading Question Types

LEARNING OBJECTIVES

After completing this chapter, you will be able to:

- Unpack PSAT Reading question stems by:
  - Distinguishing among six PSAT Reading question types
  - Determining if the correct answer is best found by researching the passage text or by consulting your big picture summary

SmartPoints®:

Inference Questions, 90/300 (Very High Yield)
Command of Evidence Questions, 60/300 (High Yield)
Detail Questions, 45/300 (Medium Yield)
Vocabulary-in-Context Questions, 45/300 (Medium Yield)
Function Questions, 40/300 (Medium Yield)
Global Questions, 20/300 (Low Yield)

How Much Do You Know?

Directions: In this chapter, you'll learn to unpack PSAT Reading question stems (step 1 of the Method for PSAT Reading Questions). Unpacking a question stem means identifying your task (as identified by the question type) and noting where the answer will be found (a specific reference within the passage text or in your big picture summary). You saw examples of these question types introduced in chapter 10. For your reference as you complete this quiz, here they are with brief descriptions:

- **Global**—asks about the big picture
- **Detail**—asks about explicitly stated points
- **Inference**—asks about points that are unstated but strongly suggested
- **Command of Evidence**—asks for evidence to support the answer to a previous question
- **Function**—asks why the author wrote specific parts of the text
- **Vocabulary-in-Context** (or Vocab-in-Context)—asks for the intended meaning of a word as it is used in the passage

For each of the following question stems, identify the question type, cite the language in the stem that helped you identify it, and indicate where you would begin to research this question: either your big picture summary or a specific part of the text.

Example

The author of the passage would most likely agree with which one of the following statements concerning hydraulic mining?

Question type: *Inference*

Identifying language: *"would most likely agree"*

Research where? *passage, where author discusses hydraulic mining*

1. Over the course of the passage, the main focus shifts from

   Question type:
   Identifying language:
   Research where?

2. In the second paragraph, the discussion of the Bangledeshi women who manufacture bamboo stools (lines 20–28) serves mainly to

   Question type:
   Identifying language:
   Research where?

3. As used in line 27, "modest" most nearly means

   Question type:
   Identifying language:
   Research where?

4. With which one of the following statements would the early advocates of microlending be most likely to agree?

   Question type:
   Identifying language:
   Research where?

5. Which choice provides the best evidence for the answer to the previous question?

    Question type:
    Identifying language:
    Research where?

6. Which one of the following is cited in the passage as a finding reached by researchers studying the efficacy of microlending?

    Question type:
    Identifying language:
    Research where?

7. Which choice provides the best evidence for the answer to the previous question?

    Question type:
    Identifying language:
    Research where?

8. As used in line 78, "cautious" most nearly means

    Question type:
    Identifying language:
    Research where?

9. The author uses "temporary or seasonal unemployment, crop failures, [and] health crises" (lines 123–125) as examples of

    Question type:
    Identifying language:
    Research where?

Check Your Work

1. Over the course of the passage, the main focus shifts from

   Question type: Global
   Identifying language: "main focus"
   Research where? big picture summary and paragraph notes

2. In the second paragraph, the discussion of the Bangledeshi women who manufacture bamboo stools (lines 20–28) serves mainly to

   Question type: Function
   Identifying language: "serves mainly to"
   Research where? passage, lines 20–28

3. As used in line 27, "modest" most nearly means

   Question type: Vocab-in-Context
   Identifying language: "most nearly means"
   Research where? passage, line 27

4. With which one of the following statements would the early advocates of microlending be most likely to agree?

   Question type: Inference
   Identifying language: "most likely to agree"
   Research where? passage, where author discusses early advocates

5. Which choice provides the best evidence for the answer to the previous question?

   Question type: Command of Evidence
   Identifying language: "provides the best evidence"
   Research where? passage, where you went to answer the previous question

6. Which one of the following is cited in the passage as a finding reached by researchers studying the efficacy of microlending?

   Question type: Detail
   Identifying language: "cited in the passage"
   Research where? passage, where the efficacy of microlending is discussed

7. Which choice provides the best evidence for the answer to the previous question?

   Question type: Command of Evidence (note that the language is identical to that used in question 5; this is the most common phrasing for this question type)
   Identifying language: "provides the best evidence"
   Research where? passage, where you went to answer the previous question

8. As used in line 78, "cautious" most nearly means

   Question type: Vocab-in-Context
   Identifying language: "most nearly means"
   Research where? passage, line 78

9. The author uses "temporary or seasonal unemployment, crop failures, [and] health crises" (lines 123–125) as examples of

   Question type: Function
   Identifying language: "author uses"
   Research where? passage, lines 123–125

How to Unpack PSAT Reading Question Stems

LEARNING OBJECTIVES

After this lesson, you will be able to:

- Unpack PSAT Reading question stems by:
  - Distinguishing among six PSAT Reading question types
  - Determining if the correct answer is best found by researching the passage text or by consulting your big picture summary

To unpack question stems like these:

1. The passage is written from the viewpoint of someone who is

2. According to the passage, which of the following explains the reason leafcutter ants bring cut vegetation into their nests?

3. Which choice provides the best evidence for the answer to the previous question?

4. As used in line 15, "dedicated" most nearly means

5. Which of the following can most reasonably be inferred about leafcutter ant activity?

6. Which choice provides the best evidence for the answer to the previous question?

7. In the fourth paragraph (lines 48–61), the mathematical figures cited serve mainly to

8. According to the graph, the ratio of refuse soil to control soil is highest for which of the following nutrients?

9. Which of the following statements is best supported by the data presented in the table?

You'll need to know this:

- The six kinds of question types, each of which defines a specific task:
  - **Global**—asks about the passage's main idea, the author's primary purpose, or the passage's overall organization

TYPICAL GLOBAL QUESTION STEMS

The central claim of the passage is that

Which choice best summarizes the passage?

The main purpose of the passage is to

Which choice best describes the developmental pattern of the passage?

Which choice best reflects the overall sequence of events in the passage?

o **Detail**—asks about something explicitly stated in the passage

TYPICAL DETAIL QUESTION STEMS

According to the passage, which of the following is true of developmental psychology?

The author indicates that people value solitude because

In the second paragraph (lines 14–27), what does the author claim are key questions the study must answer?

The passage identifies which of the following as a factor that influences economic growth?

o **Inference**—asks for something that follows from the passage without having been stated explicitly in it

TYPICAL INFERENCE QUESTION STEMS

Based on the passage, the author's statement "in response, the Federal Reserve will often lower interest rates" (lines 21–22) implies that

Which concept is supported by the passage and by the information in the graph?

Based on information in the passage, it can reasonably be inferred that

The authors of both passages would most likely agree with which of the following statements?

o **Command of Evidence**—asks you to cite the support offered in the passage for the correct answer to the previous question or for a given statement

TYPICAL COMMAND OF EVIDENCE QUESTION STEMS

Which choice provides the best evidence for the answer to the previous question?

Which choice best supports the claim that the new policy is unlikely to curtail water pollution?

o **Function**—asks about the purpose of a piece of text—why the author included it or how the author has used it

TYPICAL FUNCTION QUESTION STEMS

The sentence in lines 35–37 serves mainly to

The main purpose of the fourth paragraph (lines 42–50) is to

How do the words "must," "necessary," and "imperative" in the third paragraph (lines 35–49) help establish the tone of the paragraph?

The author uses the image of an explorer overlooking a valley (lines 23–28) most likely to

The sentence in lines 74–78 ("After . . . rest") primarily serves which function in paragraph 7?

○ **Vocabulary-in-Context** (or Vocab-in-Context)—asks you to define a word as the author used it in the passage

> ### TYPICAL VOCABULARY-IN-CONTEXT QUESTION STEMS
>
> As used in line 55, "platform" most nearly means
>
> As used in line 29, "substantial" most nearly means

- The kinds of research clues found in PSAT Reading question stems include the following:

  ○ **Line Numbers**—Mentions of "line 53" or "lines 37–40," often in parentheses, tend to stand out and give you a clear place to start your research. (In Command of Evidence questions, line numbers are found in the answer choices.)

  ○ **Paragraph Numbers**—A reference to "paragraph 5," "the third paragraph," or "the last two paragraphs" is not as precise as a line reference but will still give you an idea of where to look. Start with your margin notes for the paragraph.

  ○ **Quoted Text**—(often accompanied by line numbers)—Check the context of the quoted term or phrase to see what the author meant by it in the passage.

  ○ **Proper Nouns**—Names like "Professor James," "World War II," and "Baltimore" will likely stand out in question stems due to the capitalization. If a particular proper noun is discussed in only part of the passage, it narrows the range of text you have to research.

  ○ **Specific Content Clues**—Sometimes a question stem will repeat terminology used in part of the passage like "federalism" or "action potentials." Use your passage map to direct your research to the right part of the passage.

  ○ **Whole Passage Clues**—If a question lacks specific content clues but refers to the passage as a whole, or to the author in general, you are likely dealing with a Global question or an open-ended Inference question, which should lead you to your big picture summary rather than to rereading parts of the text.

You'll need to do this:

The Method for PSAT Reading Questions	
Step 1.	**Unpack the question stem**
Step 2.	Research the answer
Step 3.	Predict the answer
Step 4.	Find the one correct answer

Reading

- Unpack PSAT Reading question stems by:
  - Identifying the question type and anticipating how it will need to be answered
  - Noting research clues that indicate how best to research the correct answer

QUESTION TYPES

Why distinguish question types in PSAT Reading?

Unpacking the question stem puts you in control. You'll know exactly what the question is asking, where to find the correct answer, and what form the correct answer will take.

- **Global:** The correct answer must take the entire passage into account. A choice that reflects only part of the passage is incorrect.
- **Detail:** The correct answer must be stated in the passage explicitly. A choice that is not directly stated in the passage is incorrect.
- **Inference:** The correct answer will be a conclusion that can be drawn from the passage. A choice that draws too strong a conclusion from the evidence available in the passage is incorrect.
- **Command of Evidence:** The correct answer must directly support the correct answer to the previous question. A choice about the same subject but providing no direct evidence is not good enough.
- **Function:** The correct answer will say *why* a certain detail is included. Look up the detail, then ask yourself what the author was trying to accomplish by putting it there.
- **Vocab-in-Context:** The correct answer will give the meaning of a word as it is used *in the context of the passage*. Choices that give common meanings of the word are often incorrect.

Correct answers to Reading questions are never random or vague. They are tailored to the precise language of the stem, so being able to distinguish the question types will save you time and eliminate confusion during the test.

Explanations:

1. This is a Global question because it asks about the general "viewpoint" of the passage, that is, the author's overall perspective. Your big picture summary will help you find the answer.

GLOBAL STRATEGY

Start with your big picture summary:

Global questions ask for the big picture of the passage, so always start by reviewing your big picture summary. You should generally avoid rereading passage text when tackling a Global question but, if you get stuck, the first and last paragraphs are usually the best places to look.

2. "According to the passage" is a clear sign of a Detail question. The answer will be found where the author discusses what leafcutters do with the vegetation they take in.

> ### DETAIL STRATEGY
>
> **Search for the relevant information:**
>
> Don't expect a lot of precise clues such as line numbers with Detail questions. Your task will usually be to extract the stem's specific content clues and then use your passage map to help you locate that content in the text. If you can't find it within about a minute, consider skipping a Detail question and returning to it after you answer the passage's other questions. Researching them may inadvertently lead you to the detail you need.

3. The vast majority of Command of Evidence questions have this exact wording: "Which choice provides the best evidence for the answer to the previous question?" All Command of Evidence answer choices feature direct quotes with line numbers, which you should use to guide your research.

> ### COMMAND OF EVIDENCE STRATEGY
>
> **Use your work on the previous question:**
>
> The line numbers listed in Command of Evidence answer choices give you four potential locations to look for the correct answer, but preempt this extensive searching by looking first at the lines of text you used to answer the previous question (usually an Inference or Detail). Alternatively, if you're working on a different question and see a Command of Evidence coming up next, you can use the line numbers there to guide your research, increasing your efficiency by answering both questions at once.

4. A question stem that begins with a line reference, quotes a term from the passage, and ends in "most nearly means" is always a Vocab-in-Context question.

> ### VOCAB-IN-CONTEXT STRATEGY
>
> **Go back to the context:**
>
> At a minimum, go to the line cited in a Vocab-in-Context question and reread the entire sentence that contains the word. If that doesn't give you enough context, look for additional help in the surrounding sentences until you have a clear idea of what the author intended.

5.   The phrase "can most reasonably be inferred" tells you this is an Inference question. You'll want to find the discussion of leafcutter ant activity to begin your research.

INFERENCE STRATEGY

What follows from the text?

Inference questions come in a wider variety of forms than the other question types, but all are united by asking you to identify something that the author only suggests without saying outright. Fortunately for you, these questions are not asking for subtle hints, but for statements that MUST be true given what the author does state. Follow the clues to locate the relevant text, and then ask yourself, "What *must* follow from this?"

---

6.   This is another Command of Evidence question in the standard format.

7.   This is a Function question, as can be determined from the phrase "serve mainly to." To research it, you should look for the mathematical figures in paragraph 4 and determine their purpose.

FUNCTION STRATEGY

Why did the author write *that*?

Most Function questions are *why* questions, asking you to explain what the author intended to accomplish with a particular piece of text, usually singled out with precise clues like line or paragraph numbers. Start researching by looking at the appropriate location from your passage map, reviewing what you described as the author's purpose in that part of the text. If that doesn't help, reread the indicated text and ask yourself, "Why did the author include this?"

---

8.   "According to the graph" suggests that this is a Detail question connected to a graphic. To research, go to the graph after the passage and find the specified information.

9.   The phrase "best supported" suggests an Inference question. For this question, go to the table accompanying the passage.

Try on Your Own

Directions: Analyze each of the following question stems by 1) identifying the word or phrase that describes your task, 2) naming the question type, and 3) noting how best to research the correct answer (research the text or consult the big picture summary). Answers are found at the end of the chapter.

1. The main purpose of the passage is to

    Question type:

    Identifying language:

    Research where?

2. The author implies that, during the period in which the Norse settlements were initially founded, the climate in the region was

    Question type:

    Identifying language:

    Research where?

3. Which choice provides the best evidence for the answer to the previous question?

    Question type:

    Identifying language:

    Research where?

4. In line 63, the word "inadvertently" most nearly means

    Question type:

    Identifying language:

    Research where?

5. The passage indicates that the Inuit people on Greenland

    Question type:

    Identifying language:

    Research where?

6. What function does the discussion of the trade in whale and elephant ivory serve in the passage as a whole?

    Question type:

    Identifying language:

    Research where?

7. What can reasonably be inferred from the passage about the relationship between the shipping fleets of nations in the fourteenth and fifteenth centuries and the colonies established by those nations?

    Question type:

    Identifying language:

    Research where?

8. The author claims the Norse settlers did not adopt the successful survival tactics of the Inuit because

    Question type:

    Identifying language:

    Research where?

9. Which choice provides the best evidence for the answer to the previous question?

    Question type:

    Identifying language:

    Research where?

10. Which of the following best summarizes the organization of the passage?

    Question type:

    Identifying language:

    Research where?

For any question types that you misidentified, return to the definitions and question stem examples before moving on to the "How Much Have You Learned?" section.

Reading

How Much Have You Learned?

Directions: Now, complete a similar assessment under timed conditions. Take a few minutes to analyze each of the following question stems by 1) identifying the word or phrase that describes your task, 2) naming the question type, and 3) noting how best to research the correct answer (research the text or consult the big picture summary).

11. The primary purpose of the passage is to

    Question type:
    Identifying language:
    Research where?

12. According to the passage, when children begin to acquire their native language they

    Question type:
    Identifying language:
    Research where?

13. Which choice provides the best evidence for the answer to the previous question?

    Question type:
    Identifying language:
    Research where?

14. As used in line 48, "predicated" most nearly means

    Question type:
    Identifying language:
    Research where?

15. The main purpose of the third paragraph (lines 45–70) is to

    Question type:
    Identifying language:
    Research where?

16. As used in line 82, "discriminate" most nearly means

    Question type:
    Identifying language:
    Research where?

17. According to the passage, children begin to learn the rhythms, pitches, and accents of speech

    Question type:
    Identifying language:
    Research where?

18. The passage most strongly suggests that a mother who wants to assist her child in language acquisition should

    Question type:
    Identifying language:
    Research where?

19. Which choice provides the best evidence for the answer to the previous question?

    Question type:
    Identifying language:
    Research where?

20. The most likely purpose of the discussion of phonemes is to

    Question type:
    Identifying language:
    Research where?

Reflect

Directions: Take a few minutes to recall what you've learned and what you've been practicing in this chapter. Consider the following questions, jot down your best answer for each one, and then compare your reflections to the expert responses on the following page. Use your level of confidence to determine what to do next.

Why is it important to always unpack the question stem before proceeding?

_____

_____

_____

Can you name the six PSAT Reading question types and cite words or phrases that identify each one?

- _____
    - Identifying language: _____
- _____
    - Identifying language: _____
- _____
    - Identifying language: _____
- _____
    - Identifying language: _____
- _____
    - Identifying language: _____
- _____
    - Identifying language: _____

How will you approach PSAT Reading question stems differently as you continue to practice and improve your performance in the Reading section? What are the main differences you see between PSAT Reading questions and those you're used to from tests in school?

_____

_____

_____

Reading

Expert Responses

Why is it important to always unpack the question stem before proceeding?

Knowing the PSAT Reading question types makes you a more strategic and efficient reader because the test maker uses the same question types on every test. Fully analyzing each question stem helps you to research the text more effectively, predict the correct answer in a way that fits the question stem, and avoid wrong answers made from misreading the question.

Can you name the six PSAT Reading question types and cite words or phrases that identify each one?

- *Global*
  - Identifying language: *main idea of the passage, author's primary purpose*
- *Detail*
  - Identifying language: *according to the passage, identifies, claims*
- *Inference*
  - Identifying language: *implies, can be inferred, based on the passage*
- *Command of Evidence*
  - Identifying language: *provides the best evidence, best supports, the answer to the previous question*
- *Function*
  - Identifying language: *is used to, serves mainly to, functions as*
- *Vocabulary-in-Context*
  - Identifying language: *as used in line [number], most nearly means*

How will you approach PSAT Reading question stems differently as you continue to practice and improve your performance in the Reading section? What are the main differences you see between PSAT Reading questions and those you're used to from tests in school?

There is no one-size-fits-all answer here. Reflect on your own strengths and weaknesses as you consider how to best improve your performance in the PSAT Reading section. Depending on the kinds of classes and teachers you've had in high school, the skills rewarded on PSAT Reading questions may be more or less familiar, but almost every test taker needs to be aware of her own instincts as a reader, and needs to break some unhelpful reading habits, to master this section of the test. The more you give yourself an honest self-assessment, the better prepared you'll be to handle all of the PSAT Reading question types confidently.

Next Steps

If you answered most questions correctly in the "How Much Have You Learned?" section, and if your responses to the Reflect questions were similar to those of the PSAT expert, then consider identifying PSAT Reading Question Types an area of strength and move on to the next chapter. Come back to this topic periodically to prevent yourself from getting rusty.

If you don't yet feel confident, review the material in "How to Unpack PSAT Reading Question Stems," then try the questions you missed again. As always, be sure to review the explanations closely.

Answers and Explanations

1. The main purpose of the passage is to

   Question type: Global
   Identifying language: "main purpose"
   Research where? big picture summary

2. The author implies that, during the period in which the Norse settlements were initially founded, the climate in the region was

   Question type: Inference
   Identifying language: "implies"
   Research where? passage, where author discusses Norse settlement founding

3. Which choice provides the best evidence for the answer to the previous question?

   Question type: Command of Evidence
   Identifying language: "provides the best evidence"
   Research where? passage, where you went to answer the previous question

4. In line 63, the word "inadvertently" most nearly means

   Question type: Vocab-in-Context
   Identifying language: "most nearly means"
   Research where? passage, line 63

5. The passage indicates that the Inuit people on Greenland

   Question type: Detail
   Identifying language: "indicates"
   Research where? passage, where the author discusses the Inuit people

6. What function does the discussion of the trade in whale and elephant ivory serve in the passage as a whole?

   Question type: Function
   Identifying language: "function," "serve in the passage"
   Research where? passage, where the ivory trade is discussed

7. What can reasonably be inferred from the passage about the relationship between the shipping fleets of nations in the fourteenth and fifteenth centuries and the colonies established by those nations?

   Question type: Inference
   Identifying language: "reasonably be inferred"
   Research where? passage, where the author discusses fourteenth- and fifteenth-century colonization

8. The author claims the Norse settlers did not adopt the successful survival tactics of the Inuit because

   Question type: Detail
   Identifying language: "author claims"
   Research where? passage, where the author discusses the Norse response to the Inuit

9. Which choice provides the best evidence for the answer to the previous question?

   Question type: Command of Evidence
   Identifying language: "provides the best evidence"
   Research where? passage, where you went to answer the previous question

10. Which of the following best summarizes the organization of the passage?

    Question type: Global
    Identifying language: "organization of the passage"
    Research where? big picture summary and paragraph notes

11. The primary purpose of the passage is to

    Question type: Global
    Identifying language: "primary purpose"
    Research where? big picture summary

12. According to the passage, when children begin to acquire their native language they

    Question type: Detail
    Identifying language: "According to the passage"
    Research where? passage, where beginning of language acquisition is discussed

13. Which choice provides the best evidence for the answer to the previous question?

    Question type: Command of Evidence
    Identifying language: "provides the best evidence"
    Research where? passage, where you went to answer the previous question

14. As used in line 48, "predicated" most nearly means

    Question type: Vocab-in-Context
    Identifying language: "most nearly means"
    Research where? passage, line 48

15. The main purpose of the third paragraph (lines 45–70) is to

    Question type: Function
    Identifying language: "main purpose of the third paragraph"
    Research where? passage, paragraph 3

16. As used in line 82, "discriminate" most nearly means

    Question type: Vocab-in-Context
    Identifying language: "most nearly means"
    Research where? passage, line 82

17. According to the passage, children begin to learn the rhythms, pitches, and accents of speech

    Question type: Detail
    Identifying language: "According to the passage"
    Research where? passage, where author discusses rhythms, pitches, and accents

18. The passage most strongly suggests that a mother who wants to assist her child in language acquisition should

    Question type: Inference
    Identifying language: "most strongly suggests"
    Research where? passage, where author discusses factors that help language acquisition

19. Which choice provides the best evidence for the answer to the previous question?

    Question type: Command of Evidence
    Identifying language: "provides the best evidence"
    Research where? passage, where you went to answer the previous question

20. The most likely purpose of the discussion of phonemes is to

    Question type: Function
    Identifying language: "most likely purpose"
    Research where? passage, where phonemes are discussed

CHAPTER 13

Answering PSAT Reading Questions

LEARNING OBJECTIVES

After completing this chapter, you will be able to:

- Research the answer in the passage or your big picture summary
- Predict the correct answer
- Find the one correct answer choice

How Much Do You Know?

Directions: In this chapter, you'll learn how best to research, predict, and find the correct answers to PSAT Reading questions. For this quiz, first take a couple of minutes to refresh your memory of this passage from chapter 11. Then, for each question (the stems of which you categorized in chapter 12), 1) research the answer in the passage text or from your big picture summary, 2) predict the correct answer in your own words, and 3) identify the one correct answer.

Questions 1–9 refer to the following passage.

Microcredit Passage Map

This passage is adapted from a 2018 article reviewing the benefits and shortcomings of a financial model called microcredit.

Until a few decades ago, it was virtually impossible for an impoverished person to obtain credit from an institutional source like a
5 bank. Lacking collateral or verifiable income, such people—often citizens of developing nations—simply could not qualify for even a small loan from a traditional financial institution. As a
10 result, these people were unable to start businesses that could free them from the trap of poverty.

very poor could not get loans

Some financial experts put forth an intriguing theory: if impoverished
15 people had access to very small loans, called microloans, for the purpose of funding small businesses, they could lift themselves up from poverty to self-employment and perhaps even into
20 a position to employ others. In 1976, an economics professor in Bangladesh extended a microloan of 27 dollars to a group of impoverished village women for the purpose of buying supplies for
25 their business manufacturing bamboo stools. The loan allowed the women to make a modest profit and grow their business to a point of self-sufficiency.

theory: microloans could help

example

Advocates of microlending built
30 on this initial success, maintaining that microcredit was an avenue to widespread entrepreneurship among the poor that could increase individual

pro-microloan arguments

wealth and, ultimately, reduce poverty.
35 Additionally, since microloans were frequently extended to women borrowers, supporters contended that microfinance was a way to empower women. A variety of microcredit
40 organizations sprang up to serve the needs of the poor in Asia, Latin America, Africa, and Eastern Europe.

A number of different microlending business models developed, and over
45 the ensuing decades, the number of customers of microcredit grew from a few hundred to tens of millions worldwide. Microlenders and microcredit advocates told stories of
50 desperately poor people who had lifted themselves out of poverty and into self-sufficiency, and of impoverished women who had become family breadwinners through the use of
55 microloans. Microfinance, it seemed, was a tremendous success.

microloan successes

Soon, however, another side of the story came to light. Anecdotes emerged about impoverished borrowers
60 who were unable to pay their interest from their business earnings, became imprisoned in debt, and were forced to sell off their meager possessions to meet their loan obligations. Other stories
65 described customers who used their loans for consumption spending rather than to finance businesses, and who were thus unable either to pay their interest or to return the original money
70 borrowed. A backlash developed against microlending. Members of the media, politicians, and public administrators harshly criticized the industry and

microloan failure stories

75 its advocates for promoting a process
that could harm rather than help the
neediest and most vulnerable people.
Nevertheless, economists were
more cautious. They recognized that
anecdotes were not adequate to support
80 either side of the debate meaningfully.
What was needed was solid scientific
evidence that could quantify the
real impacts of microlending.
Academics focused on finance and
85 development performed a number of
studies exploring various aspects of
microfinance.

economists:
need real
data

When researchers aggregated the
findings of the best of these studies,
90 they concluded that microlending was
not the panacea claimed by its
advocates. Poverty had not been
alleviated on a widescale, or even
measurably reduced. Moreover, there
95 was little if any evidence that women
had been substantially empowered by
microcredit. Perhaps most tellingly, the
average incomes of microloan
customers had not risen above their
100 previous levels.

research
results

Critics jumped on these findings,
claiming that they proved that
microfinance as a whole was a failure.
Undeterred, advocates could still point
105 to a variety of less dramatic yet still
worthwhile positive outcomes that
resulted from microcredit. While

anti:
microcredit
a failure

VS.

pro:
still good
outcomes

borrowers had not increased their
incomes on average, they often replaced
110 longer hours of grueling wage-work
with more fulfilling and less onerous
self-employment. In many cases,
temptation spending—expenditures
on things like tobacco, alcohol, and
115 gambling—had been reduced in favor
of greater savings and expenditures
on durable goods, better food, and
healthcare. There is also evidence
that borrowers' use of microcredit
120 extended beyond financing small
businesses to "income smoothing," the
use of microloans to ease the financial
stresses of temporary or seasonal
unemployment, crop failures, health
125 crises, and the like.

While the original lofty expectations
for microfinance were overly optimistic,
it would be unfair and inaccurate to
classify the practice as a failure. Rather,
130 microfinance should be viewed as a
useful tool to help impoverished people
better their circumstances, even if only
modestly.

author:
microloans
somewhat
helpful

BIG PICTURE

Main Idea: Microcredit provides some relief for impoverished people even if it is not the total success its supporters imagined.

Author's Purpose: To analyze the claims of microcredit advocates and critics in light of research on the subject

---

1. Over the course of the passage, the main focus shifts from

   A) claims of success by advocates of microcredit to a complete refutation of these claims by critics of microcredit.

   B) a presentation of the theory of microcredit and its advantages to anecdotal evidence of its failure.

   C) claims of microcredit's successes and failures by its advocates and critics to an evaluation of these claims based on research.

   D) the success of microcredit as a financial strategy for small, impoverished villages to its failure as a worldwide business model with tens of millions of borrowers.

2. In the second paragraph, the discussion of the Bangladeshi women who manufacture bamboo stools (lines 20–28) serves mainly to

   A) highlight these women's extreme poverty.

   B) critique the lending systems of traditional financial institutions.

   C) prove that microcredit is especially helpful to women borrowers.

   D) illustrate the theory of microlending in practice.

3. As used in line 27, "modest" most nearly means

   A) small.

   B) self-effacing.

   C) immoderate.

   D) reserved.

4. With which one of the following statements would the early advocates of microlending be most likely to agree?

   A) Microlending organizations should replace traditional financial institutions in many parts of the world.

   B) The growing number of female family breadwinners prompted a backlash against microlending.

   C) Opening small businesses is a viable way for some people to lift themselves out of poverty.

   D) Some microloans are appropriate to finance consumer spending among the desperately poor.

5. Which choice provides the best evidence for the answer to the previous question?

   A) Lines 29–34 ("Advocates … poverty")

   B) Lines 39–42 ("A variety … Europe")

   C) Lines 48–55 ("Microlenders … microloans")

   D) Lines 64–70 ("Other stories … borrowed")

6. Which one of the following is cited in the passage as a finding reached by researchers studying the efficacy of microlending?

   A) Research data does not support any of the anecdotes offered by either advocates or critics of microlending.

   B) Customers who receive microloans often use the money for temptation spending.

   C) On average, microlending customers do not see their incomes rise after receiving a microloan.

   D) Women-owned businesses benefit disproportionately from microlending.

7. Which choice provides the best evidence for the answer to the previous question?

    A) Lines 78–80 ("They recognized … meaningfully")

    B) Lines 88–92 ("When researchers … advocates")

    C) Lines 97–100 ("Perhaps most … levels")

    D) Lines 112–118 ("In many … healthcare")

8. As used in line 78, "cautious" most nearly means

    A) discreet.

    B) bashful.

    C) cagey.

    D) wary.

9. The author uses "temporary or seasonal unemployment, crop failures, [and] health crises" (lines 123–125) as examples of

    A) economic hardships exacerbated by the spread of microlending.

    B) unexpected expenses that can be offset by microloans.

    C) the causes of widespread poverty in many parts of the world.

    D) obstacles to those seeking a way out of grueling wage-work.

Check Your Work

1. C

Difficulty: Medium

Category: Global

Strategic Advice: For Global questions that focus on the passage's structure, consult your big picture summary for the main idea and your paragraph notes to see how the author developed the text.

Getting to the Answer: In the passage, the author first presents the claims by both advocates and critics of microlending (paragraphs 1–4) and then turns to the results of research to evaluate those claims (paragraphs 5–9). That matches **(C)**.

(A) leaves out the evaluation of advocates' and critics' claims based on research, and it is extreme in suggesting a complete refutation of the advocates' claims. (B) also neglects the research that the author uses to evaluate the successes and failures of microcredit. (D) distorts the passage by suggesting that the reason for microcredit's disadvantages are related to its rapid growth.

2. D

Difficulty: Medium

Category: Function

Strategic Advice: The phrase "serves mainly to" identifies this as a Function question. To predict the correct answer, check your notes for the paragraph in which the detail cited in the question stem appears and ask how the author is using the detail.

Getting to the Answer: In paragraph 2, the author defines microcredit and cites the small loan to these Bangladeshi women as an example of it. That matches **(D)**, the correct answer.

(A) distorts the author's purpose; the idea of microcredit arose to address the financial difficulties of people in poverty, but the author isn't using the example to emphasize the conditions in which these women lived. (B) misuses a detail from paragraph 1; while it's true that impoverished people weren't able to get loans from "traditional financial institution[s]," it is not the author's purpose to criticize standard banking systems. (C) misapplies the example in paragraph 2 to a broader point ascribed to advocates of microcredit in paragraph 3.

3. A

Difficulty: Easy

Category: Vocab-in-Context

Strategic Advice: On Vocab-in-Context questions, read the sentence in which the word from the question stem appears. The correct answer will replace the word without changing the meaning of the sentence.

Getting to the Answer: The sentence suggests that the microloan given to the Bangladeshi women allowed them to turn a small profit that they used to further grow their business. "Small" appears in **(A)**, making it the correct answer.

(B), "self-effacing," which means displaying humility, fits the common definition of "modest," but doesn't work to modify "profits." (C), "immoderate," which means "excessive or extreme," suggests the opposite of "modest." (D), "reserved," often used to describe people who are quiet or reticent, is similar to the common definition of "modest" but can't be used to modify "profits."

4. C

Difficulty: Medium

Category: Inference

Strategic Advice: The phrase "most likely to agree" signals an Inference question, meaning that the correct answer follows from the passage text. In this case, the correct answer will be a statement that follows from what the passage told you about early advocates of microlending. The views and claims of the first wave of microlending advocates are laid out in paragraphs 3 and 4.

Getting to the Answer: The passage characterizes the advocates of microlending as very optimistic. In particular, they saw microcredit as a path to entrepreneurship and to the empowerment of women. **(C)** supports the first of those; because microlending advocates argue that entrepreneurship can increase wealth and reduce poverty, they must view small business ownership as a viable way for some people to improve their financial situations.

(A) distorts the viewpoint presented in the passage; microlending advocates never suggest that microcredit organizations should replace traditional financial institutions. (B) improperly ties together two different statements in the passage; the backlash, mentioned in paragraph 5, arose from stories indicating that microlending was not helping the poor or empowering women. (D) misuses a detail from paragraph 5; the fact that some customers were using funds for consumption spending was mentioned as a critique of microlending.

5. A

Difficulty: Medium

Category: Command of Evidence

Strategic Advice: Most Command of Evidence questions ask you to locate a specific piece of text that supports the correct answer to the preceding question. Have your answer to the previous question in mind as you use the line references in each choice to research the passage.

Getting to the Answer: In the preceding question, you may have deduced that advocates of microlending believe that getting money to open small businesses can help lift some people out of poverty. That follows directly from lines 29–34, where the author explains the view of advocates that poverty could be alleviated by means of "widespread entrepreneurship among the poor" (lines 32–33), so **(A)** is the correct answer here.

The sentence cited in (B) tells of the worldwide spread of microlending organizations; it might be tempting to test takers who like choice (A) on the preceding question. (C) is incorrect because it doesn't specifically mention starting businesses (entrepreneurship) as a means of alleviating poverty. The sentence cited in (D) comes from paragraph 5 and relates some of the negative stories offered by critics of microlending.

6. C

Difficulty: Medium

Category: Detail

Strategic Advice: When a question stem calls for something "cited" in the passage, you have a Detail question. The correct answer will paraphrase an explicit statement or claim from the passage. Use the clues or references in the question stem to guide your research in the passage.

Getting to the Answer: Here, the question stem asks about a research finding. Those are outlined in paragraphs 7 and 8. Paragraph 7 cites three broad findings: 1) microlending has not measurably reduced poverty, 2) microlending does not appear to have substantially empowered women, and 3) the average income of microlending customers has not risen. **(C)** paraphrases the last of those findings, making it the correct answer.

(A) is extreme; economists seek data, not anecdotes, for their analyses, but that doesn't mean that none of the anecdotes is supported. (B) distorts a detail from paragraph 8; research seems to indicate that microlending customers are actually less likely to indulge in temptation spending, such as gambling and buying tobacco or alcohol. (D) contradicts findings cited in paragraph 7, which show "little evidence" that microlending has empowered women.

7. C

Difficulty: Medium

Category: Command of Evidence

Strategic Advice: Most Command of Evidence questions ask you to locate a specific piece of text that supports the correct answer to the preceding question. Have your answer to the previous question in mind as you use the line references in each choice to research the passage.

Getting to the Answer: The correct answer to the preceding question states that the average incomes of microlending customers did not rise. That is directly supported by the sentence cited by **(C)**.

(A) says that the economists were not satisfied with anecdotal evidence; this answer might tempt a test taker who incorrectly chose (A) on the preceding question. (B) provides indirect support for the previous question's answer by casting doubt on advocates' views, but it does not specifically support the claim about income. (D) notes that temptation spending goes down among microloan recipients, which also does not support the claim about income.

8. D

Difficulty: Hard

Category: Vocab-in-Context

Strategic Advice: On Vocab-in-Context questions, read the sentence in which the word from the question stem appears. The correct answer will replace the word without changing the meaning of the sentence.

Getting to the Answer: The sentence contrasts economists, who were cautious, with both the advocates and critics, who rushed to their respective judgments of microlending. Predict a word that means "careful to make a conclusion." That lines up with choice **(D)**, which means "careful or watchful."

(A), "discreet," refers to someone who is private or circumspect; while it relates to a kind of judicious behavior, it doesn't describe the economists discussed in the passage. (B), "bashful," means "shy or reserved," and doesn't fit the author's use of "cautious" here. (C), "cagey," may be used to describe a cautious person but carries the implication that the subject is being tricky or shrewd.

9. B

Difficulty: Hard

Category: Function

Strategic Advice: Function questions ask you to describe how the author uses a detail in the passage or to identify the author's reason for including it. Occasionally, in a Function question like this one, the test will give you a piece of the answer in the question stem. Here, you're told that the three details are examples of something. Use the context provided by the paragraph to assess the answer choices.

Getting to the Answer: The first sentence of paragraph 8 tells you that critics of microlending jumped on the researchers' finding to declare microlending a total failure. After that, however, the paragraph shifts to the positive findings that microlending advocates use to refute the critics' broad claim. The example in this question stem is from the paragraph's final sentence on "income smoothing." The sentence explains that microloans can help impoverished people survive sudden, severe financial stresses such as the three details cited in the question stem. **(B)** correctly describes how the details are used in the passage.

(A) is a claim that microlending critics would make, but the part of the paragraph quoted in the question is outlining arguments made by microlending advocates. (C) is outside the scope of the passage; the author never discusses specific causes of poverty. (D) misuses a detail from earlier in the paragraph, which applied to a distinct advantage of microlending cited by its advocates.

How to Answer PSAT Reading Questions

LEARNING OBJECTIVES

After this lesson, you will be able to:

- Research the answer in the passage or your big picture summary
- Predict the correct answer
- Find the one correct answer choice

To answer questions like these:

Directions: Choose the best answer choice for the following questions.

Questions 1–9 refer to the following passage and supplementary material.

Leafcutter Passage Map

This passage is adapted from an article called "Nature's Tiny Farmers" that appeared in a popular biology magazine in 2018.

Leafcutter ants are among the most ecologically important animals in the American tropics. At least forty-seven species of leafcutter ants range from
5 as far south as Argentina to as far north as the southern United States. These ants, as their name implies, cut sections of vegetation—leaves, flowers, and grasses—from an array of plants,
10 taking the cut sections back into their underground nests. However, the ants don't feed on the vegetation they cut; in fact, they're unable to digest the material directly. Instead, they carry
15 the fragments into dedicated chambers within their nests, where they cultivate a particular species of nutritious fungus on the cut vegetation. It is this fungus that the ants eat and feed to their
20 larvae.

leafcutter ants "farm" fungus using cut vegetation

Remarkably, each species of leafcutter ant cultivates a different species of fungus, and each of these fungi grows nowhere but within the
25 nests of its own species of leafcutter ant. According to entomologist Ted Schultz of the Smithsonian National Museum

unique fungus for each ant species

of Natural History, "The fungi that [the ants] grow are never found in the
30 wild, they are now totally dependent on the ants." In other words, over millions of years, the ants have actually domesticated the fungi, much as we humans have domesticated the plants
35 we grow for crops.

ant domesticated fungus

The leafcutters' foraging trails extend hundreds of meters throughout the landscape. The ants harvest a wide range of vegetation but are selective,
40 preferring particular plant species and picking younger growth to cut. Research has also shown that the ants often limit how much they cut from a single plant, possibly in response to chemical
45 defenses the cut plant produces. In this way, the amount of damage they cause to individual plants is limited.

ants' plant cutting explained

Leafcutters are probably the most important environmental engineers
50 in the areas they occupy. A single leafcutter nest can extend as far as 21 meters underground, have a central mound 30 meters in diameter with branches extending out to a radius of
55 80 meters, contain upwards of 1,000 individual chambers, and house up to eight million ants. Where they are present, leafcutters are responsible for up to 25 percent or more of the
60 total consumption of vegetation by all herbivores.

why ants so impt to environment

Alejandro G. Farji-Brener of Argentina's National Scientific and Technical Research Council and

65 Mariana Tadey of the National University of Comahue wanted to better understand how the activities of leafcutter ants influence soil conditions. To do so, they analyzed the data from

70 a large number of previous studies to determine how various environmental factors play into the ants' behavior and their effects on local ecology.

The researchers found that

75 overall soil quality and fertility are dramatically higher where leafcutters are present. The ants affect the soil in two ways: first, the physical shifting of the soil that occurs as a

80 consequence of nest construction improves soil porosity, drainage, and aeration; additionally, the ants' fungus-cultivating activities generate enormous amounts of plant waste,

85 which the ants carry away, either into specialized chambers within the nest or to dedicated refuse piles outside. In fact, this movement of organic matter may be the largest performed by any

90 animal in the environment. This transfer of huge volumes of organic material results in greatly enriched soil, with nutrient levels that are orders of magnitude higher than in areas where

95 the ants are not present.

The researchers also determined that seeds germinate more easily and at higher rates in these soils. Additionally, plants grow substantially better in soils

[margin notes: 2 scientists research LC ants; review prev studies; findings: soil better where LC ants are; reason 1; reason 2; HUGE impact; more findings: seeds and plants grow better]

100 that have been modified by leafcutters. In effect, then, the ants create conditions that encourage the growth of plants, thereby greatly improving the conditions of the landscape in general.

105 Furthermore, in areas of disturbance or degradation, such as lands that have been overgrazed or deforested, or those suffering from the effects of fire or drought, leafcutters are major

110 contributors to the natural restoration of healthy plant communities and the overall recovery of the land. The study concludes that "in terms of conservation, ant-nest areas should be

115 especially protected...because they are hot spots of plant productivity and diversity."

[margin note: recommendation: protect LC ant areas]

Nutrient Ratio: Refuse Soil/Control Soil

Relative Nutrient Content of Leafcutter Ant Soils—Ratios of Leafcutter Ant Soils to Control Soil		
Nutrient	**Nest Soil: Control Soil**	**Refuse Soil: Control Soil**
Nitrogen	1.4:1	33:1
Phosphorus	2.0:1	48:1
Potassium	1.4:1	49:1
Carbon	4.2:1	47:1
Calcium	1.9:1	29:1
Magnesium	2.2:1	15:1

BIG PICTURE

Main Idea: Leafcutter ants are impressive environmental engineers with profound and positive effects on their environments.

Author's Purpose: To describe the range, nests, and fungus cultivation of the ants and to summarize the research on how they alter and improve their environments

---

1. The passage is written from the viewpoint of someone who is

    A) actively involved in conducting research on leafcutter ants.

    B) an advocate for habitat restoration.

    C) knowledgeable about advances in leafcutter ant research.

    D) a participant in a recent conference on environmental issues.

2. According to the passage, which of the following explains the reason leafcutter ants bring cut vegetation into their nests?

    A) For use as nesting material

    B) To feed the vegetation to their larvae

    C) To add nutrients to the nest soil

    D) To cultivate edible fungus on the vegetation

3. Which choice provides the best evidence for the answer to the previous question?

    A) Lines 7–11 ("These ants … nests")

    B) Lines 14–20 ("Instead … larvae")

    C) Lines 21–25 ("Remarkably … ant")

    D) Lines 31–35 ("In other … crops")

4. As used in line 15, "dedicated" most nearly means

    A) zealous.

    B) enthusiastic.

    C) faithful.

    D) special.

5. Which of the following can most reasonably be inferred about leafcutter ant activity?

    A) Leafcutter ants' actions remain consistent across species and geographic areas.

    B) Changes in environmental conditions can influence how leafcutter ants behave.

    C) The leafcutter ants' actions are the primary force for change in the environments in which they are present.

    D) Compared to the activities of large grazing animals, the activities of leafcutter ants have a less important effect on the landscape.

6. Which choice provides the best evidence for the answer to the previous question?

    A) Lines 7–11 ("These ants … nests")

    B) Lines 69–73 ("To do so … ecology")

    C) Lines 88–90 ("In fact … environment")

    D) Lines 105–112 ("Furthermore … land")

7. In the fourth paragraph (lines 48–61), the mathematical figures cited serve mainly to

    A) indicate the power leafcutter ants have to damage local ecosystems.

    B) demonstrate that leafcutter ants are more numerous than other insect species where they are present.

    C) underscore how much is known about the construction and configuration of leafcutter ant colonies.

    D) emphasize the great scope of the leafcutter ants' impact on their environment.

8. According to the graph, the ratio of refuse soil to control soil is highest for which of the following nutrients?

    A) Potassium

    B) Phosphorus

    C) Magnesium

    D) Carbon

9. Which of the following statements is best supported by the data presented in the table?

    A) Leafcutter ants greatly increase the nutrients present in their refuse soil and increase it even more in their nest soil.

    B) Leafcutter ants greatly increase the nutrients present in their nest soil and increase it even more in their refuse soil.

    C) Potassium is critical in helping plants near leafcutter ants to grow.

    D) There is approximately twice as much calcium as magnesium in refuse soil.

You need to know this:

- Use clues to direct your research to a specific portion of the passage or to your big picture summary.
  - **Line Numbers**—Reread the indicated text and possibly the lines before and after; look for keywords indicating why the referenced text has been included or how it's used.
  - **Paragraph Numbers**—Consult your margin notes to see the paragraph's purpose and scope before rereading the text. Sometimes your passage map alone is enough to find an answer.
  - **Quoted Text**—Go back to the passage to read the entire quote if the stem or answer choices use ellipses (. . .). Then check the surrounding context of the quoted term or phrase to see what the author meant by it in the passage.
  - **Proper Nouns**—Use your map or look for capital letters in the text to find the term and then check the context to see why the author included it in the passage; note whether the author had a positive, negative, or neutral evaluation of it.
  - **Specific Content Clues**—Use your margin notes to help you search the passage for terms or ideas mentioned in the question stem; these clues will usually refer to something the author offered an opinion about or emphasized.
  - **Whole Passage Clues**—Begin by reviewing your big picture summary, and only go back to the passage if you can't find the information you need. If you do get stuck, the first and last paragraphs are typically the best places to go for global takeaways.
- Predicting what you're looking for in the correct answer saves time and reduces confusion as you read each choice.
- PSAT Reading questions always have one correct answer and three incorrect answers.
  - The correct answer will match what the passage says in a way that responds to the task set out in the question stem.
  - Wrong answers often fall into one of five categories. Not every incorrect choice matches one of these types exactly, but learning to spot them can help you eliminate some wrong answers more quickly.
    - **Out of Scope**—contains a statement that is too broad, too narrow, or beyond the purview of the passage
    - **Extreme**—contains language that is too strong (*all*, *never*, *every*, *none*) to be supported by the passage
    - **Distortion**—based on details or ideas from the passage but distorts or misstates what the author says or implies
    - **Opposite**—directly contradicts what the correct answer must say
    - **Misused Detail**—accurately states something from the passage but in a manner that incorrectly answers the question

You need to do this:

We focused on step 1, unpacking the question stem, in the last chapter. Now we'll focus on steps 2–4.

The Method For PSAT Reading Questions	
Step 1.	Unpack the question stem
Step 2.	**Research the answer**
Step 3.	**Predict the answer**
Step 4.	**Find the one correct answer**

- Research the answer.
  - When clues point to a specific part of the passage (line or paragraph numbers, quotations, content discussed only in particular paragraphs), begin by rereading the specified text and immediate context.
    - If the immediate context does not provide enough info to answer the question, gradually expand outward, rereading sentences that come before and after.
  - With whole passage clues or questions that seem to lack clear content clues, begin by reviewing your big picture summary.
  - If you can't figure out where to research the question and your big picture summary doesn't help either, consider using process of elimination, skipping the question and coming back to it later, or just making a guess.
- Predict or characterize what the correct answer will say or suggest.
  - Don't worry about phrasing your prediction as a complete sentence or about repeating exactly the language used in the passage. Just try to answer the question posed in your own words based on your research.
  - If you struggle to predict, use your active reading of the passage to characterize the correct answer, setting expectations about characteristics it must possess.
    - For example, if the author has a negative view of a topic in the question, expect a correct answer with negative language and eliminate choices that suggest a positive or neutral view.
- Find the one correct answer.
  - Identify the choice that matches your prediction, if possible.
    - Don't expect a word-for-word match, but look for a correspondence of ideas.
      - For example, if you predict that the function of a detail is to "provide support for the main idea," an answer choice that says it "supplies evidence for the author's thesis" would likely be correct.

- ○ If there is no clear match, use process of elimination.
  - Eliminate any choice that contradicts your prediction or that clearly falls into one of the five wrong answer categories.
  - Choose the only answer remaining or guess among those you were unable to eliminate.

FINDING THE CORRECT ANSWER

One correct choice—three *demonstrably* incorrect choices:

Great PSAT test takers know that there is always one correct answer, written to match the meaning of the passage, and three *demonstrably* incorrect ones. The word "demonstrably" underscores that the wrong answers aren't merely worse than the credited choice, but that they fail, for one or more reasons, to accurately answer the question. PSAT experts don't compare answer choices to one another; they evaluate the choices based on the passage. They never ask themselves, "Do I like (B) or (C) more?" Instead, they ask, "Does the second paragraph imply (B)? Why or why not?"

Answers and Explanations

Question	Analysis
1. The passage is written from the viewpoint of someone who is A) actively involved in conducting research on leafcutter ants. B) an advocate for habitat restoration. C) knowledgeable about advances in leafcutter ant research. D) a participant in a recent conference on environmental issues.	**Answer: C** **Difficulty:** Medium **Category:** Global **Strategic Advice:** Use your big picture summary and paragraph notes to answer a Global question like this. **Getting to the Answer:** You know from the blurb that the article was written for a "popular biology magazine" in 2018, but this doesn't reveal exactly what the author's credentials are. What you do know from your notes is that the author cites research throughout the passage, including in paragraph 5. This paragraph discusses researchers who built on previous studies about leafcutter ants. This means that **(C)** is correct—the author is knowledgeable about advances in leafcutter ant research. The author discusses others' research, but not his own, so there is no support for (A). (B) conflates two details from the final paragraph. Leafcutter ants can help restore "areas of disturbance," and the author cites researchers who feel that areas with leafcutter ants should be protected. However, the author never advocates for restoring habitats, nor is it the author's primary focus. Finally, there is no discussion of a "recent conference" in the passage, so (D) is out.

Question	Analysis

2. According to the passage, which of the following explains the reason leafcutter ants bring cut vegetation into their nests?

A) For use as nesting material

B) To feed the vegetation to their larvae

C) To add nutrients to the nest soil

D) To cultivate edible fungus on the vegetation

Answer: D

Difficulty: Medium

Category: Detail

Strategic Advice: Use your paragraph notes to guide you toward the relevant portion of the passage, and research there. This is a Detail question, so the answer will be explicitly stated in the passage.

Getting to the Answer: The discussion of the ants bringing vegetation into their nests is in paragraph 1, which states in lines 14–20: "they carry the fragments [of vegetation] into dedicated chambers within their nests, where they cultivate a particular species of nutritious fungus on the cut vegetation. It is this fungus that the ants eat and feed to their larvae." **(D)** is correct.

Although the ants bring vegetation into their nests, this doesn't mean that the vegetation is a nesting material, so (A) is incorrect. They feed the fungus they grow (not the vegetation itself) to their larvae; eliminate (B). The ants do influence soil conditions, but adding nutrients to the nest soil is not the reason for bringing vegetation into the nest, as (C) would have you believe.

3. Which choice provides the best evidence for the answer to the previous question?

A) Lines 7–11 ("These ants … nests")

B) Lines 14–20 ("Instead … larvae")

C) Lines 21–25 ("Remarkably … ant")

D) Lines 31–35 ("In other … crops")

Answer: B

Difficulty: Medium

Category: Command of Evidence

Strategic Advice: Use the lines you researched for the previous question to make your prediction for a Command of Evidence question like this.

Getting to the Answer: The answer for the previous question came from lines 14–20. These lines explain why the ants bring vegetation into their nests. **(B)** is correct.

(A) reveals that the ants bring vegetation into their nests, but does not explain why. (C) and (D) deal with fungus cultivation, but do not not mention that the ants cultivate the fungus for food.

Question	Analysis
4. As used in line 15, "dedicated" most nearly means A) zealous. B) enthusiastic. C) faithful. D) special.	**Answer: D** **Difficulty:** Easy **Category:** Vocab-in-Context **Strategic Advice:** Use the information surrounding the given word to confirm how it's being used. **Getting to the Answer:** The text surrounding the word says that these chambers are used specifically for fungus cultivation—that is, they are uniquely or specially dedicated to that task. **(D)**, "special," is correct. (A), (B), and (C) are all alternative meanings of "dedicated," but none of them fit the context. They all describe attributes of active beings (like people or ants), rather than passive objects like chambers.

Reading

Question	Analysis
5. Which of the following can most reasonably be inferred about leafcutter ant activity?	**Answer: B**
	Difficulty: Hard
A) Leafcutter ants' actions remain consistent across species and geographic areas.	**Category:** Inference
	Strategic Advice: It's difficult to make a specific prediction given how broad the question stem is. Use your big picture summary and paragraph notes to guide you, then check the answer choices one by one to see which is supported.
B) Changes in environmental conditions can influence how leafcutter ants behave.	
C) The leafcutter ants' actions are the primary force for change in the environments in which they are present.	**Getting to the Answer:** The author states in paragraph 5 that two scientists "analyzed the data from a large number of previous studies to determine how various environmental factors play into the ants' behavior and their effects on local ecology" (lines 69–73). If environmental factors play into the ants' behaviors, then changes in environmental factors could change those ants' behaviors. Choice **(B)** is thus correct.
D) Compared to the activities of large grazing animals, the activities of leafcutter ants have a less important effect on the landscape.	
	The passage never indicates that leafcutter ants' actions are always the same. Further, different leafcutter ant species cultivate different species of fungus, so (A) is incorrect. The author explains that these ants may move more organic material than other animals in their environment, but because animals are not the only factor in environmental change, it would be extreme to claim that they are the "primary force for change" in their environments, as (B) states. Finally, the passage notes that "leafcutters are responsible for up to 25 percent or more of the total consumption of vegetation by all herbivores" (lines 58–61), but does not note what percentage is consumed by large grazing animals. Further, the author never implies that the leafcutter ants are less important in general to the landscape than large grazers, so (D) is incorrect.

Question	Analysis
6. Which choice provides the best evidence for the answer to the previous question? A) Lines 7–11 ("These ants … nests") B) Lines 69–73 ("To do so … ecology") C) Lines 88–90 ("In fact … environment") D) Lines 105–112 ("Furthermore … land")	**Answer: B** **Difficulty:** Medium **Category:** Command of Evidence **Strategic Advice:** Use your research from the previous question to make a prediction. **Getting to the Answer:** The answer to the previous question came from lines 69–73, which is **(B)**. The lines in (A) provide a fact about leafcutter ant behavior that does not help to answer the previous question. (C) and (D) are incorrect because they offer ways that the ants affect the environment surrounding them, not how environmental conditions affect the ants' behavior, as the answer to the previous question states. (C) or (D) might be a tempting trap answer if you had incorrectly answered (C) to the previous question.
7. In the fourth paragraph (lines 48–61), the mathematical figures cited serve mainly to A) indicate the power leafcutter ants have to damage local ecosystems. B) demonstrate that leafcutter ants are more numerous than other insect species where they are present. C) underscore how much is known about the construction and configuration of leafcutter ant colonies. D) emphasize the great scope of the leafcutter ants' impact on their environment.	**Answer: D** **Difficulty:** Medium **Category:** Function **Strategic Advice:** To predict the correct answer for a Function question like this, check your notes for the cited portion of the passage and ask how the author is using the relevant details. **Getting to the Answer:** Paragraph 4 opens by noting what important "environmental engineers" the leafcutter ants are. All of the numbers cited reinforce this point, demonstrating how numerous they are, how large their nests are, and how much they consume. This purpose is consistent with **(D)**. While the leafcutter ants impact their environments, the passage does not indicate that they damage it—in fact, the final paragraph explains that they can improve it—so (A) is incorrect. One statistic tells you how many ants can be present in a single nest, but there is no comparison given to other species, so (B) is incorrect as well. The point of the paragraph is how much the ants accomplish, not how much scientists know about them, so (C) is out.

Question	Analysis
8. According to the graph, the ratio of refuse soil to control soil is highest for which of the following nutrients? A) Potassium B) Phosphorus C) Magnesium D) Carbon	**Answer: A** **Difficulty:** Easy **Category:** Detail **Strategic Advice:** Read the graph for the detail that the question stem requests. **Getting to the Answer:** The graph shows the longest bar for potassium. So, the ratio of refuse soil to control soil is greater for potassium than for any other nutrient. **(A)** is correct. (B), (C), and (D) are all nutrients in the graph with lesser ratios.
9. Which of the following statements is best supported by the data presented in the table? A) Leafcutter ants greatly increase the nutrients present in their refuse soil and increase it even more in their nest soil. B) Leafcutter ants greatly increase the nutrients present in their nest soil and increase it even more in their refuse soil. C) Potassium is critical in helping plants near leafcutter ants to grow. D) There is approximately twice as much calcium as magnesium in refuse soil.	**Answer: B** **Difficulty:** Medium **Category:** Inference **Strategic Advice:** Consult your notes for the table to remind yourself of what information it contains, and then check to see which answer choice is supported by the data. **Getting to the Answer:** The ratios provided in the chart support the fact that the ants increase the amount of each nutrient in their nest soil. Further, the ratios comparing refuse soil to control soil are all greater than the ratios comparing nest soil to control soil. **(B)** is correct. (A) reverses the relationship between refuse and nest soil. (C) is incorrect because, while leafcutter ants greatly increase the potassium in their soil, there is no indication provided of which specific nutrients local plants require. (D) is unsupported because the chart does not give the total amount of any given element in any type of soil. It indicates only how much more prevalent a nutrient is in refuse soil or nest soil when compared to control soil.

Try on Your Own

Directions: Put the expert question strategies to work on the following passage. First, take a few minutes to refresh your memory of the passage, which first appeared in chapter 11. As you review the question stems (which you first saw in chapter 12 when you practiced step 1 of the Reading Question Method), try to recall the question type and research approach you previously identified, or simply repeat step 1 if you don't recall. Then, for each question, 1) conduct the needed research, 2) jot down your prediction of the answer, and 3) find the one correct answer.

> ### PREDICTIONS
>
> On the real test, you won't have time to write down your full prediction in complete sentences. If you feel the need to write something to help you hold on to your prediction, keep it very brief: a word or two, or even better, a single abbreviation. For example, if you predict that an author is including a detail as support for a broader point, you might just write "suppt" next to the choices.

Questions 1–10 are based on the following passage.

Norse Passage Map

This passage, about the decline of the Norse colonies that once existed in Greenland, is from a comprehensive 2015 research report examining this anthropological mystery.

In 1721, the Norwegian missionary Hans Egede discovered that the two known Norse settlements on Greenland were completely deserted. Ever since,
5 the reasons behind the decline and eventual disappearance of these people have been greatly debated. Greenland, established by the charismatic outlaw Erik the Red in about 986 c.e., was
10 a colony of Norway by 1000 c.e., complete with a church hierarchy and trading community. After several relatively prosperous centuries, the colony had fallen on hard times and
15 was not heard from in Europe, but it wasn't until Egede's discovery that the complete downfall of the settlement was confirmed.
Throughout the nineteenth century,
20 researchers attributed the demise of the Norse colonies to war between the colonies and Inuit groups. This

[margin notes: GL colony gone by 1721— reasons debated]

[margin notes: 1800s researchers said cause was war w/ Inuits]

is based largely on evidence from the work *Description of Greenland,*
25 written by Norse settler Ivar Bardarson around 1364, which describes strained relationships between the Norse settlers and the Inuits who had recently come to Greenland. However, because there is
30 no archaeological evidence of a war or a massacre, and the extensive body of Inuit oral history tells of no such event, modern scholars give little credence to these theories.
35 New theories about the reason for the decline of the Norse colonies are being proposed partially because the amount of information available is rapidly increasing. Advances in
40 paleoclimatology, for example, have increased the breadth and clarity of our picture of the region. Most notably, recent analyses of the central Greenland ice core, coupled with data obtained
45 from plant material and sea sediments, have indicated severe climate changes in the region that some are now calling a "mini ice age." Such studies point toward a particularly warm period
50 for Greenland that occurred between the years 800 c.e. and 1300 c.e., which

[margin notes: but no arch. evid.]

[margin notes: much new info]

[margin notes: climate data]

[margin notes: big climate change b/4 colony decline]

was then followed—unfortunately for those inhabiting even the most temperate portions of the island—by a
55 steady decline in overall temperatures that lasted for nearly 600 years. The rise and fall of the Norse colonies in Greenland, not surprisingly, roughly mirrors this climate-based chronology.
60 Researchers have also found useful data in a most surprising place—fly remains. The insect, not native to the island, was brought over inadvertently on Norse ships. Flies survived in the
65 warm and unsanitary conditions of the Norse dwellings and barns and died out when these were no longer inhabited. By carbon dating the fly remains, researchers have tracked the occupation
70 of the settlements and confirmed that the human population began to decline around 1350 c.e.

Changing economic conditions likely also conspired against the
75 settlers. The colonies had founded a moderately successful trading economy based on exporting whale ivory, especially important given their need for the imported wood and iron that
80 were in short supply on the island. Unfortunately, inexpensive and plentiful Asian and African elephant ivory flooded the European market during the fourteenth century, destroying
85 Greenland's standing in the European economy. At the same time, the trading fleet of the German Hanseatic League

fly remains

dating shows human decline ~1350

econ prob-lems, too

ivory market ↓

supplanted the previously dominant Norwegian shipping fleets. Because the
90 German merchants had little interest in the Norse colonists, Greenland soon found itself visited by fewer and fewer ships each year until its inhabitants were completely isolated by 1480 c.e.
95 Cultural and sociological factors may have also contributed to the demise of the Norse settlements. The Inuit tribes, while recent immigrants to Greenland, had come from nearby areas to the
100 west and had time-tested strategies to cope with the severe environment. The Norse settlers, however, seem to have viewed themselves as fundamentally European and did not adopt Inuit
105 techniques. Inuit apparel, for example, was far more appropriate for the cold, damp environment; the remains from even the last surviving Norse settlements indicate a costume that
110 was undeniably European in design. Likewise, the Norse settlers failed to adopt Inuit hunting techniques and tools, such as the toggle harpoon, which made it possible to capture calorie-rich
115 seal meat. Instead, the Norse relied on the farming styles that had been so successful for their European ancestors, albeit in a radically different climate. It seems likely that this stubborn cultural
120 inflexibility prevented the Norse civilization in Greenland from adapting to increasingly severe environmental and economic conditions.

+ German traders didn't visit GL

also cultural factors

Euro. clothes

hunting vs. farming

BIG PICTURE

Main Idea: New information shows that factors such as climate, economy, and culture may have caused the collapse of the Norse colonies in Greenland.

Author's Purpose: To describe current theories (and evidence for them) of what happened to the Norse in Greenland

---

1. The main purpose of the passage is to

   A) discuss possible theories explaining a historical event.

   B) refute a commonly held belief about a group of people.

   C) chronicle the conflict between immigrant settlers and a region's indigenous people.

   D) analyze the motivations behind a number of conflicting explanations.

2. The author implies that, during the period in which the Norse settlements were initially founded, the climate in the region was

   A) uncharacteristically mild.

   B) typically inhospitable.

   C) unusually harsh.

   D) increasingly cold.

3. Which choice provides the best evidence for the answer to the previous question?

   A) Lines 42–47 ("Most ... region")

   B) Lines 48–51 ("Such ... 1300 c.e.")

   C) Lines 56–59 ("The rise ... chronology")

   D) Lines 64–67 ("Flies ... inhabited")

4. In line 63, the word "inadvertently" most nearly means

   A) secretly.

   B) distractedly.

   C) unintentionally.

   D) deliberately.

5. The passage indicates that the Inuit people on Greenland

   A) were responsible for the collapse of the Norse settlements.

   B) shared their knowledge with the Norse settlers.

   C) struggled with the difficult local climate.

   D) were recent immigrants, like the Norse themselves.

6. What function does the discussion of the trade in whale and elephant ivory serve in the passage as a whole?

   A) It is evidence that strengthens the traditional view introduced in the second paragraph.

   B) It is an example that challenges the theory introduced in the fourth paragraph.

   C) It provides additional support for the main idea of the third paragraph.

   D) It contradicts the central argument of the whole passage.

7. What can reasonably be inferred from the passage about the relationship between the shipping fleets of nations in the fourteenth and fifteenth centuries and the colonies established by those nations?

   A) Ships never traded with colonies not founded by the same country.

   B) Colonies were dependent upon deliveries by ships from their own country.

   C) Colonies would surely fail without regular deliveries by ships.

   D) Shipping fleets may not have prioritized deliveries to foreign colonies.

8. The author claims the Norse settlers did not adopt the successful survival tactics of the Inuit because

   A) the Norse settlers had strained relations with the Inuit.

   B) the Inuit did not share their knowledge with the Norse settlers.

   C) the Norse settlers believed those tactics were incompatible with their culture.

   D) after attempting them, the Norse settlers found the tactics to be unsuccessful.

9. Which choice provides the best evidence for the
    answer to the previous question?

    A) Lines 22–29 ("This is ... Greenland")

    B) Lines 111–115 ("Likewise ... meat")

    C) Lines 115–118 ("Instead ... climate")

    D) Lines 118–123 ("It seems ... conditions")

10. Which of the following best summarizes the organ-
    ization of the passage?

    A) An unusual event is described, the possible
        causes of the event are evaluated, and the most
        likely cause is determined.

    B) A mystery is presented, an accepted
        explanation is proposed but challenged, and
        alternative explanations are introduced.

    C) An anomaly is noted, the traditional
        interpretation of the anomaly is reported, and
        more recent evidence is cited to support that
        interpretation.

    D) A paradox is reported, the historical solution
        is proven to be false, and a more modern
        resolution is proven to be correct.

How Much Have You Learned?

Directions: Take 12 minutes to reread this passage (from chapter 11) and answer the associated questions (first seen in chapter 12). Try to use the various PSAT Reading question strategies you learned in this chapter.

Questions 11–20 refer to the following passage.

Infant Language Passage Map

This passage, about infant language acquisition, is adapted from a research paper written in 2017 that explored early childhood development.

Infants are born as scientists, constantly interacting with and questioning the world around them. However, as any good scientist

5   knows, simply making observations is not sufficient; a large part of learning is dependent on being able to communicate ideas, observations, and feelings with others. Though most

10 infants do not produce discernible words until around age one or one-and-a-half, they begin gaining proficiency in their native languages long before that. In fact, many linguists agree that a

15 newborn baby's brain is already pre-programmed for language acquisition, meaning that it's as natural for a baby to talk as it is for a dog to dig.
According to psycholinguist Anne

20 Cutler, an infant's language acquisition actually begins well before birth. At only one day old, newborns have demonstrated the ability to recognize the voices and rhythms heard

25 during their last trimester in the muffled confines of the womb. In general, infants are more likely to attend to a specific voice stream if they perceive it as more familiar than other

30 streams. Newborns tend to be especially partial to their mother's voice and her native language, as opposed to another woman or another language. For example, when an infant is presented

35 with a voice stream spoken by his

babies start learning lang. b/4 they can talk

"pre-pro-grammed"

Cutler: learn lang. b/4 birth

— support

mother and a background stream delivered by an unfamiliar voice, he will effortlessly attend to his mother while ignoring the background stream.

40 Therefore, by using these simple yet important cues, and others like them, infants can easily learn the essential characteristics and rules of their native language.

45 However, it is important to note that an infant's ability to learn from the nuances of her mother's speech is predicated upon her ability to separate that speech from the sounds of the

50 dishwasher, the family dog, the bus stopping on the street outside, and, quite possibly, other streams of speech, like a newscaster on the television down the hall or siblings playing in

55 an adjacent room. Infants are better able to accomplish this task when the voice of interest is louder than any of the competing background noises. Conversely, when two voices are of

60 equal amplitude, infants typically demonstrate little preference for one stream over the other. Researchers have hypothesized that because an infant's ability to selectively pay attention to

65 one voice or sound, even in a mix of others, has not fully developed yet, the infant is actually interpreting competing voice streams that are equally loud as one single stream with unfamiliar

70 patterns and sounds.
During the first few months after birth, infants will subconsciously study the language being used around them, taking note of the rhythmic

75 patterns, the sequences of sounds, and the intonation of the language.

need mom's voice sep. from bkgd

+ louder than other voices

newborns learn patterns

Reading

Newborns will also start to actively process how things like differences in pitch or accented syllables further

80 affect meaning. Interestingly, up until six months of age, they can still recognize and discriminate between the phonemes (single units of sound in a language like "ba" or "pa") of other

85 languages. Though infants do display a preference for the language they heard in utero, most infants are not biased towards the specific phonemes of that language.

90   This ability to recognize and discriminate between all phonemes comes to an end by the middle of their first year, at which point infants start

<6 mos.: "hear" other lang. too

~1 yr.: prefer their own lang.

displaying a preference for phonemes

95 in their native language, culminating at age one, when they stop responding to foreign phonemes altogether. This is part of what is known as the "critical period," which begins at birth and

100 lasts until puberty. During this period, as the brain continues to grow and change, language acquisition is instinctual, explaining why young children seem to pick up languages so

105 easily.

crit. pd.: still easier to learn other lang.

BIG PICTURE

Main Idea: Infants listen to voices in their environments to acquire language instinctually, possibly starting before they are even born.

Author's Purpose: To explain the abilities and limitations of infants in acquiring language

---

11. The primary purpose of the passage is to

    A) present the background of a recent medical discovery.

    B) trace the history of a scientific inquiry.

    C) explain the research that led to a new breakthrough.

    D) describe an aspect of early childhood development.

12. According to the passage, when children begin to acquire their native language they

    A) are in about the middle of their first year.

    B) are at least one year old.

    C) are not yet able to speak.

    D) start to imitate the phonemes of that language.

13. Which choice provides the best evidence for the answer to the previous question?

    A) Lines 9–14 ("Though most ... that")

    B) Lines 80–85 ("Interestingly ... languages")

    C) Lines 90–97 ("This ability ... altogether")

    D) Lines 97–100 ("This is ... puberty")

14. As used in line 48, "predicated" most nearly means

    A) predicted.

    B) expressed.

    C) replaced.

    D) built.

15. The main purpose of the third paragraph (lines 45–70) is to

    A) illustrate how distinct speech streams increase the speed of language acquisition.

    B) discuss the mechanism by which louder volumes of speech impede language acquisition.

    C) explain the role of the relative volumes of sounds on an infant's ability to learn to process language.

    D) provide scientific data that measure the improvement in language acquisition as the volume of the speech stream increases.

16. As used in line 82, "discriminate" most nearly means

    A) differentiate.

    B) perceive.

    C) prefer.

    D) persecute.

17. According to the passage, children begin to learn the rhythms, pitches, and accents of speech

    A) before birth.

    B) in the first months of life.

    C) after the middle of the first year.

    D) at around one year of age.

18. The passage most strongly suggests that a mother who wants to assist her child in language acquisition should

    A) expose her child to as many spoken languages as possible.

    B) use short words composed of the basic phonemes of her native language.

    C) be sure her voice is louder than other background noises.

    D) use as large a vocabulary as possible when speaking to her child.

19. Which choice provides the best evidence for the answer to the previous question?

    A) Lines 14–18 ("In fact ... dig")

    B) Lines 45–55 ("However ... room")

    C) Lines 55–58 ("Infants ... noises")

    D) Lines 85–89 ("Though ... language")

20. The most likely purpose of the discussion of phonemes is to

    A) identify important stages in the process of language acquisition in children.

    B) emphasize the importance of children acquiring only one language at a time.

    C) show how children gradually build larger words from the primary sounds around them.

    D) illustrate the importance of volume in the language acquisition of children.

Reflect

Directions: Take a few minutes to recall what you've learned and what you've been practicing in this chapter. Consider the following questions, jot down your best answer for each one, and then compare your reflections to the expert responses on the following page. Use your level of confidence to determine what to do next.

Why do PSAT experts research and predict the correct answer to Reading questions before reading the answer choices?

_____

_____

_____

What are the types of research clues contained in PSAT Reading question stems?

_____

_____

_____

What are the five common wrong answer types associated with PSAT Reading questions?

- _____
- _____
- _____
- _____
- _____

How will you approach the process of answering PSAT Reading questions more strategically going forward? Are there any specific habits you will practice to make your approach to PSAT Reading more effective and efficient?

_____

_____

_____

Expert Responses

Why do PSAT experts research and predict the correct answer to Reading questions before reading the answer choices?

Expert test takers know that the correct answer to each PSAT Reading question is based on the text of the passage. They research to avoid answering based on memory or on a whim. Predicting the correct answer before reading the choices increases accuracy and speed by helping the test taker avoid rereading, confusion, and comparing answer choices to one another.

What are the types of research clues contained in PSAT Reading question stems?

Line numbers, paragraph numbers, proper nouns, quoted text, specific content clues, and whole passage clues.

What are the five common wrong answer types associated with PSAT Reading questions?

- *Out of scope*
- *Opposite*
- *Distortion*
- *Extreme*
- *Misused detail*

How will you approach the process of answering PSAT Reading questions more strategically going forward? Are there any specific habits you will practice to make your approach to PSAT Reading more effective and efficient?

There is no one-size-fits-all answer here. Reflect on your own habits in answering PSAT Reading questions and give yourself an honest assessment of your strengths and weaknesses. Consider the strategies you've seen experts use in this chapter, and put them to work in your own practice to increase your accuracy, speed, and confidence.

Next Steps

If you answered most questions correctly in the "How Much Have You Learned?" section, and if your responses to the Reflect questions were similar to those of the PSAT expert, then consider Answering PSAT Reading Questions an area of strength, and move on to the next chapter. Come back to this topic periodically to prevent yourself from getting rusty.

If you don't yet feel confident, review the material in "How to Answer PSAT Reading Questions," and then try the questions you missed again. As always, be sure to review the explanations closely.

Answers and Explanations

1. A

Difficulty: Medium

Category: Global

Strategic Advice: Use your big picture summary to make a prediction on a Global question like this. For this question, you can simply use your summary of the author's purpose.

Getting to the Answer: The author discusses the disappearance of a group of Norse settlers and offers a number of explanations for this occurrence, but doesn't advocate for any one of them in particular. Thus, the primary purpose is to introduce readers to a number of possible explanations, as suggested in correct choice **(A)**.

(B) and (C) are too narrow. The belief that there was a conflict between the Inuit and the Norse settlers is refuted in the second paragraph, and the passage continues for three more paragraphs, so (B) isn't the main purpose. The passage mentions "strained relations" between the groups at the start of the second paragraph, but does not go on to "chronicle the conflict," as (C) suggests. The motivations behind the explanations are never discussed, nor is it clear that the explanations are in conflict (climatological, economic, and cultural factors could all be partial causes of the collapse), so (D) is also incorrect.

2. A

Difficulty: Medium

Category: Inference

Strategic Advice: This question requires you to put together details from different parts of the passage to arrive at the appropriate inference.

Getting to the Answer: The important clues in the question are "the period in which the Norse settlements were initially founded" and "climate." The beginning of the passage states that the colony was founded around the year 1000 c.e. However, climate is not discussed until the third paragraph, where the author writes, "a particularly warm period for Greenland ... occurred between the years 800 c.e. and 1300 c.e." (lines 49–51). In fact, "particularly warm" is not bad for a prediction. Choice **(A)** matches and is correct. The "mild," warm weather was uncharacteristic of the usually cold, harsh climate.

All of the incorrect choices are misused details that are mentioned in the passage; they apply to the years after 1300 c.e., not to the specific time period indicated in the question stem.

3. B

Difficulty: Medium

Category: Command of Evidence

Strategic Advice: If you used a line reference to answer the previous question, use that as your prediction and start by seeing whether that line reference is one of the answer choices.

Getting to the Answer: In answering the previous question, it emerges that the climate during the initial founding of the Norse settlements was "uncharacteristically mild." This strange, "particularly warm" weather is mentioned in line 49, making choice **(B)** correct.

(A) and (C) mention the change in climate, but do not specifically mention the warmer years in the answer to the previous question. (D) connects the disappearance of the flies to that of the settlers, but does not address the climate change.

4. C

Difficulty: Easy

Category: Vocab-in-Context

Strategic Advice: Use surrounding information to figure out the meaning of a challenging word. If you can't think of a single word to use as a prediction, a short phrase is also fine.

Getting to the Answer: Return to line 63, mentioned in the question, and read a little above and a little below the line. The flies were not on the island until the Norse ships arrived, and "inadvertently" is an adverb describing how the flies were brought to the island. The suggestion there is that the flies were not brought on purpose, so "by accident" is a good prediction. Choice **(C)** matches and is thus correct.

The remaining choices are incorrect because they don't fit the context. It makes little sense that the ships would hide the flies in secret as (A) suggests. (B) almost suggests that the flies somehow diverted the attention of the colonists to bring themselves on board, which also seems implausible. Finally, (D) presents the opposite of the intended meaning.

5. D

Difficulty: Medium

Category: Detail

Strategic Advice: When an open-ended question makes prediction difficult, use elimination. Match information in the passage to the choices and eliminate choices as you go.

Getting to the Answer: The Inuit people are mentioned in the second and final paragraphs. The second paragraph states in lines 28–29 that "Inuits ... had recently come to Greenland." In lines 97–98, in the final paragraph, this point is repeated, indicating that the Norse colonists were not the only recent settlers of Greenland. **(D)** is therefore correct.

(A) is incorrect because the author dismisses the view that the Inuit are responsible for the Norse colony collapse (lines 29–34). (B) is incorrect because the author suggests in the final paragraph that the Norse were unwilling to abandon their European ways, so there's no evidence that the Inuit successfully shared knowledge with them. (C) is incorrect because, in the final paragraph, the Inuit are said to have had "time-tested strategies to cope with the severe environment" (lines 100–101), suggesting they did not struggle with the climate.

6. C

Difficulty: Medium

Category: Function

Strategic Advice: If your prediction ends up being more specific than the answer choices, try to fill in the generic descriptions with actual details from the passage to better assess which choice is a match. For example, if a choice mentions the main idea of a particular paragraph, then rephrase the choice in your mind to include that actual main idea.

Getting to the Answer: At the beginning of the third paragraph, the author notes that new information is leading to novel theories that explain the Norse

colonies' decline. The author then goes on to provide some examples of these new theories and the evidence that supports them. The fourth paragraph continues this line of thought by turning to economic factors such as the changing ivory trade. Because that discussion provides additional support for the main idea of paragraph 3, **(C)** is correct.

(A) is incorrect because the traditional view, that the colony was destroyed by war with the Inuits, is dismissed later in paragraph 2, not supported. (B) is incorrect because the discussion of the ivory trade supports, not challenges, the theory in paragraph 4 about economic factors of collapse. (D) is incorrect because the shift in the ivory trade away from whale ivory strengthens the author's claim that new explanations are emerging, which is the central idea of the passage.

7. D

Difficulty: Hard

Category: Inference

Strategic Advice: Inference questions may require you to put together pieces from different parts of the passage before arriving at a prediction.

Getting to the Answer: The shipping fleets of Norway and Germany are part of the economic discussion in the fourth paragraph. Lines 86–94 indicate that the German fleets took over the trade routes from the Norse and lost interest in the Norse colony. The suggestion is that a country's fleets are generally more interested in transacting with that country's colonies than with foreign colonies. Choice **(D)** is thus correct.

(A) is too extreme and contradicted by the passage, which suggests that at least a few non-Norwegian ships visited the colonies. (B) is incorrect because the colony was able to survive for a time even after the Norwegian fleets were supplanted, suggesting that essential deliveries could come from foreign sources. (C) is incorrect because the author presents another possibility in the last paragraph: the colonists could have adopted more of the well-adapted customs of the Inuit and learned to survive in Greenland's natural environment, instead of sticking with European practices that didn't suit the climate.

8. C

Difficulty: Medium

Category: Detail

Strategic Advice: Follow the clue in the question stem to discover the relevant detail from the passage. For Detail questions, it's fine to use phrases or sentences directly from the passage as predictions.

Getting to the Answer: The discussion of the Norse colonists refusing to adapt to the changing climate occurs in the fifth paragraph. Lines 101–104 attribute this refusal to the Norse colonists thinking of themselves as European and clinging to European traditions. The author even concludes the passage by suggesting that the Norse colonists were likely guilty of a "stubborn cultural inflexibility" (lines 119–120) that led to their collapse. Choice **(C)** is therefore correct.

(A) is a misused detail from the second paragraph. Although there were strained relations between the two groups, the text does not cite this poor relationship as the reason why the Norse did not adopt Inuit ways. (B) and (D) are not mentioned in the passage, making them incorrect as well.

9. D

Difficulty: Medium

Category: Command of Evidence

Strategic Advice: Use your work on the previous question to make a prediction: wherever you went for research will likely be correct.

Getting to the Answer: The author suggests in the concluding sentence that the Norse colonists died out because of their refusal to take on better-adapted cultural norms, which directly supports the previous question's answer. **(D)** is thus correct.

(A) is the line that supports the misused detail (from choice (A) in the previous question) in the second paragraph. There is no evidence that the difficult relations between the two groups led to the colonists' refusal to adopt Inuit practices. (B) and (C) identify two of the Inuit's survival tactics, but do not provide a reason these tactics were not adopted by the Norse.

10. B

Difficulty: Global

Category: Hard

Strategic Advice: For a question about the organization of the passage, review the marginal notes of your passage map and try to construct a story of how the passage moves from one paragraph to the next, using this as your prediction. The correct answer will best reflect the story you've constructed.

Getting to the Answer: The first paragraph introduces the topic of the unexplained disappearance of the Norse colonies and the second paragraph presents and refutes one historical explanation. In the remainder of the passage, the author presents a number of alternative explanations, but never advocates for one of them over the others. Rather, the author seems to suggest the theories are somewhat compatible, all representing factors that led to the colonies' collapse. This structure is best reflected in **(B)**, the correct answer.

(A) is incorrect because no single cause is definitively determined. (C) is incorrect because the traditional view, war between the Norse colonists and the Inuit, is discredited, not supported. (D) is too extreme; the disappearance of the colonies is not really a "paradox" so much as a mystery, and the author doesn't attempt to "prove" anything, but just offers possible explanations.

11. D

Difficulty: Easy

Category: Global

Strategic Advice: Research the answer to a Global question in your big picture summary, and keep the author's tone in mind.

Getting to the Answer: The author presented a factual description of several aspects of infant language acquisition, which matches choice **(D)**.

(A) and (C) are incorrect because the passage doesn't identify a "recent medical discovery" or "new breakthrough." (B) is incorrect because, although some of the steps in the process of language acquisition are described in the text, the history of the research into this process is not.

12. C

Difficulty: Medium

Category: Detail

Getting to the Answer: The important context clue in this question is "begin to acquire their native language." Although the entire passage is describing language acquisition, the context clue tells you to focus your research on the first paragraph. Lines 9–14 state that babies start to learn their native language before they can speak, and this prediction matches **(C)**, the correct answer.

(A) and (B) are ages mentioned in the passage, but (A) gives the age when babies begin to produce recognizable words and (B) gives the age when babies begin to prefer the phonemes of their native languages. (D) is a distortion of information presented in the last paragraph. Although the passage says that babies prefer the phonemes of their native language, it does not say that babies imitate these phonemes, nor that this preference is evident at the beginning of the language acquisition process.

13. A

Difficulty: Medium

Category: Command of Evidence

Getting to the Answer: Good research on the previous question pays off in efficient, correct answers to Command of Evidence questions. Since the answer to the previous question is found in lines 9–14, **(A)** is correct.

(B) describes the age at which infants still discriminate among phonemes, (C) describes the age when children begin to prefer the phonemes of their native languages, and (D) defines the "critical period." None of these incorrect choices identify the age when children *begin* to acquire their native languages.

14. D

Difficulty: Medium

Category: Vocab-in-Context

Getting to the Answer: The word "predicated" connects the "ability to learn from ... mother's speech" to the "ability to separate that speech" from other sounds. Logically, it would not be possible to learn from something (mother's speech) if you can't even recognize that thing in the first place, so the noted word must mean something like "dependent." **(D)** comes closest to this prediction, making it correct.

(A) is incorrect because the ability to learn from a stream of speech comes after the ability to distinguish that speech, but "predicted" seems to reverse the chronology. (B) is incorrect because it suggests the two abilities are the same, that one is only the expression of another, but the author is clear to distinguish them. (C) is incorrect because the two abilities work together; the second doesn't simply take the place of the first.

15. C

Difficulty: Hard

Category: Function

Getting to the Answer: Keep the purpose of the passage in mind, then review the passage map and predict a reason the author included the third paragraph. Within the discussion of language acquisition in infants, the third paragraph describes the importance of the volume of the mother's voice over the other background sounds. This prediction matches **(C)**, the correct answer.

Choice (A) subtly distorts the information in the paragraph. The ability of a baby to identify a specific speech stream is not connected to the *speed* of language acquisition. (B) is an opposite choice; louder volumes of speech assist, not impede, language acquisition. (D) is not discussed in the passage; no data is supplied to connect the improvement in language acquisition to different volumes of speech.

16. A

Difficulty: Medium

Category: Vocab-in-Context

Getting to the Answer: Read the sentence without "discriminate" and ask what the author is trying to communicate. Because the sentence is about infants distinguishing sounds as belonging to one or another language, *separate* or *tell the difference* are good predictions. Choice **(A)** is correct because it matches.

(B) is incorrect because it is synonymous with "recognize," which the author combines with "discriminate," so it would be redundant and lose the connotation of distinguishing between multiples phonemes. (C) is incorrect because it contradicts what the author says in the following sentence (lines 85–89) about the lack of preference toward specific phonemes. (D) is incorrect because "persecute" is a common meaning of "discriminate" that doesn't fit the context.

17. B

Difficulty: Medium

Category: Detail

Getting to the Answer: The clues in the question stem point to paragraph 4, where the author mentions "rhythmic patterns" and "differences in pitch or accented syllables." That paragraph begins, "During the first few months after birth," which directly matches with correct choice **(B)**.

(A), (C), and (D), the incorrect answers, all contain different ages of children that are mentioned in the passage, but each is associated with a different phase of language acquisition, not the stage mentioned in the question.

18. C

Difficulty: Hard

Category: Inference

Getting to the Answer: Paragraph 3 discusses how infants have difficulty separating voice streams that have equal volumes, as well as how important it is for infants to recognize their mother's speech in order to learn from it. Thus, it makes sense that a mother would aid her infant's language acquisition by speaking louder than any background sounds, which makes **(C)** correct.

(A) and (B) are distortions of information in the passage, making them incorrect. Although the passage mentions that young children learn languages easily, the text never recommends exposing children to multiple languages. Similarly, phonemes are discussed, but using phonemes to assist children in learning to speak is not. (D), using a large vocabulary, is never mentioned in the text, and so is incorrect.

19. C

Difficulty: Medium

Category: Command of Evidence

Getting to the Answer: Since the support for the previous answer came from the third paragraph, return to that paragraph and identify the line numbers that most directly state that volume helps children to learn language. Lines 55–58, choice **(C)**, are correct.

You can eliminate (A) and (D) quickly because neither comes from the third paragraph. (A) and (D) are indeed incorrect because they identify different stages in the language acquisition process, not a specific action a mother could take to assist this process. (B) is incorrect because, although it identifies the need for babies to be able to differentiate the targeted speech stream from background noises, it does not suggest how this could be done by using a louder volume.

20. A

Difficulty: Medium

Category: Function

Getting to the Answer: The author discusses phonemes in the fourth and fifth paragraphs, identifying two distinct ways that infants respond to phonemes. In paragraph 4, the author notes that infants can recognize phonemes from other languages until six months of age, while in paragraph 5, infants stop responding to foreign phonemes altogether in the "critical period." Thus, the purpose of this discussion is to highlight some important stages in the process of language acquisition, as in correct choice **(A)**.

(B) and (C) are not mentioned in the text, and so are incorrect. (D) is incorrect because volume is discussed earlier in the passage where phonemes are not the topic.

PART 4

PSAT Writing and Language

CHAPTER 14

The Method for PSAT Writing and Language Questions

LEARNING OBJECTIVE

After completing this chapter, you will be able to:

- Efficiently apply the PSAT Writing and Language Method

How to Do PSAT Writing and Language

The Writing and Language section of the PSAT tests a limited number of grammar, style, and logic issues. You should feel empowered in knowing that you can familiarize yourself with these recurring issues and learn to spot them and address them quickly and efficiently. We'll describe the issues that you're likely to see on test day and how to deal with them in the other chapters of this unit. In this chapter, we'll present a simple series of steps for tackling Writing and Language questions.

Take a look at the passage and questions that follow and think about how you would approach them on test day. Then, compare your approach to the recommendations presented.

Questions 1 and 2 refer to the following passage.

Design Museums

City museums are places where visitors can learn about various cultures by **1** glancing at objects of particular historical or artistic value. The increasingly popular "design museums" that are opening today perform quite a different function. **2** Design museums display and assess objects that are readily available to the general public, unlike most city museums. These museums place everyday household items under the spotlight, breaking down the barriers between commerce and creative invention. London's Design Museum, for instance, displays a collection of mass-produced objects ranging from electric typewriters to Norwegian sardine-tin labels.

1. A) NO CHANGE
   B) studying
   C) disregarding
   D) organizing

2. A) NO CHANGE
   B) Design museums display and assess objects that are readily available to the general public, unlike the common practice at most city museums.
   C) Unlike most city museums, design museums display and assess objects that are readily available to the general public.
   D) Unlike the common practice at most city museums, design museums display and assess objects that are readily available to the general public.

There is no need to read the entire passage before you start to answer questions. Instead, answer them as you read. When you see a number, finish the sentence you are reading and then look at the corresponding question. If you can answer the question based on what you've read so far, do so—this will likely be the case if the question is testing grammar. If you need more information—which may happen if the question is testing organization or relevance—keep reading until you have enough context to answer the question.

Sometimes the issue being tested will be obvious to you when you look at the underlined segment. If it isn't, glance at the answer choices to help you determine what the test maker is after. For instance, in question 1 from the previous page, a verb with -*ing* and a preposition are underlined. Is the question testing the verb, the preposition, or something else? A quick glance at the answer choices makes it obvious that this question is testing precise word choice, given that the choices are various -*ing* words. **Identifying the issue**, using the choices if necessary, is step 1 of the Writing and Language method.

To find the correct word choice, use the surrounding text. The sentence states that visitors can "learn about various cultures" by doing something to the museum's objects. Thus, the underlined word must be something you could do to objects that would result in learning about them. As written, merely "glancing at" the objects would not be enough to result in actual learning, so eliminate (A). You can also eliminate (C) because "disregarding" the objects would result in the *opposite* of learning about them. Finally, eliminate (D), "organizing." Although the museum staff might organize objects in the collection, the visiting public would not. Since none of the other choices correct the error, this leaves only **(B)**, "studying," which indeed matches the context of learning. So choose **(B)** as the correct answer to question 1. **Eliminating answer choices that do not address the issue** is step 2 of the Writing and Language method.

Sometimes there will be more than one choice that addresses the issue. When that happens, you'll need to base your final response on three considerations: conciseness, relevance, and the potential of a given choice to introduce a new error. Question 2 from the previous page is an example of a question in which more than one choice addresses the issue. This question features an entire sentence that is underlined. The answer choices include various placements for the descriptive phrase "unlike most city museums"—a signal to check whether this modifying phrase is correctly placed. Indeed, it is *design museums* that should be contrasted with city museums, not the "general public," so the phrase "design museums" should be right next to the phrase "unlike most city museums." That eliminates (A) and (B), but you still have to decide between **(C)** and (D), both of which fix the misplaced modifier. Both these choices are grammatically correct and relevant to the surrounding context. However, **(C)** is more concise and is therefore the correct answer for question 2. **Choosing the most concise and relevant response from those that are grammatically correct** is step 3 of the Writing and Language method.

Here are the steps we just illustrated:

The PSAT Method for Writing and Language	
Step 1.	Identify the issue (use the choices if need be)
Step 2.	Eliminate answer choices that do not address the issue
Step 3.	Plug in the remaining answer choices and select the most *correct*, *concise*, and *relevant* one

Correct, concise, and **relevant** means that the answer choice you select:

- Has no grammatical errors
- Is as short as possible while retaining the writer's intended meaning
- Is relevant to the paragraph and the passage as a whole

Correct answers do *not* change the intended meaning of the original sentence, paragraph, or passage, or introduce new grammatical errors.

Try on Your Own

Directions: Take as much time as you need on these questions. Work carefully and methodically. Practice using the steps that you just learned.

Questions 1–4 refer to the following passage.

Design Museums

One advantage that design museums have over other civic museums is that design museums are places where people feel familiar with the exhibits. Unlike average art gallery patrons, a design **1** museums visitors rarely feel intimidated or disoriented. This is partly because design museums clearly illustrate how and why mass-produced consumer objects work and look as they do and show how design contributes to the quality of our lives. **2** For example, an exhibit showcasing a collection of chair designs **3** do not simply explain how the chairs function. The display also demonstrates how such chairs' various features combine to produce an artistic effect or redefine our manner of performing the basic act of being seated. Thus, the purpose of such an exhibit is to present these concepts in novel ways and to challenge, stimulate, and inform the viewer. An art gallery chair **4** exhibit, on the other hand would provide very little information about the chairs themselves and would expect the visitor to appreciate the exhibit on some abstract level.

1. A) NO CHANGE
    B) museums visitors'
    C) museum's visitors'
    D) museum's visitors

2. A) NO CHANGE
    B) In contrast,
    C) Additionally,
    D) Next,

3. A) NO CHANGE
    B) does not
    C) will not
    D) did not

4. A) NO CHANGE
    B) exhibit, on the other hand,
    C) exhibit on the other hand
    D) exhibit on the other hand:

Answers and explanations are on the next page. ▶ ▶ ▶

Answers and Explanations

1. D

Difficulty: Medium

Category: Agreement: Modifiers

Getting to the Answer: When you encounter two nouns in a row, check to see whether the possessive form is needed. Who or what has "visitors"? The "museum." Any answer choices that do not include the apostrophe to make "museum's" possessive are incorrect: eliminate (A) and (B). The "visitors," however, are not in possession of anything in this sentence, so you do not need a possessive form. Thus, eliminate (C) and choose **(D)** as the correct answer.

2. A

Difficulty: Medium

Category: Organization: Transitions

Getting to the Answer: To determine which type of transition is correct, analyze the relationship between the ideas it connects. The previous sentence explains that design museums do two things when displaying objects: 1) show how the objects work/look and 2) show how design impacts people's lives. The sentence with the transition describes an exhibit of chair designs and states that the exhibit would not just explain "how chairs function." The next sentence describes what the display would "also" demonstrate. Thus, the chair exhibit must be an example of the two things that design museums do, so **(A)** is correct. (B) is incorrect because it introduces an illogical contrast transition. (C) is incorrect because the sentence with the transition does not provide an "additional" detail about design museums, but rather it provides a specific example of design museums' functions. (D) is incorrect because this transition is not a part of a chronological sequence of events.

3. B

Difficulty: Medium

Category: Agreement: Verbs

Getting to the Answer: When a verb is underlined, locate its subject to make sure they are in agreement. Although the noun "chair designs" is closest to the verb, the singular "exhibit" is what "does not simply explain how chairs function." Eliminate (A) since it contains a plural verb. To decide among the remaining choices, determine which verb tense matches the surrounding context. The action is happening in the present, as confirmed by the present tense "demonstrates" in the next sentence, so **(B)** is correct. The future tense in (C) and the past tense of (D) are incorrect because they result in an unnecessary verb tense shift.

4. B

Difficulty: Medium

Category: Sentence Structure: Commas, Dashes, and Colons

Getting to the Answer: The phrase "on the other hand" is parenthetical information—if you were to remove the phrase, the sentence would retain the same meaning. Parenthetical information should be set off by a set of commas or dashes, so eliminate (A) because it uses only one comma, (C) because it uses no punctuation, and (D) because it uses a colon. **(B)** is correct because it sets off the parenthetical information with a pair of commas.

Writing & Lang

CHAPTER 15

Spotting and Fixing Errors: Sentence Structure, Punctuation, and Agreement

LEARNING OBJECTIVES

After completing this chapter, you will be able to:

- Determine the correct punctuation and/or conjunctions to form a complete sentence
- Identify and correct inappropriate uses of semicolons
- Identify and correct inappropriate uses of commas, dashes, and colons
- Use punctuation to set off simple parenthetical elements
- Identify and correct verb agreement issues
- Identify and correct pronoun agreement issues
- Identify and correct modifier agreement issues
- Identify and correct inappropriate uses of apostrophes
- Identify and correct expressions that deviate from idiomatic English
- Determine the appropriate word in frequently confused pairs

145/600 SmartPoints®:
Sentence Structure and Punctuation, 85/300 (Very High Yield)
Agreement, 60/300 (High Yield, especially Verbs and Pronouns)

How Much Do You Know?

Directions: Try the questions that follow. The "Category" heading in the explanation for each question gives the title of the lesson that covers how to answer it. If you answered the question(s) for a given lesson correctly, you may be able to move quickly through that lesson. If you answered incorrectly, you may want to take your time on that lesson.

Questions 1–11 refer to the following passage.

Economic Regulation

[1] First introduced by Senator John Sherman of Ohio, the U.S. Congress passed the Sherman Antitrust Act in 1890. The Act made illegal "every contract, combination in the form of trust or otherwise, or conspiracy in the restraint of trade." However, many critics of the time charged that the decidedly vague wording introduced by the pro-business senators who rewrote the act before its final approval [2] results in the emasculation of the law's anti-monopoly intent. Nevertheless, the Act was the first law to fight, even symbolically, against economic monopolies in the "open" market economy of the United States.

From the nation's beginning, many politicians and [3] influential, business leaders had maintained that the ideal economy in a democracy was one in which the government played a very limited role in regulating commerce. They argued that, by permitting businesses to pursue their own interests, the government actually promoted the interests of the nation as a whole. A quote often attributed to [4] Charles E. Wilson, a former chairperson of General Motors, accurately captured the prevailing attitude of big [5] business. "What's good for General Motors is good for the nation." Many of the leaders of trusts and monopolies in the 1800s co-opted the then cutting-edge terminology of Charles

1.
   A) NO CHANGE
   B) In 1890, first introduced by Senator John Sherman of Ohio, the U.S. Congress passed the Sherman Antitrust Act.
   C) The U.S. Congress passed the Sherman Antitrust Act, first introduced by Senator John Sherman of Ohio, in 1890.
   D) The U.S. Congress, first introduced by Senator John Sherman of Ohio, passed the Sherman Antitrust Act in 1890.

2.
   A) NO CHANGE
   B) will result
   C) resulted
   D) has resulted

3.
   A) NO CHANGE
   B) influentially business leaders
   C) influential business leaders
   D) influential business, leaders

4.
   A) NO CHANGE
   B) Charles E. Wilson a former chairperson of General Motors
   C) Charles E. Wilson—a former chairperson of General Motors
   D) Charles E. Wilson a former chairperson of General Motors,

5. Which choice most effectively combines the two sentences at the underlined portion?
   A) business, and
   B) business;
   C) business
   D) business:

Darwin's theory of natural selection, [6] they argued that in an unrestrained economy, power and wealth would naturally flow to the most capable according to the principles of "social Darwinism." Their monopolies were thus natural and efficient outcomes of economic development.

Toward the close of the 1800s, however, an increasingly large and vocal number of lower- and middle-class dissenters felt that these hands-off economic policies of the federal government allowed monopolies like Standard Oil to manipulate consumers by fixing prices, [7] exploiting workers by cutting wages, and threaten democracy by corrupting politicians. Most directly, the trusts and monopolies completely destroyed the opportunities for competitors in their industries to do business effectively. The concerns of these working-class dissenters thus created a groundswell of support for the Sherman Antitrust [8] Act, and attempted to outlaw these monopolies and trusts. Even more important [9] then the direct effects of the Act, however, was the shift toward a new era of reform against monopolistic economic corruption and the rise of deliberate economic regulation in America. The federal government [10] realizing finally that [11] they had to take a more active role in the economy in order to protect the interests and rights of consumers, workers, and small businesses while tempering the dominating power of big business.

6. A) NO CHANGE
    B) arguing
    C) they argue
    D) to argue

7. A) NO CHANGE
    B) exploit
    C) exploits
    D) exploited

8. A) NO CHANGE
    B) Act, which were attempting
    C) Act, which attempted
    D) Act, and attempting

9. A) NO CHANGE
    B) against
    C) and
    D) than

10. A) NO CHANGE
    B) finally realizing
    C) finally will have realized
    D) had finally realized

11. A) NO CHANGE
    B) we
    C) it
    D) one

Writing & Lang

Check Your Work

1. C

Difficulty: Medium

Category: Agreement: Modifiers

Getting to the Answer: Modifying phrases must be placed as close as possible to what they modify. The intended meaning is not that the U.S. Congress was "first introduced by Senator John Sherman of Ohio"; rather, the phrase describes the Sherman Antitrust Act. Only **(C)** correctly places the modifying phrase adjacent to the Act, so **(C)** is correct.

2. C

Difficulty: Easy

Category: Agreement: Verbs

Getting to the Answer: Unless the context in the passage indicates that the time frame has changed, verb tenses should be consistent. The context makes clear that everything described in this sentence happened in the past. Choice **(C)**, which is in the simple past tense like the other verbs in the sentence ("charged" and "rewrote"), corrects the unnecessary shift in verb tense. The other answer choices are incorrect because they are in other verb tenses: (A) is in present tense, (B) is in future tense, and (D) indicates an action that occurred in the past but has present consequences.

3. C

Difficulty: Medium

Category: Agreement: Modifiers

Getting to the Answer: This question tests how to use the words "influential" and "business" to modify "leaders" in a way that maintains the intended meaning. In this context, "business" defines the type of "leaders." You can test this by reversing the order of the modifiers: "business influential leaders" does not make logical sense. "Influential" is thus modifying "business leaders," not just "leaders," so no comma is needed between the modifiers. **(C)** is correct. (B) is incorrect because the phrase "business leaders" functions as a noun, so you need an adjective, not an adverb, to modify it.

4. A

Difficulty: Hard

Category: Sentence Structure: Commas, Dashes, and Colons

Getting to the Answer: Parenthetical information in a sentence must be set off by punctuation, while essential information does not require punctuation. This question tests whether the descriptive phrase "a former chairman of General Motors" is essential in this sentence. Although the phrase adds relevant information, removing the phrase still results in a sentence that makes logical sense: the reader still knows precisely who (Charles E. Wilson) is associated with the quote. Since the phrase is parenthetical, it should be set off by a pair of commas, dashes, or parentheses—**(A)** is correct. The other choices are incorrect because they either omit the necessary punctuation entirely, as in (B), or use only one punctuation mark instead of a pair, as in (C) and (D).

5. D

Difficulty: Medium

Category: Sentence Structure: Commas, Dashes, and Colons

Getting to the Answer: You must determine the correct punctuation to use between these two independent clauses. Since several of the answer choices are technically correct, evaluate the content of the sentences to determine the relationship between them. The first sentence refers to a "quote," and the second sentence is the actual quote. Since the first sentence introduces the quote, a colon is appropriate, so **(D)** is correct. (A) and (B) are technically correct ways to join independent clauses, but they are incorrect in this context, in which the first clause introduces the second. (C) results in a run-on.

6. B

Difficulty: Medium

Category: Sentence Structure: The Basics

Getting to the Answer: The underlined portion links two independent clauses, each containing a subject and verb ("Many ... co-opted" and "they ... argued") and expressing a complete thought. As written, a comma without a FANBOYS conjunction between two independent clauses creates a run-on sentence; eliminate (A). None of the other answer choices contains a FANBOYS conjunction, so look for another way to correct the run-on. Since the comma is not underlined, look for the choice that makes the second clause dependent—in this case, choice **(B)**.

7. B

Difficulty: Hard

Category: Agreement: Verbs

Getting to the Answer: Whenever you see a series, make sure that all of the items are in parallel form. This is a series of three verb phrases that describe what "monopolies" were allowed to do. The entire series begins with "to," and the non-underlined verb phrases begin with present tense verbs: "manipulate consumers" and "threaten democracy." As written, the second item is "exploit*ing* workers," so it is not parallel with "manipulate" and "threaten." Choice **(B)** follows the pattern of the other verb phrases and is correct.

8. C

Difficulty: Hard

Category: Sentence Structure: The Basics

Getting to the Answer: Check underlined verbs for their subjects. Make sure that the sentence makes logical sense. Often, the subject of a verb can be found much earlier in the sentence. As written, the underlined segment seems to have "concerns" as its subject, but it doesn't make logical sense that the "concerns" "attempted" anything. Reading carefully, you will see that the phrase provides additional information about the Sherman Antitrust Act and should be subordinate to the main clause. Choice **(C)** fixes the issue and correctly uses the verb "attempted" to match the singular noun "Sherman Antitrust Act."

9. D

Difficulty: Easy

Category: Agreement: Idioms

Getting to the Answer: Analyze the sentence so you can determine which word is correct in context. The underlined word helps set up a comparison between the Act's "direct effects" and "a new era of reform." The correct word to use in a comparison phrase such as "more than" is *than*, so **(D)** is correct. Choice (A), "then," which is frequently confused with *than*, refers to sequence or to causation in "if/then" statements. Neither (B) nor (C) is idiomatically correct when used with the comparison "more."

10. D

Difficulty: Easy

Category: Sentence Structure: The Basics

Getting to the Answer: Read long sentences carefully to make sure they contain a subject and a predicate verb and express a complete thought. As written, this sentence is a fragment because it lacks a predicate verb for the subject "the federal government." Replacing the underlined segment with **(D)** adds a predicate verb and forms a complete sentence. (B) fails to fix the initial error. While (C) results in a complete sentence, it is incorrect because its verb tense does not match the context.

11. C

Difficulty: Medium

Category: Agreement: Pronouns

Getting to the Answer: When you see an underlined pronoun, read around the underlined segment to identify its antecedent so you can determine whether they are in agreement. Reading from the beginning of the sentence, you can see that the pronoun "they" stands in for "government." Although the government consists of many people, the noun "government" is singular, so **(C)** is correct.

Sentence Structure: The Basics

LEARNING OBJECTIVES

After this lesson, you will be able to:

- Determine the correct punctuation and/or conjunctions to form a complete sentence
- Identify and correct inappropriate uses of semicolons

To answer a question like this:

San Francisco's cable cars get their name from the long, heavy cable that runs beneath the streets along which the cars [1] travel, this cable system resembles a giant laundry clothesline with a pulley at each end. Electricity turns the wheels of the pulleys, which in turn make the cable move.

1. A) NO CHANGE
    B) travel and this cable
    C) travel this cable
    D) travel; this cable

You need to know this:

Fragments and Run-Ons

A complete sentence must have both a subject and a verb and express a complete thought. If any one of these elements is missing, the sentence is a **fragment**. You can recognize a fragment because the sentence will not make sense as written. There are some examples in the table below.

Missing Element	Example	Corrected Sentence
Subject	*Ran a marathon.*	*Lola ran a marathon.*
Verb	*Lola a marathon.*	
Complete thought	*While Lola ran a marathon.*	*While Lola ran a marathon, her friends cheered for her.*

The fragment "While Lola ran a marathon" is an example of a dependent clause: it has a subject (Lola) and a verb (ran), but it does not express a complete thought because it starts with a subordinating conjunction (while). Notice what the word "while" does to the meaning: While Lola ran a marathon, what happened? To fix this type of fragment, eliminate the subordinating conjunction or join the dependent clause to an independent clause using a comma. Subordinating conjunctions are words and phrases such as *since*, *because*, *therefore*, *unless*, *although*, and *due to*.

Unlike a dependent clause, an independent clause can stand on its own as a complete sentence. If a sentence has more than one independent clause, those clauses must be properly joined. If they are not, the sentence is a **run-on**: *Lucas enjoys hiking, he climbs a new mountain every summer.* There are several ways to correct a run-on as shown in the following table.

To Correct a Run-on	Example
Use a period	*Lucas enjoys hiking. He climbs a new mountain every summer.*
Use a semicolon	*Lucas enjoys hiking; he climbs a new mountain every summer.*
Use a colon	*Lucas enjoys hiking: he climbs a new mountain every summer.*
Make one clause dependent	*Since Lucas enjoys hiking, he climbs a new mountain every summer.*
Add a FANBOYS conjunction: For, And, Nor, But, Or, Yet, So	*Lucas enjoys hiking, so he climbs a new mountain every summer.*
Use a dash	*Lucas enjoys hiking—he climbs a new mountain every summer.*

Semicolons

Semicolons are used in two specific ways:

- A semicolon may join two independent clauses that are not connected by a FANBOYS conjunction (also called a coordinating conjunction), just as you would use a period.
- Semicolons may be used to separate items in a list if those items already include commas.

Use semicolons to ...	Example
Join two independent clauses that are not connected by a comma and FANBOYS conjunction	*Gaby knew that her term paper would take at least four hours to write; she got started in study hall and then finished it at home.*
Separate sublists within a longer list when the sublists contain commas	*The team needed to bring uniforms, helmets, and gloves; oranges, almonds, and water; and hockey sticks, pucks, and skates.*

You need to do this:

To recognize and correct errors involving fragments, run-ons, and semicolons, familiarize yourself with the ways in which they are tested.

- Fragments
  - If a sentence is missing a subject, a verb, or a complete thought, it is a fragment.
  - Correct the fragment by adding the missing element.

- Run-ons
  - If a sentence includes two independent clauses, they must be properly joined.
  - Employ one of the following options to properly punctuate independent clauses:
    - Use a period
    - Insert a semicolon
    - Use a comma and a FANBOYS (for, and, nor, but, or, yet, so) conjunction
    - Use a dash
    - Make one clause dependent by using a subordinating conjunction (since, because, unless, although, due to, etc.)
- Semicolons
  - A semicolon is used to join two independent clauses that are not connected by a comma and FANBOYS conjunction.
  - Semicolons separate sublists within a longer list. (The items inside the sublists are separated by commas.)

Explanation:

If a clause could stand alone as a complete sentence, it is independent. As written, the sentence is a run-on because two independent clauses cannot be joined by only a comma, so (A) is incorrect. Only **(D)** corrects the run-on by joining the independent clauses with a semicolon. (B) is incorrect because the FANBOYS conjunction "and" must be preceded by a comma to join independent clauses. (C) is incorrect because it eliminates all punctuation and is still a run-on.

If sentence formation or semicolons give you trouble, study the preceding information and try these Drill questions before completing the Try on Your Own questions that follow. Answers to the Drill can be found after the Try on Your Own questions.

Drill

a. <u>Correct the fragment by adding a subject</u>: Drove to the store to buy ice cream.

b. <u>Correct the fragment by completing the thought</u>: Despite arriving late to the movie.

c. <u>Correct the run-on sentence with a punctuation mark</u>: I hope that Zahra can attend the study session she has a gift for clearly explaining geometry questions.

d. <u>Correct the run-on sentence with a conjunction</u>: Visiting Washington, D.C., is a great experience because you can immerse yourself in the nation's political history, another perk is the free admission at the Smithsonian museums.

e. <u>Correct the run-on sentence by making one clause dependent</u>: The early computer ENIAC could make only simple computations, it was still a landmark achievement.

Try on Your Own

Directions: Take as much time as you need on these questions. Work carefully and methodically. There will be an opportunity for timed practice at the end of the chapter.

Questions 2–6 refer to the following passage.

Penicillin

In 1928, bacteriologist Dr. Alexander Fleming observed that a spot of mold had contaminated one of the glass plates on which he was growing a colony of bacteria. Since he did not discard the plate **2** immediately. He noticed that bacteria were flourishing everywhere on the plate except in the mold's vicinity. He decided to culture the **3** mold; and found that a broth filtered from it inhibited the growth of several species of bacteria. Nine years later, a team of scientists led by Howard Florey and Ernst Chain isolated the active antibacterial agent in Fleming's broth: penicillin. Florey and Chain went on to demonstrate that penicillin could cure bacterial infections in mice and in humans. Penicillin became a "miracle drug."

2. A) NO CHANGE
    B) immediately and he
    C) immediately, he
    D) immediately; he

3. A) NO CHANGE
    B) mold and found
    C) mold, and found
    D) mold. And found

Since these discoveries, medical specialists have prescribed penicillin to effectively combat bacterial infections, but problems concerning usage of this antibiotic have begun to emerge. Some people are allergic to [4] penicillin. Though the number of those who are truly allergic is probably low. Side effects to the antibiotic are more frequent and include common reactions such as [5] nausea; rash; and vomiting; less-common reactions such as fever; wheezing; and irregular breathing; and rare, life-threatening reactions such as anaphylaxis and seizures. However, the most significant problem with penicillin usage is the increasing prevalence of bacteria that are becoming [6] penicillin-resistant, these bacteria cannot be effectively treated with current antibiotic strains. Despite these difficulties, careful penicillin administration will continue to save lives and reduce suffering from medical conditions.

4. A) NO CHANGE
   B) penicillin,
   C) penicillin, and though
   D) penicillin, though

5. A) NO CHANGE
   B) nausea, rash, and vomiting, uncommon reactions such as fever, wheezing, and irregular breathing, and
   C) nausea, rash, and vomiting, uncommon reactions such as fever, wheezing, and irregular breathing; and
   D) nausea, rash, and vomiting; uncommon reactions such as fever, wheezing, and irregular breathing; and

6. A) NO CHANGE
   B) penicillin-resistant; these
   C) penicillin-resistant these
   D) penicillin-resistant; although these

Drill answers from before:

Note: These are not the only ways to correct the sentences; your answers may differ.

a. **Harold** drove to the store to buy ice cream.

b. Despite arriving late to the movie, **I still understood the plot.**

c. I hope that Zahra can attend the study session; she has a gift for clearly explaining geometry questions.

d. Visiting Washington, D.C., is a great experience because you can immerse yourself in the nation's political history, **and** another perk is the free admission at the Smithsonian museums.

e. **Although** the early computer ENIAC could make only simple computations, it was still a landmark achievement.

Sentence Structure: Commas, Dashes, and Colons

LEARNING OBJECTIVES

After this lesson, you will be able to:

- Identify and correct inappropriate uses of commas, dashes, and colons
- Use punctuation to set off simple parenthetical elements

To answer a question like this:

San Francisco's famous cable cars are not powered and don't generate any locomotion. Instead, each car has a powerful claw under its floor. The claw grips the cable when the car is ready to **7** move, and releases the cable when the car needs to stop. The cars simply cling to the cable, which pulls them up and down San Francisco's steep hills.

7. A) NO CHANGE
    B) move and releases
    C) move; and releases
    D) move—and releases

You need to know this:

Answer choices often move punctuation marks around, replace them with other punctuation marks, or remove them altogether. When underlined portions include commas, dashes, or colons, check to make sure the punctuation is used correctly in context.

Commas

There are two ways in which commas are not interchangeable with any other punctuation: a series of items and introductory words or phrases.

Use commas to...	Comma(s)
Set off three or more items in a series	*Jeremiah packed a sleeping bag, a raincoat, and a lantern for his upcoming camping trip.*
Separate an introductory word or phrase from the rest of the sentence	*For example, carrots are an excellent source of several vitamins and minerals.*

Commas and Dashes

In many cases, either a comma or a dash may be used to punctuate a sentence.

Use commas or dashes to...	Comma(s)	Dash(es)
Separate independent clauses connected by a FANBOYS conjunction (For, And, Nor, But, Or, Yet, So)	*Jess finished her homework earlier than expected, so she started an assignment that was due the following week.*	*Jess finished her homework earlier than expected—so she started an assignment that was due the following week.*
Separate an independent and dependent clause	*Tyson arrived at school a few minutes early, which gave him time to organize his locker before class.*	*Tyson arrived at school a few minutes early—which gave him time to organize his locker before class.*
Separate parenthetical elements from the rest of the sentence (use either two commas or two dashes, not one of each)	*Professor Mann, who is the head of the English department, is known for assigning extensive projects.*	*Professor Mann—who is the head of the English department—is known for assigning extensive projects.*

Colons and Dashes

Colons and dashes are used to include new ideas by introducing or explaining something, or by breaking the flow of the sentence. Note that the clause before the colon or dash must be able to stand on its own as a complete sentence.

Use colons and dashes to...	Colon	Dash
Introduce and/or emphasize a short phrase, quotation, explanation, example, or list	*Sanjay had two important tasks to complete: a science experiment and an expository essay.*	*Sanjay had two important tasks to complete—a science experiment and an expository essay.*
Separate two independent clauses when the second clause explains, illustrates, or expands on the first sentence	*Highway 1 in Australia is one of the longest national highways in the world: it circles the entirety of the continent and connects every mainland state capital.*	*Highway 1 in Australia is one of the longest national highways in the world—it circles the entirety of the continent and connects every mainland state capital.*

Unnecessary Punctuation

Knowing when punctuation should not be used is equally important. If an underlined portion includes punctuation, take time to consider if it should be included at all.

Do NOT use punctuation to...	Incorrect	Correct
Separate a subject from its verb	*The diligent student council, meets every week.*	*The diligent student council meets every week.*
Separate a verb from its object or a preposition from its object	*The diligent student council meets, every week.*	*The diligent student council meets every week.*
Set off elements that are essential to a sentence's meaning	*The, diligent student, council meets every week.*	*The diligent student council meets every week.*
Separate adjectives that work together to modify a noun	*The diligent, student council meets every week.*	*The diligent student council meets every week.*

Parenthetical Elements

Parenthetical elements may appear at the beginning, in the middle, or at the end of a sentence. They must be properly punctuated with parentheses, commas, or dashes for the sentence to be grammatically correct. A phrase such as *the capital of France* is considered parenthetical if the rest of the sentence is grammatically correct when it is removed. Do not mix and match; a parenthetical element must begin and end with the same type of punctuation.

Parenthetical Element Placement	Parentheses	Comma(s)	Dash(es)
Beginning	*N/A*	*The capital of France, Paris is a popular tourist destination.*	*N/A*
Middle	*Paris (the capital of France) is a popular tourist destination.*	*Paris, the capital of France, is a popular tourist destination.*	*Paris—the capital of France—is a popular tourist destination.*
End	*A popular tourist destination is Paris (the capital of France).*	*A popular tourist destination is Paris, the capital of France.*	*A popular tourist destination is Paris—the capital of France.*

Writing & Lang

K 359

You need to do this:

If the underlined portion includes punctuation, ask yourself:

- Is the punctuation used correctly?
  - The punctuation needs to be the correct type (comma, dash, or colon) and in the correct location.
- Is the punctuation necessary?
  - If you cannot identify a reason why the punctuation is included, the punctuation should be removed.

Explanation:

Make sure every underlined punctuation mark is serving a function. Commas serve a variety of purposes, but in this sentence as written, the underlined comma separates the subject ("claw") from part of its compound verb ("grips . . . and releases"). A comma should never separate a subject and verb, so eliminate (A). Only **(B)** correctly punctuates the sentence by removing the punctuation altogether. The other choices also separate the subject and verb, punctuating the sentence with a semicolon or dash as though joining two independent clauses.

If commas, dashes, and colons give you trouble, study the information above and try these Drill questions before completing the Try on Your Own questions that follow. Edit each sentence to correct the punctuation issue. Answers to the Drill can be found after the Try on Your Own questions.

Drill

a. Jamal doesn't plan to carve a jack-o'-lantern but he still had fun picking a pumpkin at the pumpkin patch.

b. Eleanor Roosevelt the longest serving First Lady of the United States considered her work on the United Nations' Declaration of Human Rights one of her greatest accomplishments.

c. I have three final exams this week Statistics, Biology, and World Literature.

d. The legendary entertainer, Johnny Carson, hosted his late-night talk show for 30 years.

e. Enabling agriculture due to its annual flooding the Nile River was truly the source of life in ancient Egypt.

Try on Your Own

Directions: Take as much time as you need on these questions. Work carefully and methodically. There will be an opportunity for timed practice at the end of the chapter.

Questions 8–15 refer to the following passage.

The Sistine Chapel

One shudders to contemplate Michelangelo's reaction if he were to gaze up today at the famous frescoes* he painted on the ceiling of the Sistine Chapel over four centuries ago. A practical **8** man: he would no doubt be unsurprised by the effects of time and environment on his masterpiece. He would be philosophical about the damage wrought by mineral salts left behind when rainwater leaked through the roof. He would probably also accept the layers of dirt and soot from coal braziers that heated the chapel and from **9** candles, and incense burned during religious functions. However, he would be appalled by the ravages recently inflicted on his work by restorers.

The Vatican restoration team reveled in inducing a jarringly colorful transformation of the frescoes with **10** special, cleaning solvents and computerized analysis equipment. However, the restorers did not achieve this **11** effect as they claimed merely by removing the dirt and animal glue (employed by earlier restorers to revive muted colors) from the **12** frescoes: the team removed Michelangelo's final touches as well. Gone from the ceiling is the quality of suppressed anger and thunderous pessimism so often commented upon by admiring scholars. That quality was not an artifact of grime, not a misleading monochrome imposed on

* *fresco*: a style of painting on plaster using water-based pigments

8. A) NO CHANGE
   B) man he
   C) man, he
   D) man—he

9. A) NO CHANGE
   B) candles—and
   C) candles. And
   D) candles and

10. A) NO CHANGE
    B) special cleaning solvents and computerized, analysis equipment.
    C) special cleaning solvents, and computerized analysis equipment.
    D) special cleaning solvents and computerized analysis equipment.

11. A) NO CHANGE
    B) effect, as they claimed, merely
    C) effect as they claimed, merely
    D) effect, as they claimed merely

12. A) NO CHANGE
    B) frescoes, the team
    C) frescoes and the team
    D) frescoes the team

the ceiling by time, for Michelangelo himself applied a veil of glaze to the frescoes to darken them after he had deemed his work too bright. The master would have felt compelled to add a few more layers of glaze had the ceiling radiated forth as it does now. The solvents of the restorers **13** stripped away the shadows of the frescoes, reacted chemically with Michelangelo's pigments, and ultimately produced hues the painter never intended for his art.

Of course, the restorers left open an avenue for the reversal of their progress toward color and brightness. Since the layers of animal glue were no longer there to serve as **14** protection the atmospheric pollutants from the city of Rome gained direct access to the frescoes. Observers already noticed significant darkening in some of the restored work a mere four years after its completion. It remains to be seen whether the measure introduced to arrest this **15** process: an extensive climate-control system—will itself have any long-term effect on the chapel's ceiling.

13. A) NO CHANGE
    B) stripped away the shadows of the frescoes reacted chemically with Michelangelo's pigments, and ultimately produced hues the painter never intended for his art.
    C) stripped away the shadows of the frescoes; reacted chemically with Michelangelo's pigments; and ultimately produced hues the painter never intended for his art.
    D) stripped away the shadows of the frescoes, reacted chemically with Michelangelo's pigments; and ultimately produced hues the painter never intended for his art.

14. A) NO CHANGE
    B) protection, the
    C) protection—the
    D) protection; the

15. A) NO CHANGE
    B) process—an extensive climate-control system—will
    C) process, an extensive climate-control system—will
    D) process; an extensive climate-control system; will

Drill answers from before:

Note: These are not the only ways to correct the sentences; your answers may differ.

a. Jamal doesn't plan to carve a jack-o'-lantern, but he still had fun picking a pumpkin at the pumpkin patch.

b. Eleanor Roosevelt, the longest serving First Lady of the United States, considered her work on the United Nations' Declaration of Human Rights one of her greatest accomplishments. OR Eleanor Roosevelt—the longest serving First Lady of the United States—considered her work on the United Nations' Declaration of Human Rights one of her greatest accomplishments.

c. I have three final exams this week: Statistics, Biology, and World Literature.

d. The legendary entertainer Johnny Carson hosted his late-night talk show for 30 years. (Commas deleted.)

e. Enabling agriculture due to its annual flooding, the Nile River was truly the source of life in ancient Egypt.

Agreement: Verbs

LEARNING OBJECTIVE

After this lesson, you will be able to:

- Identify and correct verb agreement issues

To answer a question like this:

The astronauts of Apollo 13 **16** <u>have performed</u> a routine maintenance check on the ship's equipment immediately before an explosion occurred that forced them to cancel a moon landing and greatly endangered the lives of the crew.

16. A) NO CHANGE
    B) will have performed
    C) had performed
    D) was performing

You need to know this:

Verb Tense

Verb tense indicates when an action or state of being took place: past, present, or future. The tense of the verb must fit the context of the passage. Each tense can express three different types of action.

Type of Action	Past	Present	Future
Single action occurring only once	Connor **planted** vegetables in the community garden.	Connor **plants** vegetables in the community garden.	Connor **will plant** vegetables in the community garden.
Action that is ongoing at some point in time	Connor **was planting** vegetables in the community garden this morning before noon.	Connor **is planting** vegetables in the community garden this morning before noon.	Connor **will be planting** vegetables in the community garden this morning before noon.
Action that is completed before some other action	Connor **had planted** vegetables in the community garden every year until he gave his job to Jasmine.	Connor **has planted** vegetables in the community garden since it started five years ago.	Connor **will have planted** vegetables in the community garden by the time the growing season starts.

Subject-Verb Agreement

A verb must agree with its subject in person and number:

- Person (first, second, or third)
  - First: *I **ask** a question.*
  - Second: *You **ask** a question.*
  - Third: *She **asks** a question.*
- Number (singular or plural)
  - Singular: *The apple **tastes** delicious.*
  - Plural: *Apples **taste** delicious.*

The noun closest to the verb is not always the subject: *The chair with the lion feet is an antique.* The singular verb in this sentence, "is," is closest to the plural noun "feet." However, the verb's actual subject is the singular noun "chair," so the sentence is correct as written.

When a sentence includes two nouns, only the conjunction *and* forms a compound subject requiring a plural verb form:

- Plural: *Saliyah and Taylor **are** in the running club.*
- Singular: *Either Saliyah or Taylor **is** in the running club.*
- Singular: *Neither Saliyah nor Taylor **is** in the running club.*

Collective nouns are nouns that name entities with more than one member, such as *group*, *team*, and *family*. Even though these nouns represent more than one person, they are grammatically singular and require singular verb forms:

- *The collection of paintings **is** one of the most popular art exhibits in recent years.*
- *The team **looks** promising this year.*

Parallelism

Verbs in a list, a compound, or a comparison must be parallel in form.

Feature	Example	Parallel Form
A list	Chloe **formulated** a question, **conducted** background research, and **constructed** a hypothesis before starting the experiment.	3 simple past verb phrases
A compound	**Hunting** and **fishing** were essential to the survival of Midwestern Native American tribes such as the Omaha.	2 *-ing* verb forms
A comparison	Garrett enjoys **sculpting** as much as **painting**.	2 *-ing* verb forms

Note that parallelism may be tested using other parts of speech besides verbs. In general, any items in a list, compound, or comparison must be in parallel form. For example, if a list starts with a noun, the other items in the list must also be nouns; if it starts with an adjective, the other items must be adjectives, etc.

Incorrect	Correct
Naomi likes ***pumpkin pie and to drink coffee*** on chilly weekend afternoons.	Naomi likes ***pumpkin pie and coffee*** on chilly weekend afternoons. *or* Naomi likes ***to eat pumpkin pie and drink coffee*** on chilly weekend afternoons.
Which of the dogs is the ***most docile and better behaved?***	Which of the dogs is the ***most docile and best behaved?*** or Which of the dogs is the ***more docile and better behaved?***

You need to do this:

If the underlined portion includes a verb, check that the verb:

- Reflects the correct tense: does it fit the context?
- Agrees with the subject in person and number
- Is parallel in form with other verbs in a series, list, or compound if there is one in the sentence

Explanation:

Check underlined verbs to make sure they agree with their subjects and match the tense of the passage. The subject of the underlined verb is "astronauts," so a plural verb is required; eliminate (D). Check the surrounding context to determine the correct tense. The actions of the sentence happened in the past ("occurred," "endangered"), but this performance of a maintenance check happened *before* another past action in the sentence: the explosion. "Had performed" is the appropriate way to indicate the sequence of these past actions, so **(C)** is correct. The other choices are not appropriate ways to express a single past action that happened before another past action.

If verbs give you trouble, study the information above and try the following Drill questions before completing the Try on Your Own questions that follow. Edit each sentence to correct the verb issue. Answers to the Drill can be found after the Try on Your Own questions.

Writing & Lang

Drill

a. The delicious flavors offered by the new ice cream shop (<u>ensure/ensures</u>) that many customers are typically lined up waiting to buy a scoop.

b. The manga club and the quiz team (<u>meet/meets</u>) in the student union on alternating Tuesdays.

c. Neither the teacher nor the student (<u>was/were</u>) adequately prepared for class.

d. By the time the toddler finally finished his dinner, everyone else (<u>finished/had finished</u>) eating dessert.

e. Katrina's favorite activities at the amusement park include riding the wooden roller coasters, driving the bumper cars, and (<u>eating/to eat</u>) the caramel candy apples.

Try on Your Own

Directions: Take as much time as you need on these questions. Work carefully and methodically. There will be an opportunity for timed practice at the end of the chapter.

Questions 17–22 refer to the following passage.

Woolly Mammoth

The woolly mammoth and the mastodon probably best **17** capture the public's current image of prehistoric Ice Age animals. Typically, these now-extinct, herbivorous precursors to the modern-day elephant **18** was about 10 feet tall at the shoulders and weighed nearly 6,000 pounds.

Although paleontologists have discovered remains of many woolly mammoths over the years, none has been found better preserved than the "Jarkov Mammoth" found on Siberia's Taimyr Peninsula in 1997. Soon after a 9-year-old boy out playing in the snowy hills first spotted the remains, scientists descended on the site. Then, after battling weeks of frigid weather and approximately 20,000 years' worth of dense frost coating the entire body of the mammoth, the assembled team finally **19** had completed a successful excavation. Important for numerous scientific reasons, the Jarkov Mammoth, in particular, has helped scientists settle a debate that has been raging for many years concerning the possible reasons behind the sudden extinction of these ancient giants.

Woolly mammoths roamed the cold northern plains of the globe for much of the last 2 million years, including most of the Ice Age that began roughly 70,000 years ago. Then, quite suddenly, 10,000 years ago, a time that corresponds with the end of the Ice Age, the mammoths disappeared. Scientific theories

17. A) NO CHANGE
    B) captured
    C) will have captured
    D) captures

18. A) NO CHANGE
    B) are
    C) were
    D) is

19. A) NO CHANGE
    B) completed
    C) is completing
    D) have completed

explaining this rapid extinction ranged from meteor showers pelting Earth to [20] suggestions of massive volcanic eruptions. Today, however, partially due to evidence taken from the Jarkov Mammoth, the scientific community generally [21] agree that these creatures died out from a combination of changing climate, hunting pressures from humans, and probably even disease. In fact, scientists consider it likely that the rising temperatures accompanying the end of the Ice Age [22] will work against the evolutionary adaptations of the mammoths, including their signature woolly coats of dense fur. Indeed, the demise of the Jarkov Mammoth seems to have involved a deep patch of mud, perhaps a sign that these behemoths were unaccustomed to treading on increasingly softer ground.

20. A) NO CHANGE
    B) suggesting massive volcanic eruptions.
    C) theories of massive volcanic eruptions.
    D) massive volcanic eruptions.

21. A) NO CHANGE
    B) agrees
    C) agreeing
    D) have agreed

22. A) NO CHANGE
    B) work
    C) working
    D) worked

Drill answers from before:

a. The delicious flavors offered by the new ice cream shop **ensure** that many customers are typically lined up waiting to buy a scoop.

b. The manga club and the quiz team **meet** in the student union on alternating Tuesdays.

c. Neither the teacher nor the student **was** adequately prepared for class.

d. By the time the toddler finally finished his dinner, everyone else **had finished** eating dessert.

e. Katrina's favorite activities at the amusement park include riding the wooden roller coasters, driving the bumper cars, and **eating** the caramel candy apples.

Agreement: Pronouns

> **LEARNING OBJECTIVES**
>
> After this lesson, you will be able to:
>
> ● Identify and correct pronoun agreement issues

To answer a question like this:

The public library is an invaluable treasure trove of the wisdom, research, drama, and wit of the ages, all available for easy access to eager patrons. Indeed, anyone with a card can borrow `23` <u>them</u> free of charge.

23. A) NO CHANGE
    B) it
    C) those
    D) the library's resources

You need to know this:

Pronoun Forms

A pronoun is a word that takes the place of a noun. Pronouns can take three different forms, each of which is used based on the grammatical role it plays in the sentence.

Form	Pronouns	Example
Subjective: The pronoun is used as the subject.	I, you, she, he, it, we, they, who	*Rivka is the student **who** will lead the presentation.*
Objective: The pronoun is used as the object of a verb or a preposition.	me, you, her, him, it, us, them, whom	*With **whom** will Rivka present the scientific findings?*
Possessive: The pronoun expresses ownership.	my, mine, your, yours, his, her, hers, its, our, ours, their, theirs, whose	*Rivka will likely choose a partner **whose** work is excellent.*

Note that a pronoun in subjective form can, logically, be the subject in a complete sentence. Pronouns that are in objective form cannot.

When there are two pronouns or a noun and a pronoun in a compound structure, drop the other noun or pronoun to tell which form to use—for example: *Leo and me walked into town.* If you were talking about yourself only, you would say, "I walked into town," not "Me walked into town." Therefore, the correct form is subjective, and the original sentence should read: *Leo and I walked into town.*

Pronoun-Antecedent Agreement

A pronoun's antecedent is the noun it logically represents in a sentence. If the noun is singular, the pronoun must be singular; if the noun is plural, the pronoun must be plural.

Antecedent	Incorrect	Correct
selection	*The selection of books was placed in **their** designated location.*	*The selection of books was placed in **its** designated location.*
A woman	*A woman visiting the zoo fed the giraffes all of the lettuce **they** had purchased.*	*A woman visiting the zoo fed the giraffes all of the lettuce **she** had purchased.*
sapling	*The sapling, along with dozens of flowers, was relocated to where **they** would thrive.*	*The sapling, along with dozens of flowers, was relocated to where **it** would thrive.*
apples	*If apples are unripe, **it** should not be purchased.*	*If apples are unripe, **they** should not be purchased.*

Ambiguous Pronouns

A pronoun is ambiguous if its antecedent is either missing or unclear. When you see an underlined pronoun, make sure you can identify the noun to which it refers.

Ambiguous Pronoun Use	Corrected Sentence
*Anthony walked with Cody to the ice cream shop, and **he** bought a banana split.*	*Anthony walked with Cody to the ice cream shop, and **Cody** bought a banana split.*

You need to do this:

If the underlined portion includes a pronoun, *find the logical antecedent*. If there is no clear antecedent, the pronoun is ambiguous and this error must be corrected. Then check that the pronoun:

- Uses the correct form
  - If the pronoun is the subject of the sentence, use a subjective pronoun such as *I, you, she, he, it, we, they*, or *who*.
  - If the pronoun is an object within the sentence, use an objective pronoun such as *me, you, her, him, it, us, they*, or *whom*.
  - If the pronoun indicates possession, use a possessive pronoun such as *my, mine, your, yours, his, her, hers, its, our, ours, their, theirs*, or *whose*.
- Agrees with its antecedent
  - A singular antecedent requires a singular pronoun; a plural antecedent requires a plural pronoun.

Writing & Lang

Explanation:

Every underlined pronoun on the PSAT must have a crystal-clear antecedent. In this case, although it is understood from the context that the writer means that people can borrow library materials, the pronoun "them" is ambiguous—indeed, its nearest antecedent is "eager patrons," which is not what the writer intended to mean can be borrowed! Eliminate (A), as well as the other pronoun answer choices, since they all result in ambiguity. **(D)** is correct because it identifies precisely what can be borrowed.

If pronouns give you trouble, study the information above and try these Drill questions before completing the Try on Your Own questions that follow. Edit each sentence to correct the pronoun issue. Answers to the Drill can be found on the next page.

Drill

a.   The manager let the employee go home an hour early because she was in a good mood.

b.   My parents had a great surprise for my sister and (<u>I/me</u>): a visit to the beach.

c.   The manager moved the display of vintage comic books from (<u>its/their</u>) location in the back of the store to the front.

d.   Fai was able to convince (<u>him/his</u>) teacher to give the class no homework over the long weekend.

e.   After purchasing (<u>her/their</u>) tickets, Jen watched the singers perform in the concert.

Try on Your Own

Directions: Take as much time as you need on these questions. Work carefully and methodically. There will be an opportunity for timed practice at the end of the chapter.

Questions 24–29 refer to the following passage.

James Joyce

As we contemplate the state of literature in our modern era, it is difficult to resist a longing for the epic writers of eras gone by. At times, we take great pains to merely remember that there were once authors such as Homer, Dante, and Melville: authors **24** whom were able to relate stories of heroic travels and struggles. They did not waste their time or ours with trivial affairs; they compelled **25** you to mull over the great philosophical questions of all time in stories that stand up to readers' repeated perusal from generation to generation. **26** They took extensive care to depict accurately the best and worst aspects of human nature; strove to ensure that they would be enhancing, rather than degrading, the public's intellect; and did not resort to tricks or devices in order to garner readership for their writings. In all these regards, past writers are firmly distinguished from many modern writers: the most notorious of these modern writers is the Irish novelist James Joyce.

24. A) NO CHANGE
    B) which
    C) who
    D) who're

25. A) NO CHANGE
    B) me
    C) one
    D) us

26. A) NO CHANGE
    B) Readers
    C) Such authors
    D) He

Drill answers from previous page:

a. The manager let the employee go home an hour early because **the manager** was in a good mood.

b. My parents had a great surprise for my sister and **me**: a visit to the beach.

c. The manager moved the display of vintage comic books from **its** location in the back of the store to the front.

d. Fai was able to convince **his** teacher to give the class no homework over the long weekend.

e. After purchasing **her** tickets, Jen watched the singers perform in the concert.

While literary critics typically offer vastly different assessments of its quality after [27] <u>our</u> readings of *Ulysses*, Joyce's novel that retells Homer's *The Odyssey*, my contention is that Joyce sullied the very form of the epic genre. Whereas *The Odyssey* was a great tale of a noble hero's struggle against a seemingly insurmountable series of trials in order to restore order and honor to his household, [28] <u>his</u> book is nearly the direct opposite. The protagonist is no hero: his actions are listless and forgettable, and his obsession with obscene and undignified behavior is virtually nauseating. And even more shamefully, Joyce wasted his talent; subject matter aside, the art of masterfully crafting words came naturally to [29] <u>him</u>. Sadly, it is the literary world's loss that he was not born a few centuries earlier, when his talents could have been utilized in a more dignified manner.

27. A) NO CHANGE
    B) their
    C) his or her
    D) my

28. A) NO CHANGE
    B) their
    C) Joyce's
    D) Homer's

29. A) NO CHANGE
    B) himself
    C) his own self
    D) he

Writing & Lang

Agreement: Modifiers

LEARNING OBJECTIVES

After this lesson, you will be able to:

- Identify and correct modifier agreement issues
- Identify and correct inappropriate uses of apostrophes

To answer a question like this:

Wind power development could potentially impact populations of several nocturnally migrating bird and bat species. During their seasonal migrations, **30** large numbers fly through the mountainous landforms used for wind turbine locations.

30. A) NO CHANGE
    B) large amounts
    C) many birds and bats
    D) birds and bats

You need to know this:

A **modifier** is a word or phrase that describes, clarifies, or provides additional information about another part of the sentence. Modifier questions require you to identify the part of a sentence being modified and use the appropriate modifier in the proper place.

In order to be grammatically correct, the modifier must be placed as close to the word it describes as possible. Use context clues in the passage to identify the correct placement of a modifier; a misplaced modifier can cause confusion and is always incorrect on test day.

Note that a common way the PSAT tests modifiers is with modifying phrases at the beginning of a sentence. Just like any other modifier, the modifying phrase grammatically modifies whatever is right next to it in the sentence. For example, consider the sentence, *While walking to the bus stop, the rain drenched Bob*. The initial phrase, "While walking to the bus stop," grammatically modifies "the rain," creating a nonsense sentence; the rain can't walk to the bus stop. The writer meant that Bob was walking to the bus stop, so the sentence should read, *While walking to the bus stop, Bob was drenched by the rain*.

Modifier/Modifying Phrase	Incorrect	Correct
nearly	Andre **nearly** watched the play for four hours.	Andre watched the play for **nearly** four hours.
in individual containers	The art teacher handed out paints to students **in individual containers**.	The art teacher handed out paints **in individual containers** to students.
A scholar athlete	**A scholar athlete**, maintaining high grades in addition to playing soccer were expected of Maya.	**A scholar athlete**, Maya was expected to maintain high grades in addition to playing soccer.

Adjectives and Adverbs

Use adjectives only to modify nouns and pronouns. Use adverbs to modify everything else.

- **Adjectives** are single-word modifiers that describe nouns and pronouns: *Ian conducted an* **efficient** *lab experiment.*
- **Adverbs** are single-word modifiers that describe verbs, adjectives, or other adverbs: *Ian* **efficiently** *conducted a lab experiment.*

Note that nouns can sometimes be used as adjectives. For example, in the phrase *the fashion company's autumn line*, the word "fashion" functions as an adjective modifying "company" and the word "autumn" functions as an adjective modifying "line."

Comparative/Superlative

When comparing similar things, use adjectives that match the number of items being compared. When comparing two items or people, use the **comparative** form of the adjective. When comparing three or more items or people, use the **superlative** form.

Comparative (two items)	Superlative (three or more items)
better, more, newer, older, shorter, taller, worse, younger	best, most, newest, oldest, shortest, tallest, worst, youngest

Possessive Nouns and Pronouns

Possessive nouns and pronouns indicate that something belongs to someone or something. In general, possessive nouns are written with an apostrophe, while possessive pronouns are not.

To spot errors in possessive noun or pronoun construction, look for ...	Incorrect	Correct
Two nouns in a row	The **professors lectures** were both informative and entertaining.	The **professor's lectures** were both informative and entertaining.
Pronouns with apostrophes	The book is her's.	The book is **hers**.
Words that sound alike	The three friends decided to ride **there** bicycles to the park over **they're** where **their** going to enjoy a picnic lunch.	The three friends decided to ride **their** bicycles to the park over **there** where **they're** going to enjoy a picnic lunch.

Writing & Lang

Apostrophes

Use an apostrophe to ...	Example
Indicate the possessive form of a single noun	*My oldest **sister's** soccer game is on Saturday.*
Indicate the possessive form of a plural noun	*My two older **sisters'** soccer games are on Saturday.*
Indicate a contraction (e.g., *don't, can't*)	***They've** won every soccer match this season.*

Note that plural nouns are formed without an apostrophe.

Incorrect	Correct
*Sting **ray's** are cartilaginous fish related to **shark's**.*	*Sting **rays** are cartilaginous fish related to **sharks**.*
*There are many **carnival's** in this area every summer.*	*There are many **carnivals** in this area every summer.*

To check whether *it's* is appropriate, replace it in the sentence with *it is* or *it has*. If the sentence no longer makes sense, *it's* is incorrect. The following sentence is correct:

The tree frog blends perfectly into its surroundings; when it holds still, it's nearly invisible.

Note that *its'* and *its's* are never correct.

You need to do this:

If the underlined portion includes a modifier, determine whether the modifier:

- Is placed correctly
    - Is it as near as possible to the word it logically modifies?
    - If it is not in the correct place, where should it be moved?
- Agrees with the word or words it is describing
    - Does the sentence require an adjective or an adverb?
    - Does the noun or pronoun show proper possession?

If the underlined portion includes an apostrophe, make sure it correctly indicates either possession or a contraction. If an apostrophe is missing, select the answer choice that places it in the correct location.

Explanation:

Make sure introductory modifiers are modifying the correct items. The introductory modifying phrase in this sentence is "During their seasonal migrations," which must modify what directly follows it; as written, "large numbers." It does not make sense that "numbers" migrate (as though you can see the number 17 flying across the sky). Eliminate (A) and (B), which make the same error. Even though both (C) and (D) correct the error, only choice **(C)** retains the original intended meaning: that numerous birds and bats migrate.

If modifiers give you trouble, study the information in this section and try these Drill questions before completing the Try on Your Own questions that follow. Edit each sentence to correct the modifier or apostrophe issue. Answers to the Drill can be found on the page after the Drill.

Drill

a.   The colorfully impressive plumage of the tropical birds helped make the aviary the most popular destination at the zoo.

b.   Since the gym is remodeling the womens locker room, I had to change into my workout clothes at home.

c.   The players on the baseball team all felt an immense sense of relief after a hard-fought victory over there long-time rivals.

d.   When asked if they preferred reality programs or news documentaries, viewers reported that reality programs were most entertaining.

e.   Although normally considered a children's toy, yo-yo performers are highly skilled professionals who can flawlessly execute impressive tricks.

Try on Your Own

Directions: Take as much time as you need on these questions. Work carefully and methodically. There will be an opportunity for timed practice at the end of the chapter.

Questions 31–36 refer to the following passage.

Madame Bovary

Some critics believe that *Madame Bovary*, the most famous novel by French author Gustave Flaubert, has a strange and subversive theme that undermines [31] its own medium: in short, they say that Flaubert's masterpiece of fiction is a cautionary tale about the dangers of reading novels. As evidence, they point to its unsympathetic protagonist, Emma Bovary, who lives in her books and romanticizes the simplest aspects of daily life—for example, eating rich food and buying expensive clothing—as well as her relationships. [32] Emma cares only about her immediate physical gratification and material possessions rather than the well-being of her friends and family, becoming cruel, shortsighted, and constantly dissatisfied with real life. Her fantasies lead to her downfall: her relationship with her well-meaning

31. A) NO CHANGE
    B) it's
    C) they're
    D) their

32. A) NO CHANGE
    B) Becoming cruel, shortsighted, and constantly dissatisfied with real life, friends and family do not affect Emma's well-being as she cares only about her immediate physical gratification and material possessions.
    C) Becoming cruel, shortsighted, and constantly dissatisfied with real life, Emma cares only about her immediate physical gratification and material possessions rather than the well-being of her friends and family.
    D) Caring only about her immediate physical gratification and material possessions, Emma's friends and family become cruel, shortsighted, and constantly dissatisfied with real life.

Drill answers from previous page:

Note: These are not the only ways to correct the sentences; your answers may differ.

a. The **colorful,** impressive plumage of the tropical birds helped make the aviary the most popular destination at the zoo.

b. Since the gym is remodeling the **women's** locker room, I had to change into my workout clothes at home.

c. The players on the baseball team all felt an immense sense of relief after a hard-fought victory over **their** long-time rivals.

d. When asked if they preferred reality programs or news documentaries, viewers reported that reality programs were **more** entertaining.

e. Although **the yo-yo is** normally considered a children's toy, yo-yo performers are highly skilled professionals who can flawlessly execute impressive tricks.

but naive husband gradually disintegrates, her two adulterous affairs end in disaster, her constant borrowing leads her family to financial ruin, and her desire to die in a 33 <u>glorious dramatic fashion</u> leads instead to an unexpectedly agonizing three days of death throes. She expects too much from life and is punished horribly for it.

Certainly Emma's flawed personality, as well as her literary obsession, contributes to her downfall, but it is interesting to note 34 <u>that only Emma is the only character in the novel who habitually reads for pleasure</u>. In fact, her husband spends the bulk of the story engaged in the mundane activities of daily life: running a business, tending to family members, maintaining the household. He is naive, admittedly, but happy—at least until Emma's penchant for romance begins to interfere with his responsibilities. Therefore, there really are no other appropriate characters with whom to compare her, although we can point out that the characters making up the novel's non-reading population tend to be 35 <u>more</u> socially responsible than Emma. Perhaps *Madame Bovary*, then, was not meant to be a criticism of fiction itself; rather, Flaubert intended his novel to be a caution against allowing suggestible characters like Emma to have access to novels. The permissive environment that the Bovarys permit in their household contributes to their downfall and social ruin; the 36 <u>characters'</u> unwillingness to check Emma's passions (and even their ignorance of the existence of such a problem) leads to the disintegration of their family.

33. A) NO CHANGE
    B) gloriously dramatic fashion
    C) dramatic glorious fashion
    D) glorious dramatically fashion

34. A) NO CHANGE
    B) that Emma is the only character in the novel who habitually reads for pleasure
    C) that Emma is the character in the only novel who habitually reads for pleasure
    D) that Emma is the character in the novel who only habitually reads for pleasure

35. A) NO CHANGE
    B) comparatively
    C) greater
    D) most

36. A) NO CHANGE
    B) character's
    C) characters
    D) characters's

Agreement: Idioms

LEARNING OBJECTIVES

After this lesson, you will be able to:

- Identify and correct expressions that deviate from idiomatic English
- Determine the appropriate word in frequently confused pairs

---

To answer a question like this:

The United States Geological Survey (USGS) is studying the distribution and flight patterns of birds and bats that migrate at night. Researchers analyze weather surveillance radar data **37** not only to assess the responses of migrant birds to prominent landforms but also to generate a broad overview of spring and fall migration through the Appalachians.

37. A) NO CHANGE
    B) not to assess the responses of migrant birds to prominent landforms but also to generate
    C) not only to assess the responses of migrant birds to prominent landforms but to generate
    D) to not only assess the responses of migrant birds to prominent landforms but also to generate

You need to know this:

An **idiom** is a combination of words that must be used together to convey either a figurative or literal meaning. Idioms are tested in three ways:

1. Proper preposition use in context: The preposition must reflect the writer's intended meaning.

   She waits **on** customers.

   She waits **for** the bus.

   She waits **with** her friends.

2. Idiomatic expressions: Some words or phrases must be used together to be correct.

   Simone will **either** bike **or** run to the park.

   Neither the principal **nor** the teachers will tolerate tardiness.

   This fall, Shari is playing **not only** soccer **but also** field hockey.

3. Implicit double negatives: Some words imply a negative and therefore cannot be paired with an explicit negative. The words "barely," "hardly," and "scarcely" fall into this category.

   Correct: Janie **can hardly** wait for vacation.

   Incorrect: Janie **can't hardly** wait for vacation.

Writing & Lang

Frequently Tested Prepositions	Idiomatic Expressions	Words That Can't Pair with Negative Words
at	as … as	barely
by	between … and	hardly
for	both … and	scarcely
from	either … or	
of	neither … nor	
on	just as … so too	
to	not only … but also	
with	prefer … to	

Commonly Confused Words

English contains many pairs of words that sound alike but are spelled differently and have different meanings, such as *accept* (to take or receive something that is offered) and *except* (with the exclusion of).

Other words, such as *among* (in a group of, or surrounded by, multiple things or people) and *between* (distinguishing one thing from one other thing), do not sound alike but have similar meanings that are often confused.

You'll want to familiarize yourself with the following list of commonly misused words so you can spot them on test day.

Accept: to take or receive something that is offered	*My niece **accepted** her pile of birthday gifts with great enthusiasm.*
Except: with the exclusion of	*All of the presents are toys **except** for a box containing a popular book series.*

Affect: to act on, to have influence on something	*The dreary, rainy weather negatively **affected** Rahul's mood.*
Effect: something that is produced by a cause; a consequence	*A recent study explored the **effects** of weather on mental well-being.*

Lay: to put or place something	*My boss asked me to **lay** the report on her desk before I left for the day.*
Lie: to rest or recline	*After a long day of work, I just want to **lie** down on the couch.*

Raise: to build or lift up something; to support the growth of someone	*Many books are dedicated to the topic of **raising** children.*
Rise: to get up	*Ted likes to **rise** early in the morning to exercise before his children wake up.*

| **Whose:** a possessive pronoun | ***Whose*** *uniform shirt is this?* |
| **Who's:** a contraction meaning "who is" | ***Who's*** *responsible for ordering new uniforms?* |

Their: a possessive pronoun for a plural noun or pronoun	*The college students plan to travel internationally after **their** graduation.*
They're: a contraction for "they are"	***They're*** *going to visit several countries in East Asia.*
There: at a certain point or place	*The students are excited to experience the foods and cultures **there**.*
There's: a contraction for "there is"	***There's*** *a tour of an ancient palace that they're looking forward to seeing.*

| **Among:** in a group of, or surrounded by, multiple things or people | *Navya was **among** many doctoral candidates who visited the university.* |
| **Between:** distinguishing one thing from one other thing | *Navya had to decide **between** her top two doctoral program choices.* |

| **Amount:** sum or quantity of multiple things that cannot be counted | *The **amount** of pollution in the ocean is affecting dolphin populations.* |
| **Number:** sum or quantity of a finite collection that can be counted | *Scientists report that the **number** of dolphins has decreased significantly.* |

| **Less:** a smaller extent or amount of things that cannot be counted | *The common supermarket sign "10 items or **less**" is actually incorrect.* |
| **Fewer:** of a smaller number, referring to things that can be counted | *Since the items can be counted, the sign should read "10 items or **fewer**."* |

| **Much:** great in quantity, referring to things that cannot be counted | *My sister has **much** more patience than I have.* |
| **Many:** great in quantity, referring to things that can be counted | ***Many*** *of her friends admire her ability to stay calm in difficult situations.* |

| **Good:** satisfactory in quality, quantity, or degree; adjective | *Dakota considered both the **good** and bad effects of wind energy before composing her essay.* |
| **Well:** to perform an action in a satisfactory manner; adverb | *Dakota wrote her essay so **well** that her professor used it as an example of excellent persuasive writing.* |

You need to do this:

- If the underlined portion includes a preposition, a conjunction, or *barely/hardly/scarcely*, look for a common idiom error.
- If the underlined segment includes a commonly misused word, check the context to determine whether it is used properly.

Explanation:

The underlined phrase contains the idiomatic expression *not only ... but also*, so make sure it is correctly structured. (B) and (C) both omit part of the expression: (B) is missing "not *only*" and (C) is missing "but *also*." (A) and (D) both use the correct wording, so analyze what the difference is between them. (D) places the word "to" *before* the beginning of the idiomatic phrase: "*to* not only." However, the second part of the expression in (D) places the word "to" *after* the idiomatic phrase: "but also *to*." Either placement would be acceptable, but the phrase must be structured consistently, so (D) is incorrect. **(A)** correctly structures the idiomatic expression: "not only to ... but also to."

If idioms give you trouble, study the information in this section and try these Drill questions before completing the Try on Your Own questions that follow. Edit each sentence to correct the idiom issue. Answers to the Drill can be found on the next page.

Drill

a.   My book club meets at every third Sunday of the month.

b.   Greyson made the gingerbread house by gumdrops, icing, candy buttons, and, of course, gingerbread.

c.   The cheetah's anatomy allows for extremely quick running speed not only due to its especially flexible spine but due to its unusually short skull.

d.   After accidentally getting sunburned, I couldn't hardly stand how itchy my skin felt.

e.   Since she collected less pairs then her opponent, Candace lost the matching game.

Try on Your Own

Directions: Take as much time as you need on these questions. Work carefully and methodically. There will be an opportunity for timed practice at the end of the chapter.

Questions 38–44 refer to the following passage.

Hudson River School

[38] <u>Excepted</u> by art historians as the first truly American art movement, the Hudson River School movement began in the early nineteenth century. The first works in this style were created by landscape painters Thomas Cole, Thomas Doughty, and Asher Durand, a trio of painters who worked during the 1820s in the Hudson River Valley and surrounding locations. Heavily influenced [39] <u>by</u> European romanticism, these painters set out to convey the remoteness and splendor of the American wilderness. The strongly nationalistic tone of their paintings caught the spirit of the times, and within a generation, the movement had mushroomed to include landscape painters from all over the United States.

38. A) NO CHANGE
     B) Accepted
     C) Excepting
     D) Accepting

39. A) NO CHANGE
     B) with
     C) in
     D) due to

Drill answers from previous page:

Note: These are not the only ways to correct the sentences; your answers may differ.

a. My book club meets **on** every third Sunday of the month.

b. Greyson made the gingerbread house **from** gumdrops, icing, candy buttons, and, of course, gingerbread.

c. The cheetah's anatomy allows for extremely quick running speed not only due to its especially flexible spine but **also** due to its unusually short skull.

d. After accidentally getting sunburned, I **could** hardly stand how itchy my skin felt.

e. Since she collected **fewer** pairs **than** her opponent, Candace lost the matching game.

One factor contributing to the success of the Hudson River School was the rapid growth of American nationalism in the early nineteenth century. One [40] affect of the War of 1812 was that it instilled Americans with a new sense of pride in their identity, and as the nation continued to grow, a desire grew to compete with Europe on both economic and cultural grounds. The vast panoramas of the Hudson River School fit the bill perfectly [41] to providing a new movement in [42] art, which was unmistakably American. The Hudson River School also arrived at a time when writers in the United States were turning their attention to the wilderness as a unique aspect of their nationality. The Hudson River School painters profited from this nostalgia because they effectively represented Americans' perceptions of early America. [43] Hardly not anyone questioned the view that the American character was formed by the frontier experience, and many writers wrote about their concerns regarding an increasingly urbanized country.

In keeping with this nationalistic spirit, even the painting style of the Hudson River School exhibited a strong sense of American identity. Unlike European painters, who brought to their canvases the styles and techniques of centuries past, the Hudson River School painters [44] sought neither to embellish nor to idealize their scenes, but rather to portray nature with the objectivity and attention to detail of naturalists.

40. A) NO CHANGE
    B) effect
    C) affecting
    D) effecting

41. A) NO CHANGE
    B) by providing
    C) in providing
    D) only providing

42. A) NO CHANGE
    B) art, and
    C) art that
    D) art, so

43. A) NO CHANGE
    B) Not hardly anyone
    C) Not anyone hardly
    D) Hardly anyone

44. A) NO CHANGE
    B) sought to neither embellish nor to idealize their scenes
    C) sought neither to embellish or to idealize their scenes
    D) sought to neither embellish or to idealize their scenes

How Much Have You Learned?

Directions: For testlike practice, give yourself 9 minutes to complete this question set. Be sure to study the explanations, even for questions you answered correctly. They can be found at the end of this chapter.

Questions 45–55 refer to the following passage.

Antarctica

To get some idea of what Antarctica is like, think of a place as remote as the far side of the 45 Moon as strange as Saturn, and as inhospitable as Mars. A mere 2.4 percent of 46 its 5.4 million square-mile landmass (50 percent larger than the United States) is ice-free, and that condition lasts for only a few months a year. Scientists estimate that 70 percent of the world's fresh water is locked away in Antarctica's 47 ice cap, if this ice were ever to melt, sea levels might rise 200 feet, inundating coastal lands together with their major cities. In Antarctica, winds can blow at better than 200 mph, and temperatures can plummet as low as −128.6 degrees (Fahrenheit). 48 There's 49 neither a town or a single tree, bush, or blade of grass on the entire continent.

Nevertheless, Antarctica is vital to life on Earth. The continent's vast ice fields reflect sunlight back into space, preventing the planet from overheating. The cold water that the icebergs generate flows north and mixes with equatorial warm water, producing currents and clouds that 50 create ultimate, complex weather patterns.

45. A) NO CHANGE
    B) Moon, as strange as Saturn,
    C) Moon as strange Saturn
    D) Moon, strange as Saturn,

46. A) NO CHANGE
    B) Antarctica's
    C) their
    D) it's

47. A) NO CHANGE
    B) ice cap; and if
    C) ice cap and if
    D) ice cap; if

48. A) NO CHANGE
    B) Their's
    C) There are
    D) They're

49. A) NO CHANGE
    B) either a town or a single
    C) no town nor a single
    D) neither a town nor a single

50. A) NO CHANGE
    B) ultimately complexly create
    C) ultimately create complex
    D) create

Antarctic seas teem with [51] life—from microscopic phytoplankton and tiny krill at the bottom of the food chain to killer whales and leopard seals at the top giving these waters a vital status among the Earth's ecosystems. [52] Unique species of birds and mammals make their homes in the frigid waters of the Southern Ocean that lap the continent's edge, some found nowhere else on the planet.

The relative inaccessibility and near pristine state of Antarctica [53] makes it an invaluable place for scientific research today. Clues to ancient climates lie buried deep in layers of Antarctic ice—clues such as trapped bubbles of atmospheric gases, which can help scientists draw a better picture of what Antarctica was like in the past. Until recently, most scientists thought that Antarctica has been covered by ice for 40 million to 52 million years and that the present ice cap is about 15 million years old. However, the discovery of remnants of a beech forest near the head of the Beardmore glacier, approximately 250 miles from the South Pole, [54] provides evidence that Antarctica may have been both ice-free and much more temperate 2.5 million to 5 million years ago than it is now. Similar fossil finds made elsewhere suggest that western Antarctica was perhaps completely ice-free as recently as 100,000 years [55] ago and scientists, as a result, are conducting new research to enhance their understanding of Antarctica's climate changes.

51. A) NO CHANGE
    B) life, from microscopic phytoplankton and tiny krill at the bottom of the food chain to killer whales and leopard seals at the top; giving
    C) life; from microscopic phytoplankton and tiny krill at the bottom of the food chain to killer whales and leopard seals at the top—giving
    D) life, from microscopic phytoplankton and tiny krill at the bottom of the food chain to killer whales and leopard seals at the top, giving

52. A) NO CHANGE
    B) Some found nowhere else on the planet, the frigid waters of the Southern Ocean that lap the continent's edge are home to unique species of birds and mammals.
    C) Unique species of birds and mammals, some found nowhere else on the planet, make their homes in the frigid waters of the Southern Ocean that lap the continent's edge.
    D) The frigid waters of the Southern Ocean that lap the continent's edge, some found nowhere else on the planet, are home to unique species of birds and mammals.

53. A) NO CHANGE
    B) make
    C) made
    D) is making

54. A) NO CHANGE
    B) were providing
    C) provide
    D) providing

55. A) NO CHANGE
    B) ago so scientists
    C) ago, scientists
    D) ago. Scientists

Reflect

Directions: Take a few minutes to recall what you've learned and what you've been practicing in this chapter. Consider the following questions, jot down your best answer for each one, and then compare your reflections to the expert responses on the following page. Use your level of confidence to determine what to do next.

Name at least three ways to correct a run-on sentence.

_____

_____

_____

How does the PSAT test subject-verb agreement and parallelism?

_____

_____

_____

What are the three different pronoun forms? When do you use each one?

_____

_____

_____

What is the difference between an adjective and an adverb?

_____

_____

_____

What are the three ways that apostrophes are tested on the PSAT?

_____

_____

_____

Which commonly confused words do you need to be especially careful to look out for?

_____

_____

_____

Expert Responses

Name at least three ways to correct a run-on sentence.

There are a number of ways to fix a run-on sentence on the PSAT. The six ways that you are likely to see are: 1) use a period to create two separate sentences, 2) use a semicolon between the two independent clauses, 3) use a colon between the two independent clauses, 4) make one clause dependent, 5) add a FANBOYS conjunction after the comma, or 6) use a dash between the two independent clauses.

How does the PSAT test subject-verb agreement and parallelism?

A subject and verb must always agree in person (first, second, or third) and number (singular or plural). You will need to be able to spot subject-verb mismatches and correct them. Parallelism requires that all items in a list, a compound, or a comparison are in parallel form. The PSAT may test lists or comparisons in which one item is in the wrong form.

What are the three different pronoun forms? When do you use each one?

The three forms are subjective (when the pronoun is the subject), objective (when the pronoun is the object of a verb or preposition), and possessive (when the pronoun expresses ownership).

What is the difference between an adjective and an adverb?

An adjective is a single word that modifies a noun or a pronoun, while an adverb is a single word that modifies a verb, an adjective, or another adverb.

What are the three ways that apostrophes are tested on the PSAT?

Apostrophes on the PSAT are used to 1) indicate the possessive form of a singular noun ('s), 2) indicate the possessive form of a plural noun (s'), or 3) indicate a contraction (don't = do not).

Which commonly confused words do you need to be especially careful to look out for?

The answer to this question is specific to you. If you have concerns about more than half of the words out of the list of 24, consider making flash cards to help you practice. The extra effort will ensure that you do not confuse any of the commonly confused words on test day.

Next Steps

If you answered most questions correctly in the "How Much Have You Learned?" section, and if your responses to the Reflect questions were similar to those of the PSAT expert, then consider Sentence Structure, Punctuation, and Agreement areas of strength and move on to the next chapter. Come back to these topics periodically to prevent yourself from getting rusty.

If you don't yet feel confident, review those parts of this chapter that you have not yet mastered. In particular, review punctuation usage in the Sentence Structure: The Basics and Commas, Dashes, and Colons lessons, as well as how to select the appropriate pronoun or modifier in the Agreement: Pronouns and Agreement: Modifiers lessons. Then try the questions you missed again. As always, be sure to review the explanations closely.

Answers and Explanations

1. Review the Explanation portion of the Sentence Structure: The Basics lesson.

2. C

Difficulty: Medium

Getting to the Answer: As written, the first sentence is a fragment: it does not express a complete thought. Eliminate (A). Also eliminate (D), since a semicolon joins two independent clauses. (B) is incorrect because it uses the conjunction "and" incorrectly, turning the entire sentence into a fragment. **(C)** is correct because it uses a comma to join the dependent clause beginning "Since" to the independent clause "he noticed ..."

3. B

Difficulty: Medium

Getting to the Answer: As written, the sentence uses a semicolon to join the sentence's parts. The first part of the sentence is an independent clause with subject-verb "He decided." The second part does not contain a subject or express a complete thought, so eliminate any answer choices that punctuates the sentence as if it contains two independent clauses: (A), a semicolon; (C), a comma and FANBOYS conjunction; and (D), a period that results in two sentences. **(B)** is correct because the word "and" joins the compound verb "decided ... and found"; no extra punctuation is necessary.

4. D

Difficulty: Medium

Getting to the Answer: The part of the sentence before the underline is an independent clause; it expresses a complete thought with subject "Some people" and verb "are." The part after the underline, however, is a dependent clause because it does not express a complete thought: "Though the number ..." The word "though" subordinates the second clause. You need to find a way to join the independent clause to the subordinate (dependent) clause that follows it. **(D)** is correct because a comma is the appropriate way to join an independent clause and a dependent, subordinate clause. (A) and (C) are incorrect because they punctuate the sentence as though the second part were an independent clause. (B) is incorrect because it creates a run-on.

5. D

Difficulty: Hard

Getting to the Answer: The underlined section contains part of a long list of side effects. Normally, you would separate items in a list with commas, but when a list contains sublists, the sublists must be separated by semicolons and the items within them must be separated by commas. **(D)** is correct because it correctly punctuates the list by using commas between the items in the sublists of side effects and semicolons between the distinct groups of side effects.

6. B

Difficulty: Medium

Getting to the Answer: The parts of the sentence before and after the underline are both independent clauses. Each expresses a complete thought and has a subject and predicate verb ("problem ... is" and "these bacteria cannot be"). Eliminate any answer choices that are not ways to combine two independent clauses. (A) incorrectly uses a comma. (C) is incorrect because the lack of any punctuation between independent clauses results in a run-on. (D) is incorrect because the word "although" turns the second clause into a subordinate clause, so the clauses cannot be joined by a semicolon. **(B)** is correct because it joins two independent clauses with a semicolon.

7. Review the Explanation portion of the Sentence Structure: Commas, Dashes, and Colons lesson.

8. C

Difficulty: Easy

Getting to the Answer: As written, the colon is used improperly: a colon can follow an independent clause only. Eliminate (A). The words before the punctuation mark, "A practical man," form an introductory phrase. An introductory phrase should be followed by a comma, so **(C)** is correct. (B) is incorrect because it runs the phrases together, and the use of the dash in (D) is incorrect for the same reason as is the colon in (A).

9. D

Difficulty: Hard

Getting to the Answer: This sentence is complicated, so break it down into its component parts so you can determine which punctuation is correct. The subject of the sentence is "He" and the verb is "would ... accept." The phrases after "layers" are prepositional phrases that describe the layers. The underline appears in one of these prepositional phrases: "from candles, and incense burned during religious functions." Punctuation should not separate a preposition from its object, even when the preposition ("from") has a compound object ("candles and incense"). Therefore, eliminate any choices that separate the preposition from the objects. **(D)** is the only one that doesn't separate them, so it is correct.

10. D

Difficulty: Medium

Getting to the Answer: This underline contains two nouns ("solvents" and "equipment") and their descriptive adjectives. When more than one adjective modifies a noun, there should be commas between the adjectives only if you could change the order of the adjectives without changing the meaning. For the first noun here, "solvents," the word "cleaning" specifies the type of solvents. Thus, "special" is actually modifying "cleaning solvents." You cannot change the order of the adjectives without changing the meaning—"cleaning special solvents" does not make sense. Therefore, eliminate (A), which adds a comma between "special" and "cleaning." Perform the same analysis on "equipment." Switching the order of the adjectives would result in an illogical phrase ("analysis computerized equipment"), so "analysis" specifies the type of "equipment," and no comma is necessary. Eliminate (B). There is no reason to separate the nouns "solvents" and "equipment" with a comma as in choice (C), so **(D)** is correct.

11. B

Difficulty: Medium

Getting to the Answer: Remember that punctuation must be used to set off parenthetical information. In this sentence, the phrase "as they claimed" is parenthetical in the sentence—without this nonessential phrase, the essential idea of the sentence, "the restorers did not achieve this effect merely by removing the dirt ... from the frescoes" still makes logical sense. Since punctuation must set off parenthetical information, **(B)** is correct because it is the only choice that uses a comma at both the beginning and the end of the phrase.

12. A

Difficulty: Medium

Getting to the Answer: Analyze both the types of clauses and the relationship between their ideas to determine how they should be punctuated. The clause before the punctuation is an independent clause, a complete thought with subject-verb: "the restorers did not achieve." The clause after the punctuation is also an independent clause with subject-verb: "the team removed." The ideas of the clauses are closely related: the first sentence states that the "effect" was not "merely" the result of "removing the dirt and animal glue," and the second sentence explains what else was done to achieve the effect ("remov[ing] Michelangelo's final touches"). Since the part of the sentence before the punctuation is an independent clause and the second part helps to explain the first, a colon effectively punctuates these two closely related clauses, so **(A)** is correct. The other choices create run-on sentences by improperly joining two independent clauses.

13. A

Difficulty: Easy

Getting to the Answer: Items in a series should be separated by commas. This series is lengthy, but the rule is the same. The underlined portion lists the things that the "solvents" did: "stripped," "reacted," and "produced." These should be separated by commas, so **(A)** is correct. Semicolons, as in (C) and (D), are required only in series to separate groups of related items; when this occurs, the related items are separated by commas.

14. B

Difficulty: Medium

Getting to the Answer: This sentence begins with a subordinating clause ("Since the layers ... protection"). Because this clause is not a complete thought, it is a dependent clause that must be joined to the rest of the sentence with a comma, so **(B)** is correct. (A) runs the clauses together, while (C) and (D) punctuate the sentence as though it consisted of two independent clauses.

15. B

Difficulty: Medium

Getting to the Answer: The phrase "an extensive climate-control system" is parenthetical to the meaning of the sentence. Although it provides clarifying information about what "the measure" is, the sentence would still be logical even if the phrase were removed. Parenthetical information must be set off by a pair of matching punctuation marks, such as commas or dashes, so **(B)** is correct. (A) and (C) are incorrect because they include mismatched punctuation marks around the phrase. (D) is incorrect because semicolons cannot be used to set off parenthetical information.

16. Review the Explanation portion of the Agreement: Verbs lesson.

17. A

Difficulty: Medium

Getting to the Answer: Make sure that the underlined verb matches the tense of the surrounding context and agrees with its subject. The verb should be in the present tense since it refers to the "current image," so eliminate (B) and (C). The subject of the verb "capture" is the compound subject, "The woolly mammoth and the mastodon." Since a compound subject is treated as a plural, the singular verb in (D) is incorrect. Only **(A)** is left and is correct because it has the correct tense and agrees with its subject.

18. C

Difficulty: Medium

Getting to the Answer: Check whether the subject of the underlined verb is singular or plural. Finding the subject is complicated by the fact that a prepositional phrase ("to the modern-day elephant") separates the verb from its subject, "precursors." This subject is plural, so eliminate the singular verbs in (A) and (D). You know that these animals are "now-extinct," so you need a past tense verb; eliminate (B). Only **(C)** is left and is correct.

19. B

Difficulty: Medium

Getting to the Answer: The verb's subject is the singular "team," and the action happened in the past, as indicated by verbs "descended" and "helped" in the surrounding sentences. Eliminate (C), which is not in the past tense, and (D), which is a plural verb form. One of the remaining choices, (A), is a verb form that indicates an action that occurred before another past action, "had completed." This action did *not* occur before another action in the sentence, but rather occurred "*after*" the other events described. Thus, the simple past tense, **(B)**, is correct.

20. D

Difficulty: Medium

Getting to the Answer: Comparisons on the PSAT must be written in parallel form. This comparison identifies two "scientific theories": "meteor showers" and "massive volcanic eruptions." Be very careful that the wording you choose directly compares these two ideas. The comparison begins after the word "ranged" and fits into the pattern "from … to …" So, as written, the sentence compares "meteor showers" to "*suggestions* of massive volcanic eruptions." This comparison is not parallel, so eliminate (A). (B) and (C) make similar errors, comparing the "meteor showers" to "suggesting" and "theories," respectively. **(D)** completes the comparison logically.

21. B

Difficulty: Medium

Getting to the Answer: This underlined verb has the subject "community." Although this noun refers to numerous people, the collective noun itself is treated as singular. Eliminate any answer choices that use a plural verb: (A) and (D). Using the -*ing* form of the verb, as in (C), results in a sentence fragment. **(B)** appropriately uses a present tense, singular verb and is therefore correct.

22. D

Difficulty: Easy

Getting to the Answer: Use context to determine the appropriate tense for the underlined verb. Although the scientists' action, "consider," is in present tense, the verbs referring to the mammoths, which "died out" according to the previous sentence, must be in past tense. Only **(D)** is in the past tense, so it is correct.

23. Review the Explanation portion of the Agreement: Pronouns lesson.

24. C

Difficulty: Medium

Getting to the Answer: When a pronoun is underlined, make sure it agrees with its antecedent and is in the correct form based on its placement in the sentence. The underlined pronoun refers to people ("authors"), not things, so eliminate the pronoun "which," choice (B). The subjective form of the pronoun is required since the pronoun is part of the subject of the verb "were." Therefore, the subjective pronoun "who," choice **(C)**, is correct.

25. D

Difficulty: Medium

Getting to the Answer: An underlined pronoun must match the pronouns used in the surrounding context. Determine who the writer is referring to in saying that these authors "compelled" *someone*. In surrounding sentences, the writer uses the pronouns "we" and "ours" to refer to those impacted by these authors; the writer thus includes both the reader and herself in this designation. This pronoun should include the same groups, so the first-person plural "us," **(D)**, is correct. (B) is incorrect because it includes only the writer, which does not match the other surrounding pronouns. (A) is incorrect because it is in the second person, and (C) is incorrect because it is in the third person, neither of which is used elsewhere in the passage.

26. C

Difficulty: Medium

Getting to the Answer: The pronoun "they" sounds correct in this usage, and the writer uses this pronoun in the previous sentence to refer to the authors, but carefully check to make sure this underlined pronoun has a clear antecedent. The pronoun is meant to refer to the authors, as indicated later in the sentence by the reference to "their writings." However, the nearest antecedent for the pronoun "they" is "readers" in the previous sentence. Even though you may understand the intended meaning, the pronoun here is ambiguous and thus incorrect. **(C)** is correct because it is the only choice that clarifies the subject.

27. B

Difficulty: Medium

Getting to the Answer: Determine the antecedent of the underlined pronoun. The pronoun is possessive, indicating that the "readings" of *Ulysses* belong to someone. The sentence previously refers to the plural "literary critics," so this pronoun should be plural as well; eliminate (C). Although the writer clearly read *Ulysses* and refers to her opinion about it in the remainder of the paragraph, these readings belong only to *other* literary critics, so eliminate (A) and (D). **(B)** is correct.

28. C

Difficulty: Medium

Getting to the Answer: The underlined pronoun is possessive, indicating that the "book" either belongs to or was written by someone. The antecedent is unclear, as the sentence previously refers to *The Odyssey*, written by Homer, and *The Odyssey*'s "hero." However, the context indicates that the "book" referred to in this case is the "opposite" of *The Odyssey*, so it must be the book written by Joyce. Although you can logically determine the pronoun's antecedent, the writer should eliminate the grammatical ambiguity by using Joyce's name rather than a pronoun, so **(C)** is correct.

29. A

Difficulty: Medium

Getting to the Answer: Besides matching their antecedent, pronouns must also be in the correct form: subjective, objective, or possessive. The underlined pronoun should be in the objective form since it is the object of the preposition "of." **(A)** is correct. (B) and (D) are incorrect because they use pronoun forms that are not appropriate for the context. (C) is incorrect because it is not a grammatically correct pronoun form.

30. Review the Explanation portion of the Agreement: Modifiers lesson.

31. A

Difficulty: Medium

Getting to the Answer: The answer choices contain frequently confused versions of possessive pronouns and contractions, so carefully assess the context of the sentence to determine which is correct. A possessive pronoun is appropriate because the sentence is referring to the "medium" *that belongs to the* "novel," so eliminate the contractions "it's" and "they're," which mean "it is" and "they are," respectively. The "novel" is singular, so the singular possessive pronoun "its," **(A)**, is correct.

32. C

Difficulty: Hard

Getting to the Answer: The placement of a modifying phrase affects the meaning of a sentence, so make sure every phrase is placed correctly. The writer intends to use the modifying phrase "becoming cruel, shortsighted, and constantly dissatisfied with real life" to describe Emma; however, as written, the phrase describes her "friends and family." Eliminate (A). Only **(C)** places the modifying phrase next to "Emma," so it is correct.

33. B

Difficulty: Hard

Getting to the Answer: The underlined words modify the noun "fashion." Unless one of the adjectives is a defining modifier of the noun (as in the phrase "red dump truck," which could not be written "dump red truck"), two adjectives cannot be placed together without a comma between them, so (A) and (C) are incorrect. Only **(B)** uses the modifiers correctly, the adverb "gloriously" describing the adjective "dramatic" and the adjective "dramatic" describing the noun "fashion." (D) is incorrect because it uses an adverb, "dramatically," to modify a noun, "fashion."

34. B

Difficulty: Medium

Getting to the Answer: Sometimes the trickiest modifier placement questions concern the shortest words, such as "only." In such cases, carefully analyze the writer's intended meaning. The writer is comparing Emma with the other characters in the novel, making the point that *no other character* "habitually reads for pleasure."

Therefore, it is Emma who is "the *only* character" who reads in this way, so **(B)** is correct. (A) is incorrect because it unnecessarily repeats the modifier "only." (C) and (D) both change the intended meaning. (C) singles out "novel," as though more than one novel were being discussed. (D) implies that Emma *only* does one thing: "habitually reads for pleasure."

35. A

Difficulty: Easy

Getting to the Answer: When you see an underlined comparison, determine how many things are being compared. The underlined modifier compares "the characters making up the novel's non-reading population" with "Emma" in regard to social responsibility. Since only two groups are part of the comparison, a comparative word is appropriate, so **(A)**, "more," is correct. (B) and (C) both result in an improperly worded comparison, and (D) is incorrect because "most" is a superlative, used when comparing three or more items.

36. A

Difficulty: Medium

Getting to the Answer: This question concerns correct apostrophe placement in a possessive noun. You know the underlined word must be in a possessive form because the sentence is referring to the "unwillingness" of the characters; eliminate (C). There are many other characters in *Madame Bovary*—her husband, her household, and her family are all mentioned in the passage. **(A)** is correct because it is the correct way to punctuate a plural possessive: place the apostrophe immediately after the letter that makes the word plural. (B) is incorrect because it is a singular possessive. (D) is not written with the correct structure for a plural possessive.

37. Review the Explanation portion of the Agreement: Idioms lesson.

38. B

Difficulty: Easy

Getting to the Answer: This question is testing two commonly confused words: *accept* and *except*. *Except* denotes an exclusion, while *accept* can mean to either receive or recognize something. In this context, "art historians" are recognizing the status of an art movement, so eliminate any choice containing "except": (A) and (C). The *-ed* form of the word fits in this context, so **(B)** is correct.

39. A
Difficulty: Easy

Getting to the Answer: You need to identify the correct preposition for the idiom *influenced ____ something*. Since the correct idiom is *influenced by*, **(A)** is correct.

40. B
Difficulty: Easy

Getting to the Answer: This question is testing two commonly confused words: *affect* and *effect*. *Affect* means "to influence" and is most often used as a verb. While *effect* can be used as a verb (meaning "to bring something about," as in *effected a solution*), it is usually used as a noun meaning "result." In this sentence, the word is used as a noun (try substituting the word *result*—if you can, you can use *effect)*, so *effect* must be correct. Adding the *-ing* ending does not make sense in context, so **(B)** is correct.

41. B
Difficulty: Easy

Getting to the Answer: The correct preposition can often only be determined in the context of the sentence. This sentence states that the Hudson River School was suited to the task of competing with Europe. The function of the prepositional phrase is to explain how that was accomplished, and the phrase "*by* providing" best serves that function, so **(B)** is correct.

42. C
Difficulty: Hard

Getting to the Answer: This question is testing two commonly confused words: *that* and *which*. *That* is used with essential, or defining, information. *Which* is used with nonessential, or parenthetical, information. In this case, *that* is correct because it is necessary to specify that the "art" is "unmistakably American." The phrase "art, which was unmistakably American" indicates that *all* art is unmistakably American, which is clearly not the intended meaning. **(C)** is correct. (B) and (D) result in ungrammatical sentences.

43. D
Difficulty: Medium

Getting to the Answer: While explicit double negatives are easier to catch and avoid, you must also be on the lookout for implicit double negatives. *Hardly* is a word that cannot be directly paired with a negative, such as *not*. The only answer choice that avoids an implicit double negative construction is **(D)**, so it is correct.

44. A
Difficulty: Medium

Getting to the Answer: This question requires you to select the correct construction of the idiomatic expression *neither . . . nor*. (C) and (D) use the phrasing "neither . . . or," so eliminate them. The preposition "to" must be consistently placed in the expression. As written, the word "to" appears after each word in the expression: "neither *to* embellish nor *to* idealize," so **(A)** is correct. (B) incorrectly places the word "to" both before and within the phrase: "*to* neither embellish nor *to* idealize."

45. B
Difficulty: Easy

Category: Sentence Structure: Commas, Dashes, and Colons

Getting to the Answer: The sentence creates a series: attributes of locations in space that help the reader picture Antarctica. Each item in the series is worded "as (*adjective*) as *Moon/Saturn/Mars*." Basic series should be punctuated with commas between each of the items, so **(B)** is correct. (A) and (C) each omit necessary commas from the series, and (D) incorrectly omits the word "as" in the second series item.

46. B
Difficulty: Hard

Category: Agreement: Pronouns

Getting to the Answer: Always check underlined pronouns for ambiguity. In this case, the antecedent of the pronoun is unclear: although the writer is clearly describing qualities of Antarctica, the nearest antecedent is "Mars." After eliminating the pronouns that are ambiguous, you're left with **(B)**, which correctly clarifies the intended location. Note that even if a pronoun in this location were not ambiguous, (C) would be incorrect because it is plural and (D) would be incorrect because it is the contraction of *it is*.

47. D

Difficulty: Medium

Category: Sentence Structure: The Basics

Getting to the Answer: The underlined comma separates two independent clauses, each expressing a complete thought with a subject and predicate verb ("Scientists estimate" and "sea levels might rise"). Remember that semicolons combine two independent clauses, while commas can join independent clauses only when followed by a FANBOYS conjunction. Choice **(D)** is correct because it properly joins the independent clauses with a semicolon. The other answer choices are not valid ways to join independent clauses. (A) creates a run-on because it joins independent clauses with only a comma. (B) adds an unnecessary "and" after the semicolon. (C) omits the necessary comma before "and."

48. A

Difficulty: Medium

Category: Agreement: Idioms

Getting to the Answer: The word *their* and *theirs* are possessive pronouns, but "their's" is never correct, so eliminate (B). The singular "a town" that follows the underlined portion for this question requires a singular verb. Only **(A)** offers the singular verb "is" and is therefore correct. The remaining choices are incorrect because they use the plural verb "are" either outright as (C) does, or hidden in a contraction, as in (D), where "they're" is a shortened version of *they are*.

49. D

Difficulty: Medium

Category: Agreement: Idioms

Getting to the Answer: The underlined phrase contains an idiomatic expression. The writer is identifying things that are *not* in Antarctica, not expressing that the continent could logically only have either a town *or* vegetation, so eliminate (B). The correct idiomatic expression is "neither ... nor." Only correct answer **(D)** uses this structure.

50. C

Difficulty: Medium

Category: Agreement: Modifiers

Getting to the Answer: When modifiers are underlined, make sure they are in the correct format to modify the intended word. The underlined modifiers are in the last part of a sentence that describes the impact of Antarctic water. The modifier "ultimate" is not intended to modify "weather patterns," as written, but to indicate that the creation of these weather patterns is the final part of a process; eliminate (A). Only (C) structures the modifiers so that "ultimately" modifies the verb "create" and "complex" modifies "weather patterns," so **(C)** is correct. (D) is incorrect because it alters the original intended meaning of the sentence.

51. D

Difficulty: Hard

Category: Sentence Structure: Commas, Dashes, and Colons

Getting to the Answer: You must determine what punctuation is correct around this long phrase that appears in the middle of a sentence. As written, the descriptive phrase that begins "giving these waters" confusingly runs into the previous part of the sentence, so eliminate (A). The underlined prepositional phrases are best viewed as parenthetical information that describes the type of life in Antarctic seas. If the phrases were removed, the sentence would still stand on its own: "Antarctic seas teem with life, ... giving these waters a vital status among the Earth's ecosystems." Look for an answer choice that punctuates the parenthetical information appropriately, using either a pair of commas or dashes to set off the nonessential phrase. **(D)** does this with commas and is correct. (B) and (C) are incorrect because the use of a semicolon would indicate that two independent clauses are being joined, but each creates one dependent clause.

52. C

Difficulty: Medium

Category: Agreement: Modifiers

Getting to the Answer: The answer choices place the descriptive phrase "some found nowhere else on the planet" in different locations. The phrase should be placed near "unique species of birds and mammals," since it describes these living creatures rather than "frigid waters" or "the continent's edge." Only correct answer **(C)** places these phrases together.

53. B

Difficulty: Medium

Category: Agreement: Verbs

Getting to the Answer: Check underlined verbs for tense consistency and agreement with their subjects. The context of the paragraph makes it clear that research in Antarctica occurs "today," so eliminate (C), which confines the action to only the past. To determine which present tense verb is correct, find the verb's subject. Although the noun "Antarctica" is nearest, the subject is actually the compound "relative inaccessibility *and* near pristine state." Compound subjects with *and* should be treated as plural, so the plural verb "make," **(B)**, is correct.

54. A

Difficulty: Medium

Category: Agreement: Verbs

Getting to the Answer: Determine the subject of the underlined verb so you can ensure the subject and verb are in agreement. Although there are many words in between, the subject of the verb is "discovery"; all the words in between are prepositional or descriptive phrases that describe the discovery or its location. Since "discovery" is singular, the singular "provides," **(A)**, is correct. (B) and (C) are incorrect because they are plural verbs. (D) is incorrect because it would result in a sentence fragment.

55. D

Difficulty: Easy

Category: Sentence Structure: The Basics

Getting to the Answer: A sentence is a run-on if it has two improperly joined independent clauses that could be stand-alone sentences. The parts of the sentence before and after the underline are both independent clauses that express complete thoughts. Both a comma and a FANBOYS conjunction are required when combining two independent clauses. Eliminate (A) and (B) because they are missing the comma, and eliminate (C) because it is missing a FANBOYS conjunction. Choice **(D)** correctly divides the two independent clauses into two separate sentences.

PART 5

Countdown to Test Day

CHAPTER 16

Countdown to Test Day

The Week Before the Test

- Focus your additional practice on the question types and/or subject areas in which you usually score highest. Now is the time to sharpen your best skills, not cram new information.

- Make sure you are registered for the test. Remember, Kaplan cannot register you. If you missed the registration deadlines, you can request Waitlist Status on the test maker's website, collegeboard.org.

- Confirm the location of your test site. Never been there before? Make a practice run to make sure you know exactly how long it will take to get from your home to your test site. Build in extra time in case you hit traffic or construction on the morning of the test.

- Get a great night's sleep the two days before the test.

The Day Before the Test

- Review the methods and strategies you learned in this book.

- Put new batteries in your calculator.

- Pack your backpack or bag for test day with the following items:

  - Photo ID
  - Registration slip or printout
  - Directions to your test site location
  - Five or more sharpened no. 2 pencils (no mechanical pencils)
  - Pencil sharpener
  - Eraser
  - Calculator
  - Extra batteries
  - Non-prohibited timepiece
  - Tissues
  - Prepackaged snacks, like granola bars
  - Bottled water, juice, or sports drink
  - Sweatshirt, sweater, or jacket

The Night Before the Test

- No studying!
- Do something relaxing that will take your mind off the test, such as watching a movie or playing video games with friends.
- Set your alarm to wake up early enough so that you won't feel rushed.
- Go to bed early, but not too much earlier than you usually do. You want to fall asleep quickly, not spend hours tossing and turning.

The Morning of the Test

- Dress comfortably and in layers. You need to be prepared for any temperature.
- Eat a filling breakfast, but don't stray too far from your usual routine. If you normally aren't a breakfast eater, don't eat a huge meal, but make sure you have something substantial.
- Read something over breakfast. You need to warm up your brain so you don't go into the test cold. Read a few pages of a newspaper, magazine, or favorite novel.
- Get to your test site early. There is likely to be some confusion about where to go and how to sign in, so allow yourself plenty of time, even if you are taking the test at your own school.
- Leave your cell phone at home. Many test sites do not allow them in the building.
- While you're waiting to sign in or be seated, read more of what you read over breakfast to stay in reading mode.

During the Test

- Be calm and confident. You're ready for this!
- Remember that while the PSAT is an almost-three-hour marathon, it is also a series of shorter sections. Focus on the section you're working on at that moment; don't think about previous or upcoming sections.
- Use the methods and strategies you have learned in this book as often as you can. Allow yourself to fall into the good habits you built during your practice.
- Don't linger too long on any one question. Mark it and come back to it later.
- Can't figure out an answer? Try to eliminate some choices and take a strategic guess. Remember, there is no penalty for an incorrect answer, so even if you can't eliminate any choices, you should take a guess.
- There will be plenty of questions you *can* answer, so spend your time on those first!
- Maintain good posture throughout the test. It will help you stay alert.
- If you find yourself losing concentration, getting frustrated, or stressing about the time, stop for 30 seconds. Close your eyes, put your pencil down, take a few deep breaths, and relax your shoulders. You'll be much more productive after taking a few moments to relax.
- Use your breaks effectively. During the five-minute breaks, go to the restroom, eat your snacks, and get your energy up for the next section.

After the Test

- Congratulate yourself! Then, reward yourself by doing something fun. You've earned it!
- Your scores will be available online in early December, about six to eight weeks after you took the PSAT.

PART 6

Practice Tests

HOW TO SCORE YOUR PRACTICE TESTS

For each subject area in the practice test, convert your raw score, or the number of questions you answered correctly, to a scaled score using the table below. To get your raw score for Evidence-Based Reading & Writing, add the total number of Reading questions you answered correctly to the total number of Writing questions you answered correctly; for Math, add the number of questions you answered correctly for the Math (No-Calculator) and Math (Calculator) sections.

Evidence-Based Reading and Writing		Math		Evidence-Based Reading and Writing		Math	
TOTAL Raw Score	Scaled Score	Raw Score	Scaled Score	TOTAL Raw Score	Scaled Score	Raw Score	Scaled Score
0	160	0	160	46	490	46	750
1	160	1	190	47	490	47	760
2	180	2	210	48	500	48	760
3	190	3	240	49	510		
4	200	4	270	50	520		
5	210	5	290	51	520		
6	220	6	320	52	530		
7	230	7	340	53	540		
8	240	8	360	54	540		
9	250	9	370	55	540		
10	280	10	390	56	550		
11	280	11	400	57	550		
12	290	12	420	58	560		
13	300	13	430	59	560		
14	310	14	440	60	570		
15	320	15	460	61	580		
16	320	16	470	62	580		
17	340	17	480	63	580		
18	340	18	490	64	590		
19	350	19	500	65	590		
20	350	20	510	66	600		
21	360	21	520	67	610		
22	360	22	530	68	610		
23	360	23	540	69	620		
24	380	24	550	70	620		
25	380	25	560	71	630		
26	380	26	570	72	630		
27	390	27	580	73	640		
28	390	28	580	74	640		
29	400	29	590	75	640		
30	400	30	600	76	650		
31	420	31	610	77	660		
32	420	32	620	78	670		
33	420	33	630	79	680		
34	420	34	640	80	680		
35	430	35	650	81	690		
36	430	36	670	82	700		
37	440	37	680	83	710		
38	440	38	690	84	720		
39	450	39	710	85	720		
40	460	40	720	86	730		
41	460	41	730	87	740		
42	460	42	730	88	740		
43	470	43	740	89	750		
44	480	44	740	90	750		
45	480	45	750	91	760		

PSAT Practice Test 1 Answer Sheet

Remove (or photocopy) this answer sheet and use it to complete the test. See the answer key following the test when finished.

Start with number 1 for each section. If a section has fewer questions than answer spaces, leave the extra spaces blank.

SECTION 1

1. (A) (B) (C) (D)
2. (A) (B) (C) (D)
3. (A) (B) (C) (D)
4. (A) (B) (C) (D)
5. (A) (B) (C) (D)
6. (A) (B) (C) (D)
7. (A) (B) (C) (D)
8. (A) (B) (C) (D)
9. (A) (B) (C) (D)
10. (A) (B) (C) (D)
11. (A) (B) (C) (D)
12. (A) (B) (C) (D)
13. (A) (B) (C) (D)

14. (A) (B) (C) (D)
15. (A) (B) (C) (D)
16. (A) (B) (C) (D)
17. (A) (B) (C) (D)
18. (A) (B) (C) (D)
19. (A) (B) (C) (D)
20. (A) (B) (C) (D)
21. (A) (B) (C) (D)
22. (A) (B) (C) (D)
23. (A) (B) (C) (D)
24. (A) (B) (C) (D)
25. (A) (B) (C) (D)
26. (A) (B) (C) (D)

27. (A) (B) (C) (D)
28. (A) (B) (C) (D)
29. (A) (B) (C) (D)
30. (A) (B) (C) (D)
31. (A) (B) (C) (D)
32. (A) (B) (C) (D)
33. (A) (B) (C) (D)
34. (A) (B) (C) (D)
35. (A) (B) (C) (D)
36. (A) (B) (C) (D)
37. (A) (B) (C) (D)
38. (A) (B) (C) (D)
39. (A) (B) (C) (D)

40. (A) (B) (C) (D)
41. (A) (B) (C) (D)
42. (A) (B) (C) (D)
43. (A) (B) (C) (D)
44. (A) (B) (C) (D)
45. (A) (B) (C) (D)
46. (A) (B) (C) (D)
47. (A) (B) (C) (D)

correct in Section 1

incorrect in Section 1

SECTION 2

1. (A) (B) (C) (D)
2. (A) (B) (C) (D)
3. (A) (B) (C) (D)
4. (A) (B) (C) (D)
5. (A) (B) (C) (D)
6. (A) (B) (C) (D)
7. (A) (B) (C) (D)
8. (A) (B) (C) (D)
9. (A) (B) (C) (D)
10. (A) (B) (C) (D)
11. (A) (B) (C) (D)

12. (A) (B) (C) (D)
13. (A) (B) (C) (D)
14. (A) (B) (C) (D)
15. (A) (B) (C) (D)
16. (A) (B) (C) (D)
17. (A) (B) (C) (D)
18. (A) (B) (C) (D)
19. (A) (B) (C) (D)
20. (A) (B) (C) (D)
21. (A) (B) (C) (D)
22. (A) (B) (C) (D)

23. (A) (B) (C) (D)
24. (A) (B) (C) (D)
25. (A) (B) (C) (D)
26. (A) (B) (C) (D)
27. (A) (B) (C) (D)
28. (A) (B) (C) (D)
29. (A) (B) (C) (D)
30. (A) (B) (C) (D)
31. (A) (B) (C) (D)
32. (A) (B) (C) (D)
33. (A) (B) (C) (D)

34. (A) (B) (C) (D)
35. (A) (B) (C) (D)
36. (A) (B) (C) (D)
37. (A) (B) (C) (D)
38. (A) (B) (C) (D)
39. (A) (B) (C) (D)
40. (A) (B) (C) (D)
41. (A) (B) (C) (D)
42. (A) (B) (C) (D)
43. (A) (B) (C) (D)
44. (A) (B) (C) (D)

correct in Section 2

incorrect in Section 2

Practice Tests

SECTION 3

1. Ⓐ Ⓑ Ⓒ Ⓓ   5. Ⓐ Ⓑ Ⓒ Ⓓ   9. Ⓐ Ⓑ Ⓒ Ⓓ   13. Ⓐ Ⓑ Ⓒ Ⓓ
2. Ⓐ Ⓑ Ⓒ Ⓓ   6. Ⓐ Ⓑ Ⓒ Ⓓ   10. Ⓐ Ⓑ Ⓒ Ⓓ
3. Ⓐ Ⓑ Ⓒ Ⓓ   7. Ⓐ Ⓑ Ⓒ Ⓓ   11. Ⓐ Ⓑ Ⓒ Ⓓ
4. Ⓐ Ⓑ Ⓒ Ⓓ   8. Ⓐ Ⓑ Ⓒ Ⓓ   12. Ⓐ Ⓑ Ⓒ Ⓓ

☐ # correct in Section 3

☐ # incorrect in Section 3

14.   15.   16.   17.

SECTION 4

1. Ⓐ Ⓑ Ⓒ Ⓓ   9. Ⓐ Ⓑ Ⓒ Ⓓ   17. Ⓐ Ⓑ Ⓒ Ⓓ   25. Ⓐ Ⓑ Ⓒ Ⓓ
2. Ⓐ Ⓑ Ⓒ Ⓓ   10. Ⓐ Ⓑ Ⓒ Ⓓ   18. Ⓐ Ⓑ Ⓒ Ⓓ   26. Ⓐ Ⓑ Ⓒ Ⓓ
3. Ⓐ Ⓑ Ⓒ Ⓓ   11. Ⓐ Ⓑ Ⓒ Ⓓ   19. Ⓐ Ⓑ Ⓒ Ⓓ   27. Ⓐ Ⓑ Ⓒ Ⓓ
4. Ⓐ Ⓑ Ⓒ Ⓓ   12. Ⓐ Ⓑ Ⓒ Ⓓ   20. Ⓐ Ⓑ Ⓒ Ⓓ
5. Ⓐ Ⓑ Ⓒ Ⓓ   13. Ⓐ Ⓑ Ⓒ Ⓓ   21. Ⓐ Ⓑ Ⓒ Ⓓ
6. Ⓐ Ⓑ Ⓒ Ⓓ   14. Ⓐ Ⓑ Ⓒ Ⓓ   22. Ⓐ Ⓑ Ⓒ Ⓓ
7. Ⓐ Ⓑ Ⓒ Ⓓ   15. Ⓐ Ⓑ Ⓒ Ⓓ   23. Ⓐ Ⓑ Ⓒ Ⓓ
8. Ⓐ Ⓑ Ⓒ Ⓓ   16. Ⓐ Ⓑ Ⓒ Ⓓ   24. Ⓐ Ⓑ Ⓒ Ⓓ

☐ # correct in Section 4

☐ # incorrect in Section 4

28.   29.   30.   31.

Reading Test

60 Minutes—47 Questions

This section corresponds to Section 1 of your answer sheet.

Directions: Read each passage or pair of passages, then answer the questions that follow. Choose your answers based on what the passage(s) and any accompanying graphics state or imply.

Questions 1–9 are based on the following passage.

The following passage is adapted from Charles Dickens's 1860 novel *Great Expectations.* In this scene, the narrator, a boy named Pip, eats breakfast with his older sister's acquaintance, Mr. Pumblechook. Pumblechook has agreed to take Pip to see Miss Havisham, a wealthy woman who has requested this visit, although Pip has never met her.

Mr. Pumblechook and I breakfasted at eight o'clock in the parlor behind the shop, while the shopman took his mug of tea and hunch of bread and butter on a sack of peas in the front premises.
5 I considered Mr. Pumblechook wretched company. Besides being possessed by my sister's idea that a mortifying and penitential character ought to be imparted to my diet,[1]—besides giving me as much crumb as possible in combination with as
10 little butter, and putting such a quantity of warm water into my milk that it would have been more candid to have left the milk out altogether,—his conversation consisted of nothing but arithmetic. On my politely bidding him Good morning, he
15 said, pompously, "Seven times nine, boy?" And how should I be able to answer, dodged in that way, in a strange place, on an empty stomach! I was hungry, but before I had swallowed a morsel, he began a running sum that lasted all through the
20 breakfast. "Seven?" "And four?" "And eight?" . . . And so on. And after each figure was disposed of, it was as much as I could do to get a bite or a sup, before the next came; while he sat at his ease

guessing nothing, and eating bacon and hot roll, in
25 (if I may be allowed the expression) a gorging and gormandizing manner.

For such reasons, I was very glad when ten o'clock came and we started for Miss Havisham's; though I was not at all at my ease regarding the
30 manner in which I should acquit myself under that lady's roof. Within a quarter of an hour we came to Miss Havisham's house, which was of old brick, and dismal, and had a great many iron bars to it. Some of the windows had been walled
35 up; of those that remained, all the lower were rustily barred. There was a courtyard in front, and that was barred; so we had to wait, after ringing the bell, until some one should come to open it. While we waited at the gate, I peeped in (even
40 then Mr. Pumblechook said, "And fourteen?" but I pretended not to hear him), and saw that at the side of the house there was a large brewery. No brewing was going on in it, and none seemed to have gone on for a long long time.
45 A window was raised, and a clear voice demanded "What name?" To which my conductor replied, "Pumblechook." The voice returned, "Quite right," and the window was shut again, and a young lady came across the court-yard, with keys in her
50 hand.

"This," said Mr. Pumblechook, "is Pip."

"This is Pip, is it?" returned the young lady, who was very pretty and seemed very proud; "come in, Pip."

---

[1]Pip's sister indicated to Pumblechook that Pip should be grateful, even penitent (unreasonably so) for his help.

55   Mr. Pumblechook was coming in also, when she stopped him with the gate.

    "Oh!" she said. "Did you wish to see Miss Havisham?"

    "If Miss Havisham wished to see me," returned
60 Mr. Pumblechook, discomfited.

    "Ah!" said the girl; "but you see she don't."

    She said it so finally, and in such an undiscussible way, that Mr. Pumblechook, though in a condition of ruffled dignity, could not protest. But he eyed me
65 severely,—as if I had done anything to him!—and departed with the words reproachfully delivered: "Boy! Let your behavior here be a credit unto them which brought you up by hand!"[2] I was not free from apprehension that he would come back to
70 propound through the gate, "And sixteen?" But he didn't.

[2]Pumblechook is speaking of Pip's sister, who often boasts that she raised him "by hand."

1. According to the first paragraph, Pip's breakfast with Mr. Pumblechook is

  A) eaten on the run.

  B) small and of poor quality.

  C) better than Pip usually receives.

  D) carefully cooked and served.

2. As used in line 5, "wretched" most nearly means

  A) shameful.

  B) deprived.

  C) distressing.

  D) heartbroken.

3. Based on the passage, it can be inferred that Mr. Pumblechook

  A) has looked forward to his morning with Pip.

  B) is as uncomfortable as Pip is during breakfast.

  C) has known Pip and his sister for a very long time.

  D) is indifferent to Pip's discomfort during breakfast.

4. Which choice provides the best support for the answer to the previous question?

  A) Lines 1–4 ("Mr. Pumblechook and I . . . premises")

  B) Lines 6–13 ("Besides . . . arithmetic")

  C) Lines 46–47 ("To which my . . . Pumblechook")

  D) Lines 62–64 ("She said . . . not protest")

5. What theme is communicated through the experiences of Pip, the narrator?

  A) The world can be a puzzling and sometimes cruel place.

  B) Young people are misunderstood by their elders.

  C) Mean-spirited people deserve to be treated harshly.

  D) The favors one receives in life should be reciprocated.

GO ON TO THE NEXT PAGE

6. Which of the following is true when Mr. Pumblechook leaves Pip at Miss Havisham's house?

    A) Pip is excited to finally meet Miss Havisham.

    B) Pip is nervous about being away from his sister for so long.

    C) Pip is relieved to be away from Mr. Pumblechook.

    D) Pip is anxious about spending time with the young lady who greets them.

7. Which choice provides the best support for the answer to the previous question?

    A) Lines 1–4 ("Mr. Pumblechook . . . premises")

    B) Lines 45–46 ("A window . . . name")

    C) Lines 62–64 ("She said it . . . protest")

    D) Lines 68–71 ("I was not . . . he didn't")

8. As used in line 63, "condition" most nearly means

    A) illness.

    B) prerequisite.

    C) state.

    D) limitation.

9. The function of the parenthetical comment in line 25 is to reveal that

    A) Pip is usually more polite in his references to others.

    B) Mr. Pumblechook appreciates gourmet food.

    C) Pip is very angered that his own breakfast is so meager.

    D) Mr. Pumblechook has no qualms about over-eating in public.

Questions 10–18 are based on the following passage.

This passage is adapted from Martin Luther King Jr.'s "Letter from Birmingham Jail."

. . . I think I should give the reason for my being in Birmingham, since you have been influenced by the argument of "outsiders coming in." I have the honor of serving as president of the Southern
5 Christian Leadership Conference, an organization operating in every Southern state with headquarters in Atlanta, Georgia. We have some eighty-five affiliate organizations all across the South, one being the Alabama Christian Movement for Human
10 Rights. Whenever necessary and possible we share staff, educational, and financial resources with our affiliates. Several months ago our local affiliate here in Birmingham invited us to be on call to engage in a nonviolent direct action program if such were
15 deemed necessary. We readily consented and when the hour came we lived up to our promises. So I am here, along with several members of my staff, because we were invited here. I am here because I have basic organizational ties here. Beyond this, I
20 am in Birmingham because injustice is here. . . .

Moreover, I am cognizant of the interrelatedness of all communities and states. I cannot sit idly by in Atlanta and not be concerned about what happens in Birmingham. Injustice anywhere is a threat to
25 justice everywhere. We are caught in an inescapable network of mutuality, tied in a single garment of destiny. Whatever affects one directly affects all indirectly. Never again can we afford to live with the narrow, provincial "outside agitator" idea. Anyone
30 who lives inside the United States can never be considered an outsider anywhere in this country. . . .

You may well ask, "Why direct action? Why sit-ins, marches, etc.? Isn't negotiation a better
35 path?" You are exactly right in your call for negotiation. Indeed, this is the purpose of direct action. Nonviolent direct action seeks to create such a crisis and establish such creative tension that a community that has constantly refused to
40 negotiate is forced to confront the issue. It seeks

so to dramatize the issue that it can no longer be ignored. I just referred to the creation of tension as a part of the work of the nonviolent resister. This may sound rather shocking. But I must confess that

45 I am not afraid of the word tension. I have earnestly worked and preached against violent tension, but there is a type of constructive nonviolent tension that is necessary for growth. Just as Socrates felt that it was necessary to create a tension in the mind

50 so that individuals could rise from the bondage of myths and half-truths to the unfettered realm of creative analysis and objective appraisal, we must see the need of having nonviolent gadflies to create the kind of tension in society that will help men rise

55 from the dark depths of prejudice and racism to the majestic heights of understanding and brotherhood. So the purpose of the direct action is to create a situation so crisis-packed that it will inevitably open the door to negotiation. We, therefore, concur

60 with you in your call for negotiation. Too long has our beloved Southland been bogged down in the tragic attempt to live in monologue rather than dialogue. . . .

My friends, I must say to you that we have

65 not made a single gain in civil rights without determined legal and nonviolent pressure. History is the long and tragic story of the fact that privileged groups seldom give up their privileges voluntarily. Individuals may see the moral light

70 and voluntarily give up their unjust posture; but as Reinhold Niebuhr has reminded us, groups are more immoral than individuals.

We know through painful experience that freedom is never voluntarily given by the oppressor;

75 it must be demanded by the oppressed. . . . For years now I have heard the word "Wait!" It rings in the ear of every African American with a piercing familiarity. This "wait" has almost always meant "never." It has been a tranquilizing thalidomide,

80 relieving the emotional stress for a moment, only

to give birth to an ill-formed infant of frustration. We must come to see with the distinguished jurist of yesterday that "justice too long delayed is justice denied." We have waited for more than three

85 hundred and forty years for our constitutional and God-given rights. The nations of Asia and Africa are moving with jet-like speed toward the goal of political independence, and we still creep at horse and buggy pace toward the gaining of a cup of

90 coffee at a lunch counter. . . .

10. King's purpose for writing this letter is

A) to explain why he came to Birmingham to protest.

B) to launch a nonviolent protest movement in Birmingham.

C) to open an affiliate of the Southern Christian Leadership Conference in Birmingham.

D) to support fellow civil rights activists in Birmingham.

11. Which choice provides the best evidence for the answer to the previous question?

A) Lines 1–2 ("I think . . . in Birmingham")

B) Lines 3–7 ("I have . . . Atlanta, Georgia")

C) Lines 7–10 ("We have some . . . Rights")

D) Lines 24–25 ("Injustice anywhere . . . everywhere")

GO ON TO THE NEXT PAGE →

12. As used in lines 21–22, "interrelatedness of all communities and states" most nearly means that

    A) King has personal connections to people in the town.

    B) the Southern Christian Leadership Conference needs national support.

    C) events in one part of the country affect everyone in the nation.

    D) local civil rights groups operate independently of one another.

13. Based on paragraph 3, it can be reasonably inferred that King believed circumstances in Birmingham at the time

    A) were unfair and wrong.

    B) constituted an isolated event.

    C) justified his arrest.

    D) required federal intervention.

14. Which choice provides the best evidence for the answer to the previous question?

    A) Lines 21–22 ("Moreover, . . . states")

    B) Lines 24–25 ("Injustice anywhere . . . every-where")

    C) Lines 25–27 ("We are caught . . . destiny")

    D) Lines 28–29 ("Never again . . . idea")

15. As used in line 41, "dramatize" most nearly means

    A) cast events in an appealing light.

    B) draw attention to significant events.

    C) exaggerate events to seem more important.

    D) turn events into a popular performance.

16. Which choice most clearly paraphrases a claim made by King in paragraph 4?

    A) A failure to negotiate in the South has provoked secret action by civil rights activists.

    B) A focus on dialogue blinds reformers to the necessity for direct action to promote change.

    C) Direct action is necessary to motivate people to talk about prejudice and racism.

    D) Nonviolent protest encourages a sense of brotherhood and understanding among citizens.

17. Paragraph 4 best supports the claims made in paragraph 3 by

    A) arguing that nonviolent pressure is most likely to spur just action by individuals.

    B) clarifying that throughout history, privileged classes have been reluctant to let go of privilege.

    C) drawing a distinction between the morality of individuals and of groups.

    D) pointing out that few gains in civil rights have been made without nonviolent pressure.

18. King refers to "the gaining of a cup of coffee at a lunch counter" (lines 89–90) primarily to

    A) call attention to the sedative effect of delaying civil rights reform in the United States.

    B) emphasize that white Americans will not willingly end oppression against black Americans.

    C) describe the progress made toward the winning of equal rights in other countries.

    D) underscore the contrast between progress made in other countries and the United States.

Questions 19–28 are based on the following passages and supplementary material.

The idea of a World Bank became a reality in 1944 when delegates to the Bretton Woods Conference pledged to "outlaw practices which are agreed to be harmful to world prosperity." Passage 1 discusses the benefits of the World Bank, while Passage 2 focuses on the limited life span of the Bretton Woods system.

Passage 1

In 1944, 730 delegates from forty-four Allied nations met in Bretton Woods, New Hampshire, just as World War II was ending. They were attending an important conference. This mostly
5 forgotten event shaped our modern world because delegates at the Bretton Woods Conference agreed on the establishment of an international banking system.

To ensure that all nations would prosper,
10 the United States and other allied nations set rules for a postwar international economy. The Bretton Woods system created the International Monetary Fund (IMF). The IMF was founded as a kind of global central bank from which member
15 countries could borrow money. The countries needed money to pay for their war costs. Today, the IMF facilitates international trade by ensuring the stability of the international monetary and financial system.
20 The Bretton Woods system also established the World Bank. Although the World Bank shares similarities with the IMF, the two institutions remain distinct. While the IMF maintains an orderly system of payments and receipts between
25 nations, the World Bank is mainly a development institution. The World Bank initially gave loans to European countries devastated by World War II, and today it lends money and technical assistance specifically to economic projects in developing
30 countries. For example, the World Bank might provide a low-interest loan to a country attempting to improve education or health. The goal of the World Bank is to "bridge the economic divide between poor and rich countries." In short, the
35 organizations differ in their purposes. The Bank

promotes economic and social progress so people can live better lives, while the IMF represents the entire world in its goal to foster global monetary cooperation and financial stability.
40 These two specific accomplishments of the Bretton Woods Conference were major. However, the Bretton Woods system particularly benefited the United States. It effectively established the U.S. dollar as a global currency. A global
45 currency is one that countries worldwide accept for all trade, or international transactions of buying and selling. Because only the U.S. could print dollars, the United States became the primary power behind both the IMF and the
50 World Bank. Today, global currencies include the U.S. dollar, the euro (European Union countries), and the yen (Japan).

The years after Bretton Woods have been considered the golden age of the U.S. dollar. More
55 importantly, the conference profoundly shaped foreign trade for decades to come.

Passage 2

The financial system established at the 1944 Bretton Woods Conference endured for many years. Even after the United States abrogated
60 agreements made at the conference, the nation continued to experience a powerful position in international trade by having other countries tie their currencies to the U.S. dollar. The world, however, is changing.
65 In reality, the Bretton Woods system lasted only three decades. Then, in 1971, President Richard Nixon introduced a new economic policy by ending the convertibility of the dollar to gold. It marked the end of the Bretton Woods
70 international monetary framework, and the action resulted in worldwide financial crisis. Two cornerstones of Bretton Woods, however, endured: the International Monetary Fund (IMF) and the World Bank.
75 Since the collapse of the Bretton Woods system, IMF members have been trading using a

GO ON TO THE NEXT PAGE ⟶

flexible exchange system. Namely, countries allow their exchange rates to fluctuate in response to changing conditions. The exchange rate between
80 two currencies, such as the Japanese yen and the U.S. dollar, for example, specifies how much one currency is worth in terms of the other. An exchange rate of 120 yen to dollars means that 120 yen are worth the same as one dollar.

85 Even so, the U.S. dollar has remained the most widely used money for international trade, and having one currency for all trade may be better than using a flexible exchange system.

This seems to be the thinking of a powerful
90 group of countries. The Group of Twenty (G20), which has called for a new Bretton Woods, consists of governments and leaders from 20 of the world's largest economies including China, the United States, and the European Union. In 2009, for
95 example, the G20 announced plans to create a new global currency to replace the U.S. dollar's role as the anchor currency. Many believe that China's yuan, quickly climbing the financial ranks, is well on its way to becoming a major world reserve
100 currency.

In fact, an earlier 1988 article in *The Economist* stated, "30 years from now, Americans, Japanese, Europeans, and people in many other rich countries and some relatively poor ones will probably be
105 paying for their shopping with the same currency."

The article predicted that the world supply of currency would be set by a new central bank of the IMF. This prediction seems to be coming to fruition since the G20 indicated that a "world currency is
110 in waiting." For an international construct such as the original Bretton Woods to last some 26 years is nothing less than amazing. But move over Bretton Woods; a new world order in finance could be on the fast track.

Top 10 International Currencies						
(Percent Shares of Average Daily Currency Trading)						
	2007		**2010**		**2013**	
	Share	*Rank*	*Share*	*Rank*	*Share*	*Rank*
U.S. Dollar (USD)	85.6%	1	84.9%	1	87.0%	1
Euro (EUR)	37.0%	2	39.1%	2	33.4%	2
Japanese Yen (JPY)	17.2%	3	19.0%	3	23.0%	3
UK Pound (GBP)	14.9%	4	12.9%	4	11.8%	4
Australian Dollar (AUD)	6.6%	6	7.6%	5	8.6%	5
Swiss Franc (CHF)	6.8%	5	6.3%	6	5.2%	6
Canadian Dollar (CAD)	4.3%	7	5.3%	7	4.6%	7
Mexican Peso (MXN)	1.3%	12	1.3%	14	2.5%	8
Chinese Yuan (CNY)	0.5%	20	0.9%	17	2.2%	9
New Zealand Dollar	1.9%	11	1.6%	10	2.0%	10

Adapted from Mauldin Economics; Bank for International Settlements, September 2013 Triennial Central Bank Survey.

19. Based on Passage 1, it can reasonably be inferred that

    A) world leaders recognized the need for markets to function independently.

    B) Bretton Woods increased U.S. economic influence around the world.

    C) the IMF and the World Bank work closely together to ensure prosperity.

    D) the conclusion of World War II had little influence on events at Bretton Woods.

20. Which choice provides the best evidence for the answer to the previous question?

    A) Lines 9–11 ("To ensure . . . economy")

    B) Lines 11–13 ("The Bretton . . . Fund")

    C) Lines 47–50 ("Because only . . . World Bank")

    D) Lines 54–56 ("More importantly . . . to come")

21. As used in line 38, "foster" most nearly means

    A) publicize.

    B) rear.

    C) stabilize.

    D) encourage.

22. Which statement best explains the difference between the purposes of the IMF and the World Bank?

    A) The IMF provides money to pay for war costs, while the World Bank offers assistance to rebuild countries recovering from war across the globe.

    B) The IMF encourages stability in the global financial system, while the World Bank promotes economic development in relatively poor nations.

    C) The IMF supports the U.S. dollar in international markets, while the World Bank provides low-interest loans to many nations around the world.

    D) The IMF offers governments advice about participation in global markets, while the World Bank encourages monetary cooperation between nations.

23. Based on the second paragraph in Passage 2, it can be reasonably inferred that

    A) the United States did not support the goals of the IMF and the World Bank.

    B) Bretton Woods was originally intended to last for three decades.

    C) President Nixon acted to reinforce the decisions made at Bretton Woods.

    D) some U.S. policy decisions differed from international consensus over Bretton Woods.

24. Which choice provides the best evidence for the answer to the previous question?

    A) Lines 65–66 ("In reality . . . three decades")

    B) Lines 66–69 ("Then, in 1971 . . . to gold")

    C) Lines 71–74 ("Two cornerstones . . . World Bank")

    D) Lines 75–77 ("Since the collapse . . . exchange system")

25. As used in line 97, "anchor" most nearly means

    A) key.

    B) fastening.

    C) rigid.

    D) supporting.

26. It can reasonably be inferred from both Passage 2 and the graphic that

    A) international markets are increasingly comfortable using the yuan as trade currency.

    B) the United States favors using the yuan as one of the world's reserve currencies.

    C) the G20 wants to replace the yuan and other currencies with a new global currency.

    D) the IMF continues to support the yuan and other currencies in a flexible exchange system.

27. Which statement most effectively compares the authors' purposes in both passages?

A) Passage 1's purpose is to contrast the functions of the IMF and World Bank, while Passage 2's purpose is to outline the benefits of a flexible trade system to the United States.

B) Passage 1's purpose is to describe the history of international trade in the 20th century, while Passage 2's purpose is to explain why the Bretton Woods system collapsed.

C) Passage 1's purpose is to describe Bretton Woods's effect on the global economy, while Passage 2's purpose is to suggest that a new currency for global trade may soon be implemented.

D) Passage 1's purpose is to promote the economic benefits of the IMF and World Bank, while Passage 2's purpose is to encourage the reestablishment of the Bretton Woods system.

28. Both passages support which generalization about the global economy?

A) U.S. influence on global trade has continued under a flexible exchange system.

B) The purposes of the International Monetary Fund and the World Bank are indirectly related.

C) The Group of Twenty represents the financial interests of the world's largest economies.

D) International institutions such as the IMF continue to influence economic trade and development.

Questions 29–38 are based on the following passage.

This passage is adapted from an article about treating paralysis.

According to a study conducted by the Christopher and Dana Reeve Foundation, more than six million people in the United States suffer from debilitating paralysis. That's close to
5 one person in every fifty who suffers from a loss of the ability to move or feel in areas of his or her body. Paralysis is often caused by illnesses, such as stroke or multiple sclerosis, or injuries to the spinal cord. Research scientists have made
10 advances in the treatment of paralysis, which means retraining affected individuals to become as independent as possible. Patients learn how to use wheelchairs and prevent complications that are caused by restricted movement. This
15 retraining is key in maintaining paralytics' quality of life; however, an actual cure for paralysis has remained elusive—until now.

In 2014, surgeons in Poland collaborated with the University College London's Institute of Neurology
20 to treat a Polish man who was paralyzed from the chest down as a result of a spinal cord injury. The scientists chose this patient for their study because of the countless hours of physical therapy he had undergone with no signs of progress. Twenty-one
25 months after their test subject's initial spinal cord injury, his condition was considered complete as defined by the American Spinal Injury Association (ASIA)'s Impairment Scale. This meant that he experienced no sensory or motor function in the
30 segments of his spinal cord nearest to his injury.

The doctors used a technique refined during forty years of spinal cord research on rats. They removed one of two of the patient's olfactory bulbs, which are structures found at the top of the human
35 nose. From this structure, samples of olfactory ensheathing cells, responsible for a portion of the sense of smell, were harvested. These cells allow the olfactory system to renew its cells over the course of a human life. It is because of this constant

40 regeneration that scientists chose these particular
cells to implant into the patient's spinal cord.
After being harvested, the cells were reproduced
in a culture. Then, the cells were injected into the
patient's spinal cord in 100 mini-injections above
45 and below the location of his injury. Four strips of
nerve tissue were then placed across a small gap in
the spinal cord.

      After surgery, the patient underwent a
tailormade neurorehabilitation program. In the
50 nineteen months following the operation, not only
did the patient experience no adverse effects, but
his condition improved from ASIA's class A to class
C. Class C is considered an incomplete spinal cord
injury, meaning that motor function is preserved to
55 a certain extent and there is some muscle activity.
The patient experienced increased stability in the
trunk of his body, as well as partial recovery of
voluntary movements in his lower extremities. As
a result, he was able to increase the muscle mass in
60 his thighs and regain sensation in those areas. In
late 2014, he took his first steps with the support of
only a walker.

      These exciting improvements suggest that the
nerve grafts doctors placed in the patient's spinal
65 cord bridged the injured area and prompted the
regeneration of fibers. This was the first-ever
clinical study that showed beneficial effects of cells
transplanted into the spinal cord. The same team
of scientists plans to treat ten more patients using
70 this "smell cell" transplant technique. If they have
continued success, patients around the world can
have both their mobility and their hope restored.

29. The passage is primarily concerned with

A) how various diseases and injuries can cause permanent paralysis.

B) ways in which doctors and therapists work to improve patients' quality of life.

C) one treatment being developed to return mobility to patients suffering paralysis.

D) methods of physical therapy that can help patients with spinal cord injuries.

30. Based on the information in the passage, it can be inferred that the author

A) believes more research should be done before patients with paralysis are subjected to the treatment described in the passage.

B) feels that increased mobility will have a positive impact on patients suffering from all levels of paralysis.

C) thinks that more scientists should study paralysis and ways to improve the quality of life for patients with limited mobility.

D) was part of the research team that developed the new method of treating paralysis described in the passage.

31. Which choice provides the best support for the answer to the previous question?

A) Lines 7–9 ("Paralysis is . . . spinal cord")

B) Lines 18–21 ("In 2014 . . . injury")

C) Lines 56–58 ("The patient . . . extremities")

D) Lines 70–72 ("If they . . . restored")

GO ON TO THE NEXT PAGE ⟹

32. As used in line 14, "restricted" most nearly means

    A) confidential.

    B) dependent.

    C) increased.

    D) limited.

33. In line 49, the author's use of the word "tailor-made" helps reinforce the idea that

    A) the injected cells were from the patient and were therefore well-suited to work in his own body.

    B) spinal cord cells were replaced during the transplant portion of the individualized treatment.

    C) olfactory bulbs were removed from rats and placed in the patient's spinal cord during surgery.

    D) the method used by doctors to locate the damaged area required expertise and precision.

34. It reasonably can be inferred from the passage that

    A) the patient's treatment would have been more successful if scientists had used cells from another area of his body instead of from his olfactory bulbs.

    B) cells from olfactory bulbs will be used to cure diseases that affect areas of the body other than the spinal cord.

    C) the patient who received the experimental treatment using cells from olfactory bulbs would not have regained mobility without this treatment.

    D) soon doctors will be able to treat spinal injuries without time-consuming and demanding physical therapy.

35. Which choice provides the best evidence for the answer to the previous question?

    A) Lines 9–12 ("Research scientists . . . possible")

    B) Lines 21–24 ("The scientists . . . progress")

    C) Lines 32–35 ("They removed . . . nose")

    D) Lines 63–66 ("These exciting . . . fibers")

36. As used in line 31, "refined" most nearly means

    A) advanced.

    B) improved.

    C) experienced.

    D) treated.

37. The success of the patient's treatment was due in large part to

    A) studies done on other patients.

    B) research conducted by other doctors in Poland.

    C) many experiments performed on rats.

    D) multiple attempts on various types of animals.

38. The procedure described in which cells from olfactory bulbs are injected into a damaged area of the spinal cord is most analogous to which of the following?

    A) Replacing a diseased organ in a patient with an organ from a donor who has the same tissue type

    B) Giving a patient with a high fever an injection of medication to bring the core body temperature down

    C) Placing a cast on a limb to hold the bone in place to encourage healing after suffering a break

    D) Grafting skin from a healthy area of the body and transplanting it to an area that has suffered severe burns

Practice Tests

Questions 39–47 are based on the following passage and supplementary material.

The following passage is adapted from an essay about mercury in fish.

Mercury is an unusual element; it is a metal but is liquid at room temperature. It is also a neurotoxin and a teratogen, as it causes nerve damage and birth defects. Mercury can be found just about
5 everywhere; it is in soil, in air, in household items, and even in our food. Everyday objects, such as thermometers, light switches, and fluorescent light bulbs, contain mercury in its elemental form. Batteries can also contain mercury, but they
10 contain it in the form of the inorganic compound mercury chloride. Mercury can also exist as an organic compound, the most common of which is methylmercury. While we can take steps to avoid both elemental and inorganic mercury, it is much
15 harder to avoid methylmercury.

Most of the mercury in the environment comes from the emissions of coal-burning power plants; coal contains small amounts of mercury, which are released into the air when coal burns.
20 The concentration of mercury in the air from power plants is very low, so it is not immediately dangerous. However, the mercury is then washed out of the air by rainstorms and eventually ends up in lakes and oceans.

25 The mercury deposited in the water does not instantaneously get absorbed by fish, as elemental mercury does not easily diffuse through cell membranes. However, methylmercury diffuses into cells easily, and certain anaerobic bacteria
30 in the water convert the elemental mercury to methylmercury as a byproduct of their metabolic processes. Methylmercury released into the water by the bacteria diffuses into small single-celled organisms called plankton. Small shrimp and other
35 small animals eat the plankton and absorb the methylmercury in the plankton during digestion. Small fish eat the shrimp and then larger fish eat the smaller fish; each time an animal preys on another animal, the predator absorbs the
40 methylmercury. Because each animal excretes the methylmercury much more slowly than it absorbs it, methylmercury builds up in the animal over

time and is passed on to whatever animal eats it, resulting in a process called bioaccumulation.

45 As people became aware of the bioaccumulation of mercury in fish, many reacted by eliminating seafood from their diet. However, seafood contains certain omega-3 fatty acids that are important for good health. People who do not eat enough
50 of these fatty acids, especially eicosapentaenoic acid (EPA) and docosahexaenoic acid (DHA), are more likely to have heart attacks than people who have enough EPA and DHA in their diet. Because fish and shellfish, along with some algae, are the
55 only sources of these fatty acids, eliminating them from our diet might have worse health effects than consuming small amounts of mercury.

Scientists have studied the effects of mercury by conducting tests on animals and by studying
60 various human populations and recording the amount of mercury in their blood. By determining the levels of mercury consumption that cause any of the known symptoms of mercury poisoning, they were able to identify a safe level of mercury
65 consumption. The current recommendation is for humans to take in less than 0.1 microgram of mercury for every kilogram of weight per day. This means that a 70-kilogram person (about 155 pounds) could safely consume 7 micrograms of
70 mercury per day. Because haddock averages about 0.055 micrograms of mercury per gram, that person could safely eat 127 grams (about 4.5 ounces) of haddock per day. On the other hand, swordfish averages about 0.995 micrograms of mercury per
75 gram of fish, so the 70-kilogram person could safely eat only about 7 grams (about one-quarter of an ounce) of swordfish per day.

Nutritionists recommend that, rather than eliminate fish from our diet, we try to eat more of
80 the low-mercury fish and less of the high-mercury fish. Low-mercury species tend to be smaller omnivorous fish while high-mercury species tend to be the largest carnivorous fish. Awareness of the particulars of this problem, accompanied by
85 mindful eating habits, will keep us on the best course for healthy eating.

GO ON TO THE NEXT PAGE

Species	Average Weight Range (grams)	Average Mercury Concentration (parts per billion)
Alaskan Pollock	227–1,000	31
Atlantic Haddock	900–1,800	55
Atlantic Herring	100–600	84
Chub Mackerel	100–750	88
Cod	800–4,000	111
Skipjack Tuna	2,000–10,000	144
Black-Striped Bass	6,820–15,900	152
Albacore Tuna	4,540–21,364	358
Marlin	180,000	485

39. The author of the passage would most likely agree with which of the following statements?

A) Mercury poisoning is only one of many concerns that should be considered when choosing which fish to add to one's diet.

B) More should be done by scientists and nutritionists to inform people about the dangers of mercury poisoning.

C) Fish is an essential part of a healthy diet and can be eaten safely if recommendations for mercury consumption are kept in mind.

D) The mercury present in the air is more dangerous to people than the mercury consumed by eating fish with high mercury levels.

40. Which choice provides the best evidence for the answer to the previous question?

A) Lines 16–18 ("Most of . . . plants")

B) Lines 32–34 ("Methylmercury released . . . plankton")

C) Lines 58–61 ("Scientists . . . their blood")

D) Lines 83–86 ("Awareness . . . eating")

41. In addition to the levels of mercury in a specific species of fish, people should also consider which of the following when determining a safe level of consumption?

A) Their own body weight

B) Where the fish was caught

C) The other meats they are eating

D) What they ate the day before

42. As used in line 20, "concentration" most nearly means

A) focus.

B) application.

C) density.

D) awareness.

43. The passage most strongly suggests which of the following statements is accurate?

A) It is not possible to completely avoid environmental exposure to mercury.

B) Inorganic mercury is more dangerous to humans than organic mercury.

C) Most of the exposure to mercury experienced by humans comes from fish consumption.

D) Mercury is one of the most abundant elements found in nature.

44. Which choice provides the best evidence for the answer to the previous question?

A) Lines 1–2 ("Mercury is an unusual . . . temperature")

B) Lines 4–6 ("Mercury . . . our food")

C) Lines 20–22 ("The concentration . . . dangerous")

D) Lines 28–32 ("However, methylmercury . . . processes")

GO ON TO THE NEXT PAGE

45. Which of the following pieces of evidence would most strengthen the author's line of reasoning?

   A) More examples in paragraph 1 of places mercury is found

   B) Details in paragraph 2 about the levels of mercury found in the air

   C) An explanation in paragraph 4 of how to treat mercury poisoning

   D) More examples in paragraph 5 of how many micrograms of mercury people of different weights could eat

46. As used in line 84, "particulars" most nearly means

   A) data.

   B) specifics.

   C) points.

   D) evidence.

47. Based on the information in the passage and the graphic, which of the following statements is true?

   A) The fish with the lowest average weight is the safest to eat.

   B) A person can safely eat more marlin than albacore tuna in one day.

   C) Eating large fish carries a lower risk of mercury poisoning than eating small fish.

   D) A person can safely eat more Alaskan pollock than black-striped bass in one day.

IF YOU FINISH BEFORE TIME IS CALLED, YOU MAY CHECK YOUR WORK ON THIS SECTION ONLY.
DO NOT TURN TO ANY OTHER SECTION IN THE TEST.   STOP

Writing and Language Test

35 Minutes—44 Questions

This section corresponds to Section 2 of your answer sheet.

Directions: Each passage in this section is followed by several questions. Some questions will reference an underlined portion in the passage; others will ask you to consider a part of a passage or the passage as a whole. For each question, choose the answer that reflects the best use of grammar, punctuation, and style. If a passage or question is accompanied by a graphic, take the graphic into account in choosing your response(s). Some questions will have "NO CHANGE" as a possible response. Choose that answer if you think the best choice is to leave the sentence as written.

Questions 1–11 are based on the following passage and supplementary material.

The UN: Promoting World Peace

The United Nations (UN) is perhaps the most important political contribution of the 20th century. Some may argue that the work of the UN **1** ; an international peacekeeping organization—has proven futile, given persisting global conflict. But the UN's worldwide influence demands a closer look. This organization's global impact is undeniable. The UN is a strong political organization determined to create opportunities for its member nations to enjoy a peaceful and productive world. **2**

1. A) NO CHANGE
   B) —an international peacekeeping organization;
   C) —an international peacekeeping organization—
   D) ; an international peacekeeping organization,

2. Which choice would most clearly end the paragraph with a restatement of the author's claim?
   A) The UN is an organization dedicated to advancing social and political justice around the world.
   B) Those who argue otherwise are not well educated about geopolitical issues in the 20th century or today.
   C) The UN has had its share of corruption over the years, but it has a well-earned reputation of effectively settling international disputes.
   D) A better understanding of the UN suggests that the UN enables far greater peace in today's world than could have been possible otherwise.

3 Decades ago, provoked by the events of World Wars I and II, world leaders began imagining a politically neutral force for international peace. The UN was born in 1945 with 51 participating nations. It was to be a collective political authority for global peace and security. Today, 193 nations are UN members. **4** In keeping with the original hope, the UN still strives toward peaceful international relations.

Understandably, no single organization can perfectly solve the world's countless, complex problems. But the UN has offered consistent relief for many of the past half-century's most difficult disasters and conflicts. It also provides a safe space for international conversation. Moreover, it advocates for issues such as justice, trade, hunger relief, human rights, health, and gender **5** equality, the UN also coordinates care for those displaced by disaster and conflict, **6** dictates environmental protection, and works toward conflict reconciliation.

3. A) NO CHANGE
   B) Recently,
   C) Consequently,
   D) In other words,

4. A) NO CHANGE
   B) In having kept with the original hope, the UN still strives toward peaceful international relations.
   C) In keeping with the original hope, the UN still strived toward peaceful international relations.
   D) In keeping with the original hope, the UN still strove toward peaceful international relations.

5. A) NO CHANGE
   B) equality. The UN
   C) equality: the UN
   D) equality, The UN

6. A) NO CHANGE
   B) prefers
   C) promotes
   D) celebrates

GO ON TO THE NEXT PAGE

[7] The UN's budget, goals, and personnel count have significantly expanded with time to meet more needs. **[8]** The year 2014 witnessed the UN peacekeeping force grow to over 100,000 strong. These uniformed, volunteer, civilian personnel represent 128 nations. The UN's budget has also grown over the years to support an international court system, as well as countless agencies, committees, and centers addressing sociopolitical topics. Today's UN undertakes important work, and it functions with remarkable organization and efficiency. Critics highlight shortcomings to discount the UN's effectiveness. But considering the countless disasters to which the UN has responded over its six decades of existence, today's world might enjoy **[9]** far less peace, freedom, and safety without the UN.

7. Which choice provides the most logical introduction to the paragraph?

A) NO CHANGE

B) The UN has developed over the years, but critics charge it has met with limited success.

C) The responsibilities of the UN have expanded in recent years in response to challenging events.

D) The UN has maintained a quiet but effective voice on the world stage in spite of criticism.

8. Which choice best completes the sentence with accurate data based on the graphic?

A) NO CHANGE

B) The year 2010 led to an increase of approximately 100,000 in the UN peacekeeping force.

C) The year 2010 saw the UN peacekeeping force grow to approximately 100,000 strong.

D) The year 2010 saw the UN peacekeeping force decrease to just over 100,000 strong.

9. A) NO CHANGE

B) considerably less peace, less freedom, and less safety

C) much less peace, less freedom, and less safety

D) significantly less peace and freedom, and less safety

[1] From promoting overarching sociopolitical change to offering food and care for displaced groups, the UN serves to protect human rights. [2] Equally 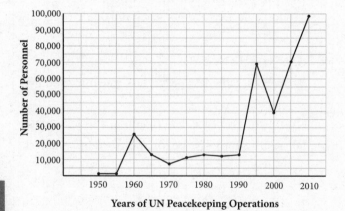10 quotable are its initiatives to foster international collaboration, justice, and peace. [3] The UN provided aid to the Philippines after the disastrous 2013 typhoon. [4] Certainly, this work is not finished. [5] But no other organization's scope of work compares with the influence of the UN. [6] This brave endeavor to insist on and strive for peace, whatever the obstacles, has indeed united hundreds of once-divided nations. [7] Today, with eleven Nobel Peace Prizes to its name, the UN is undoubtedly an irreplaceable and profoundly successful force for peace. 11

UN Peacekeeping Personnel Numbers Since 1950

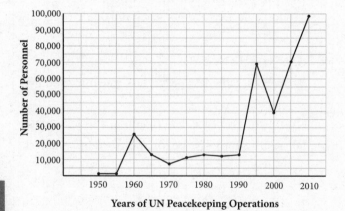

Years of UN Peacekeeping Operations

10. A) NO CHANGE
    B) luminous
    C) noteworthy
    D) repeatable

11. Which sentence should be removed to improve the focus of the concluding paragraph?

    A) Sentence 1
    B) Sentence 3
    C) Sentence 5
    D) Sentence 6

GO ON TO THE NEXT PAGE

Questions 12–22 are based on the following passage.

DNA Analysis in a Day

Jane Saunders, a forensic DNA specialist, arrives at work and finds a request waiting for her: She needs to determine if the DNA of a fingernail with a few skin cells on it [12] match any records in the criminal database.

"Human DNA is a long, double-stranded [13] molecule; each strand consists of a complementary set of nucleotides," she explains. "DNA has four nucleotides: [14] adenine (A), thymine (T), guanine (G), and, cytosine (C). On each strand is a sequence of nucleotides that 'match,' or pair up with the nucleotides on the other, or complementary, strand. [15] On the other hand, when there is an adenine on one strand, there is a thymine on the complementary strand, and where there is guanine on one strand, there is cytosine on the complementary strand."

She begins by [16] moving the DNA from the rest of the sample, transferring it to a [17] reaction tube. She adds a solution of primers, DNA polymerase, and nucleotides. Her goal is to separate the two strands of the DNA molecules and then make complementary copies of each strand.

12. A) NO CHANGE
    B) matches
    C) has matched
    D) will be matching

13. A) NO CHANGE
    B) molecule, each strand consists
    C) molecule each strand consists
    D) molecule but each strand consists

14. A) NO CHANGE
    B) adenine (A), thymine (T), guanine (G), and cytosine (C).
    C) adenine (A), thymine (T) guanine (G) and cytosine (C).
    D) adenine (A) thymine (T), guanine (G) and cytosine (C).

15. A) NO CHANGE
    B) Specifically,
    C) However,
    D) Similarly,

16. A) NO CHANGE
    B) reviewing
    C) changing
    D) detaching

17. Which choice most effectively combines the sentences at the underlined portion?
    A) reaction tube since she adds
    B) reaction tube, however, she adds
    C) reaction tube, and adding
    D) reaction tube, she adds

[18] The process of testing the DNA includes several steps and many changes in temperature. After mixing the primers, DNA polymerase, and nucleotides with the evidence DNA, Saunders closes the reaction tube and puts it in a thermocycler. It is programmed to raise the temperature to 94°C to separate the double strands into single strands, and then lower the temperature to 59°C to attach the primers to the single strands. Finally, it raises the temperature to 72°C for the DNA polymerase to build the complementary strands. The thermocycler holds each temperature for one minute and repeats the cycle of three temperatures for at least 30 cycles. At the end of each cycle, the number of DNA segments containing the sequence marked by the primers doubles. If the original sample contains only 100 DNA strands, [19] the absolute final sample will have billions of segments.

[1] After a short lunch break, Saunders needs to separate and identify the copied DNA segments. [2] She had used primers that bind to 13 specific sites in human DNA called short tandem repeats, or STRs. [3] The 13 STRs are segments of four nucleotides that repeat, such as GATAGATAGATA. [4] "Now here's where the real magic happens!" Saunders says excitedly. [5] "Most DNA is identical for all humans. [6] But STRs vary greatly. [7] The chances of any two humans—other than identical twins—having the same set of 13 STRs is less than one in one trillion." [20]

18. Which sentence most effectively establishes the central idea?

A) NO CHANGE

B) The object of testing the DNA is to re-create many strands of the DNA in question.

C) Saunders uses a variety of machines in order to analyze the DNA.

D) Saunders would be unable to identify the DNA without the thermocycler.

19. A) NO CHANGE

B) absolutely the final sample

C) the final sample

D) the most final sample

20. Where should sentence 1 be placed to make the paragraph feel cohesive?

A) Where it is now

B) After sentence 2

C) After sentence 3

D) After sentence 4

Saunders knows that the detectives will be [21] prepared to hear her findings, so she sits down at her desk to compare her results with the criminal database in the hopes of finding a match. [22] Is it possible that too much time is spent identifying DNA in cases that are relatively easy to solve?

21. A) NO CHANGE
     B) eager
     C) impatient
     D) conditioned

22. At this point, the writer wants to add a conclusion that best reflects Jane's feelings conveyed in the passage. Which choice accomplishes that?

     A) NO CHANGE
     B) It takes a good deal of work and expense to identify DNA in the world of modern forensics.
     C) She takes pride in the fact that her scientific expertise plays such a key role in bringing criminals to justice.
     D) She marvels at how far science has come in DNA analysis.

GO ON TO THE NEXT PAGE

Questions 23–33 are based on the following passage.

Will Your Start-Up Succeed?

According to research from Harvard Business School, the majority of small businesses [23] fail in fact the success rate for a first-time company owner is a meager 18 percent. With odds so dismal, why would anyone become a business entrepreneur?

[24] Veteran entrepreneurs achieve a higher 30 percent success rate, so the most predictive factor for success appears to be the number of innovations that a person has "pushed out." More specifically, the people who succeed at building a robust start-up are the ones who have previously tried. Finally, many entrepreneurs [25] grab the idea for their business by solving practical problems, and it's more than luck; 320 new entrepreneurs out of 100,000 *do* succeed by starting a company at the right time in the right industry.

Mitch Gomez is evidence of this data. He [26] did graduate from college with a degree in accounting. "I quickly realized that I have too big of a personality to be content practicing accounting," he laughs. He first built a successful insurance claims [27] service, and next founded his own independent insurance agency. "I continually employ my accounting skills, but I've ascertained that I'm an even more effective salesperson."

23. A) NO CHANGE
    B) fail, in fact,
    C) fail; in fact,
    D) fail: in fact

24. Which sentence most effectively establishes the central idea?

    A) NO CHANGE
    B) The Small Business Administration defines a small business as one with fewer than 500 employees and less than $7 million in sales annually.
    C) Many small businesses fail because company founders are not realistic about the amount of time it takes for a company to become profitable.
    D) Running a small business can take up a lot more time than punching a clock for someone else and might not be enjoyable for everyone.

25. A) NO CHANGE
    B) derive
    C) achieve
    D) grasp

26. A) NO CHANGE
    B) has graduated
    C) graduated
    D) would have graduated

27. A) NO CHANGE
    B) service. And next
    C) service and next
    D) service; and next

GO ON TO THE NEXT PAGE ⟹

Similarly, Barbara Vital, the woman behind Vital Studio, explains, "I love spending as much time with my family as possible." Vital saw an opportunity to [28] launch a monogramming business when her two young sons started school, so she founded a company that offers monogrammed backpacks and water bottles for kids, as well as [29] totes, rain boots; and baseball caps for college students. What is the secret to Vital's success? "I'm always learning how to incorporate social media and add functionality to my product website to keep customers happy," she says.

Finally, Chris Roth is an entrepreneur who can step out of his comfort zone. Always seeking a new [30] challenge his company designed and manufactured technology to keep the nozzles of water misting systems clean. Roth has also established a corporate travel agency and a truck customization company, most recently claiming he has become an innovator who beat the odds by "striving to serve customers better than my competition." [31] Large companies often employ corporate travel agencies to arrange travel for their employees and clients.

Gomez, Vital, and Roth [32] agrees that although being an entrepreneur can be a formidable challenge, exceptionally skillful entrepreneurs have important strategies for success, including stretching [33] his personal boundaries and recovering from failures. "And nothing beats being your own boss," adds Gomez.

28. A) NO CHANGE
    B) present
    C) propel
    D) impact

29. A) NO CHANGE
    B) totes; rain boots; and
    C) totes, rain boots, and,
    D) totes, rain boots, and

30. A) NO CHANGE
    B) challenge: his company
    C) challenge; his company
    D) challenge, his company

31. Which sentence would best support the central idea?
    A) NO CHANGE
    B) Savvy entrepreneurs know which risks are worth taking and which risks can tank their business before their doors open.
    C) Now Roth's small business installs water misters on restaurant patios and even sets up misting stations at outdoor music festivals.
    D) Many new small businesses fail because company founders fail to do market research and identify the needs of their community.

32. A) NO CHANGE
    B) agree
    C) should agree
    D) had agreed

33. A) NO CHANGE
    B) their
    C) our
    D) her

Questions 34–44 are based on the following passage and supplementary material.

Edgard Varèse's Influence

Today's music, from rock to jazz, has many [34] influences. And perhaps none is as unique as the ideas from French composer Edgard Varèse. Called "the father of electronic music," he approached compositions from a different theoretical perspective than classical composers such as Bartók and Debussy. He called his [35] works "organized sound"; they did not [36] endear melodies but waged assaults of percussion, piano, and human voices. He thought of sounds as having intelligence and treated music spatially, as "sound objects floating in space."

His unique vision can be credited to his education in science. Born in 1883 in France, Varèse was raised by a great-uncle and grandfather in the Burgundy region. He was interested in classical music and composed his first opera as a teenager. While the family lived [37] in Italy he studied engineering in Turin, where he learned math and science and was inspired by the work of the artist Leonardo da Vinci.

In 1903, he returned to France to study music at the Paris Conservatory. There, he composed the radical percussion performance piece *Ionisation*, which featured cymbals, snares, bass drum, xylophone, and sirens wailing. Later compositions were scored for the theremin, a new electronic instrument controlled by [38] the player's hands waving over its antennae, which sense their position. No composer had ever scored music for the theremin before.

34. A) NO CHANGE
    B) influences, and perhaps none is as
    C) influences, but perhaps none is as
    D) influences. Or perhaps none is as

35. A) NO CHANGE
    B) works "organized sound": They
    C) works "organized sound," they
    D) works—"organized sound"—they

36. A) NO CHANGE
    B) amplify
    C) deprive
    D) employ

37. A) NO CHANGE
    B) in Italy, he studied engineering in Turin, where he
    C) in Italy he studied engineering in Turin where he
    D) in Italy, he studied engineering in Turin; where he

38. A) NO CHANGE
    B) the players' hands
    C) the players hands
    D) the player's hands'

GO ON TO THE NEXT PAGE ⇨

In his thirties, Varèse moved to New York City, where he played piano in a café and conducted other composers' works until his own compositions gained success. His piece *Amériques* was performed in Philadelphia in 1926. Varèse went on to travel to the western United States, where he recorded, lectured, and collaborated with other musicians. By the 1950s, he was using tape recordings in **39** contention with symphonic performance. His piece *Déserts* was aired on a radio program amid selections by Mozart and Tchaikovsky but was received by listeners with hostility. **40**

Varèse's ideas were more forward-thinking than could be realized. One of his most ambitious scores, called *Espace*, was a choral symphony with multilingual lyrics, which was to be sung simultaneously by choirs in Paris, Moscow, Peking, and New York. He wanted the timing to be orchestrated by radio, but radio technology did not support worldwide transmission. If only Varèse **41** had had the Internet!

Although many of **42** their written compositions were lost in a fire in 1918, many modern musicians and composers have been influenced by Varèse, including Frank Zappa, John Luther Adams, and John Cage, who

39. A) NO CHANGE
    B) conjunction
    C) appropriation
    D) supplication

40. If added to the paragraph, which fact would best support the author's claims?
    A) The critical response to his 1926 performance in Philadelphia
    B) The selections by Mozart and Tchaikovsky that were played on the radio
    C) Which specific states he traveled to in the western United States
    D) The cities in which the radio program was aired

41. A) NO CHANGE
    B) would have had
    C) would have
    D) have had

42. A) NO CHANGE
    B) its
    C) our
    D) his

wrote that Varèse is "more relevant to present musical necessity than even the Viennese masters." **43** Despite being less famous than Stravinsky or Shostakovich, his impact is undeniable. **44** Varèse's love of science and mathematics is shown in his later compositions, but less so in his early works.

Composer	Number of Surviving Works
Edgard Varèse	14
Benjamin Britten	84
Charles Ives	106
Igor Stravinsky	129
Arnold Schoenberg	290
Dmitri Shostakovich	320

43. Which choice most accurately and effectively represents the information in the graph?

A) NO CHANGE

B) Despite having fewer surviving works than his contemporaries, his impact is undeniable.

C) Even though he wrote pieces using a wider range of instruments than other composers, his impact is undeniable.

D) Even though far fewer of his works are now performed compared with those of his contemporaries, his impact is undeniable.

44. Which sentence best summarizes the central idea?

A) NO CHANGE

B) In contrast with his newfound popularity, Varèse's early works have long been ignored due to increasing critical hostility.

C) Varèse and his innovative compositions became an inspiration for artists seeking to challenge traditional musical beliefs.

D) Though Varèse's contemporary critics failed to call him a "Viennese master," this distinction is changing.

IF YOU FINISH BEFORE TIME IS CALLED, YOU MAY CHECK YOUR WORK ON THIS SECTION ONLY. DO NOT TURN TO ANY OTHER SECTION IN THE TEST.   **STOP**

Math Test

25 Minutes—17 Questions

NO-CALCULATOR SECTION

This section corresponds to Section 3 of your answer sheet.

Directions: For this section, solve each problem and decide which is the best of the choices given. Fill in the corresponding oval on the answer sheet. You may use any available space for scratch work.

Notes:

1. Calculator use is NOT permitted.
2. All numbers used are real numbers, and all variables used represent real numbers, unless otherwise indicated.
3. Figures are drawn to scale and lie in a plane unless otherwise indicated.
4. Unless stated otherwise, the domain of any function f is assumed to be the set of all real numbers x for which $f(x)$ is a real number.

Information:

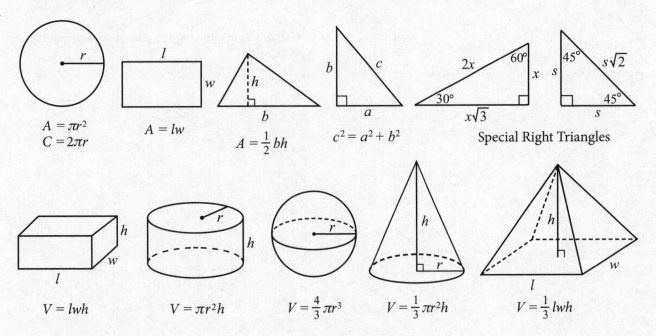

$$A = \pi r^2$$
$$C = 2\pi r$$

$$A = lw$$

$$A = \tfrac{1}{2} bh$$

$$c^2 = a^2 + b^2$$

Special Right Triangles

$$V = lwh$$

$$V = \pi r^2 h$$

$$V = \tfrac{4}{3}\pi r^3$$

$$V = \tfrac{1}{3}\pi r^2 h$$

$$V = \tfrac{1}{3} lwh$$

The sum of the degree measures of the angles in a triangle is 180.

The number of degrees of arc in a circle is 360.

The number of radians of arc in a circle is 2π.

$$\frac{4(n-2)+5}{2}=\frac{13-(9+4n)}{4}$$

1. In the equation above, what is the value of n?

A) $\frac{5}{6}$

B) $\frac{5}{2}$

C) There is no value of n that satisfies the equation.

D) There are infinitely many values of n that satisfy the equation.

$$\frac{18x^3+9x^2-36x}{9x^2}$$

2. Which of the following is equivalent to the expression above?

A) $2x-\frac{4}{x}$

B) $18x^3-36x$

C) $2x+1-\frac{4}{x}$

D) $18x^3-36x+1$

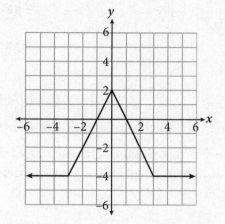

3. The figure above shows the graph of $f(x)$. For which value(s) of x does $f(x)$ equal 0?

A) -3 and 3

B) -1 and 1

C) -1, 1, and 2

D) 2 only

4. Which of the following systems of inequalities has no solution?

A) $\begin{cases} y \geq x \\ y \leq 2x \end{cases}$

B) $\begin{cases} y \geq x \\ y \leq -x \end{cases}$

C) $\begin{cases} y \geq x+1 \\ y \leq x-1 \end{cases}$

D) $\begin{cases} y \geq -x+1 \\ y \leq x-1 \end{cases}$

GO ON TO THE NEXT PAGE

5. At what value(s) of x do the graphs of $y = -2x + 1$ and $y = 2x^2 + 5x + 4$ intersect?

A) -8 and $\frac{1}{2}$

B) -3 and $-\frac{1}{2}$

C) -3 and 3

D) $-\frac{1}{2}$ and 3

6. If line P shown in the graph above is reflected over the x-axis and shifted up 3 units, what is the new y-intercept?

A) $(0, -4)$

B) $(0, -2)$

C) $(0, 2)$

D) $(0, 4)$

7. Which of the following are roots of the equation $3x^2 - 6x - 5 = 0$?

A) $1 \pm 2\sqrt{6}$

B) $\dfrac{1 \pm 2\sqrt{2}}{3}$

C) $\dfrac{3 \pm 2\sqrt{2}}{3}$

D) $\dfrac{3 \pm 2\sqrt{6}}{3}$

8. If $m = \dfrac{1}{n^{-\frac{1}{4}}}$, where both $m > 0$ and $n > 0$, which of the following gives n in terms of m?

A) $n = m^4$

B) $n = \dfrac{1}{m^4}$

C) $n = \dfrac{1}{\sqrt[4]{m}}$

D) $n = m^{\frac{1}{4}}$

$$\begin{cases} y = 3x - 1 \\ y = \dfrac{5x + 8}{2} \end{cases}$$

9. If (x, y) represents the solution to the system of equations shown above, what is the value of y?

A) 10

B) 19

C) 29

D) 31

10. If $0 < \dfrac{d}{2} + 1 \leq \dfrac{8}{5}$, which of the following is not a possible value of d?

A) -2

B) $-\dfrac{6}{5}$

C) 0

D) $\dfrac{6}{5}$

11. A business's "break-even point" is the point at which revenue (sales) equals expenses. When a company breaks even, no profit is being made, but the company is not losing any money either. Suppose a manufacturer buys materials for producing a particular item at a cost of $4.85 per unit and has fixed monthly expenses of $11,625 related to this item. The manufacturer sells this particular item to several retailers for $9.50 per unit. How many units must the manufacturer sell per month to reach the break-even point for this item?

A) 810

B) 1,225

C) 2,100

D) 2,500

12. If $\frac{1}{2}y - \frac{3}{5}x = -16$, what is the value of $6x - 5y$?

A) 32

B) 80

C) 96

D) 160

13. If $f(g(2)) = -1$ and $f(x) = x + 1$, then which of the following could define $g(x)$?

A) $g(x) = x - 6$

B) $g(x) = x - 4$

C) $g(x) = x - 2$

D) $g(x) = x - 1$

GO ON TO THE NEXT PAGE

Directions: For questions 14–17, enter your responses into the appropriate grid on your answer sheet, in accordance with the following:

1. You will receive credit only if the circles are filled in correctly, but you may write your answers in the boxes above each grid to help you fill in the circles accurately.
2. Don't mark more than one circle per column.
3. None of the questions with grid-in responses will have a negative solution.
4. Only grid in a single answer, even if there is more than one correct answer to a given question.
5. A **mixed number** must be gridded as a decimal or an improper fraction. For example, you would grid $7\frac{1}{2}$ as 7.5 or 15/2.

    (Were you to grid it as $\boxed{7\ 1\ /\ 2}$, this response would be read as $\frac{71}{2}$.)
6. A **decimal** that has more digits than there are places on the grid may be either rounded or truncated, but every column in the grid must be filled in to receive credit.

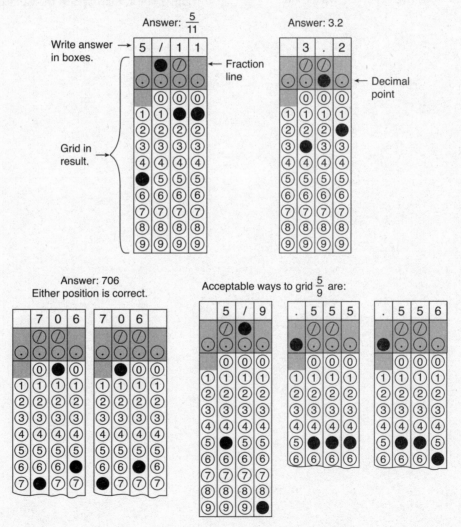

$$k(10x - 5) = 2(3 + x) - 7$$

14. If the equation above has infinitely many solutions and k is a constant, what is the value of k?

15. A right triangle has leg lengths of 18 and 24 and a hypotenuse of $15n$. What is the value of n?

$$\frac{\sqrt{x} \cdot x^{\frac{5}{4}} \cdot x^2}{\sqrt[4]{x^3}}$$

16. If the expression above is combined into a single power of x with a positive exponent, what is that exponent?

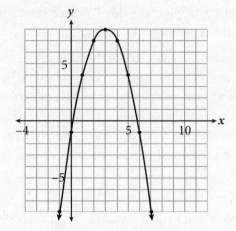

17. If the equation of the parabola shown in the graph is written in standard quadratic form, $y = ax^2 + bx + c$, and $a = -1$, then what is the value of b?

Math Test

45 Minutes—31 Questions

CALCULATOR SECTION

This section corresponds to Section 4 of your answer sheet.

Directions: For this section, solve each problem and decide which is the best of the choices given. Fill in the corresponding oval on the answer sheet. You may use any available space for scratch work.

Notes:

1. Calculator use is permitted.
2. All numbers used are real numbers, and all variables used represent real numbers, unless otherwise indicated.
3. Figures are drawn to scale and lie in a plane unless otherwise indicated.
4. Unless stated otherwise, the domain of any function f is assumed to be the set of all real numbers x for which $f(x)$ is a real number.

Information:

$A = \pi r^2$
$C = 2\pi r$

$A = lw$

$A = \frac{1}{2}bh$

$c^2 = a^2 + b^2$

Special Right Triangles

$V = lwh$

$V = \pi r^2 h$

$V = \frac{4}{3}\pi r^3$

$V = \frac{1}{3}\pi r^2 h$

$V = \frac{1}{3}lwh$

The sum of the degree measures of the angles in a triangle is 180.

The number of degrees of arc in a circle is 360.

The number of radians of arc in a circle is 2π.

GO ON TO THE NEXT PAGE

Hours Spent in Batting Practice

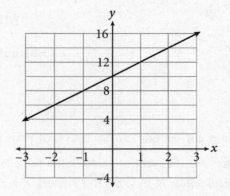

1. The scatterplot above shows data collected from 10 major league baseball players comparing the average weekly time each one spent in batting practice and the number of home runs he hit in a single season. The line of best fit for the data is also shown. What does the slope of the line represent in this context?

   A) The estimated time spent in batting practice by a player who hits zero home runs

   B) The estimated number of single-season home runs hit by a player who spends zero hours in batting practice

   C) The estimated increase in time that a player spends in batting practice for each home run that he hits in a single season

   D) The estimated increase in the number of single-season home runs hit by a player for each hour he spends in batting practice

2. Where will the line shown in the graph above intersect the x-axis?

   A) -5.5

   B) -5

   C) -4.5

   D) -4

3. The function $f(x)$ is defined as $f(x) = -3g(x)$, where $g(x) = x + 2$. What is the value of $f(5)$?

   A) -21

   B) -1

   C) 4

   D) 7

GO ON TO THE NEXT PAGE

4. The graph above shows the average cost of back surgery followed by a hospital stay in the United States. The hospital charges for the surgery itself plus all the costs associated with recovery care for each night the patient remains in the hospital. Based on the graph, what is the average cost per night spent in the hospital?

A) $2,600

B) $4,000

C) $6,600

D) $8,000

5. The figure above represents a click-through rate curve, which shows the relationship between a search result position in a list of Internet search results and the number of people who clicked on advertisements on that result's page. Which of the following regression types would be the best model for this data?

A) A linear function

B) A quadratic function

C) A polynomial function

D) An exponential function

GO ON TO THE NEXT PAGE

6. Kudzu is a vine-like plant that grows indigenously in Asia. It was brought over to the United States in the early 20th century to help combat soil erosion. As can often happen when foreign species are introduced into a non-native habitat, kudzu growth exploded and it became invasive. In one area of Virginia, kudzu covered approximately 3,200 acres of a farmer's cropland, so the farmer tried a new herbicide. After two weeks of use, 2,800 acres of the cropland were free of the kudzu. Based on these results, and assuming the same general conditions, how many of the 30,000 acres of kudzu-infested cropland in that region would still be covered if all the farmers in the entire region had used the herbicide?

A)   3,750

B)   4,000

C)   26,000

D)   26,250

x	−2	−1	0	1	2	3
$g(x)$	5	3	1	−1	−3	−5
$h(x)$	−3	−2	−1	0	1	2

7. Several values for the functions $g(x)$ and $h(x)$ are shown in the table above. What is the value of $g(h(3))$?

A)   −5

B)   −3

C)   −1

D)   2

8. Mae-Ling made 15 shots during a basketball game. Some were 3-pointers and others were worth 2 points each. If s shots were 3-pointers, which expression represents her total score?

A) $3s$

B) $s + 30$

C) $3s + 2$

D) $5s + 30$

9. Crude oil is sold by the barrel, which refers to both the physical container and a unit of measure, abbreviated as bbl. One barrel holds 42 gallons and, consequently, 1 bbl = 42 gallons. An oil company is filling an order for 2,500 barrels. The machine the company uses to fill the barrels pumps at a rate of 37.5 gallons per minute. If the oil company has 8 machines working simultaneously, how long will it take to fill all the barrels in the order?

A)   5 hours and 50 minutes

B)   12 hours and 45 minutes

C)   28 hours and 30 minutes

D)   46 hours and 40 minutes

GO ON TO THE NEXT PAGE

	Jan	Feb	Mar	Apr
Company A	54	146	238	330
Company B	15	30	60	120

10. Company A and company B are selling two similar toys. The sales figures for each toy are recorded in the table above. The marketing department at company A predicts that its monthly sales for this particular toy will continue to be higher than company B's through the end of the year. Based on the data in the table, and assuming that each company sustains the pattern of growth the data suggests, which company will sell more of this toy in December of that year and how much more?

A) Company A; 182

B) Company A; 978

C) Company B; 29,654

D) Company B; 60,282

11. Which symbol correctly completes the inequality whose solution is shown above?

A) $<$

B) $>$

C) $\leq$

D) $\geq$

Questions 12 and 13 refer to the following information.

A student is drawing the human skeleton to scale for a school assignment. The assignment permits the student to omit all bones under a certain size because they would be too small to draw. The longest bone in the human body is the femur, or thighbone, with an average length of 19.9 inches. The tenth longest bone is the sternum, or breastbone, with an average length of 6.7 inches.

12. If the scale factor of the drawing is one-eighth, about how long in inches should the student draw the femur?

A) 2

B) 2.5

C) 2.8

D) 3

13. The student draws the femur, but then realizes she drew it too long, at 3.5 inches. She doesn't want to erase and start over, so she decides she will adjust the scale factor to match her current drawing instead. Based on the new scale factor, about how long in inches should she draw the sternum?

A) 0.8

B) 1

C) 1.2

D) 1.5

14. If a line that passes through the ordered pairs $(4 - c, 2c)$ and $(-c, -8)$ has a slope of $\frac{1}{2}$, what is the value of c?

   A) −5

   B) −3

   C) −2

   D)   2

From	Distance to LHR
DCA	3,718
MIA	4,470

15. Two airplanes departed from different airports at 5:30 a.m., both traveling nonstop to London Heathrow Airport (LHR). The distances the planes traveled are recorded in the table. The Washington, D.C. (DCA) flight flew through moderate cloud cover and as a result only averaged 338 miles per hour. The flight from Miami (MIA) had good weather conditions for the first two-thirds of the trip and averaged 596 miles per hour, but then encountered some turbulence and only averaged 447 miles per hour for the last part of the trip. Which plane arrived first and how long was it at the London airport before the other plane arrived?

   A) MIA; 2 hours, 40 minutes

   B) MIA; 3 hours, 30 minutes

   C) DCA; 1 hour, 20 minutes

   D) DCA; 3 hours, 40 minutes

16. Which of the following quadratic equations has no real solution?

   A) $0 = -3(x + 1)(x - 8)$

   B) $0 = 3(x + 1)(x - 8)$

   C) $0 = -3(x + 1)^2 + 8$

   D) $0 = 3(x + 1)^2 + 8$

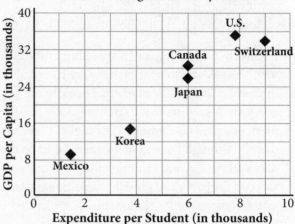

Annual Expenditures per Student as a Percentage of Country's GDP

Adapted from the Organization for Economic Cooperation and Development (OECD), 2003.

17. A student looked at the graph above and determined based on the data that spending more money per student causes the gross domestic product (GDP) to increase. Which of the following statements is true?

   A) The student is correct; the data shows that increased spending on students causes an increase in the GDP.

   B) The student is incorrect; the data shows that having a higher GDP causes an increase in the amount of money a country spends on students.

   C) The student is incorrect; there is no correlation and, therefore, no causation between GDP and expenditures on students.

   D) The student is incorrect; the two variables are correlated, but changes in one do not necessarily cause changes in the other.

GO ON TO THE NEXT PAGE

18. In chemistry, the combined gas law formula

$\dfrac{p_1 V_1}{T_1} = \dfrac{p_2 V_2}{T_2}$ gives the relationship between the

volumes, temperatures, and pressures for two fixed amounts of gas. Which of the following gives p_2 in terms of the other variables?

A) $p_1 = p_2$

B) $\dfrac{p_1 T}{V} = p_2$

C) $\dfrac{p_1 V_1 T_2}{T_1 V_2} = p_2$

D) $\dfrac{p_1 V_1 V_2}{T_1 T_2} = p_2$

19. An object's weight is dependent upon the gravitational force being exerted upon the object. This is why objects in space are weightless. If 1 pound on Earth is equal to 0.377 pounds on Mars and 2.364 pounds on Jupiter, how many more pounds does an object weighing 1.5 tons on Earth weigh on Jupiter than on Mars? (Note: 1 ton = 2,000 pounds.)

A) 1,131

B) 4,092

C) 5,961

D) 7,092

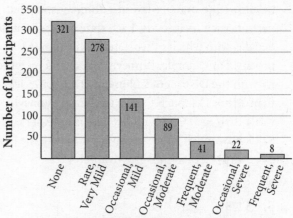

Clinical Trial: Headache Side Effect 900-Participant Study

Frequency and Severity of Headaches

20. When a drug company wants to introduce a new drug, it must subject the drug to rigorous testing. The final stage of this testing is human clinical trials, in which progressively larger groups of volunteers are given the drug and carefully monitored. One aspect of this monitoring is keeping track of the frequency and severity of side effects. The figure above shows the results for the side effect of headaches for a certain drug. According to the trial guidelines, all moderate and severe headaches are considered to be adverse reactions. Which of the following best describes the data?

A) The data is symmetric with more than 50 percent of participants having adverse reactions.

B) The data is skewed to the right with more than 50 percent of participants having adverse reactions.

C) The data is skewed to the right with more than 75 percent of participants failing to have adverse reactions.

D) The data is skewed to the right with approximately 50 percent of participants having no reaction at all.

21. In the legal field, "reciprocity" means that an attorney can take and pass a bar exam in one state and be allowed to practice law in a different state that permits such reciprocity. Each state bar association decides with which other states it will allow reciprocity. For example, Pennsylvania allows reciprocity with the District of Columbia. It costs $25 less than 3 times as much to take the bar in Pennsylvania than in D.C. If both bar exams together cost $775, how much less expensive is it to take the bar exam in D.C. than in Pennsylvania?

A) $200

B) $275

C) $375

D) $575

Driver's Education Test Results

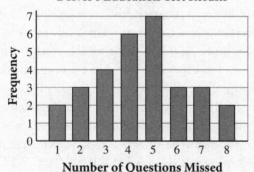

Number of Questions Missed

22. Mr. Juno took his driver's education class to the Department of Motor Vehicles to take their driver's license tests. The number of questions missed by each student in the class is recorded in the bar graph above. Which of the following statements is true?

A) More than half of the students missed 5 or more questions.

B) The mean number of questions missed was between 4 and 5.

C) More students missed 3 questions than any other number of questions.

D) Thirty-six students from Mr. Juno's class took the driver's license test that day.

23. If the graph of the equation $y = ax^2 + bx + c$ passes through the points $(0, 2)$, $(-6, -7)$, and $(8, -14)$, what is the value of $a + b + c$?

A) -19

B) -2

C) 1.75

D) 2.25

24. A bakery sells three sizes of muffins—mini, regular, and jumbo. The baker plans daily muffin counts based on the size of his pans and how they fit in the oven, which result in the following ratios: mini to regular equals 5 to 2 and regular to jumbo equals 5 to 4. When the bakery caters events, it usually offers only the regular size, but it recently decided to offer a mix of mini and jumbo instead of regular. If the baker wants to keep the sizes in the same ratio as his daily counts, what ratio of mini to jumbo should he use?

A) 1:1

B) 4:2

C) 5:2

D) 25:8

$$\begin{cases} \dfrac{1}{3}x + \dfrac{1}{2}y = 5 \\ kx - 4y = 16 \end{cases}$$

25. If the system of linear equations shown above has no solution, and k is a constant, what is the value of k?

A) $-\dfrac{8}{3}$

B) -2

C) $\dfrac{1}{3}$

D) 3

GO ON TO THE NEXT PAGE

26. What is the value of $3^{90} \times 27^{90} \div \left(\dfrac{1}{9}\right)^{30}$?

    A) 9^{60}

    B) 9^{120}

    C) 9^{150}

    D) 9^{210}

27. If a right cone is three times as wide at its base as it is tall, and the volume of the cone is 384π cubic inches, what is the diameter in inches of the base of the cone?

    A) 8

    B) 12

    C) 16

    D) 24

Directions: For questions 28–31, enter your responses into the appropriate grid on your answer sheet, in accordance with the following:

1. You will receive credit only if the circles are filled in correctly, but you may write your answers in the boxes above each grid to help you fill in the circles accurately.

2. Don't mark more than one circle per column.

3. None of the questions with grid-in responses will have a negative solution.

4. Only grid in a single answer, even if there is more than one correct answer to a given question.

5. A **mixed number** must be gridded as a decimal or an improper fraction. For example, you would grid $7\frac{1}{2}$ as 7.5 or 15/2.

   (Were you to grid it as , this response would be read as $\frac{71}{2}$.)

6. A **decimal** that has more digits than there are places on the grid may be either rounded or truncated, but every column in the grid must be filled in to receive credit.

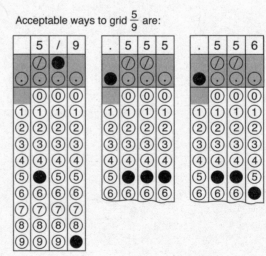

GO ON TO THE NEXT PAGE

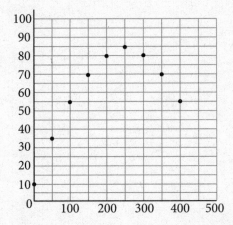

28. Nine data points were used to generate the scatterplot shown above. Assuming all whole number values for the data points, what is the maximum value in the range of the data?

29. If $Ax + By = C$ is the standard form of the line that passes through the points $(-4, 1)$ and $(3, -2)$, where A is an integer greater than 1, what is the value of B?

Questions 30 and 31 refer to the following information.

The Great Depression began in 1929 and lasted until 1939. It was a period of extreme poverty, marked by low prices and high unemployment. The main catalytic event to the Great Depression was the Wall Street Crash (stock market crash). The Dow, which measures the health of the stock market, started Black Thursday (October 24, 1929) at approximately 306 points.

30. The stock market had been in steady decline since its record high the month before. If the market had declined by 19.5 percent between its record high and opening on Black Thursday, what was the approximate value of the Dow at its record high? Round your answer to the nearest whole point.

31. By the end of business on Black Thursday, the Dow had dropped by 2 percent. Over the course of Friday and the half-day Saturday session, there was no significant change. Unfortunately, the market lost 13 percent on Black Monday, followed by another 12 percent on Black Tuesday. What was the total percent decrease from opening on Black Thursday to closing on Black Tuesday? Round your answer to the nearest whole percent and ignore the percent sign when entering your answer.

Answer Key

Reading Test

1. B	13. A	25. A	37. C
2. C	14. B	26. A	38. D
3. D	15. B	27. C	39. C
4. B	16. C	28. D	40. D
5. A	17. D	29. C	41. A
6. C	18. D	30. B	42. C
7. D	19. B	31. D	43. A
8. C	20. C	32. D	44. B
9. A	21. D	33. A	45. D
10. A	22. B	34. C	46. B
11. A	23. D	35. B	47. D
12. C	24. B	36. B	

Writing and Language Test

1. C	12. B	23. C	34. C
2. D	13. A	24. A	35. A
3. A	14. B	25. B	36. D
4. A	15. B	26. C	37. B
5. B	16. D	27. C	38. A
6. C	17. C	28. A	39. B
7. A	18. A	29. D	40. A
8. C	19. C	30. D	41. A
9. A	20. A	31. C	42. D
10. C	21. B	32. B	43. B
11. B	22. C	33. B	44. C

Math Test—No-Calculator

1. A	6. D	11. D	16. 3
2. C	7. D	12. D	17. 6
3. B	8. A	13. B	
4. C	9. C	14. 1/5 or .2	
5. B	10. A	15. 2	

Math Test—Calculator

1. D	9. A	17. D	25. A
2. B	10. C	18. C	26. D
3. A	11. A	19. C	27. D
4. B	12. B	20. C	28. 85
5. D	13. C	21. C	29. 7
6. A	14. B	22. B	30. 380
7. B	15. A	23. C	31. 25
8. B	16. D	24. D	

Answers and Explanations

Reading Test

Suggested passage map notes:

¶1: Pip eating paltry breakfast, Mr. P making him do math while he eats, Pip does not like Mr. P

¶2: Pip visiting Miss H, Miss H's house in disrepair

¶3–9: lady lets in Pip, makes Mr. P go away

¶10: Pip happy to be rid of Mr. P for now

1.   B

Difficulty: Easy

Category: Detail

Getting to the Answer: Examine the description of breakfast in the first paragraph before choosing the correct answer. In lines 9–10, Pip uses "crumb" and "little butter" to describe what he ate, and he also says that "a quantity of warm water" had been added to his milk. Therefore, it's clear that Pip's breakfast with Mr. Pumblechook is **(B)**, "small and of poor quality."

2.   C

Difficulty: Medium

Category: Vocab-in-Context

Getting to the Answer: Eliminate answer choices that might be synonyms of "wretched" but don't make sense in the context of the passage. When Pip describes Mr. Pumblechook's company to be "wretched," he means "distressing" or "causing misery." Choice **(C)** is the correct answer.

3.   D

Difficulty: Medium

Category: Inference

Getting to the Answer: Review the passage for details that reveal Mr. Pumblechook's attitude. By his actions, you can infer that Mr. Pumblechook is indifferent to Pip's discomfort. Choice **(D)** is the correct answer.

4.   B

Difficulty: Medium

Category: Command of Evidence

Getting to the Answer: Find each answer choice in the passage. Think about your answer for the previous question, and determine which lines provide the strongest support for that answer. In the first paragraph, Pip describes how Mr. Pumblechook offers him a meager breakfast and quizzes him on arithmetic during their meal rather than making conversation. Choice **(B)** is the correct answer.

5.   A

Difficulty: Hard

Category: Global

Getting to the Answer: Study the answer choices. Eliminate any that go too far in their interpretation of characters and events in the passage. Though (B) seems to reflect what might be true of Pip and Mr. Pumblechook's relationship, and one might believe that (C) and (D) are true, the correct answer is **(A)**. This theme most clearly reflects the message conveyed through Pip's experiences in this passage.

6.   C

Difficulty: Medium

Category: Inference

Getting to the Answer: Think about details in the passage that relate to the characters' relationships. What do they reveal about how Pip probably feels at the end of the passage? It is reasonable to infer that Pip is relieved when he is no longer in Mr. Pumblechook's company. Therefore, **(C)** is the correct answer.

7. D

Difficulty: Hard

Category: Command of Evidence

Getting to the Answer: Locate each answer in the passage and decide which one provides the best support for the answer to the previous question. At the end of the passage, Pip "was not free from apprehension" (lines 68–69) that Mr. Pumblechook would return but then tells the reader that no return took place. Choice **(D)** best supports the idea that Pip is relieved to be away from Mr. Pumblechook.

8. C

Difficulty: Easy

Category: Vocab-in-Context

Getting to the Answer: Substitute each answer choice for "condition." The correct answer will not change the meaning of the sentence. Choice **(C)** is the correct answer. The narrator says that Mr. Pumblechook is "in a condition of ruffled dignity." In this context, "state" means the same as "condition."

9. A

Difficulty: Medium

Category: Function

Getting to the Answer: Think of what the parenthetical comment by Pip tells you about his personality. In a sense, Pip is apologizing for what he is about to say of Mr. Pumblechook. The parenthetical comment reveals that Pip is usually more polite in his references to others. Choice **(A)** is the correct answer.

Suggested passage map notes:

¶1: MLK states why he is in Birmingham, history of SCLC, in Birmingham due to injustice

¶2: MLK cannot let injustice continue, we are one people

¶3: MLK explains why peaceful protests are needed, benefits of tension to open negotiations

¶4: nonviolent pressure only way to enact change

¶5: justice must be demanded by the oppressed

10. A

Difficulty: Medium

Category: Global

Getting to the Answer: Avoid answer choices that deal with related issues but do not address the main purpose of the letter. The passage as a whole addresses why King came to Birmingham, and then builds on his explanation for being in Birmingham to explore his cause. Choice **(A)** is correct.

11. A

Difficulty: Easy

Category: Command of Evidence

Getting to the Answer: Choose the answer that relates directly to the purpose you identified in the previous question. King begins the letter by stating, "I think I should give the reason for my being in Birmingham," which clearly explains his purpose for writing the letter from the jail. Choice **(A)** is correct.

12. C

Difficulty: Easy

Category: Vocab-in-Context

Getting to the Answer: Read the complete sentence and the surrounding paragraph to best understand the meaning of the phrase within its greater context. In the paragraph, King goes on to explain that events in Birmingham must necessarily concern him. He states that an injustice in one place threatens justice everywhere and even writes, "Whatever affects one directly affects all indirectly" (lines 27–28). This suggests that events in Birmingham affect people throughout the nation. Choice **(C)** is correct as it explains that the "interrelatedness of all communities and states" refers to the idea that events in one part of the country affect the entire nation.

13. A

Difficulty: Easy

Category: Inference

Getting to the Answer: Predict King's opinions before reviewing the answer choices. The correct answer can be inferred directly from King's views as expressed in the paragraph. In this paragraph, King refers specifically to injustice and how it affects people everywhere. From this, you can most clearly infer that King considered circumstances in Birmingham to be unfair and wrong. Choice **(A)** is correct.

14. B

Difficulty: Easy

Category: Command of Evidence

Getting to the Answer: Review the answer to the previous question. Read the answer choices to identify the one whose rhetoric provides clear support for the inference. Although the entire paragraph provides general support and context for the inference, only **(B)** suggests that circumstances in Birmingham were unjust, that is, unfair and wrong.

15. B

Difficulty: Medium

Category: Vocab-in-Context

Getting to the Answer: Before viewing the answer choices, think about the purpose of the word in the sentence and form an alternate explanation of the word. Then, identify the answer choice that best reflects that meaning and intent. King says that direct action in Birmingham aims to "dramatize the issue that it can no longer be ignored." This suggests that the issue, or events, in Birmingham are of great significance and demand attention that they have not received. Therefore, **(B)** is correct.

16. C

Difficulty: Hard

Category: Detail

Getting to the Answer: Consider the overall thrust of King's argument in this paragraph. Choose the answer that encapsulates this idea. In paragraph 4, King responds to charges that activists should focus on negotiation, not direct action. He argues that direct action is needed to spur negotiations. King reasons that nonviolent protests create the tension between forces in society needed to bring people to the table to discuss the relevant issues of prejudice and racism. His claim in the paragraph is that direct action is needed to spur negotiation, making choice **(C)** correct.

17. D

Difficulty: Hard

Category: Inference

Getting to the Answer: Identify an idea in paragraph 4 that provides clear support to the claim made in the previous paragraph. In paragraph 3, King claims that nonviolent direct action is needed to prompt negotiations on civil rights. In paragraph 4, he supports that argument by explaining that no gains have been made in civil rights without such nonviolent action, as choice **(D)** states.

18. D

Difficulty: Medium

Category: Function

Getting to the Answer: Read the complete paragraph to best understand the context and purpose of the cited line. The correct answer will identify what the phrase helps achieve in the paragraph. At the start of the paragraph, King argues that oppressors do not willingly give more freedom to the people whom they oppress. He goes on to explain the delay tactics that have kept African Americans from winning equal rights, and concludes that oppressed peoples in other nations are winning independence while African Americans still cannot get a cup of coffee at a lunch counter. The phrase helps King underscore the contrast between these two scenarios, so **(D)** is the correct answer.

Suggested passage map notes:

Passage 1

¶1: background of Bretton Woods

¶2: created IMF to facilitate international trade

¶3: created World Bank to give loans to war affected countries, bridge rich and poor countries

¶4: BW made U.S. dollar global currency

¶5: shaped foreign trade

¶6: BW made U.S. powerful

Passage 2:

¶1: BW only lasted 3 decades, Nixon changed economic policy

¶2: BW collapsed, IMF began flexible exchange system for currency

¶3: U.S. dollar still widely used

¶4: G20 wants to create global currency

¶5–6: predicts worldwide currency, new world order in finance coming

19. B

Difficulty: Medium

Category: Inference

Getting to the Answer: Remember that you are being asked to choose an inference suggested by Passage 1, not a statement of fact. The passage notes that the U.S. dollar became a global currency that nations around the world accept for trade, leaving the United States in a stronger position to influence international markets. Choice **(B)** is the correct answer.

20. C

Difficulty: Medium

Category: Command of Evidence

Getting to the Answer: The correct choice should support your answer to the previous question. Consider which choice best shows a clear relationship with your answer to the item above. Choice **(C)** explicitly states the United States became the "primary power" behind the institutions established at Bretton Woods.

21. D

Difficulty: Medium

Category: Vocab-in-Context

Getting to the Answer: Predict an answer based on the context of the passage. The correct answer should not alter the meaning of the sentence in the passage. Then, choose the option that best fits your prediction. The passage states that the IMF gives loans to member countries to ensure their continued stability. Choice **(D)** is correct because it most closely reflects the IMF's goals of proactively promoting global economic growth and stability.

22. B

Difficulty: Medium

Category: Inference

Getting to the Answer: Locate information in the passage that accurately summarizes the purposes of both institutions. Then, ask yourself how these purposes differ. Both institutions encourage economic growth. However, Passage 1 notes that the IMF maintains payments and receipts between nations. The World Bank, on the other hand, focuses on "economic and social progress" (line 36) in individual countries. Choice **(B)** is the correct answer.

23. D

Difficulty: Hard

Category: Inference

Getting to the Answer: Eliminate any answer choices that are not suggested in the passage. Choice **(D)** is correct. The paragraph states that President Nixon's decision broke with the Bretton Woods framework. It can be reasonably inferred that the decision differed from the consensus of other nations, given the fact that many nations had agreed to Bretton Woods.

24. B

Difficulty: Medium

Category: Command of Evidence

Getting to the Answer: The answer choice should support your answer to the previous question. The paragraph states that President Nixon's decision "marked the end" of the Bretton Woods framework, which best supports the inference that the United States did not have the support of other nations. The correct answer is **(B)**.

25. A

Difficulty: Medium

Category: Vocab-in-Context

Getting to the Answer: Reread the sentence in which the word appears and decide which meaning makes the most sense in context. The sentence is referring to a new global currency that might take the place of the U.S. dollar as the major, or key, currency. Therefore, **(A)** is the correct definition of "anchor" in this context.

26. A

Difficulty: Hard

Category: Inference

Getting to the Answer: Study the yuan's percent share of use in daily trading relative to other currencies in the graphic over time. What does this suggest about global views of the yuan? Passage 2 explicitly states that the yuan is "becoming a major world reserve currency" (lines 99–100). This is supported by the data in the chart, which shows the yuan's percent share of use in daily trading climbing from 0.5 percent in 2007 to 2.2 percent in 2013. Choice **(A)** is correct.

27. C

Difficulty: Medium

Category: Global

Getting to the Answer: Identify the overall purpose of each passage. Then, consider which answer choice accurately describes these purposes. Choice **(C)** is the correct answer. Passage 1 focuses on the effects of Bretton Woods, while Passage 2 focuses on the reasons why the international economy may transition to a new global currency.

28. D

Difficulty: Medium

Category: Inference

Getting to the Answer: Keep in mind that the correct answer will be a statement that is evident in both passages. The role of the IMF is mentioned prominently in both passages. Therefore, **(D)** is the correct answer.

Suggested passage map notes:

¶1: six million U.S. people paralyzed; causes of paralysis
¶2: patient in Poland became subject of study
¶3: spinal cord research on rats, now used to develop treatment
¶4: patient responded well to treatment
¶5: future benefits of treatment

29. C

Difficulty: Easy

Category: Global

Getting to the Answer: Keep in mind that the correct answer will be supported by all of the information in the text rather than just a few details. The passage is concerned with one experimental treatment that doctors are exploring to help patients regain mobility. Choice **(C)** is the correct answer.

30. B

Difficulty: Medium

Category: Inference

Getting to the Answer: Consider the main points the author makes throughout the passage. The correct answer will be directly related to these points, even if it is not directly stated in the passage. Choice **(B)** is the correct answer. It can be inferred that the author feels that increased mobility will have a positive impact on patients suffering from all levels of paralysis.

31. D

Difficulty: Easy

Category: Command of Evidence

Getting to the Answer: Locate each answer choice in the passage. Decide which one provides the best support for the answer to the previous question. In the last lines of the passage, the author says that patients with paralysis "can have both their mobility and their hope restored" (lines 71–72). Thus, **(D)** offers the strongest support for the answer to the previous question.

32. D

Difficulty: Easy

Category: Vocab-in-Context

Getting to the Answer: The correct answer will not only be a synonym for "restricted" but will also make sense in the context of the sentence in the passage. Eliminate answers, such as (A) that are synonyms for "restricted" but do not make sense in context. Here, the author is explaining that patients in wheelchairs must learn to prevent complications from restricted movement. In this context, "restricted" most nearly means "limited," answer choice **(D)**.

33. A

Difficulty: Hard

Category: Function

Getting to the Answer: Locate lines 46–47 in the passage and then read the paragraph that comes before them. This will help you identify why the author chose "tailor-made" to describe the patient's treatment. The patient received his own cells during the treatment, meaning that the treatment was tailored to his own body. Choice **(A)** fits this situation and is therefore the correct answer.

34. C

Difficulty: Hard

Category: Inference

Getting to the Answer: Remember that when a question is asking you to infer something, the answer is not stated explicitly in the passage. In paragraph 2, the author explains that the patient who received the experimental treatment had not seen an increase in mobility despite "countless hours" (line 23) of physical therapy. Therefore, it is logical to infer that the patient would not have regained mobility without this experimental treatment. Choice **(C)** is the correct answer.

35. B

Difficulty: Medium

Category: Command of Evidence

Getting to the Answer: Think about how you selected the correct answer for the previous question. Use that information to help you choose the correct answer to this question. In paragraph 2, the author explains that the patient selected for the experimental treatment had not regained mobility despite intensive physical therapy. This provides the strongest support for the answer to the previous question, so **(B)** is correct.

36. B

Difficulty: Easy

Category: Vocab-in-Context

Getting to the Answer: Substitute each of the answer choices for "refined." Select the one that makes the most sense in context and does not change the meaning of the sentence. In this context, "refined" most nearly means "improved." Choice **(B)** is the correct answer.

37. C

Difficulty: Easy

Category: Inference

Getting to the Answer: Skim the passage and look for details about how doctors came to use the treatment described. In paragraph 3, the author explains that the doctors used a technique that was developed during years of research on rats. Therefore, **(C)** is the correct answer.

38. D

Difficulty: Medium

Category: Inference

Getting to the Answer: Compare and contrast each answer choice with the procedure described in the passage. As in the procedure described in the passage, skin transplants for burn victims involve taking tissue containing healthy cells from one area of the body and using it to repair damage done to another area. Choice **(D)** is the correct answer.

Suggested passage map notes:

¶1: what mercury is, uses for mercury

¶2: causes of mercury pollution

¶3: water affected by mercury, issue for many organisms

¶4: consumption of mercury-laden seafood, risks and benefits

¶5: explanation of safe levels of mercury based on bodyweight and fish type

¶6: nutritionists' recommendations

39. C

Difficulty: Medium

Category: Inference

Getting to the Answer: The correct answer will be directly supported by the evidence in the passage. Avoid answers like (A) and (B) that go beyond what can logically be inferred about the author. The author explains how mercury gets into the fish that humans eat and goes on to say that it is possible to eat fish that contain mercury without getting mercury poisoning. Choice **(C)** is the correct answer because it is directly supported by the evidence in the passage.

40. D

Difficulty: Medium

Category: Command of Evidence

Getting to the Answer: The correct answer will provide direct support for the answer to the previous question. Avoid answers like (B) that include relevant details but do not provide direct support. In the last paragraph, the author says that nutritionists recommend eating low-mercury fish instead of eliminating fish altogether, adding that an awareness of the issues with mercury can help us make healthy eating choices. This statement supports the answer to the previous question, so **(D)** is the correct answer.

41. A

Difficulty: Easy

Category: Detail

Getting to the Answer: Review the details provided in the passage about how to determine a safe level of mercury consumption. In paragraph 5, the author explains that humans should consume less than 0.1 microgram of mercury for every kilogram of their own weight. Therefore, **(A)** is the correct answer.

42. C

Difficulty: Easy

Category: Vocab-in-Context

Getting to the Answer: Eliminate answer choices that are synonyms for "concentration" but do not make sense in context. In this sentence, the author is describing the amount of mercury in the air from power plants. "Concentration" most nearly means "density" in this context, so **(C)** is the correct answer.

43. A

Difficulty: Medium

Category: Inference

Getting to the Answer: Eliminate any answer choices that are not directly supported by information in the passage. The passage strongly suggests that it is impossible to avoid exposure to mercury. Therefore, **(A)** is the correct answer.

44. B

Difficulty: Easy

Category: Command of Evidence

Getting to the Answer: Locate each of the answer choices in the passage. The correct answer should provide support for the answer to the previous question. In paragraph 1, the author explains that mercury can be found in many places. This supports the conclusion that it is impossible to avoid mercury completely. Choice **(B)** is the correct answer.

45. D

Difficulty: Hard

Category: Inference

Getting to the Answer: Consider one of the central ideas of the passage. The correct answer would help provide additional support for this idea. One central idea in the passage is that people can eat fish if they know what mercury levels are safe for human consumption. The author states that scientists have determined safe mercury levels by studying at what point symptoms of mercury poisoning occur. However, the author only provides one example weight of how many micrograms of mercury a person could eat. Therefore, **(D)** is the correct answer.

46. B

Difficulty: Easy

Category: Vocab-in-Context

Getting to the Answer: Reread the sentence and replace "particulars" with each answer choice. Though the answer choices are similar in meaning to a certain degree, one of them makes the most sense when substituted for "particulars." In this context, "particulars" most nearly means "specifics"; therefore, **(B)** is the correct answer.

47. D

Difficulty: Hard

Category: Inference

Getting to the Answer: Remember that the correct answer will be supported by information in both the passage and the graphic. Refer to the passage to draw conclusions about the information in the graphic. The passage states that it is safe to eat fish that contain mercury as long as certain guidelines are followed regarding daily consumption. The graphic shows that Alaskan pollock has the lowest concentration of mercury of the fish listed. Therefore, **(D)** is the correct answer; a person can safely eat more Alaskan pollock than black-striped bass in one day.

Writing and Language Test

1. C

Difficulty: Medium

Category: Sentence Structure: Commas, Dashes, and Colons

Getting to the Answer: Examine the passage to determine whether the current punctuation is incorrect. Then consider which set of punctuation marks correctly emphasizes the selected part of the sentence. The dashes provide emphasis for the idea that the UN is a peacekeeping organization; the dashes help set off this part of the sentence from the remaining content. The correct answer is **(C)**.

2. D

Difficulty: Hard

Category: Development: Introductions and Conclusions

Getting to the Answer: Review the main points made so far. The correct answer should touch on or summarize previous ideas in the paragraph. Choice **(D)** is correct. This concluding sentence effectively summarizes the ideas that compose the paragraph's main claim.

3. A

Difficulty: Medium

Category: Organization: Transitions

Getting to the Answer: Read the previous paragraph and identify the word or phrase that is the best transition between the two paragraphs. The previous paragraph describes the UN today, and the paragraph beginning with the phrase in question explains the origins of the UN in the 1940s. Choice **(A)** indicates the correct shift in time period and provides the most effective transition between paragraphs.

4. A

Difficulty: Medium

Category: Agreement: Verbs

Getting to the Answer: Pay close attention to the context of the previous sentence to help you establish the correct verb tense for this particular sentence. The correct answer is **(A)**. It uses the present tense to logically follow the previous sentence that refers to the UN in the present tense as well.

5. B

Difficulty: Easy

Category: Sentence Structure: The Basics

Getting to the Answer: Watch out for choices that may create a run-on sentence. The correct choice is **(B)**, which provides a clear separation between one complete sentence and the next.

6. C

Difficulty: Easy

Category: Development: Word Choice

Getting to the Answer: Substitute each choice in the complete paragraph. The correct answer will most appropriately fit within the context of the sentence and the paragraph. The correct answer is **(C)**. The UN encourages, or promotes, environmental protection.

7. A

Difficulty: Medium

Category: Development: Introductions and Conclusions

Getting to the Answer: The correct choice should introduce a central idea that is supported by subsequent sentences in the paragraph. The correct answer is **(A)**. The expansion of the UN's budget, goals, and personnel number connects to specific evidence in the rest of the paragraph.

8. C

Difficulty: Medium

Category: Graphs

Getting to the Answer: Notice that the graphic gives specific information about the increases and decreases in the UN peacekeeping force over a period of time. Study the answer choices to find the one that best relates to the paragraph while using accurate information from the graphic. The graphic shows data

through the year 2010 and does not indicate that personnel levels rose above 100,000. Choice **(C)** is the correct answer.

9. A

Difficulty: Medium

Category: Conciseness

Getting to the Answer: Watch out for unnecessarily wordy choices like (B). The correct answer is **(A)** because it effectively communicates an idea without additional words that distract from the content.

10. C

Difficulty: Easy

Category: Development: Word Choice

Getting to the Answer: Look at the context of the sentence in which the word appears as well as the paragraph itself to choose the answer that works best. Choice **(C)**, "noteworthy," is synonymous with "worth mentioning," which clearly fits within the context of the paragraph and the author's intent to highlight the accomplishments of the UN.

11. B

Difficulty: Medium

Category: Development: Revising Text

Getting to the Answer: Read the entire paragraph. Identify the sentence that is least relevant to the paragraph's topic and purpose. The purpose of this paragraph is to sum up the central ideas of the passage. Choice **(B)** introduces a detail that, while important, does not summarize the central ideas of the passage and therefore detracts from the paragraph's focus.

12. B

Difficulty: Easy

Category: Agreement: Verbs

Getting to the Answer: Read the sentence and notice that the verb in question is in a clause with intervening prepositional phrases that come between the subject and the verb. Check to see what the subject is and whether the verb agrees with the subject. The verb "match" is in a plural form, but the subject is "DNA," not one of the other nouns in the prepositional phrases. "DNA" is singular. Choice **(B)** is the correct answer because it is the singular form of the verb "to match."

13. A

Difficulty: Medium

Category: Sentence Structure: The Basics

Getting to the Answer: Read the sentence to determine whether the two clauses separated by the semicolon are independent or not. If they are both independent, a semicolon is the appropriate punctuation. Be careful of answer choices with inappropriate transition words. A semicolon is the correct way to separate two independent but related clauses, so **(A)** is the correct answer.

14. B

Difficulty: Easy

Category: Sentence Structure: Commas, Dashes, and Colons

Getting to the Answer: Study the words in a series and see where a comma might need to be inserted or eliminated. Choice **(B)** is correct.

15. B

Difficulty: Hard

Category: Organization: Transitions

Getting to the Answer: When you see an underlined transition, identify how the sentence relates to the previous one to determine what kind of transition is appropriate. Choice **(B)** is correct because the sentence to which the transition belongs provides more detail about a general statement that preceded it.

16. D

Difficulty: Easy

Category: Development: Word Choice

Getting to the Answer: Imagine that the sentence has a blank where the word in question is. Read the entire paragraph for context, and predict what word could complete the blank. Review the answer choices to find the word closest in meaning to your prediction. The paragraph later states that Jane Saunders's goal is to separate the two strands of DNA. Only answer choice **(D)** has the correct connotation and fits within the context of the sentence.

17. C

Difficulty: Medium

Category: Conciseness

Getting to the Answer: It is important to combine sentences in order to vary sentence structures. But the correct choice should not only be the most effective way to combine the two sentences, it must also be in parallel construction with the first sentence. Watch out for choices that may have incorrect transition words as well. Choice **(C)** is the correct answer. It joins the sentences concisely and correctly because the verb "adding" is in parallel construction with the earlier verbs "detaching" and "transferring." The subject in both sentences is the same, "she," so it can be dropped when combining the two sentences.

18. A

Difficulty: Medium

Category: Development: Introductions and Conclusions

Getting to the Answer: Read the entire paragraph and then put each answer choice at the beginning. Choose the one that makes the most sense and is further explained by subsequent details in the paragraph. The paragraph discusses the process of identifying DNA, which is lengthy and involves changing the temperature of the DNA several times. Choice **(A)** is closest to this summation of what is to follow and is the correct answer.

19. C

Difficulty: Easy

Category: Conciseness

Getting to the Answer: Watch out for choices that are wordy or redundant. Choice **(C)** is the most concise and effective way of stating the information in the passage.

20. A

Difficulty: Medium

Category: Organization: Sentence Placement

Getting to the Answer: Consider the function of this sentence. At what point in the paragraph should this function be employed? The sentence is setting the scene, so it should be placed where it is now, at the beginning of the paragraph. To place it later would make the meaning of the paragraph unclear. Choice **(A)** is the correct answer.

21. B

Difficulty: Easy

Category: Development: Word Choice

Getting to the Answer: Think about the connotations of each answer choice and be sure to pick the one that fits with the context of the sentence. Substitute each answer choice for the word to see which word works best. "Eager" best reflects how the detectives would be feeling while waiting for important test results. They would be eagerly anticipating this important information and would want it as quickly as possible. Choice **(B)** is the correct answer.

22. C

Difficulty: Hard

Category: Development: Introductions and Conclusions

Getting to the Answer: Decide which sentence sounds like the most appropriate way to conclude the passage. The rhetorical question currently in the passage, choice (A), introduces an opinion that the passage never reveals; there is no sign that Jane Saunders would feel this way. Likewise, there is no indication in the passage of how expensive modern DNA analysis is, choice (B), nor that Saunders marvels about how far science has come in DNA analysis, choice (D). Choice **(C)** is the correct answer; it presents a fairly natural way for Saunders to feel given her accomplishments for the day.

23. C

Difficulty: Medium

Category: Sentence Structure: The Basics

Getting to the Answer: Check to see whether there are two independent clauses within this sentence. Two independent clauses without punctuation indicate a run-on sentence. As written, this is a run-on sentence. Choice **(C)** is the correct answer because it separates the two complete but related thoughts with a semicolon.

24. A

Difficulty: Medium

Category: Development: Introductions and Conclusions

Getting to the Answer: Eliminate answers that might contain details related to the central idea but do not properly express the central idea. This paragraph is mostly about the characteristics of people who are successful entrepreneurs. Choice **(A)** is the correct

answer because it introduces the main idea by summarizing the traits people must have to achieve success as a business owner.

25. B

Difficulty: Hard

Category: Development: Word Choice

Getting to the Answer: Eliminate answers such as (D) that mean nearly the same thing as "grab" but do not clarify the meaning of the sentence. In this context, "derive" best clarifies the meaning of the sentence, which explains how entrepreneurs get ideas for their businesses. Choice **(B)** is the correct answer.

26. C

Difficulty: Easy

Category: Agreement: Verbs

Getting to the Answer: Read the rest of the paragraph, and pay attention to the verb tense used. The verbs in the rest of this paragraph are in past tense. "Graduated" is the past tense of the verb "to graduate," so **(C)** is the correct answer.

27. C

Difficulty: Medium

Category: Sentence Structure: Commas, Dashes, and Colons

Getting to the Answer: Examine the structure of the whole sentence. Consider whether the punctuation is correct or even necessary. The subject of this sentence is "he," and it is followed by a compound predicate containing the verbs "built" and "founded." When a compound predicate contains only two items, a comma should not separate either verb from the subject. No punctuation is necessary, so **(C)** is the correct answer.

28. A

Difficulty: Medium

Category: Development: Word Choice

Getting to the Answer: Replace the underlined word with each answer choice. Consider which word makes the most sense in context and conveys the clearest meaning. The sentence discusses how Vital began her own business. In this context, "launch" conveys the most precise meaning because it connotes the start of a major endeavor. Choice **(A)** is the correct answer because no change is needed.

29. D

Difficulty: Easy

Category: Sentence Structure: Commas, Dashes, and Colons

Getting to the Answer: This sentence contains a list of items in a series. Think about the rules of punctuation for items in a series. Items in a series should be separated by commas, with a comma following each word except the last item in the series. The word "and" is not an item in the series and, therefore, should not be followed by a comma. Therefore, **(D)** is the correct answer.

30. D

Difficulty: Easy

Category: Sentence Structure: Commas, Dashes, and Colons

Getting to the Answer: Identify the main elements of this sentence, such as the subject, predicate, and any restrictive or nonrestrictive clauses. Remember that a nonrestrictive clause should be set off with a comma. The clause "always seeking a new challenge" is nonrestrictive and should be set off from the rest of the sentence with a comma. Choice **(D)** is the correct answer.

31. C

Difficulty: Hard

Category: Development: Relevance

Getting to the Answer: Identify the central idea of the paragraph. Read each answer choice and consider which sentence could be added to the paragraph to provide support for the central idea you identified. This paragraph is mostly about Chris Roth, an entrepreneur who now has several companies. **(C)** is the correct answer because it provides specific details about one of the companies Roth owns.

32. B

Difficulty: Easy

Category: Agreement: Verbs

Getting to the Answer: Read the entire sentence. Identify the subject and determine whether it is plural or singular. Determine the correct verb tense for the sentence. The subject of this sentence is plural (Gomez, Vital, and Roth), so the verb must be plural as well. **(B)** is the correct answer because "agree" is the plural present tense of the verb "to agree."

33. B

Difficulty: Easy

Category: Agreement: Pronouns

Getting to the Answer: Read the entire sentence and identify the antecedent for the underlined pronoun. The correct answer will be the pronoun that is in agreement with the antecedent. In this sentence, the antecedent is "entrepreneurs," which requires a third-person plural pronoun. Therefore, **(B)** is the correct answer.

34. C

Difficulty: Medium

Category: Organization: Transitions

Getting to the Answer: Read the two sentences connected by the underlined portion and decide which answer choice creates a grammatically correct and logical sentence. Choice **(C)** is correct. Using the coordinating conjunction "but" with a comma to combine the sentences shows that the second portion, which mentions Varèse as being unique, stands in contrast to the first portion, which mentions many influential artists. The other options, featuring "and" and "or," do not show this necessary contrast.

35. A

Difficulty: Hard

Category: Sentence Structure: The Basics

Getting to the Answer: Reread the entire sentence to assess how the punctuation in the answer choices affects how each portion of the sentence relates to one another. The correct answer is **(A)**. The semicolon correctly links the two independent clauses that have a direct relationship with one another.

36. D

Difficulty: Medium

Category: Development: Word Choice

Getting to the Answer: Read the sentence for context clues and think about the author's intention. Then, determine which answer provides the most appropriate word choice. "Employ" is the only word that matches the meaning of the sentence, which states that Varèse did not use traditional melodies. Thus, choice **(D)** is correct.

37. B

Difficulty: Medium

Category: Sentence Structure: Commas, Dashes, and Colons

Getting to the Answer: Reread the sentence to determine how each portion relates to the others. Then, examine how the punctuation in the answer choices affects these relationships. The portion of the sentence discussing the family's move to Italy is an introductory element and needs a comma to offset it from the rest of the sentence. The portion discussing what Varèse learned in Turin is a parenthetical element and also requires a comma. Therefore, choice **(B)** is correct.

38. A

Difficulty: Medium

Category: Agreement: Modifiers

Getting to the Answer: Review the sentence for context clues and to assess the subject's ownership of the objects in the sentence. Then, determine which form of the possessive noun correctly reflects this ownership. The hands in the sentence belong to a single player using a single theremin; therefore, the correct answer will use the singular possessive noun "player's." Choice **(A)** is correct.

39. B

Difficulty: Medium

Category: Development: Word Choice

Getting to the Answer: Read the sentence for context clues. Decide on the answer choice that makes the sentence's meaning precise and clear. "Conjunction" is the only word that relates to two things occurring at the same time to create a single outcome, which is the intended meaning of the sentence. Choice **(B)** is correct.

40. A

Difficulty: Hard

Category: Development: Relevance

Getting to the Answer: Assess the central idea of the introductory sentence in the paragraph and determine which additional fact noted in the answer choices would have the greatest benefit to the reader. The introductory sentence states that Varèse worked in New York until he secured his first success. Describing the critical reaction to the next event mentioned would help strengthen the idea that the Philadelphia performance was a successful event in Varèse's career. Choice **(A)** is the correct answer.

41. A

Difficulty: Hard

Category: Agreement: Verbs

Getting to the Answer: Consider what kind of situation the author is presenting here and decide which tense of the verb "has" creates a grammatically correct sentence that reflects this meaning. Keep in mind the time of the events in the sentence. The sentence imagines a situation in which Varèse had been able to use the Internet, an unrealistic action. The double "had had" is correct; it describes past-tense actions that might have occurred in the past but didn't. Choice **(A)** is correct.

42. D

Difficulty: Easy

Category: Agreement: Pronouns

Getting to the Answer: Read the entire sentence to figure out who is the owner of the burned compositions. Then, select the proper personal pronoun for this antecedent. Choice **(D)** is the correct singular possessive pronoun because the burned compositions belonged to Varèse, one person, and not a group of artists.

43. B

Difficulty: Medium

Category: Graphs

Getting to the Answer: Study the information in the graphic to determine which answer choice most accurately finishes the sentence. Choice **(B)** is correct because it accurately reflects information included in the graphic.

44. C

Difficulty: Medium

Category: Development: Introductions and Conclusions

Getting to the Answer: After reading the final paragraph, examine each answer choice to determine which best summarizes the paragraph's overall message. Choice **(C)** is correct. It is the one sentence that sets up the idea that Varèse's challenging work has been an inspiration to many later artists, an idea supported by the rest of the paragraph.

Math Test—No-Calculator

1. A

Difficulty: Easy

Category: Heart of Algebra/Linear Equations

Getting to the Answer: You could start by cross-multiplying to get rid of the denominators, but simplifying the numerators first will make the calculations easier. Don't forget to distribute the negative to both terms in the parentheses on the right-hand side of the equation:

$$\frac{4(n-2)+5}{2} = \frac{13-(9+4n)}{4}$$

$$\frac{4n-8+5}{2} = \frac{13-9-4n}{4}$$

$$\frac{4n-3}{2} = \frac{4-4n}{4}$$

$$4(4n-3) = 2(4-4n)$$

$$16n-12 = 8-8n$$

$$16n = 20-8n$$

$$24n = 20$$

$$n = \frac{20}{24} = \frac{5}{6}$$

Choice **(A)** is correct.

2. C

Difficulty: Easy

Category: Passport to Advanced Math/Rational Expressions

Getting to the Answer: Don't be tempted—you can't simply cancel one term when a polynomial is divided by a monomial. You can, however, split the expression into three terms, each with a denominator of $9x^2$, and simplify. You could also use polynomial long division to answer the question. Use whichever method gets you to the answer more quickly on test day. For example:

$$\frac{18x^3 + 9x^2 - 36x}{9x^2} = \frac{18x^3}{9x^2} + \frac{9x^2}{9x^2} - \frac{36x}{9x^2}$$

$$= 2x + 1 - \frac{4}{x}$$

Choice **(C)** is correct.

3. B

Difficulty: Easy

Category: Passport to Advanced Math/Functions

Getting to the Answer: When using function notation, $f(x)$ is simply another way of saying y, so this question is asking you to find the value(s) of x for which $y = 0$, or in other words, where the graph crosses the x-axis. Don't be tempted by the flat parts of the graph—they have a slope of 0, but the function itself does not equal 0 here (it equals -4). The graph crosses the x-axis at the points $(-1, 0)$ and $(1, 0)$, so the values of x for which $f(x) = 0$ are -1 and 1. **(B)** is correct.

4. C

Difficulty: Medium

Category: Heart of Algebra/Inequalities

Getting to the Answer: You don't need to use algebra to answer this question, and you also don't need to graph each system. Instead, think about how the graphs would look. The only time a system of linear inequalities has no solution is when it consists of two parallel lines shaded in opposite directions. All the inequalities are written in slope-intercept form, so look for parallel lines (two lines that have the same slope but different y-intercepts). The slopes in (A) are different ($m = 1$ and $m = 2$), so eliminate this choice. The same is true for (B) ($m = 1$ and $m = -1$) and (D) ($m = -1$ and $m = 1$). This means **(C)** must be correct ($m = 1$ and $m = 1$, $b = 1$ and $b = -1$). The graph of the system is shown here:

Because the shading never overlaps, the system has no solution.

5. B

Difficulty: Medium

Category: Passport to Advanced Math/Quadratics

Getting to the Answer: Although this question asks where the graphs intersect, it is not necessary to actually graph them. The point(s) at which the two graphs intersect are the points where the two equations are equal to each other. Therefore, set the equations equal and use algebra to solve for x. Because the question only asks for the x-values, you don't need to substitute the results back into the equations to solve for y.

$$-2x + 1 = 2x^2 + 5x + 4$$
$$-2x = 2x^2 + 5x + 3$$
$$0 = 2x^2 + 7x + 3$$
$$0 = (2x + 1)(x + 3)$$

Now that the equation is factored, solve for x:

$$2x + 1 = 0 \quad \text{and} \quad x + 3 = 0$$
$$2x = -1 \qquad\qquad x = -3$$
$$x = -\frac{1}{2}$$

Choice **(B)** is correct.

6. D

Difficulty: Medium

Category: Heart of Algebra/Linear Equations

Getting to the Answer: You can approach this question conceptually or concretely. When dealing with simple transformations, drawing a quick sketch is most likely the safest approach. You are only concerned about the y-intercept, so keep your focus there. When the graph is reflected over the x-axis, the y-intercept will go from $(0, -1)$ to $(0, 1)$. Next, the line is shifted up 3 units, which adds 3 to the y-coordinates of all the points on the line, making the new y-intercept $(0, 4)$. Choice **(D)** is correct, as shown in the sketch below:

7. D

Difficulty: Medium

Category: Passport to Advanced Math/Quadratics

Getting to the Answer: The roots of an equation are the same as its solutions. Take a peek at the answer choices—they contain radicals, which tells you that the equation can't be factored. Instead, either complete the square or solve the equation using the quadratic formula, whichever you are most comfortable with. The equation is already written in the form $y = ax^2 + bx + c$, and the coefficients are fairly small, so using the quadratic formula is probably the quickest method. Jot down the values that you'll need: $a = 3$, $b = -6$, and $c = -5$. Then, substitute these values into the quadratic formula and simplify:

$$x = \frac{-b \pm \sqrt{b^2 - 4ac}}{2a}$$
$$= \frac{-(-6) \pm \sqrt{(-6)^2 - 4(3)(-5)}}{2(3)}$$
$$= \frac{6 \pm \sqrt{36 + 60}}{6}$$
$$= \frac{6 \pm \sqrt{96}}{6}$$

This is not one of the answer choices, so simplify the radical. To do this, look for a perfect square that divides into 96 and take its square root. Then, if possible, cancel any factors that are common to the numerator and the denominator:

$$x = \frac{6 \pm \sqrt{16 \times 6}}{6}$$
$$= \frac{6 \pm 4\sqrt{6}}{6}$$
$$= \frac{\cancel{2}(3 \pm 2\sqrt{6})}{\cancel{2}(3)}$$
$$= \frac{3 \pm 2\sqrt{6}}{3}$$

Choice **(D)** is correct. Be careful—you can't simplify the answer any further because you cannot divide the square root of 6 by 3.

8. A

Difficulty: Medium

Category: Passport to Advanced Math/Exponents

Getting to the Answer: When you write an equation in terms of a specific variable, you are simply solving the equation for that variable. To do this, you'll need to use the property that raising a quantity to the one-fourth power is the same as taking its fourth root and that applying a negative exponent to a quantity is the same as writing its reciprocal. Rewrite the equation using these properties and then solve for n using inverse operations. Note that the inverse of taking a fourth root of a quantity is raising the quantity to the fourth power:

$$m = \frac{1}{n^{-\frac{1}{4}}}$$

$$m = \frac{\sqrt[4]{n}}{1}$$

$$(m)^4 = \left(\sqrt[4]{n}\right)^4$$

$$m^4 = n$$

Choice **(A)** is correct.

9. C

Difficulty: Medium

Category: Heart of Algebra/Systems of Linear Equations

Getting to the Answer: When a system consists of two equations already written in terms of y, the quickest way to solve the system is to set the equations equal to each other and then use inverse operations. Don't let the fraction intimidate you—you can write the first equation as a fraction over 1 and use cross-multiplication:

$$\frac{3x-1}{1} = \frac{5x+8}{2}$$

$$2(3x-1) = 5x+8$$

$$6x-2 = 5x+8$$

$$6x = 5x+10$$

$$x = 10$$

Don't let (A) fool you—the question is asking for the value of y, not the value of x. To find y, substitute 10 for x in either equation and simplify:

$$y = 3(10)-1$$

$$= 30-1$$

$$= 29$$

Choice **(C)** is correct.

10. A

Difficulty: Medium

Category: Heart of Algebra/Inequalities

Getting to the Answer: You don't need to separate this compound inequality into pieces. Just remember, whatever you do to one piece, you must do to all three pieces. The fractions in this question make it look more complicated than it really is, so start by clearing them. To do this, multiply everything by the least common denominator, 10:

$$0 < \frac{d}{2}+1 \le \frac{8}{5}$$

$$10(0) < 10\left(\frac{d}{2}+1\right) \le \left(\frac{8}{5}\right)10$$

$$0 < 5d+10 \le 16$$

$$-10 < 5d \le 6$$

$$-2 < d \le \frac{6}{5}$$

Now, read the inequality symbols carefully. The value of d is between -2 and $\frac{6}{5}$, not including -2 because of the $<$ symbol, so **(A)** is the correct answer. Don't let (C) fool you—you can't have a 0 *denominator* in a rational expression, but in this expression, the variable is in the numerator, so it *can* equal 0.

11. D

Difficulty: Medium

Category: Heart of Algebra/Linear Equations

Getting to the Answer: Assign a variable to the unknown and then create an equation that represents the scenario. Let n be the number of units the manufacturer sells in a month. Sales must equal expenses for the manufacturer to break even (sales = expenses). The sales are equal to the selling price ($9.50) times the number of units sold (n), so write $9.5n$ on one side of the equal sign. The monthly expenses are the fixed expenses ($11,625) plus the amount paid for the materials needed to produce one unit ($4.85) times the number of units (n), so write $11,625 + 4.85n$ on the other side of the equal sign. Then, solve for n:

$$9.5n = 11,625 + 4.85n$$
$$4.65n = 11,625$$
$$n = 2,500$$

Choice **(D)** is correct.

12. D

Difficulty: Medium

Category: Heart of Algebra/Linear Equations

Getting to the Answer: There is only one equation given and it has two variables. This means that you don't have enough information to solve for either variable. Instead, look for the relationship between the left side of the equation and the other expression that you are trying to find. The expression you are trying to find ($6x - 5y$) has the x-term first and then the y-term, so start by reversing the order of the terms on the left side of the given equation. Also, notice that the x term in $6x - 5y$ is not negative, so multiply the equation by -1:

$$\frac{1}{2}y - \frac{3}{5}x = -16 \quad \rightarrow \quad -\frac{3}{5}x + \frac{1}{2}y = -16$$

$$-1\left(-\frac{3}{5}x + \frac{1}{2}y = -16\right) \quad \rightarrow \quad \frac{3}{5}x - \frac{1}{2}y = 16$$

Finally, there are no fractions in the desired expression, so clear the fractions by multiplying both sides of the equation by 10. This yields the expression that you are looking for, so no further work is required—just read the value on the right-hand side of the equation, which is 160:

$$10\left(\frac{3}{5}x - \frac{1}{2}y\right) = 16(10)$$
$$6x - 5y = 160$$

Choice **(D)** is correct.

13. B

Difficulty: Medium

Category: Passport to Advanced Math/Functions

Getting to the Answer: Understanding the language of functions will make questions that seem complicated much more doable. When you know the output of a function (or in this question, a composition of two functions), you can work backward to find the input. Because $g(x)$ is the inside function for this composition, its output becomes the input for $f(x)$. Unfortunately, you don't have any information about g yet. You do know, however, that f of some number, $g(2)$, is -1, so set $f(x)$ equal to -1 and solve for x:

$$-1 = x + 1$$
$$-2 = x$$

You now know that $f(-2) = -1$. In the equation for the composition, $g(2)$ represents x, so you also know that $g(2)$ must be -2. Your only option now is to use brute force to determine which equation for g, when evaluated at 2, results in -2.

(A): $g(2) = 2 - 6 = -4$ (not -2), eliminate.

(B): $g(2) = 2 - 4 = -2$

You don't need to go any further; **(B)** is correct.

You could check your answer by working forward, starting with $g(2)$:

$$g(2) = 2 - 4 = -2$$
$$f(g(2)) = f(-2) = -2 + 1 = -1$$

14. 1/5 or .2

Difficulty: Medium

Category: Heart of Algebra/Linear Equations

Getting to the Answer: There are two variables but only one equation, so you can't actually solve the equation for k. Instead, recall that an equation has infinitely many solutions when the left side is identical to the right side. When this happens, everything cancels out and you get $0 = 0$, which is always true. Start by simplifying the right-hand side of the equation. Don't simplify the left side because k is already in a good position:

$$k(10x - 5) = 2(3 + x) - 7$$
$$k(10x - 5) = 6 + 2x - 7$$
$$k(10x - 5) = 2x - 1$$

Next, compare the left side of the equation to the right side. Rather than distributing the k, notice that $2x$ is a fifth of $10x$ and -1 is a fifth of -5, so if k were $\frac{1}{5}$ (or 0.2), then both sides of the equation would equal $2x - 1$, and it would therefore have infinitely many solutions. Thus, k is **1/5 or .2**. Grid in either of these responses.

15. 2

Difficulty: Medium

Category: Additional Topics in Math/Geometry

Getting to the Answer: You could use the Pythagorean theorem to solve this, but it will save valuable time on test day if you recognize that this question is testing your knowledge of Pythagorean triples. The triangle is a right triangle with leg lengths of 18 and 24, which, when divided by 6, are in the proportion 3:4. This means that the triangle is a scaled up 3:4:5 right triangle with a scale factor of 6. To keep the same proportion, the hypotenuse must be $5 \times 6 = 30$. For $15n$ to equal 30, n must be **2**.

16. 3

Difficulty: Hard

Category: Passport to Advanced Math/Exponents

Getting to the Answer: You need to use rules of exponents to simplify the expression. Before you can do that, you must rewrite the radicals as fraction exponents. Use the phrase "power over root" to help you convert the radicals: $\sqrt{x} = \sqrt[\text{root} \to 2]{x^{1 \leftarrow \text{power}}} = x^{\frac{1}{2}}$

and $\sqrt[\text{root} \to 4]{x^{3 \leftarrow \text{power}}} = x^{\frac{3}{4}}$. Then, use rules of exponents

to simplify the expression. Add the exponents of the factors that are being multiplied and subtract the exponent of the factor that is being divided:

$$\frac{\sqrt{x} \cdot x^{\frac{5}{4}} \cdot x^2}{\sqrt[4]{x^3}} = \frac{x^{\frac{1}{2}} \cdot x^{\frac{5}{4}} \cdot x^{\frac{2}{1}}}{x^{\frac{3}{4}}}$$
$$= x^{\frac{1}{2} + \frac{5}{4} + \frac{2}{1} - \frac{3}{4}} = x^{\frac{2}{4} + \frac{5}{4} + \frac{8}{4} - \frac{3}{4}} = x^{\frac{12}{4}} = x^3$$

The exponent of the simplified expression is **3**.

17. 6

Difficulty: Hard

Category: Passport to Advanced Math/Quadratics

Getting to the Answer: When you are given the graph of a parabola, try to use what you know about intercepts, the vertex, and the axis of symmetry to answer the question. Here, you could try to use points from the graph to find its equation, but this is not necessary because the question only asks for the value of b. As a shortcut, recall that you can find the vertex of a parabola using the formula $x = -\frac{b}{2a}$ (the quadratic formula without the radical part). You are given that $a = -1$. Now, look at the graph—the vertex of the parabola is (3, 8), so substitute 3 for x, -1 for a, and solve for b:

$$3 = -\frac{b}{2(-1)}$$
$$3 = -\left(\frac{b}{-2}\right)$$
$$3 = \frac{b}{2}$$
$$3(2) = b$$
$$6 = b$$

As an alternate method, you could plug the value of a and the vertex (from the graph) into vertex form of a quadratic equation and simplify:

$$y = a(x - h)^2 + k$$
$$= -1(x - 3)^2 + 8$$
$$= -1\left(x^2 - 6x + 9\right) + 8$$
$$= -x^2 + 6x - 9 + 8$$
$$= -x^2 + 6x - 1$$

The coefficient of x is b, so $b = $ **6**.

Math Test—Calculator

1. D

Difficulty: Easy

Category: Problem Solving and Data Analysis/ Scatterplots

Getting to the Answer: Graphically, slope is the ratio of the change in the *y*-values (rise) to the change in the *x*-values (run). In a real-world scenario, this is the same as the unit rate. In this context, the rise describes the change in the number of home runs hit in a single season, and the run describes the change in the number of hours a player spends in batting practice. Thus, the unit rate, or slope, represents the estimated increase (since the data trends upward) in the number of single-season home runs hit by a player for each hour he spends in batting practice. **(D)** is correct.

2. B

Difficulty: Easy

Category: Heart of Algebra/Linear Equations

Getting to the Answer: Finding an *x*-intercept is easy when you know the equation of the line—it's the value of *x* when *y* is 0. Notice that the answer choices are very close together. This means you shouldn't just estimate visually. Take the time to do the math. Everything you need to write the equation is shown on the graph—just pay careful attention to how the grid lines are labeled. The *y*-intercept is 10 and the line rises 2 units and runs 1 unit from one point to the next, so the slope is $\frac{2}{1} = 2$. This means the equation of the line, in slope-intercept form, is $y = 2x + 10$. Now, set the equation equal to zero and solve for *x*:

$$0 = 2x + 10$$
$$-10 = 2x$$
$$-5 = x$$

The line will intersect the *x*-axis at -5, which is **(B)**.

3. A

Difficulty: Easy

Category: Passport to Advanced Math/Functions

Getting to the Answer: When you see an expression like $f(x)$, it means to substitute the given value for *x* in the function's equation. When there is more than one function involved, pay careful attention to which

function should be evaluated first. You are looking for the value of $f(x)$ at $x = 5$. Because $f(x)$ is defined in terms of $g(x)$, evaluate $g(5)$ first by substituting 5 for *x* in the expression $x + 2$:

$$g(5) = 5 + 2 = 7$$
$$f(5) = -3g(5) = -3(7) = -21$$

Therefore, **(A)** is correct.

4. B

Difficulty: Medium

Category: Heart of Algebra/Linear Equations

Getting to the Answer: The cost per night in the hospital is the same as the unit rate, which is represented by the slope of the line. Use the grid lines and the axis labels to count the rise and the run from the *y*-intercept of the line (0, 26,000) to the next point that hits an intersection of two grid lines, (2, 34,000). Pay careful attention to how the grid lines are marked (by 2s on the *x*-axis and by 2,000s on the *y*-axis). The line rises 8,000 units and runs 2 units, so the slope is $\frac{8,000}{2}$, which means it costs an average of $4,000 per night to stay in the hospital. Note that you could also use the slope formula and the two points to find the slope:

$$\frac{34,000 - 26,000}{2 - 0} = \frac{8,000}{2} = 4,000$$

Choice **(B)** is correct.

5. D

Difficulty: Medium

Category: Problem Solving and Data Analysis/ Scatterplots

Getting to the Answer: You aren't given much information to go on except the shape of the graph, so you'll need to think about what the shape means. Remember, linear functions increase at a constant rate, exponential functions increase at either an increasing or decreasing rate, gradually at first and then more quickly or vice versa, and quadratics and polynomials reverse direction one or more times. The graph begins by decreasing extremely quickly, but then it almost (but not quite) levels off. Therefore, it can't be linear, and because it doesn't change direction, an exponential function, **(D)**, would be the best model for the data.

6. A

Difficulty: Medium

Category: Problem Solving and Data Analysis/Statistics and Probability

Getting to the Answer: This is a science crossover question. Read the first three sentences quickly—they are simply describing the context. The second half of the paragraph poses the question, so read that more carefully. In the sample, 2,800 out of 3,200 acres were free of kudzu after applying the herbicide. This is $\frac{2,800}{3,200} = 0.875 = 87.5\%$ of the area. For the whole region, assuming the same general conditions, $0.875(30,000) = 26,250$ acres should be free of the kudzu. Be careful—this is not the answer. The question asks how much of the cropland would *still be covered* by kudzu, so subtract to get $30,000 - 26,250 = 3,750$ acres. **(A)** is correct.

7. B

Difficulty: Medium

Category: Passport to Advanced Math/Functions

Getting to the Answer: The notation $g(h(x))$ indicates a composition of two functions, which can be read "g of h of x." It means that the output when x is substituted in $h(x)$ becomes the input for $g(x)$. First, use the top and bottom rows of the table to find that $h(3)$ is 2. This is your new input. Now, use the top and middle rows of the table to find $g(2)$, which is -3, so **(B)** is correct.

8. B

Difficulty: Medium

Category: Heart of Algebra/Linear Equations

Getting to the Answer: The key to answering this type of question is determining how many results fit in each category. Here, you need to know how many shots were 3-pointers and how many were 2-pointers. Mae-Ling successfully made 15 shots total and *s* were 3-pointers, so the rest, or $15 - s$, must have been 2-pointers. Write the expression in words first: points per 3-pointers (3) times number of shots that were 3-pointers (*s*), plus points per regular goal (2) times number of regular goals $(15 - s)$. Now, translate from English into math: $3s + 2(15 - s)$. This is not one of the answer choices, so simplify the expression by distributing the 2 and then combining like terms: $3s + 2(15 - s) = 3s + 30 - 2s = s + 30$. This matches **(B)**.

9. A

Difficulty: Medium

Category: Problem Solving and Data Analysis/Rates, Ratios, Proportions, and Percentages

Getting to the Answer: Let the units in this question guide you to the answer. You can do one conversion at a time or all of them at once. Just be sure to line up the units so they'll cancel correctly. The company uses 8 machines, each of which pumps at a rate of 37.5 gallons per minute, so the rate is actually $8 \times 37.5 = 300$ gallons per minute. Find the total number of gallons needed and then use the rate to find the time:

$$2,500 \; \cancel{\text{bbl}} \times \frac{42 \; \cancel{\text{gallons}}}{1 \; \cancel{\text{bbl}}} \times \frac{1 \; \text{minute}}{300 \; \cancel{\text{gallons}}} = 350 \; \text{minutes}$$

The answers are given in hours and minutes, so change 350 minutes to $350 \div 60 = 5.833$ hours, which is 5 hours and 50 minutes. **(A)** is correct.

10. C

Difficulty: Medium

Category: Problem Solving and Data Analysis/Functions

Getting to the Answer: Look for a pattern for the sales of each company. Then, apply that pattern to see which one will sell more in the last month of the year. Writing a function that represents each pattern will also help, but you have to be careful that you evaluate the function at the correct input value. Company A's sales can be represented by a linear function because each month the company sells 92 more of the toy than the month before, which is a constant difference. The sales can be represented by the function $f(t) = 92t + 54$, where *t* is the number of months *after January*. December is 11 months (not 12) after January, so during the last month of the year company A should sell $f(11) = 92(11) + 54 = 1,066$ of the toy. Company B's sales can be represented by an exponential function because the sales are doubling each month, which is a constant ratio (2 for doubling). The function is $g(t) = 15(2)^t$, where *t* is again the number of months *after January*. In December, company B should sell $g(11) = 15(2)^{11} = 30,720$. This means that in December, company B should sell $30,720 - 1,066 = 29,654$ more of the toy than company A. Choice **(C)** is correct.

11. A

Difficulty: Medium

Category: Heart of Algebra/Inequalities

Getting to the Answer: Apply logic to this question first and then algebra. The dot at the beginning of the shaded portion is an open dot, so -2 is not included in the solution set of the inequality. This means you can eliminate (C) and (D) because those symbols *would* include the endpoint. Don't immediately choose (B) just because the arrow is pointing to the right, which typically indicates *greater than*. When dealing with an inequality, if you multiply or divide by a negative number, you must flip the symbol, so the answer is not necessarily what you might think. Because you were able to eliminate two of the choices, the quickest approach is to pick one of the remaining symbols, plug it in, and see if it works. If it does, choose that answer. If it doesn't, then it must be the other symbol. Try (A):

$$5(x-2)-3x < 4x-6$$
$$5x-10-3x < 4x-6$$
$$2x-10 < 4x-6$$
$$-2x < 4$$
$$x > -2$$

The resulting inequality, $x > -2$, means all the values on the number line greater than (or to the right of) -2, so the initial inequality symbol must have been $<$. Choice **(A)** is correct.

12. B

Difficulty: Easy

Category: Problem Solving and Data Analysis/Rates, Ratios, Proportions, and Percents

Getting to the Answer: When a question involves scale factors, set up a proportion and solve for the missing value:

$$\frac{1}{8} = \frac{x}{19.9}$$
$$8x = 19.9$$
$$x = 2.4875 \approx 2.5$$

Choice **(B)** is correct.

13. C

Difficulty: Easy

Category: Problem Solving and Data Analysis/Rates, Ratios, Proportions, and Percents

Getting to the Answer: Don't make this question harder than it actually is. You don't need to find the new scale factor. Instead, use the length that the student drew the femur and the actual length to set up and solve a new proportion:

$$\frac{\text{drawing of sternum}}{\text{actual sternum}} = \frac{\text{drawing of femur}}{\text{actual femur}}$$
$$\frac{x}{6.7} = \frac{3.5}{19.9}$$
$$23.45 = 19.9x$$
$$1.1783 = x$$
$$x \approx 1.2$$

Choice **(C)** is correct.

14. B

Difficulty: Medium

Category: Heart of Algebra/Linear Equations

Getting to the Answer: Given two points (even when the coordinates are variables), the slope of the line between the points can be found using the formula $m = \frac{y_2 - y_1}{x_2 - x_1}$. You are given a numerical value for the slope and a pair of ordered pairs that have variables in them. To find the value of c, plug the points into the slope formula and then solve for c. Be careful of all the negative signs:

$$m = \frac{y_2 - y_1}{x_2 - x_1}$$
$$\frac{1}{2} = \frac{-8-2c}{-c-(4-c)}$$
$$\frac{1}{2} = \frac{-8-2c}{-c-4+c}$$
$$\frac{1}{2} = \frac{-8-2c}{-4}$$
$$1(-4) = 2(-8-2c)$$
$$-4 = -16-4c$$
$$12 = -4c$$
$$-3 = c$$

Choice **(B)** is correct.

Practice Tests

15. A

Difficulty: Medium

Category: Problem Solving and Data Analysis/Rates, Ratios, Proportions, and Percents

Getting to the Answer: Questions that involve distance, rate, and time can almost always be solved using the formula Distance = rate × time. Break the question into short steps (first part of trip, second part of trip). Start with the plane from DCA. Use the speed, or rate, of the plane, 338 miles per hour, and its distance from London, 3,718 miles, to determine when it arrived. You don't know the time, so call it t:

$$\text{Distance} = \text{rate} \times \text{time}$$
$$3,718 = 338t$$
$$11 = t$$

It took the DCA flight 11 hours. Now, determine how long it took the plane from MIA. You'll need to find the distance for each part of the trip—the question only tells you the total distance. Then, use the formula to find how long the plane flew at 596 miles per hour and how long it flew at 447 miles per hour.

First Part of Trip	*Second Part of Trip*
$\frac{2}{3} \times 4,470 = 2,980$ miles	$\frac{1}{3} \times 4,470 = 1,490$ miles
$2,980 = 596t$	$1,490 = 447t$
$5 = t$	$3.\overline{3} = t$

This means it took the MIA flight 5 hours + 3 hours, 20 minutes = 8 hours, 20 minutes. So, the plane from MIA arrived first. It arrived 11 hours − 8 hours, 20 minutes = 2 hours, 40 minutes before the plane from DCA, so **(A)** is correct.

16. D

Difficulty: Medium

Category: Passport to Advanced Math/Quadratics

Getting to the Answer: The graph of every quadratic equation is a parabola, which may or may not cross the x-axis, depending on where its vertex is and which way it opens. When an equation has no solution, its graph does not cross the x-axis, so try to envision the graph of each of the answer choices (or you could graph each one in your graphing calculator, but this will probably take longer). Don't forget—if the equation is written in vertex form, $y = a(x − h)^2 + k$, then the vertex is (h, k) and the value of a tells you which way the parabola opens. When

a quadratic equation is written in factored form, the factors tell you the x-intercepts, which means (A) and (B) (which are factored) must cross the x-axis, so eliminate them. Now, imagine the graph of the equation in (C): The vertex is $(−1, 8)$ and a is negative, so the parabola opens downward and consequently must cross the x-axis. This means **(D)** must be correct. The vertex is also $(−1, 8)$, but a is positive, so the graph opens up and does not cross the x-axis.

17. D

Difficulty: Medium

Category: Problem Solving and Data Analysis/Statistics and Probability

Getting to the Answer: The two variables are certainly correlated—as one goes up, the other goes up. A linear regression model would fit the data fairly well, so you can eliminate (C). The spending is graphed on the x-axis, so it is the independent variable and therefore does not depend on the GDP, graphed on the y-axis, so you can eliminate (B) as well. The data does show that as spending on students increases, so does the GDP, but this is simply correlation, not causation. Without additional data, no statements can be made about whether spending more on students is the reason for the increased GDP, so **(D)** is correct.

18. C

Difficulty: Easy

Category: Passport to Advanced Math/Rational Equations

Getting to the Answer: Focus on the question at the very end—it's just asking you to solve the equation for p_2. Multiply both sides by T_2 to get rid of the denominator on the right-hand side of the equation. Then divide by V_2 to isolate p_2:

$$\frac{p_1 V_1}{T_1} = \frac{p_2 V_2}{T_2}$$
$$\frac{p_1 V_1 T_2}{T_1} = p_2 V_2$$
$$\frac{p_1 V_1 T_2}{T_1 V_2} = p_2$$

Stop here! You cannot cancel the V's and T's because the subscripts indicate that they are not the same variable. In math, subscripts do not behave the same way superscripts (exponents) do. Choice **(C)** is correct.

19. C

Difficulty: Medium

Category: Problem Solving and Data Analysis/Rates, Ratios, Proportions, and Percents

Getting to the Answer: The factor-label method (canceling units) is a great strategy for this question. You're starting with tons, so work from that unit, arranging conversions so that units cancel. To keep units straight, use an E for Earth, an M for Mars, and a J for Jupiter:

$$1.5 \, \cancel{T} \times \frac{2{,}000 \, \text{lb} \, \cancel{(E)}}{1 \, \cancel{T}} \times \frac{0.377 \, \text{lb (M)}}{1 \, \text{lb} \, \cancel{(E)}} = 1{,}131 \, \text{lb (M)}$$

$$1.5 \, \cancel{T} \times \frac{2{,}000 \, \text{lb} \, \cancel{(E)}}{1 \, \cancel{T}} \times \frac{2.364 \, \text{lb (J)}}{1 \, \text{lb} \, \cancel{(E)}} = 7{,}092 \, \text{lb (J)}$$

The object weighs 1,131 pounds on Mars and 7,092 pounds on Jupiter, so it weighs $7{,}092 - 1{,}131 = 5{,}961$ more pounds on Jupiter. **(C)** is correct.

20. C

Difficulty: Medium

Category: Problem Solving and Data Analysis/Statistics and Probability

Getting to the Answer: Examine the shape of the data and familiarize yourself with the title and the axis labels on the graph. Data is *symmetric* if it is fairly evenly spread out, and it is *skewed* if it has a long tail on either side. Notice that the data is skewed to the right, so you can immediately eliminate (A). Choices (B), (C), and (D) all describe the data as skewed to the right, so you'll need to examine those statements more closely. For (B), "adverse reactions" include the last four bars, which represent $89 + 41 + 22 + 8 = 160$ participants total, which is not even close to 50 percent of 900, so eliminate (B). Note that you don't need to add all the bar heights to find that there were 900 participants—the title of the graph tells you that. Now look at (C)—"failed

to have adverse reactions" means "None" or "Mild" (the first three bars), which represent $900 - 160 = 740$ of the 900 participants. Since, 75% of $900 = 675$, and 740 is more than 675, **(C)** is correct. For (D), the "None" column contains 320 participants, which does not equal approximately 50% of 900, so it too is incorrect.

21. C

Difficulty: Medium

Category: Heart of Algebra/Systems of Linear Equations

Getting to the Answer: Use the Kaplan Method for Translating English into Math. Write a system of equations with p = the cost in dollars of the Pennsylvania bar exam and d = the cost of the D.C. bar exam. The Pennsylvania bar exam (p) costs \$25 less (-25) than 3 times as much ($3d$) as the D.C. bar exam, or $p = 3d - 25$. Together, both bar exams cost \$775, so $d + p = 775$. The system is:

$$\begin{cases} p = 3d - 25 \\ d + p = 775 \end{cases}$$

The top equation is already solved for p, so substitute $3d - 25$ into the second equation for p, and solve for d:

$$d + (3d - 25) = 775$$
$$4d = 800$$
$$d = 200$$

Be careful—that's not the answer. The D.C. bar exam costs \$200, which means the Pennsylvania bar exam costs \$775 − \$200 = \$575. This means the D.C. bar exam is \$575 − \$200 = \$375 less expensive than the Pennsylvania bar exam. Choice **(C)** is correct.

22. B

Difficulty: Medium

Category: Problem Solving and Data Analysis/Statistics and Probability

Getting to the Answer: Always read the axis labels carefully when a question involves a chart or graph. *Frequency*, which is plotted along the vertical axis, tells you how many students missed the number of questions indicated under each bar. Evaluate each statement as quickly as you can.

(A): Add the bar heights (frequencies) that represent students that missed 5 or more questions: $7 + 3 + 3 + 2 = 15$. Then, find the total number of students represented, which is the number that missed less than 5 questions plus the 15 you just found: $2 + 3 + 4 + 6 = 15$, plus the 15 you already found, for a total of 30 students. The statement is not true because 15 is exactly half (not more than half) of 30. Eliminate.

(B): This calculation will take a bit of time so skip it for now.

(C): The tallest bar tells you which number of questions was missed most often, which was 5 questions, not 3 questions, so this statement is not true. Eliminate.

(D): The number of students from Mr. Juno's class who took the test that day is the sum of the heights of the bars, which you already know is 30, not 36. Eliminate.

This means **(B)** must be correct. Mark it and move on to the next question. In case you're curious, find the mean by multiplying each number of questions missed by the corresponding frequency, adding all the products, and dividing by the total number of students, which you already know is 30:

$$\text{mean} = \frac{2 + 6 + 12 + 24 + 35 + 18 + 21 + 16}{30}$$

$$= \frac{134}{30} = 4.4\overline{6}$$

The mean is indeed between 4 and 5.

23. C

Difficulty: Hard

Category: Passport to Advanced Math/Quadratics

Getting to the Answer: Writing quadratic equations can be tricky and time-consuming. If you know the roots, you can use factors to write the equation. If you don't know the roots, you need to create a system of equations to find the coefficients of the variable terms. You don't know the roots of this equation, so start with the point that

has the nicest values $(0, 2)$ and substitute them into the equation, $y = ax^2 + bx + c$, to get $2 = a(0)^2 + b(0) + c$, or $2 = c$. Now your equation looks like $y = ax^2 + bx + 2$. Next, use the other two points to create a system of two equations in two variables:

$$(-6, -7) \rightarrow -7 = a(-6)^2 + b(-6) + 2 \rightarrow -9 = 36a - 6b$$
$$(8, -14) \rightarrow -14 = a(8)^2 + b(8) + 2 \rightarrow -16 = 64a + 8b$$

You now have a system of equations to solve. If you multiply the top equation by 4 and the bottom equation by 3, and then add the equations, the b terms will eliminate each other:

$$4[-9 = 36a - 6b] \quad \rightarrow \quad -36 = 144a - 24b$$
$$3[-16 = 64a + 8b] \quad \rightarrow \quad -48 = 192a + 24b$$
$$\overline{}$$
$$-84 = 336a$$
$$-0.25 = a$$

Now, find b by substituting $a = -0.25$ into either of the original equations. Using the top equation, you get:

$$-9 = 36(-0.25) - 6b$$
$$-9 = -9 - 6b$$
$$0 = 6b$$
$$0 = b$$

The value of $a + b + c$ is $(-0.25) + 0 + 2 = 1.75$, so **(C)** is correct.

24. D

Difficulty: Hard

Category: Problem Solving and Data Analysis/Rates, Ratios, Proportions, and Percentages

Getting to the Answer: Read the question, organizing important information as you go. You need to find the ratio of mini muffins to jumbo muffins. You're given two ratios: mini to regular and regular to jumbo. Both of the given ratios contain regular muffin size units, but the regular amounts (2 and 5) are not identical. To directly compare them, find a common multiple (10). Multiply each ratio by the factor that will make the number of regular muffins equal to 10:

Mini to regular: $(5{:}2) \times (5{:}5) = 25{:}10$

Regular to jumbo: $(5{:}4) \times (2{:}2) = 10{:}8$

Now that the number of regular muffins is the same in both ratios (10), you can merge the two ratios to compare mini to jumbo directly: 25:10:8. So, the proper ratio of mini muffins to jumbo muffins is 25:8, which is **(D)**.

25. A

Difficulty: Medium

Category: Heart of Algebra/Systems of Linear Equations

Getting to the Answer: Graphically, a system of linear equations that has no solution indicates two parallel lines, or in other words, two lines that have the same slope. So, write each of the equations in slope-intercept form ($y = mx + b$) and set their slopes (m) equal to each other to solve for k. Before finding the slopes, multiply the top equation by 6 to make it easier to manipulate.

$$6\left(\frac{1}{3}x + \frac{1}{2}y = 5\right) \rightarrow 2x + 3y = 30 \rightarrow y = -\frac{2}{3}x + 10$$

$$kx - 4y = 16 \rightarrow -4y = -kx + 16 \rightarrow y = \frac{k}{4}x - 4$$

The slope of the first line is $-\frac{2}{3}$ and the slope of the second line is $\frac{k}{4}$. Set them equal and solve for k:

$$-\frac{2}{3} = \frac{k}{4}$$
$$-8 = 3k$$
$$-\frac{8}{3} = k$$

Choice **(A)** is correct.

26. D

Difficulty: Hard

Category: Passport to Advanced Math/Exponents

Getting to the Answer: The numbers in some questions are simply too large to use a calculator (you get an "overflow" error message). Instead, you'll have to rely on rules of exponents. Notice that all of the base numbers have 3 as a factor, so rewrite everything in terms of 3. This will allow you to use the rules of exponents. Because 27 is the cube of 3, you can rewrite 27^{90} as a power of 3:

$$27^{90} = \left(3^3\right)^{90}$$
$$= 3^{3 \times 90}$$
$$= 3^{270}$$

Now, the product should read: $3^{90} \times 3^{270}$, which is equal to $3^{90+270} = 3^{360}$. Repeat this process for the quantity that is being divided:

$$\left(\frac{1}{9}\right)^{30} = \left(\frac{1}{3^2}\right)^{30} = \left(3^{-2}\right)^{30} = 3^{-60}$$

Finally, use rules of exponents one more time to simplify the new expression:

$$\frac{3^{360}}{3^{-60}} = 3^{360+60} = 3^{420}$$

All the answer choices are given as powers of 9, so rewrite your answer as a power of 9:

$$3^{420} = 3^{2 \times 210} = \left(3^2\right)^{210} = 9^{210}$$

Choice **(D)** is correct.

27. D

Difficulty: Hard

Category: Additional Topics in Math/Geometry

Getting to the Answer: If needed, don't forget to check the formulas provided for you at the beginning of each Math section. The volume of a right cone is given by $V = \frac{1}{3}\pi r^2 h$. Here, you only know the value of one of the variables, V, so you'll need to use the information in the question to somehow write r and h in terms of just one variable. If the cone is three times as wide at the base as it is tall, then call the diameter $3x$ and the height of the cone one-third of that, or x. The volume formula calls for the radius, which is half the diameter, or $\frac{3x}{2}$. Substitute these values into the formula and solve for x:

$$V = \frac{1}{3}\pi r^2 h$$
$$384\pi = \frac{1}{3}\pi\left(\frac{3}{2}x\right)^2 x$$
$$384 = \left(\frac{1}{3}\right)\left(\frac{9}{4}x^2\right)x$$
$$384 = \frac{3}{4}x^3$$
$$512 = x^3$$
$$\sqrt[3]{512} = x$$
$$8 = x$$

The question asks for the diameter of the base, which is $3x = 3(8) = 24$, choice **(D)**.

28. 85

Difficulty: Easy

Category: Problem Solving and Data Analysis/ Scatterplots

Getting to the Answer: The *range* of a set of data points is the set of outputs, which correspond to the y-values of the data points on the graph. To find the maximum value in the range of the data, look for the highest point on the graph, which is (250, 85). The y-value is 85, so **85** is the maximum value in the range.

29. 7

Difficulty: Hard

Category: Heart of Algebra/Linear Equations

Getting to the Answer: To write the equation of a line, you need two things: the slope and the y-intercept. Start by finding these, substituting them into slope-intercept form of a line ($y = mx + b$), and then manipulate the equation so that it is written in standard form. Use the given points, $(-4, 1)$ and $(3, -2)$, and the slope formula to find m:

$$m = \frac{y_2 - y_1}{x_2 - x_1} = \frac{-2 - 1}{3 - (-4)} = -\frac{3}{7}$$

Next, find the y-intercept, b, using the slope and one of the points:

$$y = -\frac{3}{7}x + b$$
$$1 = -\frac{3}{7}(-4) + b$$
$$1 = \frac{12}{7} + b$$
$$-\frac{5}{7} = b$$

Write the equation in slope-intercept form:

$$y = -\frac{3}{7}x - \frac{5}{7}$$

Now, rewrite the equation in the form $Ax + By = C$, making sure that A is a positive integer (a whole number greater than 0):

$$y = -\frac{3}{7}x - \frac{5}{7}$$
$$\frac{3}{7}x + y = -\frac{5}{7}$$
$$7\left(\frac{3}{7}x + y = -\frac{5}{7}\right)7$$
$$3x + 7y = -5$$

The question asks for the value of B (the coefficient of y), so the correct answer is **7**.

30. 380

Difficulty: Medium

Category: Problem Solving and Data Analysis/Rates, Ratios, Proportions, and Percents

Getting to the Answer: You can use the formula Percent $\times$ whole $=$ part to solve this problem, but you will first need to think conceptually about what the question is asking. The question is asking for the Dow value *before* the 19.5% decrease to 306. This means that 306 represents $100 - 19.5 = 80.5\%$ of what the stock market was at its record high. Fill these amounts into the equation and solve for the original whole, the record high Dow value:

$$0.805 \times w = 306$$
$$w = \frac{306}{0.805}$$
$$w = 380.124$$

Rounded to the nearest whole point, the record high was approximately **380** points.

31. 25

Difficulty: Hard

Category: Problem Solving and Data Analysis/Rates, Ratios, Proportions, and Percents

Getting to the Answer: Percent change is given by the ratio $\frac{\text{amount of change}}{\text{original amount}}$. To find the total percent change, you'll need to work your way through each of the days, and then use the ratio. Jot down the Dow value at the end of each day as you go. Do not round until you reach your final answer. First, calculate the value of the Dow at closing on Black Thursday: it opened at 306 and decreased by 2%, which means the value at the end of the day was $100 - 2 = 98\%$ of the starting amount, or $306 \times 0.98 = 299.88$. Then, it decreased again on Monday by 13% to close at $100 - 13 = 87\%$ of the opening amount, or $299.88 \times 0.87 = 260.8956$. Finally, it decreased on Tuesday by another 12% to end at $100 - 12 = 88\%$ of the starting amount, or $260.8956 \times 0.88 = 229.588$. Now, use the percent change formula to calculate the percent decrease from opening on Black Thursday (306) to closing on Black Tuesday (229.588):

$$\text{Percent decrease} = \frac{306 - 229.588}{306} = \frac{76.412}{306} = 0.2497$$

The Dow had a total percent decrease of approximately **25%** between opening on Black Thursday and closing on Black Tuesday.

PSAT Practice Test 2 Answer Sheet

You will see an answer sheet like the one below on test day. Review the answer key following the test when finished.

When testing, start with number 1 for each section. If a section has fewer questions than answer spaces, leave the extra spaces blank.

SECTION 1

1. Ⓐ Ⓑ Ⓒ Ⓓ	14. Ⓐ Ⓑ Ⓒ Ⓓ	27. Ⓐ Ⓑ Ⓒ Ⓓ	40. Ⓐ Ⓑ Ⓒ Ⓓ
2. Ⓐ Ⓑ Ⓒ Ⓓ	15. Ⓐ Ⓑ Ⓒ Ⓓ	28. Ⓐ Ⓑ Ⓒ Ⓓ	41. Ⓐ Ⓑ Ⓒ Ⓓ
3. Ⓐ Ⓑ Ⓒ Ⓓ	16. Ⓐ Ⓑ Ⓒ Ⓓ	29. Ⓐ Ⓑ Ⓒ Ⓓ	42. Ⓐ Ⓑ Ⓒ Ⓓ
4. Ⓐ Ⓑ Ⓒ Ⓓ	17. Ⓐ Ⓑ Ⓒ Ⓓ	30. Ⓐ Ⓑ Ⓒ Ⓓ	43. Ⓐ Ⓑ Ⓒ Ⓓ
5. Ⓐ Ⓑ Ⓒ Ⓓ	18. Ⓐ Ⓑ Ⓒ Ⓓ	31. Ⓐ Ⓑ Ⓒ Ⓓ	44. Ⓐ Ⓑ Ⓒ Ⓓ
6. Ⓐ Ⓑ Ⓒ Ⓓ	19. Ⓐ Ⓑ Ⓒ Ⓓ	32. Ⓐ Ⓑ Ⓒ Ⓓ	45. Ⓐ Ⓑ Ⓒ Ⓓ
7. Ⓐ Ⓑ Ⓒ Ⓓ	20. Ⓐ Ⓑ Ⓒ Ⓓ	33. Ⓐ Ⓑ Ⓒ Ⓓ	46. Ⓐ Ⓑ Ⓒ Ⓓ
8. Ⓐ Ⓑ Ⓒ Ⓓ	21. Ⓐ Ⓑ Ⓒ Ⓓ	34. Ⓐ Ⓑ Ⓒ Ⓓ	47. Ⓐ Ⓑ Ⓒ Ⓓ
9. Ⓐ Ⓑ Ⓒ Ⓓ	22. Ⓐ Ⓑ Ⓒ Ⓓ	35. Ⓐ Ⓑ Ⓒ Ⓓ	
10. Ⓐ Ⓑ Ⓒ Ⓓ	23. Ⓐ Ⓑ Ⓒ Ⓓ	36. Ⓐ Ⓑ Ⓒ Ⓓ	
11. Ⓐ Ⓑ Ⓒ Ⓓ	24. Ⓐ Ⓑ Ⓒ Ⓓ	37. Ⓐ Ⓑ Ⓒ Ⓓ	
12. Ⓐ Ⓑ Ⓒ Ⓓ	25. Ⓐ Ⓑ Ⓒ Ⓓ	38. Ⓐ Ⓑ Ⓒ Ⓓ	
13. Ⓐ Ⓑ Ⓒ Ⓓ	26. Ⓐ Ⓑ Ⓒ Ⓓ	39. Ⓐ Ⓑ Ⓒ Ⓓ	

☐ # correct in Section 1

☐ # incorrect in Section 1

SECTION 2

1. Ⓐ Ⓑ Ⓒ Ⓓ	12. Ⓐ Ⓑ Ⓒ Ⓓ	23. Ⓐ Ⓑ Ⓒ Ⓓ	34. Ⓐ Ⓑ Ⓒ Ⓓ
2. Ⓐ Ⓑ Ⓒ Ⓓ	13. Ⓐ Ⓑ Ⓒ Ⓓ	24. Ⓐ Ⓑ Ⓒ Ⓓ	35. Ⓐ Ⓑ Ⓒ Ⓓ
3. Ⓐ Ⓑ Ⓒ Ⓓ	14. Ⓐ Ⓑ Ⓒ Ⓓ	25. Ⓐ Ⓑ Ⓒ Ⓓ	36. Ⓐ Ⓑ Ⓒ Ⓓ
4. Ⓐ Ⓑ Ⓒ Ⓓ	15. Ⓐ Ⓑ Ⓒ Ⓓ	26. Ⓐ Ⓑ Ⓒ Ⓓ	37. Ⓐ Ⓑ Ⓒ Ⓓ
5. Ⓐ Ⓑ Ⓒ Ⓓ	16. Ⓐ Ⓑ Ⓒ Ⓓ	27. Ⓐ Ⓑ Ⓒ Ⓓ	38. Ⓐ Ⓑ Ⓒ Ⓓ
6. Ⓐ Ⓑ Ⓒ Ⓓ	17. Ⓐ Ⓑ Ⓒ Ⓓ	28. Ⓐ Ⓑ Ⓒ Ⓓ	39. Ⓐ Ⓑ Ⓒ Ⓓ
7. Ⓐ Ⓑ Ⓒ Ⓓ	18. Ⓐ Ⓑ Ⓒ Ⓓ	29. Ⓐ Ⓑ Ⓒ Ⓓ	40. Ⓐ Ⓑ Ⓒ Ⓓ
8. Ⓐ Ⓑ Ⓒ Ⓓ	19. Ⓐ Ⓑ Ⓒ Ⓓ	30. Ⓐ Ⓑ Ⓒ Ⓓ	41. Ⓐ Ⓑ Ⓒ Ⓓ
9. Ⓐ Ⓑ Ⓒ Ⓓ	20. Ⓐ Ⓑ Ⓒ Ⓓ	31. Ⓐ Ⓑ Ⓒ Ⓓ	42. Ⓐ Ⓑ Ⓒ Ⓓ
10. Ⓐ Ⓑ Ⓒ Ⓓ	21. Ⓐ Ⓑ Ⓒ Ⓓ	32. Ⓐ Ⓑ Ⓒ Ⓓ	43. Ⓐ Ⓑ Ⓒ Ⓓ
11. Ⓐ Ⓑ Ⓒ Ⓓ	22. Ⓐ Ⓑ Ⓒ Ⓓ	33. Ⓐ Ⓑ Ⓒ Ⓓ	44. Ⓐ Ⓑ Ⓒ Ⓓ

☐ # correct in Section 2

☐ # incorrect in Section 2

Practice Tests

SECTION

3

1. Ⓐ Ⓑ Ⓒ Ⓓ   5. Ⓐ Ⓑ Ⓒ Ⓓ   9. Ⓐ Ⓑ Ⓒ Ⓓ   13. Ⓐ Ⓑ Ⓒ Ⓓ
2. Ⓐ Ⓑ Ⓒ Ⓓ   6. Ⓐ Ⓑ Ⓒ Ⓓ   10. Ⓐ Ⓑ Ⓒ Ⓓ
3. Ⓐ Ⓑ Ⓒ Ⓓ   7. Ⓐ Ⓑ Ⓒ Ⓓ   11. Ⓐ Ⓑ Ⓒ Ⓓ
4. Ⓐ Ⓑ Ⓒ Ⓓ   8. Ⓐ Ⓑ Ⓒ Ⓓ   12. Ⓐ Ⓑ Ⓒ Ⓓ

correct in
Section 3

incorrect in
Section 3

14.   15.   16.   17.

SECTION

4

1. Ⓐ Ⓑ Ⓒ Ⓓ   9. Ⓐ Ⓑ Ⓒ Ⓓ   17. Ⓐ Ⓑ Ⓒ Ⓓ   25. Ⓐ Ⓑ Ⓒ Ⓓ
2. Ⓐ Ⓑ Ⓒ Ⓓ   10. Ⓐ Ⓑ Ⓒ Ⓓ   18. Ⓐ Ⓑ Ⓒ Ⓓ   26. Ⓐ Ⓑ Ⓒ Ⓓ
3. Ⓐ Ⓑ Ⓒ Ⓓ   11. Ⓐ Ⓑ Ⓒ Ⓓ   19. Ⓐ Ⓑ Ⓒ Ⓓ   27. Ⓐ Ⓑ Ⓒ Ⓓ
4. Ⓐ Ⓑ Ⓒ Ⓓ   12. Ⓐ Ⓑ Ⓒ Ⓓ   20. Ⓐ Ⓑ Ⓒ Ⓓ
5. Ⓐ Ⓑ Ⓒ Ⓓ   13. Ⓐ Ⓑ Ⓒ Ⓓ   21. Ⓐ Ⓑ Ⓒ Ⓓ
6. Ⓐ Ⓑ Ⓒ Ⓓ   14. Ⓐ Ⓑ Ⓒ Ⓓ   22. Ⓐ Ⓑ Ⓒ Ⓓ
7. Ⓐ Ⓑ Ⓒ Ⓓ   15. Ⓐ Ⓑ Ⓒ Ⓓ   23. Ⓐ Ⓑ Ⓒ Ⓓ
8. Ⓐ Ⓑ Ⓒ Ⓓ   16. Ⓐ Ⓑ Ⓒ Ⓓ   24. Ⓐ Ⓑ Ⓒ Ⓓ

correct in
Section 4

incorrect in
Section 4

28.   29.   30.   31.

Reading Test

60 Minutes—47 Questions

This section corresponds to Section 1 of your answer sheet.

Directions: Read each passage or pair of passages, then answer the questions that follow. Choose your answers based on what the passage(s) and any accompanying graphics state or imply.

Questions 1–9 are based on the following passage.

This passage is adapted from "Metamorphosis" by Franz Kafka, a famous story that combines elements of fantasy and reality. This excerpt begins with the protagonist realizing he has literally turned into a giant, beetle-like insect.

One morning, when Gregor Samsa woke from troubled dreams, he found himself transformed in his bed into a horrible vermin. He lay on his armor-like back, and if he lifted his head a little
5 he could see his brown belly, slightly domed and divided by arches into stiff sections. The bedding was hardly able to cover it and seemed ready to slide off any moment. His many legs, pitifully thin compared with the size of the rest of him, waved
10 about helplessly as he looked.

"What's happened to me?" he thought. It wasn't a dream. His room, a proper human room although a little too small, lay peacefully between its four familiar walls. A collection of textile samples lay
15 spread out on the table—Samsa was a travelling salesman—and above it there hung a picture that he had recently cut out of an illustrated magazine and housed in a nice, gilded frame. It showed a lady fitted out with a fur hat and fur boa who sat
20 upright, raising a heavy fur muff that covered the whole of her lower arm towards the viewer.

Gregor then turned to look out the window at the dull weather. Drops of rain could be heard hitting the pane, which made him feel quite sad.
25 "How about if I sleep a little bit longer and forget all this nonsense," he thought, but that was something he was unable to do because he was used to sleeping on his right, and in his present state couldn't get into that position. However hard he
30 threw himself onto his right, he always rolled back to where he was. He must have tried it a hundred times,

shut his eyes so that he wouldn't have to look at the floundering legs, and only stopped when he began to feel a mild, dull pain there that he had never felt before.

35 He thought, "What a strenuous career it is that I've chosen! Travelling day in and day out. Doing business like this takes much more effort than doing your own business at home, and on top of that there's the curse of travelling, worries about
40 making train connections, bad and irregular food, contact with different people all the time so that you can never get to know anyone or become friendly with them." He felt a slight itch up on his belly; pushed himself slowly up on his back
45 towards the headboard so that he could lift his head better; found where the itch was, and saw that it was covered with lots of little white spots which he didn't know what to make of; and when he tried to feel the place with one of his legs he drew it quickly
50 back because as soon as he touched it he was overcome by a cold shudder.

He slid back into his former position. "Getting up early all the time," he thought, "it makes you stupid. You've got to get enough sleep. Other
55 travelling salesmen live a life of luxury. For instance, whenever I go back to the guest house during the morning to copy out the contract, these gentlemen are always still sitting there eating their breakfasts. I ought to just try that with my boss; I'd
60 get kicked out on the spot. But who knows, maybe that would be the best thing for me. If I didn't have my parents to think about I'd have given in my notice a long time ago, I'd have gone up to the boss and told him just what I think, tell him everything
65 I would, let him know just what I feel. He'd fall right off his desk! And it's a funny sort of business to be sitting up there at your desk, talking down at your subordinates from up there, especially when you

GO ON TO THE NEXT PAGE

have to go right up close because the boss is hard
70 of hearing. Well, there's still some hope; once I've
got the money together to pay off my parents' debt
to him—another five or six years I suppose—that's
definitely what I'll do. That's when I'll make the big
change. First of all though, I've got to get up, my
75 train leaves at five."

1. According to the passage, Gregor initially believes
his transformation is a

A) curse.

B) disease.

C) nightmare.

D) hoax.

2. As used in line 12, "proper" most nearly means

A) called for by rules or conventions.

B) showing politeness.

C) naturally belonging or peculiar to.

D) suitably appropriate.

3. The passage most strongly suggests which of the
following about Gregor's attitude toward his
profession?

A) He is resentful.

B) He is diligent.

C) He is depressed.

D) He is eager to please.

4. Which choice provides the best evidence for the
answer to the previous question?

A) Lines 14–18 ("A collection…gilded frame")

B) Lines 22–24 ("Gregor then turned…quite
sad")

C) Lines 54–60 ("Other…the spot")

D) Lines 66–70 ("And it's…hard of hearing")

5. What central idea does the passage communicate
through Gregor's experiences?

A) Imagination is a dangerous thing.

B) People are fearful of change.

C) Dreams become our reality.

D) Humankind is a slave to work.

6. The passage most strongly suggests that which of
the following is true of Gregor?

A) He feels a strong sense of duty toward his
family.

B) He is unable to cope with change.

C) He excels in his profession.

D) He is fearful about his transformation.

7. Which choice provides the best evidence for the
answer to the previous question?

A) Lines 11–14 ("What's happened…familiar
walls")

B) Lines 22–24 ("Gregor then turned…quite
sad")

C) Lines 36–43 ("Doing business…with them")

D) Lines 70–73 ("Well, there's still…what I'll do")

8. As used in line 33, "floundering" most nearly means

A) thrashing.

B) painful.

C) pitiful.

D) trembling.

9. The function of the final sentence of the excerpt
("First of all though, I've got to get up, my train
leaves at five") is to

A) provide a resolution to the conflict Gregor
faces.

B) foreshadow the conflict between Gregor and
his boss.

C) illustrate Gregor's resilience and ability to
move on.

D) emphasize Gregor's extreme sense of duty.

GO ON TO THE NEXT PAGE

Questions 10–18 are based on the following passage.

This passage is adapted from Hillary Rodham Clinton's speech titled "Women's Rights Are Human Rights," addressed to the UN Fourth World Conference on Women in 1995.

If there is one message that echoes forth from this conference, it is that human rights are women's rights.... And women's rights are human rights.

Let us not forget that among those rights are the
5   right to speak freely and the right to be heard.

Women must enjoy the right to participate fully in the social and political lives of their countries if we want freedom and democracy to thrive and endure.

It is indefensible that many women in
10   nongovernmental organizations who wished to participate in this conference have not been able to attend—or have been prohibited from fully taking part.

Let me be clear. Freedom means the right of people to assemble, organize, and debate openly.
15   It means respecting the views of those who may disagree with the views of their governments. It means not taking citizens away from their loved ones and jailing them, mistreating them, or denying them their freedom or dignity because of
20   the peaceful expression of their ideas and opinions.

In my country, we recently celebrated the seventy-fifth anniversary of women's suffrage. It took one hundred and fifty years after the signing of our Declaration of Independence for women to
25   win the right to vote. It took seventy-two years of organized struggle on the part of many courageous women and men.

It was one of America's most divisive philosophical wars. But it was also a bloodless war.
30   Suffrage was achieved without a shot fired.

We have also been reminded, in V-J Day observances last weekend, of the good that comes when men and women join together to combat the forces of tyranny and build a better world.
35   We have seen peace prevail in most places for a half century. We have avoided another world war. But we have not solved older, deeply-rooted problems that continue to diminish the potential of half the world's population.
40   Now it is time to act on behalf of women everywhere.

If we take bold steps to better the lives of women, we will be taking bold steps to better the lives of children and families too. Families rely on mothers and
45   wives for emotional support and care; families rely on women for labor in the home; and increasingly, families rely on women for income needed to raise healthy children and care for other relatives.

As long as discrimination and inequities remain
50   so commonplace around the world—as long as girls and women are valued less, fed less, fed last, overworked, underpaid, not schooled and subjected to violence in and out of their homes—the potential of the human family to create a
55   peaceful, prosperous world will not be realized.

Let this conference be our—and the world's—call to action.

And let us heed the call so that we can create a world in which every woman is treated with respect
60   and dignity, every boy and girl is loved and cared for equally, and every family has the hope of a strong and stable future.

10.   What is the primary purpose of the passage?

  A) To chastise those who have prevented women from attending the conference

  B) To argue that women continue to experience discrimination

  C) To explain that human rights are of more concern than women's rights

  D) To encourage people to think of women's rights as an issue important to all

11.   Which choice provides the best evidence for the answer to the previous question?

  A) Lines 4–5 ("Let us...be heard")

  B) Lines 9–12 ("It is indefensible...taking part")

  C) Lines 37–39 ("But we have...population")

  D) Lines 44–48 ("Families...other relatives")

12. As used in line 28, "divisive" most nearly means

   A) conflict-producing.

   B) carefully watched.

   C) multi-purpose.

   D) time-consuming.

13. Based on the speech, with which statement would Clinton most likely agree?

   A) More men should be the primary caregivers of their children in order to provide career opportunities for women.

   B) Women do not need the support and cooperation of men as they work toward equality.

   C) Solutions for global problems would be found faster if women had more access to power.

   D) The American movement for women's suffrage should have been violent in order to achieve success more quickly.

14. Which choice provides the best evidence for the answer to the previous question?

   A) Lines 6–8 ("Women…endure")

   B) Line 30 ("Suffrage…shot fired")

   C) Lines 44–48 ("Families…other relatives")

   D) Lines 49–55 ("As long…realized")

15. As used in line 26, "organized" most nearly means

   A) arranged.

   B) cooperative.

   C) hierarchical.

   D) patient.

16. Which claim does Clinton make in her speech?

   A) The conference itself is a model of nondiscrimination toward women.

   B) Democracy cannot prosper unless women can participate fully in it.

   C) Women's rights are restricted globally by the demands on them as parents.

   D) Women are being forced to provide income for their families as a result of sexism.

17. Clinton uses the example of V-J Day observations to support the argument that

   A) campaigns succeed when they are nonviolent.

   B) historical wrongs against women must be corrected.

   C) many tragedies could have been avoided with more female participation.

   D) cooperation between men and women leads to positive developments.

18. The fifth paragraph (lines 13–20) can be described as

   A) a distillation of the author's main argument.

   B) an acknowledgment of a counterargument.

   C) a veiled criticism of a group.

   D) a defense against an accusation.

Questions 19–28 are based on the following passages and supplementary material.

The following passages discuss the history and traditions associated with tea.

Passage 1

Europe was a coffee-drinking continent before it became a tea-drinking one. Tea was grown in China, thousands of miles away. The opening of trade routes with the Far East in the fifteenth and sixteenth
5 centuries gave Europeans their first taste of tea.

However, it was an unpromising start for the beverage, because shipments arrived stale, and European tea drinkers miscalculated the steeping time and measurements. This was a far cry from
10 the Chinese preparation techniques, known as a "tea ceremony," which had strict steps and called for steeping in iron pots at precise temperatures and pouring into porcelain bowls.

China had a monopoly on the tea trade and
15 kept their tea cultivation techniques secret. Yet as worldwide demand grew, tea caught on in Europe. Some proprietors touted tea as a cure for maladies. Several European tea companies formed, including the English East India Company. In

GO ON TO THE NEXT PAGE

20 1669, it imported 143.5 pounds of tea—very little compared to the 32 million pounds that were imported by 1834.

Europeans looked for ways to circumvent China's monopoly, but their attempts to grow the
25 tea plant (Latin name *Camellia sinensis*) failed. Some plants perished in transit from the East. But most often the growing climate wasn't right, not even in the equatorial colonies that the British, Dutch, and French controlled. In 1763, the French
30 Academy of Sciences gave up, declaring the tea plant unique to China and unable to be grown anywhere else. Swedish and English botanists grew tea in botanical gardens, but this was not enough to meet demand.

35 After trial and error with a plant variety discovered in the Assam district of India, the British managed to establish a source to meet the growing demands of British tea drinkers. In May 1838, the first batch of India-grown tea shipped
40 to London. The harvest was a mere 350 pounds and arrived in November. It sold for between 16 and 34 shillings per pound. Perfecting production methods took many years, but ultimately, India became the world's largest tea-producing country.
45 By the early 1900s, annual production of India tea exceeded 350 million pounds. This voluminous source was a major factor in tea becoming the staple of European households that it is today.

Passage 2

In Europe, there's a long tradition of taking
50 afternoon tea. Tea time, typically four o'clock, means not just enjoying a beverage, but taking time out to gather and socialize. The occasion is not identical across Europe, though; just about every culture has its own way of doing things.

55 In France, for example, black tea is served with sugar, milk, or lemon and is almost always accompanied by a pastry. Rather than sweet pastries, the French prefer the savory kind, such as the *gougère*, or puff pastry, infused with cheese.
60 Germans, by contrast, put a layer of slowly melting candy at the bottom of their teacup and top the tea with cream. German tea culture is strongest in the eastern part of the country, and during the week tea is served with cookies, while on the weekend
65 or for special events, cakes are served. The Germans think of tea as a good cure for headaches and stress.

Russia also has a unique tea culture, rooted in the formalism of its aristocratic classes. Loose leaf black tea is served in a glass held by a *podstakannik*,
70 an ornate holder with a handle typically made from silver or chrome—though sometimes it may be goldplated. Brewed separately, the tea is then diluted with boiled water and served strong. The strength of the tea is seen as a measure of the host's hospitality.
75 Traditionally, tea is taken by the entire family and served after a large meal with jams and pastries.

Great Britain has a rich tradition of its own. Prior to the introduction of tea into Britain, the English had two main meals, breakfast and a
80 second, dinner-like meal called "tea," which was held around noon. However, during the middle of the eighteenth century, dinner shifted to an evening meal at a late hour; it was then called "high tea." That meant the necessary introduction of an
85 afternoon snack to tide one over, and "low tea" or "tea time" was introduced by British royalty. In present-day Britain, your afternoon tea might be served with scones and jam, small sandwiches, or cookies (called "biscuits"), depending on whether
90 you're in Ireland, England, or Scotland.

Wherever they are and however they take it, Europeans know the value of savoring an afternoon cup of tea.

**Average Annual Tea Consumption
(Pounds per Person)**

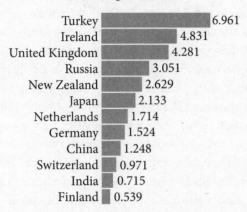

Turkey	6.961
Ireland	4.831
United Kingdom	4.281
Russia	3.051
New Zealand	2.629
Japan	2.133
Netherlands	1.714
Germany	1.524
China	1.248
Switzerland	0.971
India	0.715
Finland	0.539

Data from Euromonitor International and World Bank.

19. Based on the information provided in Passage 1, it can be inferred that

 A) European nations tried to grow tea in their colonies.

 B) European tea growers never learned Chinese cultivation techniques.

 C) Europeans' purpose in opening trade routes with the Far East was to gain access to tea.

 D) Europeans believed tea was ineffective as a treatment against illness.

20. Which choice provides the best evidence for the answer to the previous question?

 A) Lines 6–9 ("However…measurements")

 B) Lines 17–18 ("Some…maladies")

 C) Lines 26–29 ("But…French controlled")

 D) Lines 40–42 ("The harvest…per pound")

21. As used in line 23, "circumvent" most nearly means

 A) destroy.

 B) get around.

 C) ignore.

 D) compete with.

22. It can be inferred from both Passage 1 and the graphic that

 A) English botanical gardens helped make the United Kingdom one of the highest tea-consuming countries in the world.

 B) if the French Academy of Sciences hadn't given up growing tea in 1763, France would be one of the highest tea-consuming countries in the world.

 C) Britain's success at growing tea in India in the 1800s helped make the United Kingdom one of the highest tea-consuming nations in the world.

 D) China's production of tea would be higher if Britain hadn't discovered a way to grow tea in India in the 1800s.

23. It is reasonable to infer, based on Passage 2, that

 A) serving tea is an important part of hosting guests in Russia.

 B) Germans generally avoid medicine for stress.

 C) drinking tea in modern Britain is confined to the upper classes.

 D) the usual hour for drinking tea varies across Europe.

24. Which choice provides the best evidence for the answer to the previous question?

 A) Lines 50–52 ("Tea time…socialize")

 B) Lines 65–66 ("The Germans…stress")

 C) Lines 73–74 ("The strength…hospitality")

 D) Lines 84–86 ("That meant…royalty")

GO ON TO THE NEXT PAGE

25. As used in line 68, "aristocratic" most nearly means

    A) culinary.

    B) political.

    C) rigid.

    D) noble.

26. Compared with France's tradition of tea-drinking, having tea in Germany

    A) is more formal.

    B) involves sweeter food.

    C) requires greater solitude.

    D) is more of a meal than a snack.

27. Which statement is the most effective comparison of the two passages' purposes?

    A) Passage 1's purpose is to describe the early history of tea in Europe, while Passage 2's purpose is to compare European cultural practices relating to tea.

    B) Passage 1's purpose is to argue against the Chinese monopoly of tea, while Passage 2's purpose is to argue that Europeans perfected the art of tea drinking.

    C) Passage 1's purpose is to express admiration for the difficult task of tea cultivation, while Passage 2's purpose is to celebrate the rituals surrounding tea.

    D) Passage 1's purpose is to compare Chinese and European relationships with tea, while Passage 2's purpose is to describe the diffusion of tea culture in Europe.

28. Both passages support which generalization about tea?

    A) Tea drinking in Europe is less ritualized than in China.

    B) Coffee was once more popular in Europe than tea was.

    C) India grows a great deal of tea.

    D) Tea is a staple of European households.

Questions 29–38 are based on the following passage.

The following passage is adapted from an article about the *Spinosaurus*, a theropod dinosaur that lived during the Cretaceous period.

At long last, paleontologists have solved a century-old mystery, piecing together information discovered by scientists from different times and places.

The mystery began when, in 1911, German
5 paleontologist Ernst Stromer discovered the first evidence of dinosaurs having lived in Egypt. Stromer, who expected to encounter fossils of early mammals, instead found bones that dated back to the Cretaceous period, some 97
10 to 112 million years prior. His finding consisted of three large bones, which he preserved and transported back to Germany for examination. After careful consideration, he announced that he had discovered a new genus of sauropod, or a
15 large, four-legged herbivore with a long neck. He called the genus *Aegyptosaurus*, which is Greek for Egyptian lizard. One of these Aegyptosaurs, he claimed, was the *Spinosaurus*. Tragically, the fossils that supported his claim were destroyed during
20 a raid on Munich by the Royal Air Force during World War II. The scientific world was left with Stromer's notes and sketches, but no hard evidence that the *Spinosaurus* ever existed.

It was not until 2008, when a cardboard box
25 of bones was delivered to paleontologist Nizar Ibrahim by a nomad in Morocco's Sahara desert, that a clue to solving the mystery was revealed. Intrigued, Ibrahim took the bones to a university in Casablanca for further study. One specific bone
30 struck him as interesting, as it contained a red line coursing through it. The following year, Ibrahim and his colleagues at Italy's Milan Natural History Museum were looking at bones that resembled the ones delivered the year before. An important
35 clue was hidden in the cross-section they were examining, as it contained the same red line Ibrahim had seen in Morocco. Against all odds, the Italians were studying bones that belonged to the very same skeleton as the bones Ibrahim received
40 in the desert. Together, these bones make up the

Practice Tests

partial skeleton of the very first *Spinosaurus* that humans have been able to discover since Stromer's fossils were destroyed.

Ibrahim and his colleagues published a study
45 describing the features of the dinosaur, which point to the *Spinosaurus* being the first known swimming dinosaur. At 36 feet long, this particular *Spinosaurus* had long front legs and short back legs, each with a paddle-shaped foot and claws that
50 suggest a carnivorous diet. These features made the dinosaur a deft swimmer and excellent hunter, able to prey on large river fish.

Scientists also discovered significant aquatic adaptations that made the *Spinosaurus* unique
55 compared to dinosaurs that lived on land but ate fish. Similar to a crocodile, the *Spinosaurus* had a long snout, with nostrils positioned so that the dinosaur could breathe while part of its head was submerged in water. Unlike predatory
60 land dinosaurs, the *Spinosaurus* had powerful front legs. The weight of these legs would have made walking upright like a *Tyrannosaurus rex* impossible, but in water, their strong legs gave the *Spinosaurus* the power it needed to swim quickly
65 and hunt fiercely. Most notable, though, was the discovery of the *Spinosaurus*'s massive sail. Made up of dorsal spines, the sail was mostly meant for display.

Ibrahim and his fellow researchers used both
70 modern digital modeling programs and Stromer's basic sketches to create and mount a life-size replica of the *Spinosaurus* skeleton. The sketches gave them a starting point, and by arranging and rearranging the excavated fossils they had in their
75 possession, they were able to use technology to piece together hypothetical bone structures until the mystery of this semiaquatic dinosaur finally emerged from the murky depths of the past.

29. Which of the following best summarizes the central idea of this passage?

A) Paleontologists were able to identify a new species of dinosaur after overcoming a series of obstacles.

B) Most dinosaur fossils are found in pieces and must be reconstructed using the latest technology.

C) The first evidence of the *Spinosaurus* was uncovered by German paleontologist Ernst Stromer.

D) Fossils of an aquatic dinosaur called the *Spinosaurus* were first found in Egypt in the early twentieth century.

30. Based on the information in the passage, the author would most likely agree that

A) aquatic dinosaurs were more vicious than dinosaurs that lived on land.

B) too much emphasis is placed on creating realistic models of ancient dinosaurs.

C) most mysteries presented by randomly found fossils are unlikely to be solved.

D) the study of fossils and ancient life provides important scientific insights.

31. Which choice provides the best evidence for the answer to the previous question?

A) Lines 13–15 ("After careful…long neck")

B) Lines 53–56 ("Scientists also…fish")

C) Lines 59–61 ("Unlike…front legs")

D) Lines 72–78 ("The sketches…past")

GO ON TO THE NEXT PAGE ⟹

32. As used in line 37, the phrase "against all odds" most nearly means

    A) by contrast.

    B) at the exact same time.

    C) to their dismay.

    D) despite low probability.

33. The author uses the phrases "deft swimmer" and "excellent hunter" in line 51 to

    A) produce a clear visual image of the *Spinosaurus*.

    B) show how the *Spinosaurus* searched for prey.

    C) create an impression of a graceful but powerful animal.

    D) emphasize the differences between aquatic and land dinosaurs.

34. The information presented in the passage strongly suggests that Ibrahim

    A) chose to go into the field of paleontology after reading Stromer's work.

    B) was familiar with Stromer's work when he found the fossils with the red lines.

    C) did not have the proper training to solve the mystery of the *Spinosaurus* on his own.

    D) went on to study other aquatic dinosaurs after completing his research on the *Spinosaurus*.

35. Which choice provides the best evidence for the answer to the previous question?

    A) Lines 24–27 ("It was…revealed")

    B) Lines 44–47 ("Ibrahim…swimming dinosaur")

    C) Lines 53–56 ("Scientists also…fish")

    D) Lines 69–72 ("Ibrahim and…skeleton")

36. As used in line 76, "hypothetical" most nearly means

    A) imaginary.

    B) actual.

    C) possible.

    D) interesting.

37. Which statement best describes the relationship between Stromer's and Ibrahim's work with fossils?

    A) Stromer's work was dependent on Ibrahim's work.

    B) Stromer's work was contradicted by Ibrahim's work.

    C) Ibrahim's work built on Stromer's work.

    D) Ibrahim's work copied Stromer's work.

38. Which of the following is most similar to the methods used by Ibrahim to create a life-size replica of the *Spinosaurus*?

    A) An architect using computer software and drawings to create a scale model of a building

    B) A student building a model rocket from a kit in order to demonstrate propulsion

    C) A doctor using a microscope to study micro-organisms unable to be seen with the naked eye

    D) A marine biologist creating an artificial reef in an aquarium to study fish

Questions 39–47 are based on the following passage and supplementary material.

The following passage is adapted from an essay about intricacies and implications of laughter.

Today's technology and resources enable people to educate themselves on any topic imaginable, and human health is one of particular interest to all. From diet fads to exercise trends, sleep studies
5 to nutrition supplements, people strive to adopt healthier lifestyles. And while some people may associate diets and gym memberships with sheer enjoyment, most of the population tends to think of personal healthcare as a necessary but time-consuming,
10 energy-draining, less-than-fun aspect of daily life.

Yet for centuries, or perhaps for as long as conscious life has existed, sneaking suspicion has suggested that fun, or more accurately, *funniness*, is essential to human health. Finally, in recent years
15 this notion, often phrased in the adage, "Laughter is the best medicine," has materialized into scientific evidence.

 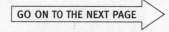

When a person laughs, a chemical reaction in the brain produces hormones called endorphins.
20 Other known endorphin-producing activities include exercise, physical pain, and certain food choices, but laughter's appearance on this list has drawn increasing empirical interest. Endorphins function as natural opiates for the human body,
25 causing what are more commonly referred to as "good feelings." A boost of endorphins can thwart lethargy and promote the mental energy and positivity necessary to accomplish challenging tasks. Furthermore, recent data reveal that the
30 laughter-induced endorphins are therapeutic and stress reducing.

This stress reduction alone indicates significant implications regarding the role of laughter in personal health. However, humor seems to address
35 many other medical conditions as well. One study from Loma Linda University in California found that the act of laughing induced immediate and significant effects on senior adults' memory capacities. This result was in addition to declines
40 in the patients' cortisol, or stress hormone, measurements. Another university study found that a mere quarter hour of laughter burns up to 40 calories. Pain tolerance, one group of Oxford researchers noticed, is also strengthened
45 by laughter—probably due to the release of those same endorphins already described. And a group of Maryland scientists discovered that those who laugh more frequently seem to have stronger protection against heart disease, the illness that
50 takes more lives annually than any other in America. Studies have shown that stress releases hormones that cause blood vessels to constrict, but laughter, on the other hand, releases chemicals that cause blood vessels to dilate, or expand. This dilation
55 can have the same positive effects on blood flow as aerobic exercise or drugs that help lower cholesterol.

Already from these reputable studies, empirical data indicates that laughter's health benefits include heart disease prevention, good physical exertion,
60 memory retention, anxiety reduction, and pain resilience—not to mention laughter's more self-evident effects on social and psychological wellness. Many believe that these findings are only

the beginning; these studies pave the way for more
65 research with even stronger evidence regarding the powerful healing and preventative properties of laughter. As is true for most fields of science, far more can be learned.

As for how laughter is achieved, these studies
70 used various methods to provoke or measure laughter or humor. Some used comedy films or television clips; others chose humor-gauging questionnaires and social—or group—laughter scenarios. Such variance suggests that the means
75 by which people incorporate laughter into their daily routine matters less than the fact that they do incorporate it. However, it should be said that humor shared in an uplifting community probably offers greater benefits than that found on a screen.

80 It is believed that young people begin to laugh less and less as they transition to adulthood. Time-pressed millennials might, in the interest of wellness, choose isolated exercise instead of social- or fun-oriented leisure activities. However,
85 this growing pool of evidence exposes the reality that amusement, too, can powerfully nourish the health of both mind and body. Humor is no less relevant to well-being than a kale smoothie or track workout. But, then, some combination of
90 the three might be most enjoyable (and, of course, beneficial) of all.

Laughter and Its Effect on Pain

Adapted from I.M. Dunbar, et al., "Social Laughter Is Correlated with an Elevated Pain Threshold." © 2011 by The Royal Society of Biological Sciences.

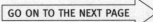 GO ON TO THE NEXT PAGE

39. The author would most likely characterize the study findings mentioned in the passage as

    A) irrelevant.

    B) very promising.

    C) inconclusive.

    D) mildly interesting.

40. Which choice provides the best evidence for the answer to the previous question?

    A) Lines 4–6 ("From diet…lifestyles")

    B) Lines 14–17 ("Finally,…evidence")

    C) Lines 18–19 ("When a person… endorphins")

    D) Lines 74–77 ("Such variance…incorporate it")

41. Which statement best explains the relationship between endorphin production and mental outlook?

    A) Increasing a person's amount of endorphins encourages a positive state of mind.

    B) The act of laughing produces endorphins, which can offer a person protection against heart disease.

    C) Research indicates that chemical reactions in the brain produce endorphins.

    D) If a person has more endorphins, he or she has a difficult time tolerating pain.

42. As used in line 57, "reputable" most nearly means

    A) honorable.

    B) distinguished.

    C) celebrated.

    D) credible.

43. Which of the following statements can be concluded from the passage?

    A) Laughing alone or in the company of others benefits people's health equally.

    B) There is reason for optimism about future research into laughter's health benefits.

    C) Public support for the idea that laughter is healthy is somewhat limited.

    D) Physical exercise is sufficient to maintain and improve mental health.

44. Which choice provides the best evidence for the answer to the previous question?

    A) Lines 11–14 ("Yet for centuries,…health")

    B) Lines 32–35 ("This stress…well")

    C) Lines 63–67 ("Many believe…of laughter")

    D) Lines 87–91 ("Humor is…of all")

45. Which reason best explains why the author chose to discuss the function of endorphins in lines 23–26 ("Endorphins…good feelings")?

    A) To reach a wider audience without a background in physiology

    B) To support the claim that laughter affects an individual's mental state

    C) To show that laughter is one of several endorphin-producing activities

    D) To demonstrate why scientists have an interest in studying laughter

46. As used in line 15, "adage" most nearly means

    A) remark.

    B) comment.

    C) cliché.

    D) proverb.

47. Which value shown on the graph most closely relates to the idea in line 78 that "humor shared in an uplifting community" increases resilience to pain?

    A)   −25

    B)   0

    C)   20

    D)   75

Writing and Language Test

35 Minutes—44 Questions

This section corresponds to Section 2 of your answer sheet.

Directions: Each passage in this section is followed by several questions. Some questions will reference an underlined portion in the passage; others will ask you to consider a part of a passage or the passage as a whole. For each question, choose the answer that reflects the best use of grammar, punctuation, and style. If a passage or question is accompanied by a graphic, take the graphic into account in choosing your response(s). Some questions will have "NO CHANGE" as a possible response. Choose that answer if you think the best choice is to leave the sentence as written.

Questions 1–11 are based on the following passage.

From Here to the Stars

Gene Kranz hadn't slept in ages. **1** The flight director, pacing between rows of monitors in NASA's Mission Control Center, an impossible problem weighing heavy in his weary mind: Three astronauts were operating a crippled spacecraft nearly 200,000 miles from Earth. And time was running out.

Kranz was no stranger to **2** issues. After losing his father at an early age, Kranz turned to the stars for guidance—and found inspiration. His high school thesis was about the possibility of **3** space travel; an idea that prompted Kranz to set a path for the stars. Kranz pursued a degree in aeronautical engineering after high school graduation. After the Wright brothers had pioneered powered, controlled flight only half a century earlier, aviation milestones like breaking the sound barrier changed the future of flight. Aeronautical engineering required a thorough understanding of **4** physics—like lift and drag on wings—as well as proficiency in mathematics to determine maximum weight on an aircraft. After graduating from Saint Louis University's Parks College of Engineering, Aviation,

1. A) NO CHANGE
    B) The flight director paced
    C) The pacing flight director
    D) The flight director pacing

2. A) NO CHANGE
    B) adversity.
    C) deadlines.
    D) maladies.

3. A) NO CHANGE
    B) space travel: an idea
    C) space travel, an idea
    D) space travel. An idea

4. A) NO CHANGE
    B) physics; like lift and drag on wings, as well as proficiency
    C) physics like lift and drag on wings, as well as proficiency
    D) physics: like lift and drag on wings—as well as proficiency

and Technology, Kranz piloted jets for the Air Force Reserve before performing research and development on missiles and rockets. Kranz later joined NASA and directed the successful *Apollo 11* mission to the moon in 1969.

[5] Without his unusual vest, no one would have noticed Kranz in the crowd. One year after the launch, the mood had drastically changed; there were no cheers, no celebratory pats on the back or teary-eyed congratulations. Coffee and adrenaline fueled the scientists and engineers communicating with the astronauts on *Apollo 13*. [6] Kranz was easy to spot among the avalanche of moving bodies and shifting papers. He was dressed, as ever, in his signature handmade vest. [7] The engineers looked to the calm man in the homemade vest.

Kranz's wife, Marta, had begun making vests at his request in the early '60s. [8] Their was power in a uniform, something Kranz understood from his years serving overseas. The vests served not as an authoritative mark or [9] sartorial flair, but a defining symbol for his team to rally behind. During the effort to save the *Apollo 13* crew, Kranz wore his white vest around the clock like perspiration-mottled battle armor.

5. Which sentence would serve as the most effective introduction to the paragraph?

   A) NO CHANGE

   B) During the mission, Kranz stood out as a pillar of strength in the chaos of the command center.

   C) Kranz earned the badges of honor that now adorned his vest.

   D) Kranz possessed more years of experience than anyone in the control center.

6. A) NO CHANGE

   B) Among the avalanche of moving bodies and shifting papers, it is easy to spot Kranz.

   C) Kranz easily spotted the avalanche of moving bodies and shifting papers.

   D) Kranz is easy to spot among the avalanche of moving bodies and shifting papers.

7. Which sentence provides effective evidence to support the main focus of the paragraph?

   A) NO CHANGE

   B) Many of the men in the Mission Control Center had lengthy military careers.

   C) Kranz's thoughts returned to the many tribulations he had experienced.

   D) Several engineers joined together as a bastion of calm in a sea of uncertainty.

8. A) NO CHANGE

   B) They're was

   C) There was

   D) They were

9. A) NO CHANGE

   B) sanguine

   C) military

   D) martial

10 <u>Among</u> meetings and calculations, Kranz and the NASA staff hatched a wild plan. By using the gravitational force of the moon, **11** <u>it</u> could slingshot the injured spacecraft back on an earthbound course. It was a long shot, of course, but also their best and only one. And, due to the tireless efforts of support staff on earth and the intrepid spirit of the *Apollo 13* crew, it worked. Six days after takeoff, all three astronauts splashed down safely in the Pacific Ocean.

Questions 12–22 are based on the following passage.

The UK and the Euro

[1] The United Kingdom is a long-standing member of the European Union (EU), a multinational political organization and economic world leader **12** <u>elected</u> over the course of the past half-century. [2] However, there is one key feature of the EU in which the UK does not **13** <u>participate; the monetary</u> union known as the Eurozone, consisting of countries that share the euro as currency. [3] While the nation's public opinion has remained generally supportive of that decision, evidence suggests that the euro's benefits for the UK might, in fact, outweigh the risks. [4] When the EU first implemented the euro in 1999, intending to strengthen the collective economy across the union, Britain was permitted exclusion and continued using the pound instead. [5] This, UK leaders hoped, would shield Britain from financial dangers that the euro might suffer. **14**

10. A) NO CHANGE
    B) In spite of
    C) Despite
    D) Between

11. A) NO CHANGE
    B) he
    C) they
    D) one

12. A) NO CHANGE
    B) determined
    C) advanced
    D) built

13. A) NO CHANGE
    B) participate: the monetary
    C) participate, the monetary
    D) participate. The monetary

14. To make this paragraph most logical, sentence 3 should be placed
    A) where it is now.
    B) after sentence 1.
    C) after sentence 4.
    D) after sentence 5.

Practice Tests

Proponents for avoiding the euro point <u>15 to faltering economies in the Eurozone region throughout the Eurozone.</u> To join a massive, multinational economy would involve surrendering taxable wealth from one's own region to aid impoverished countries that may be some thousands of miles away. If a few economies in the Eurozone suffer, all of the participating nations suffer, too. Other proponents point to details of financial policy such as interest rates and territory responsibilities, fearing loss of agency and political traction. 16 <u>The UK's taxable wealth would decrease if it assisted impoverished countries.</u>

But complications loom: the UK's current EU status may be untenable. In recent years, EU leaders seem to want to transition all members 17 <u>toward the Eurozone, for many reasons,</u> this action appears necessary for protecting nations involved and ensuring the monetary union's long-term success. These conditions may potentially force the UK to choose either the security of its multi-decade EU membership, or the pound and all it entails for Britain's economy. Enjoying both may not remain possible. 18 <u>The UK wants to maintain the pound as its currency.</u>

[1] Regarding Britain's intent to be protected from the Eurozone's economic dangers, this hope never quite materialized. [2] The UK saw economic downturns of its own during the euro's problematic years thus far. [3] Many families in the UK still struggle to pay their bills in the face of higher than normal unemployment rates. [4] It seems that regardless of shared currency, the economies of Britain and its Eurozone neighbors are too closely 19 <u>intertwined</u>

15. Which choice best completes the sentence?

   A) NO CHANGE
   B) to financial dangers that the euro might suffer.
   C) to faltering economies in most if not all Eurozone countries.
   D) to financial dangers and faltering economies in Eurozone countries throughout Europe.

16. Which statement most clearly communicates the main claim of the paragraph?

   A) NO CHANGE
   B) Economic independence from impoverished countries would still be possible.
   C) The UK would take on significant economic risk if it adopted the euro as its currency.
   D) Euro adoption would require subsequent economic assistance on the UK's behalf.

17. A) NO CHANGE
   B) toward the Eurozone. For many reasons,
   C) toward the Eurozone, for many reasons.
   D) toward the Eurozone. For many reasons.

18. Which sentence most effectively concludes the paragraph?

   A) NO CHANGE
   B) All EU members may soon have to accept the euro.
   C) The UK faces a difficult decision regarding its EU membership.
   D) All member nations want to ensure the success of the EU.

19. A) NO CHANGE
   B) disparate
   C) identical
   D) relevant

 GO ON TO THE NEXT PAGE

for one to remain unscathed by another's crises. **20**

Perhaps this question of economic security has been the wrong one. Due to Britain's location and long-standing trade relationships with its neighbors, economies will continue to be somewhat reliant on each other, euro or not. **21** Furthermore, political security, power, and protection bear more significance for the future. If the UK hopes to maintain and expand its influential presence in world leadership, its association and close involvement with greater Europe is invaluable. Considering that the euro probably offers a lower risk margin than many have supposed, the benefits of euro **22** adoption: to secure EU membership and strengthen its cause, made Britain carefully reconsider.

20. Which sentence is least relevant to the central idea of this paragraph?

A) Sentence 1

B) Sentence 2

C) Sentence 3

D) Sentence 4

21. A) NO CHANGE

B) Or,

C) Also,

D) However,

22. A) NO CHANGE

B) adoption—to secure EU membership and strengthen its cause—

C) adoption: to secure EU membership and strengthen its cause—

D) adoption; to secure EU membership and strengthen its cause,

Questions 23–33 are based on the following passage.

Coffee: The Buzz on Beans

Americans love coffee. **23** Some days you can find a coffee shop in nearly every American city. But this wasn't always true. How did coffee, which was first grown in Africa over five hundred years ago, come to America?

The coffee plant, from which makers get the "cherries" that **24** is dried and roasted into what we call beans, first appeared in the East African country Ethiopia, in the province of Kaffa. From there, it spread to the Arabian Peninsula, where the coffeehouse, or *qahveh khaneh* in Arabic, was very popular. Like spices and cloth, coffee was traded internationally as European explorers reached far lands and **25** establishing shipping routes. The first European coffeehouse opened in Venice, Italy, in 1683, and

23. A) NO CHANGE

B) Many

C) The

D) These

24. A) NO CHANGE

B) are being dried and roasted

C) are dried and roasted

D) is being dried and roasted

25. A) NO CHANGE

B) established

C) having established

D) was establishing

not long after London [26] displayed over three hundred coffeehouses.

There is no record of coffee being among the cargo of the *Mayflower*, which reached the New World in 1620. It was not until 1668 that the first written reference to coffee in America was made. The reference described a beverage made from roasted beans and flavored with sugar or honey and cinnamon. Coffee was then chronicled in the New England colony's official records of 1670. In 1683, William Penn, who lived in a settlement on the Delaware River, wrote of buying supplies of coffee in a [27] New York market, he paid eighteen shillings and nine pence per pound. [28]

Coffeehouses like those in Europe were soon established in American colonies, and as America expanded westward, coffee consumption grew. In their settlement days, [29] Chicago St. Louis and New Orleans each had famous coffeehouses. By the mid-twentieth century, coffeehouses were abundant. In places like New York and San Francisco, they became [30] confused with counterculture, as a place where intellectuals and artists gathered to share ideas. In American homes, coffee was a social lubricant, bringing people together to socialize as afternoon tea had done in English society. With the invention of the electric coffee pot, it became a common courtesy to ask a guest if she wanted "coffee or tea?"

26. A) NO CHANGE
    B) bragged
    C) highlighted
    D) boasted

27. A) NO CHANGE
    B) New York market and William Penn
    C) New York market so he paid
    D) New York market, paying

28. Which choice best establishes a concluding sentence for the paragraph?
    A) Coffee's appearance in the historical record shows it was becoming more and more established in the New World.
    B) The colonies probably used more tea than coffee because there are records of it being imported from England.
    C) William Penn founded Pennsylvania Colony, which became the state of Pennsylvania after the Revolutionary War with England ended.
    D) The Mayflower did carry a number of items that the colonists needed for settlement, including animals and tools.

29. A) NO CHANGE
    B) Chicago, St. Louis, and New Orleans
    C) Chicago, St. Louis, and, New Orleans
    D) Chicago St. Louis and, New Orleans

30. A) NO CHANGE
    B) related
    C) associated
    D) coupled

GO ON TO THE NEXT PAGE

31 There were many coffee shops in New York and in Chicago.

However, by the 1950s, U.S. manufacturing did to coffee what it had done to **32** other foods; produced it cheaply, mass-marketed it, and lowered its quality. Coffee was roasted and ground in manufacturing plants and freeze-dried for a long storage life, which compromised its flavor. An "evangelism" began to bring back the original bracing, dark-roasted taste of coffee and spread quickly.

33 In every major city of the world, now travelers around the world, expect to be able to grab an uplifting, fresh, and delicious cup of coffee—and they can.

31. Which choice most effectively concludes the paragraph?
   A) NO CHANGE
   B) Electric coffee machines changed how people entertained at home.
   C) Over time, it was clear that coffee had become a part of everyday American life.
   D) People went to coffeehouses to discuss major issues.

32. A) NO CHANGE
   B) other foods produced
   C) other foods, produced
   D) other foods: produced

33. A) NO CHANGE
   B) Now travelers, in every major city of the world, around the world expect to be able to grab an uplifting, fresh, and delicious cup of coffee—and they can.
   C) Now in every major city of the world, travelers around the world expect to be able to grab an uplifting, fresh, and delicious cup of coffee—and they can.
   D) Now travelers around the world expect to be able to grab an uplifting, fresh, and delicious cup of coffee in every major city of the world—and they can.

Questions 34–44 are based on the following passage and supplementary material.

Predicting Nature's Light Show

One of the most beautiful of nature's displays is the aurora borealis, commonly known as the Northern Lights. As 34 their informal name suggests, the best place to view this phenomenon 35 is the Northern Hemisphere. How far north one needs to be to witness auroras depends not on conditions here on Earth, but on the Sun. 36

As with hurricane season on Earth, the Sun 37 observes a cycle of storm activity, called the solar cycle, which lasts approximately 11 years. Also referred to as the sunspot cycle, this period is caused by the amount of magnetic flux that rises to the surface of the Sun, causing sunspots, or areas of intense magnetic activity. The magnetic energy is sometimes so great it causes a storm that explodes away from the Sun's surface in a solar flare.

These powerful magnetic storms eject high-speed electrons and protons into space. Called a coronal mass ejection, this ejection is far more powerful than the hot gases the Sun constantly emits. The speed at which the atoms are shot away from the Sun is almost triple that of a normal solar wind. It takes this shot of energy one to three days to arrive at Earth's upper atmosphere. Once it arrives, it is captured by Earth's own magnetic field. It is this newly captured energy that causes the Northern Lights. 38 Scientists and interested amateurs in the

34. A) NO CHANGE
    B) an
    C) its
    D) that

35. A) NO CHANGE
    B) is through the Northern Hemisphere.
    C) is over the Northern Hemisphere.
    D) is in the Northern Hemisphere.

36. Which of the following would most strengthen the passage's introduction?
    A) A statement about the Kp-Index and other necessary tracking tools scientists use
    B) A mention that the National Oceanic and Atmospheric Administration monitors solar flares
    C) An explanation about why conditions on the Sun rather than on Earth affect the Northern Lights
    D) A statement about what scientists think people should study before viewing auroras

37. A) NO CHANGE
    B) experiences
    C) perceives
    D) witnesses

38. A) NO CHANGE
    B) Interested scientists and amateurs
    C) Scientists and amateurs interested
    D) Scientists interested and amateurs

GO ON TO THE NEXT PAGE ⟩

Northern Hemisphere [39] use tools readily available to all in order to predict the likelihood of seeing auroras in their location at a specific time. One such tool is the Kp-Index, a number that determines the potential visibility of an aurora. The Kp-Index measures the energy added to Earth's magnetic field from the Sun on a scale of 0-9, with 1 representing a solar calm and 5 or more indicating a magnetic storm, or solar flare. The magnetic fluctuations are measured in three-hour intervals (12 a.m. to 3 a.m., 3 a.m. to 6 a.m., and so on) so that deviations can be factored in and accurate data can be presented. [40]

Magnetometers, tools that measure the strength of Earth's magnetic field, are located around the world. When the energy from solar flares reaches Earth, the strength and direction of the energy [41] is recorded by these tools and analyzed by scientists at the National Oceanic and Atmospheric Administration, who calculate the difference between the average strength of the magnetic field and spikes due to solar flares. They plot this information on the Kp-Index and [42] update the public with information on viewing the auroras as well as other impacts solar flares may have on life on Earth. [43] While solar flares can sometimes have negative effects

39. A) NO CHANGE
    B) use tools for prediction
    C) use specific tools to predict
    D) use all tools readily available to predict

40. Which of the following, if added to this paragraph, would best support the author's claims?
    A) The speeds of normal solar winds and coronal mass ejections
    B) The strength of Earth's magnetic field
    C) The temperature of normal solar wind
    D) The definition of coronal mass ejection

41. A) NO CHANGE
    B) are
    C) will be
    D) has been

42. A) NO CHANGE
    B) update aurora viewing information
    C) update information on viewing the auroras
    D) update aurora viewing information for the public

43. A) NO CHANGE
    B) However,
    C) Since
    D) Whereas

on our communications systems and weather patterns, the most common effect is also the most enchanting: a beautiful light show, such as the solar flare that took place from ▪44 3 p.m. to 6 p.m. on September 11.

Potential Visibility of an Aurora

Each bar = 3 hours

Data from National Oceanic and Atmospheric Administration.

44. Which choice competes the sentence with accurate data based on the graphic?

A) NO CHANGE

B) 12 a.m. on September 11 to 3 a.m. on September 12.

C) 9 a.m. on September 10 to 12 p.m. on September 12.

D) 9 a.m. on September 11 to 12 a.m. on September 12.

IF YOU FINISH BEFORE TIME IS CALLED, YOU MAY CHECK YOUR WORK ON THIS SECTION ONLY. DO NOT TURN TO ANY OTHER SECTION IN THE TEST. **STOP**

502 K

Math Test

25 Minutes—17 Questions

NO-CALCULATOR SECTION

This section corresponds to Section 3 of your answer sheet.

Directions: For this section, solve each problem and decide which is the best of the choices given. Fill in the corresponding oval on the answer sheet. You may use any available space for scratch work.

Notes:

1. Calculator use is NOT permitted.
2. All numbers used are real numbers, and all variables used represent real numbers, unless otherwise indicated.
3. Figures are drawn to scale and lie in a plane unless otherwise indicated.
4. Unless stated otherwise, the domain of any function f is assumed to be the set of all real numbers x, for which $f(x)$ is a real number.

Information:

$A = \pi r^2$
$C = 2\pi r$

$A = lw$

$A = \frac{1}{2} bh$

$c^2 = a^2 + b^2$

Special Right Triangles

$V = lwh$

$V = \pi r^2 h$

$V = \frac{4}{3} \pi r^3$

$V = \frac{1}{3} \pi r^2 h$

$V = \frac{1}{3} lwh$

The sum of the degree measures of the angles in a triangle is 180.

The number of degrees of arc in a circle is 360.

The number of radians of arc in a circle is 2π.

GO ON TO THE NEXT PAGE

1. What is the average rate of change for the line graphed in the figure above?

   A) $\dfrac{3}{5}$

   B) $\dfrac{5}{8}$

   C) $\dfrac{8}{5}$

   D) $\dfrac{5}{3}$

2. Which of the following could be the factored form of the equation graphed in the figure above?

   A) $y = \dfrac{1}{5}(x - 2)(x + 6)$

   B) $y = \dfrac{1}{5}(x + 2)(x - 6)$

   C) $y = \dfrac{2}{3}(x - 1)(x + 5)$

   D) $y = \dfrac{2}{3}(x + 1)(x - 5)$

3. Kinetic energy is the energy of motion. The equation $E_K = \dfrac{1}{2}mv^2$ represents the kinetic energy in joules of an object with a mass of m kilograms traveling at a speed of v meters per second. What is the kinetic energy in joules of an unmanned aircraft that has a mass of 2×10^3 kilograms traveling at a speed of approximately 3×10^3 meters per second?

   A) 9×5^9

   B) 9×10^8

   C) 9×10^9

   D) 1.8×10^{10}

4. $\dfrac{3(k-1)+5}{2} = \dfrac{17-(8+k)}{4}$

   In the equation above, what is the value of k?

   A) $\dfrac{9}{13}$

   B) $\dfrac{5}{7}$

   C) $\dfrac{8}{7}$

   D) $\dfrac{8}{5}$

5. An environmental protection group had its members sign a pledge to try to reduce the amount of garbage they throw out by 3 percent each year. On the year that the pledge was signed, each person threw out an average of 1,800 pounds of garbage. Which exponential function could be used to model the average amount of garbage each person who signed the pledge should throw out each year after signing the pledge?

   A) $y = 0.97 \times 1,800^t$

   B) $y = 1,800 \times t^{0.97}$

   C) $y = 1,800 \times 1.97^t$

   D) $y = 1,800 \times 0.97^t$

GO ON TO THE NEXT PAGE ⟹

6. If the equation of the line shown in the figure above is written in the form $\dfrac{y}{x} = m$, which of the following could be the value of m?

A) -3

B) $-\dfrac{1}{3}$

C) $\dfrac{1}{3}$

D) 3

7. If $4x^2 + 7x + 1$ is multiplied by $3x + 5$, what is the coefficient of x in the resulting polynomial?

A) 3

B) 12

C) 35

D) 38

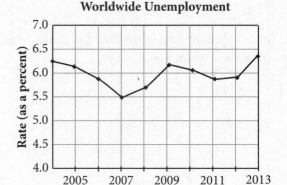

8. The figure above shows worldwide unemployment rates from 2004 to 2013. Which of the following statements is true?

A) The graph is decreasing everywhere.

B) The graph is increasing from 2007 to 2010.

C) The graph is decreasing from 2004 to 2007 and from 2009 to 2011.

D) The graph is increasing from 2007 to 2010 and decreasing from 2011 to 2013.

9. The solution to which inequality is represented in the graph above?

A) $\dfrac{1}{4}x - y > 3$

B) $\dfrac{1}{4}x - y < 3$

C) $\dfrac{1}{4}x + y > -3$

D) $\dfrac{1}{4}x + y < -3$

Practice Tests

$$\frac{1}{2}(4a + 10b) = b$$

10. If (a, b) is a solution to the equation above, what is the ratio $\frac{b}{a}$, given that $a \neq 0$?

    A) -3

    B) -2

    C) $-\frac{1}{2}$

    D) $-\frac{1}{3}$

$$\begin{cases} \frac{1}{3}x + \frac{2}{3}y = -8 \\ ax + 6y = 15 \end{cases}$$

11. If the system of linear equations above has no solution, and a is a constant, what is the value of a ?

    A) $-\frac{1}{3}$

    B) $\frac{1}{3}$

    C) $\frac{3}{2}$

    D) 3

12. A taxi in the city charges \$3.00 for the first $\frac{1}{4}$ mile, plus \$0.25 for each additional $\frac{1}{8}$ mile. Eric plans to spend no more than \$20.00 on a taxi ride around the city. Which inequality represents the number of miles, m, that Eric could travel without exceeding his limit?

    A) $2.5 + 2m \leq 20$

    B) $3 + 0.25m \leq 20$

    C) $3 + 2m \leq 20$

    D) $12 + 2m \leq 20$

13. A projectile is any moving object that is thrown near the Earth's surface. The path of the projectile is called the trajectory and can be modeled by a quadratic equation, assuming the only force acting on the motion is gravity (no friction). If a projectile is launched from a platform 8 feet above the ground with an initial velocity of 64 feet per second, then its trajectory can be modeled by the equation $h = -16t^2 + 64t + 8$, where h represents the height of the projectile t seconds after it was launched. Based on this model, what is the maximum height in feet that the projectile will reach?

    A) 72

    B) 80

    C) 92

    D) 108

GO ON TO THE NEXT PAGE

Directions: For questions 14–17, enter your responses into the appropriate grid on your answer sheet, in accordance with the following:

1. You will receive credit only if the circles are filled in correctly, but you may write your answers in the boxes above each grid to help you fill in the circles accurately.
2. Don't mark more than one circle per column.
3. None of the questions with grid-in responses will have a negative solution.
4. Only grid in a single answer, even if there is more than one correct answer to a given question.
5. A **mixed number** must be gridded as a decimal or an improper fraction. For example, you would grid $7\frac{1}{2}$ as 7.5 or 15/2.

    (Were you to grid it as $\boxed{7\ 1\ /\ 2}$, this response would be read as $\frac{71}{2}$.)

6. A **decimal** that has more digits than there are places on the grid may be either rounded or truncated, but every column in the grid must be filled in order to receive credit.

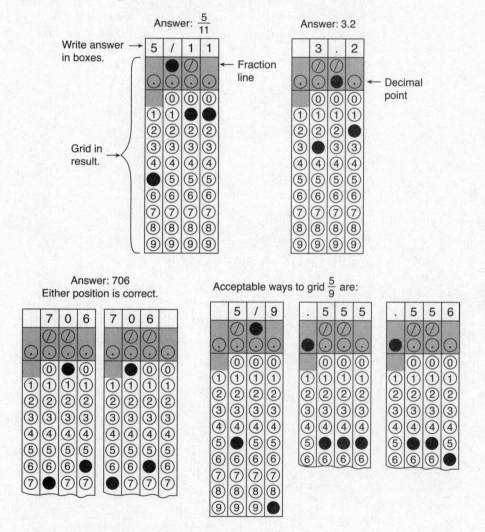

14. If $\dfrac{3}{4}x + \dfrac{5}{6}y = 12$, what is the value of $9x + 10y$?

15. How many degrees does the minute hand of an analog clock rotate from 3:20 p.m. to 3:45 p.m.?

$$\dfrac{3x^{\frac{3}{2}} \cdot \left(16x^2\right)^3}{8x^{-\frac{1}{2}}}$$

16. What is the exponent on x when the expression above is written in simplest form?

17. An exponential function is given in the form $f(x) = a \cdot b^x$. If $f(0) = 3$ and $f(1) = 15$, what is the value of $f(-2)$?

IF YOU FINISH BEFORE TIME IS CALLED, YOU MAY CHECK YOUR WORK ON THIS SECTION ONLY. DO NOT TURN TO ANY OTHER SECTION IN THE TEST.

STOP

Math Test

45 Minutes—31 Questions

CALCULATOR SECTION

This section corresponds to Section 4 of your answer sheet.

Directions: For this section, solve each problem and decide which is the best of the choices given. Fill in the corresponding oval on the answer sheet. You may use any available space for scratch work.

Notes:

1. Calculator use is permitted.
2. All numbers used are real numbers, and all variables used represent real numbers, unless otherwise indicated.
3. Figures are drawn to scale and lie in a plane unless otherwise indicated.
4. Unless stated otherwise, the domain of any function f is assumed to be the set of all real numbers x, for which $f(x)$ is a real number.

Information:

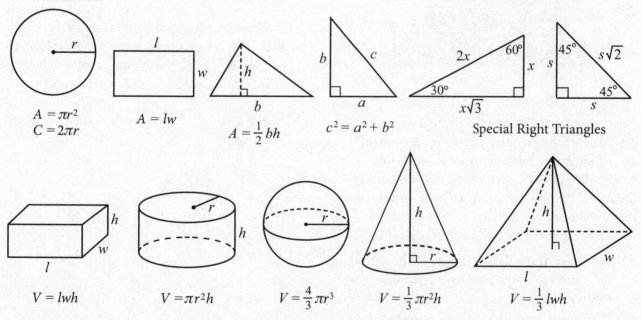

$A = \pi r^2$
$C = 2\pi r$

$A = lw$

$A = \frac{1}{2} bh$

$c^2 = a^2 + b^2$

Special Right Triangles

$V = lwh$

$V = \pi r^2 h$

$V = \frac{4}{3}\pi r^3$

$V = \frac{1}{3}\pi r^2 h$

$V = \frac{1}{3} lwh$

The sum of the degree measures of the angles in a triangle is 180.

The number of degrees of arc in a circle is 360.

The number of radians of arc in a circle is 2π.

GO ON TO THE NEXT PAGE

1. A home improvement store that sells carpeting charges a flat installation fee and a certain amount per square foot of carpet ordered. If the total cost for f square feet of carpet is given by the function $C(f) = 3.29f + 199$, then the value 3.29 best represents which of the following?

   A) The installation fee

   B) The cost of 1 square foot of carpet

   C) The number of square feet of carpet ordered

   D) The total cost not including the installation fee

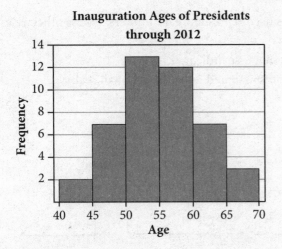

Inauguration Ages of Presidents through 2012

2. The United States Constitution requires that any candidate for the presidency be at least 35 years of age, although no president to date has been that young. The figure above shows the distribution of the ages of the presidents through 2012 at the time they were inaugurated. Based on the information shown, which of the following statements is true?

   A) The shape of the data is skewed to the left, so the mean age of the presidents is greater than the median.

   B) The shape of the data is fairly symmetric, so the mean age of the presidents is approximately equal to the median.

   C) The data has no clear shape, so it is impossible to make a reliable statement comparing the mean and the median.

   D) The same number of 55-or-older presidents have been inaugurated as ones who were younger than 55, so the mean age is exactly 55.

$$\frac{1}{3}(5x - 8) = 3x + 4$$

3. Which value of x satisfies the equation above?

   A) -5

   B) -3

   C) -1

   D) 1

4. The following quadratic equations are all representations of the graph shown above. Which equation could you use to find the minimum value of the function without doing any additional work?

   A) $y = \frac{3}{8}(x - 3)^2 - \frac{3}{2}$

   B) $y = \frac{3}{8}(x - 1)(x - 5)$

   C) $y - \frac{15}{8} = \frac{3}{8}x^2 - \frac{9}{4}x$

   D) $y = \frac{3}{8}x^2 - \frac{9}{4}x + \frac{15}{8}$

GO ON TO THE NEXT PAGE

5. Marion is a city planner. The city she works for recently purchased new property on which it plans to build administrative offices. Marion has been given the task of sizing the lots for new buildings, using the following guidelines:

   • The square footage of each lot should be greater than or equal to 3,000 square feet, but less than or equal to 15,000 square feet.

   • Each lot size should be at least 30 percent greater in area than the size before it.

   • To simplify tax assessment calculations, the square footage of each lot must be a multiple of 1,000 square feet.

   Which list of lot sizes meets the city guidelines and includes as many lots as possible?

   A) 3,000; 5,000; 10,000; 15,000

   B) 3,000; 4,500; 6,000; 7,500; 10,000; 15,000

   C) 3,000; 4,000; 6,000; 8,000; 11,000; 15,000

   D) 3,000; 3,900; 5,100; 6,600; 8,600; 11,200; 14,600

6. One function of the Environmental Protection Agency (EPA) is to reduce air pollution. After implementing several pollution reduction programs in a certain city, EPA calculated that the air pollution should decrease by approximately 8 percent each year. What kind of function could be used to model the amount of air pollution in this city over the next several years, assuming no other significant changes?

   A) A linear function

   B) A quadratic function

   C) A polynomial function

   D) An exponential function

7. Escape velocity is the speed that a traveling object needs to break free of a planet or moon's gravitational field without additional propulsion (for example, without using fuel). The formula used to calculate escape velocity is $v = \sqrt{\frac{2Gm}{r}}$, where G represents the universal gravitational constant, m is the mass of the body from which the object is escaping, and r is the distance between the object and the body's center of gravity. Which equation represents the value of r in terms of v, G, and m?

   A) $r = \frac{2Gm}{v^2}$

   B) $r = \frac{4G^2m^2}{v^2}$

   C) $r = \sqrt{\frac{2Gm}{v}}$

   D) $r = \sqrt{\frac{v}{2Gm}}$

8. A movie rental kiosk dispenses DVDs and Blu-rays. DVDs cost $2.00 per night and Blu-rays cost $3.50 per night. Between 5 p.m. and 9 p.m. on Saturday, the kiosk dispensed 209 movies and collected $562.00. Solving which system of equations would yield the number of DVDs, d, and the number of Blu-rays, b, that the kiosk dispensed during the 4-hour period?

A) $\begin{cases} d + b = 209 \\ 2d + 3.5b = \dfrac{562}{4} \end{cases}$

B) $\begin{cases} d + b = 562 \\ 2d + 3.5b = 209 \end{cases}$

C) $\begin{cases} d + b = 562 \\ 2d + 3.5b = 209 \times 4 \end{cases}$

D) $\begin{cases} d + b = 209 \\ 2d + 3.5b = 562 \end{cases}$

9. The United States Senate has two voting members for each of the 50 states. The 113th Congress had a 4:1 male-to-female ratio in the Senate. Forty-five of the male senators were Republican. Only 20 percent of the female senators were Republican. How many senators in the 113th Congress were Republican?

A) 20

B) 49

C) 55

D) 65

10. According to the *Project on Student Debt* prepared by The Institute for College Access and Success, 7 out of 10 students graduating in 2012 from a four-year college in the United States had student loan debt. The average amount borrowed per student was $29,400, which is up from $18,750 in 2004. If student debt experiences the same total percent increase over the next eight years, approximately how much will a college student graduating in 2020 owe, assuming he takes out student loans to pay for his education?

A) $40,100

B) $44,300

C) $46,100

D) $48,200

11. Annalisa has 10 beanbags to throw in a game. She gets 7 points if a beanbag lands in the smaller basket and 3 points if it lands in the larger basket. If she gets b beanbags into the larger basket and the rest into the smaller basket, which expression represents her total score?

A) $3b$

B) $3b + 7$

C) $30 + 4b$

D) $70 - 4b$

GO ON TO THE NEXT PAGE

Questions 12 and 13 refer to the following information.

In a 2010 poll, surveyors asked registered voters in four different New York voting districts whether they would consider voting to ban fracking in the state. Hydraulic fracturing, or "fracking," is a mining process that involves splitting rocks underground to remove natural gas. According to ecologists, environmental damage can occur as a result of fracking, including contamination of water. The results of the 2010 survey are shown in the following table.

	In Favor of Ban	Against Ban	No Opinion	Total
District A	23,247	17,106	3,509	43,862
District B	13,024	12,760	2,117	27,901
District C	43,228	49,125	5,891	98,244
District D	30,563	29,771	3,205	63,539
Total	110,062	108,762	14,722	233,546

12. According to the data, which district had the smallest percentage of voters with no opinion on fracking?

A) District A

B) District B

C) District C

D) District D

13. A random follow-up survey was administered to 500 of the respondents in District C. They were asked if they planned to vote in the next election. The follow-up survey results were 218 said they planned to vote, 174 said they did not plan to vote, and 108 said they were unsure. Based on the data from both the initial survey and the follow-up survey, which of the following is most likely an accurate statement?

A) Approximately 19,000 people in District C who support a ban on fracking can be expected to vote in the next election.

B) Approximately 21,000 people in District C who support a ban on fracking can be expected to vote in the next election.

C) Approximately 43,000 people in District C who support a ban on fracking can be expected to vote in the next election.

D) Approximately 48,000 people in District C who support a ban on fracking can be expected to vote in the next election.

$$\begin{cases} 2x + 4y = 13 \\ x - 3y = -11 \end{cases}$$

14. Based on the system of equations above, what is the value of the sum of x and y ?

A) $-\dfrac{1}{2}$

B) 3

C) $3\dfrac{1}{2}$

D) 4

GO ON TO THE NEXT PAGE

Bowling Scores			
	Ian	Mae	Jin
Game 1	160	110	120
Game 2	135	160	180
Game 3	185	140	105
Game 4	135	130	160
Game 5	185	110	135
Mean Score	160	130	140
Standard Deviation	22	19	27

15. Ian, Mae, and Jin bowled five games during a bowling tournament. The table above shows their scores. According to the data, which of the following conclusions is correct?

    A) Ian bowled the most consistently because the mean of his scores is the highest.

    B) Mae bowled the least consistently because the standard deviation of her scores is the lowest.

    C) Mae bowled the most consistently because the standard deviation of her scores is the lowest.

    D) Jin bowled the most consistently because the standard deviation of his scores is the highest.

16. Which of the following are solutions to the quadratic equation $(x + 3)^2 = 16$?

    A) $x = -19$ and $x = 13$

    B) $x = -7$ and $x = 1$

    C) $x = -1$ and $x = 1$

    D) $x = -1$ and $x = 7$

17. An architect is building a scale model of the Statue of Liberty. The real statue measures 305 feet, 6 inches from the bottom of the base to the tip of the torch. The architect plans to make her model 26 inches tall. If Lady Liberty's nose on the actual statue is 4 feet, 6 inches long, how long in inches should the nose on the model be?

    A) $\dfrac{1}{26}$

    B) $\dfrac{26}{141}$

    C) $\dfrac{18}{47}$

    D) $\dfrac{13}{27}$

18. If $f(x) = 3x + 5$, what is $f(6) - f(2)$?

    A) 11

    B) 12

    C) 17

    D) 23

GO ON TO THE NEXT PAGE

Northern Spotted Owls
West Oregon, 1994–2014

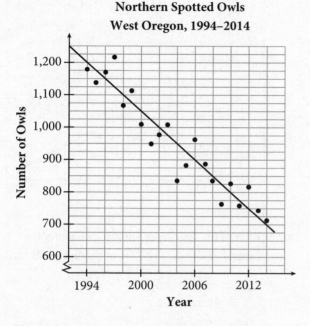

19. The United States Fish and Wildlife Service classifies animals whose populations are at low levels as either threatened or endangered. Endangered species are animals that are currently on the brink of extinction, whereas threatened species have a high probability of being on the brink in the near future. Since 1990, the Northern Spotted Owl has been listed as threatened. The figure above shows the populations of the Northern Spotted Owl in a certain region in Oregon from 1994 to 2014. Based on the line of best fit shown in the figure, which of the following values most accurately reflects the average change per year in the number of Northern Spotted Owls?

A) −25

B) −0.04

C) 0.04

D) 25

20. The x-coordinates of the solutions to a system of equations are −4 and 2. Which of the following could be the system?

A) $\begin{cases} y = 2x - 4 \\ y = (x + 4)^2 \end{cases}$

B) $\begin{cases} y = x - 2 \\ y = (x + 4)^2 + 2 \end{cases}$

C) $\begin{cases} y = x - 2 \\ y = (x - 4)^2 - 16 \end{cases}$

D) $\begin{cases} y = 2x - 4 \\ y = (x + 2)^2 - 16 \end{cases}$

21. The White-footed Mouse, named for its darker body fur and white feet, is primarily found on the east coast of the United States, living in warm, dry forests and brushland. A scientist in Virginia studied a sample of 200 white-footed mice to see how many offspring they had per birth. The results of the study are recorded in the figure above. Based on the data, given a population of 35,000 female white-footed mice living in Virginia, how many would you expect to have a litter of seven or more pups?

A) 3,325

B) 4,375

C) 7,700

D) 15,400

22. Human beings have a resting heart rate and an active heart rate. The resting heart rate is the rate at which the heart beats when a person is at rest, engaging in no activity. The active heart rate rises as activity rises. For a fairly active woman in her 20s, eight minutes of moderate exercise results in a heart rate of about 90 beats per minute. After 20 minutes, the same woman's heart rate will be about 117 beats per minute. If the human heart rate increases at a constant rate as the time spent exercising increases, which of the following linear models represents this same woman's heart rate, r, after t minutes of moderate exercise?

   A) $r = 0.15t - 5.3$

   B) $r = 0.44t - 32$

   C) $r = 2.25t + 72$

   D) $r = 6.75t + 36$

23. Chantal buys new furniture using store credit, which offers five-year no-interest financing. She sets up a payment plan to pay the debt off as soon as possible. The function $40x + y = 1,400$ can be used to model her payment plan where x is the number of payments Chantal has made and y is the amount of debt remaining. If a solution to the equation is $(21, 560)$, which of the following statements is true?

   A) Chantal pays \$21 per month.

   B) Chantal pays \$560 per month.

   C) After 21 payments, \$560 remains to be paid.

   D) After 21 payments, Chantal will have paid off \$560 of the debt.

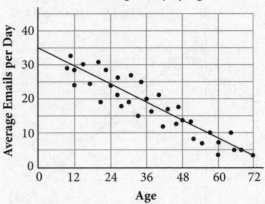

24. Which of the following equations best represents the trend of the data shown in the figure above?

   A) $y = -2.4x + 30$

   B) $y = -1.2x + 40$

   C) $y = -0.8x + 40$

   D) $y = -0.4x + 36$

25. The graph of $f(x)$ passes through the point $(5, 1)$. Through which point does the graph of $-f(x + 3) - 2$ pass?

   A) $(-2, -1)$

   B) $(2, -3)$

   C) $(2, 1)$

   D) $(8, -3)$

GO ON TO THE NEXT PAGE

26. When a certain kitchen appliance store decides to sell a floor model, it marks the retail price of the model down 25 percent and puts a "Floor Model Sale" sign on it. Every 30 days after that, the price is marked down an additional 10 percent until it is sold. The store decides to sell a floor model refrigerator on January 15th. If the retail price of the refrigerator was $1,500 and it is sold on April 2nd of the same year, what is the final selling price, not including tax?

    A) $820.13

    B) $825.00

    C) $911.25

    D) $1,012.50

27. When New York City built its 34th Street subway station, which has multiple underground levels, it built an elevator that runs along a diagonal track approximately 170 feet long to connect the upper and lower levels. The angle formed between the elevator track and the bottom level is just under 30 degrees. What is the approximate vertical distance in feet between the upper and lower levels of the subway station?

    A) 85

    B) 98

    C) 120

    D) 147

Directions: For questions 28–31, enter your responses into the appropriate grid on your answer sheet, in accordance with the following:

1. You will receive credit only if the circles are filled in correctly, but you may write your answers in the boxes above each grid to help you fill in the circles accurately.

2. Don't mark more than one circle per column.

3. None of the questions with grid-in responses will have a negative solution.

4. Only grid in a single answer, even if there is more than one correct answer to a given question.

5. A **mixed number** must be gridded as a decimal or an improper fraction. For example, you would grid $7\frac{1}{2}$ as 7.5 or 15/2.

(Were you to grid it as [7 1 / 2 grid], this response would be interpreted as $\frac{71}{2}$.)

6. A **decimal** that has more digits than there are places on the grid may be either rounded or truncated, but every column in the grid must be filled in order to receive credit.

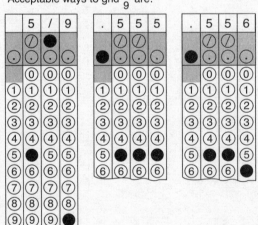

GO ON TO THE NEXT PAGE

Boeing Jets	Coach	Business	First Class
747-400	310	52	12
767-300	151	26	6
777-200	194	37	16
777-300	227	52	8

28. The table above shows the seating configuration for several commercial airplanes. The day before a particular flight departs, a travel agent books the last seat available for a client. If the seat is on one of the two Boeing 777s, what is the probability that the seat is a Business Class seat, assuming that all seats have an equal chance of being the last one available?

29. Heating water accounts for a good portion of the average home's energy consumption. Tankless water heaters, which run on natural gas, are about 22 percent more energy efficient on average than electric hot water heaters. However, a tankless hot water heater typically costs significantly more. Suppose one tankless water heater costs $160 more than twice as much as a conventional hot water heater. If both water heaters cost $1,000 together, how many more dollars does the tankless water heater cost than the conventional one?

Questions 30 and 31 refer to the following information.

Daniel works for a pest control company and is spraying all the lawns in a neighborhood. The figure above shows the layout of the neighborhood and the times that Daniel started spraying the lawns at two of the houses. Each lawn in the neighborhood is approximately 0.2 acres in size and takes the same amount of time to spray.

30. How many minutes will it take Daniel to spray all of the lawns in the neighborhood?

31. Daniel uses a mobile spray rig that holds 20 gallons of liquid. It takes 1 gallon to spray 2,500 square feet of lawn. How many times, including the first time, will Daniel need to fill the spray rig, assuming he fills it to the very top each time? (Note: 1 acre = 43,560 square feet.)

Answer Key

Reading Test

1. C	13. C	25. D	37. C
2. D	14. D	26. B	38. A
3. A	15. B	27. A	39. B
4. C	16. B	28. D	40. B
5. D	17. D	29. A	41. A
6. A	18. C	30. D	42. D
7. D	19. A	31. B	43. B
8. A	20. C	32. D	44. C
9. D	21. B	33. C	45. B
10. D	22. C	34. B	46. D
11. D	23. A	35. D	47. D
12. A	24. C	36. C	

Writing and Language Test

1. B	12. D	23. D	34. C
2. B	13. B	24. C	35. D
3. C	14. D	25. B	36. C
4. A	15. B	26. D	37. B
5. B	16. C	27. D	38. B
6. A	17. B	28. A	39. C
7. A	18. C	29. B	40. A
8. C	19. A	30. C	41. B
9. A	20. C	31. C	42. B
10. D	21. D	32. D	43. A
11. C	22. B	33. D	44. D

Math Test—No-Calculator

1. B	6. C	11. D	16. 8
2. D	7. D	12. A	17. 3/25 or .12
3. C	8. C	13. A	
4. B	9. A	14. 144	
5. D	10. C	15. 150	

Math Test—Calculator

1. B	9. B	17. C	25. B
2. B	10. C	18. B	26. C
3. A	11. D	19. A	27. A
4. A	12. D	20. D	28. 1/6 or .166 or .167
5. C	13. A	21. C	29. 440
6. D	14. B	22. C	30. 252
7. A	15. C	23. C	31. 4
8. D	16. B	24. D	

Answers and Explanations

Reading Test

Suggested passage map notes:

¶1: Gregor woke up not himself

¶2: description of Gregor's room, job

¶3: thought sleep would make him normal, couldn't roll over

¶4: thought job stress was to blame for how he was

¶5: thinks he needs more sleep, wants more luxury but has to help parents

1. C

Difficulty: Easy

Category: Detail

Getting to the Answer: Skim the passage to locate Gregor's first reaction to his transformation. The first sentence states that Gregor woke "from troubled dreams." He only realizes "it wasn't a dream" (lines 11–12) after he has examined his new body and looked around his room to orient himself. Choice **(C)** is the correct answer. "Nightmare" describes a dream that is "troubled."

2. D

Difficulty: Hard

Category: Vocab-in-Context

Getting to the Answer: Use context clues and tone to help determine the meaning of the word. Use the surrounding text to paint a mental picture of descriptive words. Finally, make sure the answer choice does not alter the meaning of the sentence when inserted. The paragraph in which the word appears describes an average room appropriate for a person. Therefore, **(D)** is the correct answer. "Proper" means "suitably appropriate" in this context.

3. A

Difficulty: Medium

Category: Inference

Getting to the Answer: Look for Gregor's thoughts and statements about work. Use this as evidence of his attitude. Paragraphs 4 and 5 are essentially rants about Gregor's dissatisfaction with his job. He dislikes travelling, feels that he works much harder than others, and expresses anger toward his boss. Gregor feels that it is unfair that other salesmen have a life of "luxury" while he has to wake up early. Choice **(A)** is the correct answer. Gregor is resentful and bitter about his job.

4. C

Difficulty: Medium

Category: Command of Evidence

Getting to the Answer: Review your answer to the previous question. Decide which lines of text give clues to how Gregor feels about his job. Choice **(C)** offers the best support. These lines describe Gregor's bitterness and the unfairness he perceives. He feels he works much harder than the other salesmen, but that he would be fired if he asked for better treatment or less work.

5. D

Difficulty: Hard

Category: Global

Getting to the Answer: Ask yourself what purpose the author has in writing the passage. What main point does the majority of the excerpt support? The events in the passage show that despite a dramatic physical transformation, Gregor still plans to go to work. Gregor consistently expresses unhappiness and bitterness about his job but ignores his transformation into an insect because he feels he must still go to work or he will be fired. In this situation, **(D)** is the correct answer. Gregor's duty to his job overrides reason and sense when he plans to attend work despite the physical transformation that has left him inhuman and helpless.

6. A

Difficulty: Medium

Category: Inference

Getting to the Answer: Reread the text, looking for evidence to support each of the answer choices. Examine Gregor's thoughts and statements for clues about his personality. Based on Gregor's statements about his work, it is clear that he continues to work at a job he dislikes in order to support his parents. He largely ignores his physical transformation, and there is no evidence as to whether he excels at his work. Choice **(A)** is the correct answer.

7. D

Difficulty: Medium

Category: Command of Evidence

Getting to the Answer: Review your answer to the previous question. Read each choice and figure out which one provides specific support for that answer. Choice **(D)** provides the best support. These lines show that Gregor thinks it may be best to quit the job he hates, but he will continue to work until he can pay off his parents' debt.

8. A

Difficulty: Medium

Category: Vocab-in-Context

Getting to the Answer: Use context clues from the target sentence and surrounding sentence. Predict the meaning of the word and look for a match in the answer choices. Gregor is attempting to turn over in his bed, but finds his legs and body are useless and unable to turn him over into his preferred position. Choice **(A)** is the nearest match to the meaning of "floundering" in this context.

9. D

Difficulty: Medium

Category: Function

Getting to the Answer: Contrast Gregor's thoughts with the dark tone of the rest of the excerpt. Think about how this phrase adds to or supports the interpretations you made in previous questions. The author ends the excerpt with Gregor completely disregarding the fact that he is now an insect. Gregor plans to go to work as he always does, and the author draws attention to the absurdity of this decision. Choice **(D)** is the correct choice. The author uses the matter-of-fact tone in the sentence to emphasize that Gregor will ignore his physical condition and go to work because he has such a strong sense of duty to his family.

Suggested passage map notes:

> ¶1–3: women are equal and deserve to be treated as such
> ¶4: what freedom is
> ¶5–6: history of women fighting for equality
> ¶7–8: men and women do great things when they work together
> ¶9–13: must help women in other countries achieve equality and fight discrimination

10. D

Difficulty: Easy

Category: Global

Getting to the Answer: Consider the word choices Clinton uses throughout her speech. Notice any recurring themes. Choice **(D)** is the correct answer. Clinton says that working to improve the lives of women will improve others' lives as well.

11. D

Difficulty: Medium

Category: Command of Evidence

Getting to the Answer: Beware of answer choices that are only vaguely related to Clinton's point. The correct answer will follow her purpose closely. Clinton indicates that women's rights issues affect more than just women. Choice **(D)** is the best fit. These lines from the text provide concrete examples of how improving the lives of women improves their families' lives as well.

12. A

Difficulty: Medium

Category: Vocab-in-Context

Getting to the Answer: Sometimes you can recognize similarities between the word in question and a more familiar word. "Divisive" is similar to "divide" and "division," both of which have to do with things being split or made separate. Clinton is saying that though suffrage produced great conflict and divided people more than other philosophical wars, it was "bloodless." Choice **(A)** is correct; "divisive" means "conflict-producing."

13. C

Difficulty: Hard

Category: Inference

Getting to the Answer: You're being asked to decide which statement Clinton is most likely to agree with. Because the statement isn't explicitly mentioned in the speech, you must infer, or make a logical guess, based on information in the speech. Clinton states that the world would be improved if women were able to contribute more. She provides specific examples of her vision for an improved world. Choice **(C)** is correct as it suggests that if women did not experience discrimination and had more power, the world would be better off.

14. D

Difficulty: Medium

Category: Command of Evidence

Getting to the Answer: Try paraphrasing the answer you chose for the previous test item. Then, decide which quote from the speech supports this idea. Choice **(D)** provides the best evidence. This quote notes that women are discriminated against and that it is not just women who suffer from this discrimination; there are global problems that could benefit from women's ideas.

15. B

Difficulty: Hard

Category: Vocab-in-Context

Getting to the Answer: A word like "organized" can have several meanings, depending on the context. Beware of choosing the most common meaning, as it may not fit this situation. Choice **(B)** successfully conveys the idea of the women's suffrage movement being one in which many different people worked together over a long period of time.

16. B

Difficulty: Hard

Category: Detail

Getting to the Answer: Be careful to assess not only what topics are mentioned but also how Clinton discusses them. Choice **(B)** is supported by the passage, which claims in lines 6–8: "Women must enjoy the right to participate fully in the social and political lives of their countries if we want freedom and democracy to thrive and endure."

17. D

Difficulty: Medium

Category: Detail

Getting to the Answer: Notice how the stem of the question doesn't ask you to find evidence for an argument; it instead gives you the evidence (the example of V-J Day) and then asks you to figure out what argument this evidence supports. Choice **(D)** is correct. Clinton mentions V-J Day as an example of something that resulted from cooperation between men and women.

18. C

Difficulty: Medium

Category: Function

Getting to the Answer: Notice how the question is asking you to figure out how the paragraph functions in relation to other parts of the speech. Clinton goes into specific detail in this paragraph to provide examples of freedom. She very specifically states what she means by freedom and accuses some of failing to respect others' freedom. Therefore, **(C)** is the correct answer.

Suggested passage map notes:

Passage 1

¶1: history of tea, Europe and China
¶2: tea not received well in Europe at first
¶3: China controlled tea production
¶4: Europe wanted to produce tea
¶5: finally had tea growing success in India

Passage 2

¶1: history of tea time in Europe
¶2: tea in France served with savory
¶3: tea in Germany served with sweet
¶4: tea in Russia sign of class
¶5: tea in GB

19. A

Difficulty: Medium

Category: Inference

Getting to the Answer: Be careful to choose an answer that is clearly supported by the information in the passage. The passage states that the climate was not right for growing tea "even in the equatorial colonies" (line 28). Choice **(A)** is the correct answer. Clearly, European tea-drinking nations tried to grow tea in their equatorial colonies; that's how they learned that the climate there wasn't right.

20. C

Difficulty: Medium

Category: Command of Evidence

Getting to the Answer: The correct answer will be the reason you were able to make the inference in the previous question. Choice **(C)** works logically. Europeans knew that tea would not grow well in their colonies; this leads to the conclusion that they tried.

21. B

Difficulty: Medium

Category: Vocab-in-Context

Getting to the Answer: You should be able to replace the original word with the correct answer in the sentence. The passage states that in order to "circumvent" the monopoly, European growers tried growing their own tea. It makes sense that Europeans' attempt at growing their own tea was a way to "get around" the Chinese monopoly. Therefore, **(B)** is the best choice.

22. C

Difficulty: Hard

Category: Inference

Getting to the Answer: Keep in mind that the graphic focuses on tea consumption, not tea production. The last paragraph of Passage 1 describes Britain's great success growing tea in India, which resulted in great increases in the amount of tea arriving in London. Therefore, **(C)** is a reasonable conclusion that may be drawn by synthesizing information in Passage 1 and the graphic.

23. A

Difficulty: Hard

Category: Inference

Getting to the Answer: Be careful to deduce only information that can reasonably be inferred from the passage. It can logically be inferred that hosting guests in Russia generally involves tea. Passage 2 emphasizes that Russian hosts are judged based on the strength of their tea and that Russians have elaborate tea-making equipment. Choice **(A)** is the correct answer.

24. C

Difficulty: Medium

Category: Command of Evidence

Getting to the Answer: Identify the country associated with the correct answer to the previous question and see what evidence fits. The passage states that Russian tea ceremonies are highly formal and that hosts are judged on their tea making. Choice **(C)** is the correct answer. The referenced lines support the conclusions about Russia.

25. D

Difficulty: Medium

Category: Vocab-in-Context

Getting to the Answer: Look for other words in this sentence that offer clues to the word's meaning. A noble, or high-ranking, class is likely to have associations with formalism, so **(D)** is the correct answer.

26. B

Difficulty: Easy

Category: Inference

Getting to the Answer: Make sure to compare only the two countries being asked about. Choice **(B)** is correct. The passage notes that cookies and cakes are served with tea in Germany, while foods served with tea in France are "savory" and include puff pastry with cheese.

27. A

Difficulty: Easy

Category: Inference

Getting to the Answer: Look for true statements about Passage 1. Then, do the same for Passage 2. Choice **(A)** is correct. Passage 1 focuses on an earlier period in European history, while Passage 2 compares different cultures within Europe.

28. D

Difficulty: Medium

Category: Inference

Getting to the Answer: For this question, you're looking for a statement that is reflected in both passages. Choice **(D)** is the only choice supported by both passages.

Suggested passage map notes:

¶1: Stromer discovered dinosaur fossils in Egypt, new genus, fossils destroyed in WWII, notes and sketches survived

¶2: Ibrahim rediscovered similar fossils, able to make partial skeleton

¶3: description of *Spinosaurus*

¶4: *Spino* unique—lived on land, hunted in water

¶5: Ibrahim used digital model and Stromer sketches to create replica

29. A

Difficulty: Easy

Category: Global

Getting to the Answer: Look for the answer choice that describes an important idea that is supported throughout the text rather than a specific detail. The passage is mostly about how the mystery of the *Spinosaurus* fossils was decoded. Choice **(A)** is the best summary of the central idea of the passage.

30. D

Difficulty: Medium

Category: Inference

Getting to the Answer: Think about the overall message of the passage and consider why the author would choose to write about this topic. The author's tone, or attitude, toward the topic of the passage demonstrates the point of view that the study of fossils and ancient life has value. Choice **(D)** is the correct answer. The evidence in the passage supports the idea that the author thinks the study of fossils and ancient life is important.

31. B

Difficulty: Medium

Category: Command of Evidence

Getting to the Answer: Some answer choices may seem important. However, if they don't support your answer to the previous question, they aren't what you should choose. Choice **(B)** is correct. The author's use of the word "significant" in this quote shows that he or she thinks the study of fossils and ancient life is important.

32. D

Difficulty: Medium

Category: Vocab-in-Context

Getting to the Answer: Though more than one answer choice might seem acceptable, one comes closest to meaning the same as the phrase in question. Earlier in the paragraph, the author explains that two different bones gathered at different times both had a red line coursing through them. This means that the bones were from the same animal. Choice **(D)** fits best. "Against all odds" most nearly means "despite low probability."

33. C

Difficulty: Medium

Category: Function

Getting to the Answer: Be careful to avoid answers that don't make sense in the context of the paragraph. These phrases help the author describe the animal in a generally positive way. Choice **(C)** is the correct answer.

34. B

Difficulty: Hard

Category: Inference

Getting to the Answer: Be careful of answers that make sense but are not implied by the information presented in the passage. Choice **(B)** is correct. The passage does not explicitly state how Ibrahim became familiar with Stromer's work, but it is implied that he was familiar with Stromer's work when he found the fossils with the red lines and used Stromer's sketches to aid with the modern digital models as mentioned in the last paragraph.

35. D

Difficulty: Hard

Category: Command of Evidence

Getting to the Answer: Eliminate any answer choices that have nothing to do with your answer to the previous question. Choice **(D)** is correct. It directly supports the inference that Ibrahim was familiar with Stromer's work, showing that he used Stromer's sketches to aid in creating his life-size replica of the *Spinosaurus*.

36. C

Difficulty: Easy

Category: Vocab-in-Context

Getting to the Answer: Ibrahim and his fellow researchers didn't know how the bones went together. They were making an educated guess with the help of technology and Stromer's sketches. Choice **(C)** is correct. "Hypothetical" in this sentence means "possible."

37. C

Difficulty: Easy

Category: Inference

Getting to the Answer: Think about the order in which Stromer and Ibrahim's work with the fossils occurred. Choice **(C)** is correct. Ibrahim used Stromer's sketches to create his models of the *Spinosaurus*. He built on Stromer's work to complete his own.

38. A

Difficulty: Hard

Category: Inference

Getting to the Answer: Think about the process described in each answer choice and compare it to how Ibrahim went about building his replica of the *Spinosaurus*. Choice **(A)** is the correct choice. An architect creating a model of a building would use tools and methods similar to those used by Ibrahim, such as drawings and digital technologies.

Suggested passage map notes:

¶1: people willing to try anything to be healthy
¶2: laughter important part of health
¶3: what happens to body when you laugh
¶4: humor helps many medical conditions, laugh more = better health
¶5: benefits of laughter
¶6: various methods to provoke laughter, best achieved in person, not through watching shows
¶7: laughter decreases with age

39. B

Difficulty: Easy

Category: Inference

Getting to the Answer: When a question asks you about the point of view of an author, look for words and phrases in the passage that hint at the author's feelings or attitude toward the topic. Choice **(B)** is the correct answer because the author speaks quite positively of the studies throughout the passage.

40. B

Difficulty: Medium

Category: Command of Evidence

Getting to the Answer: Reread each quote in the context of the passage. Consider which one is the best evidence of the author's point of view toward laughter research. The word "finally" in line 14 helps demonstrate that the author finds laughter research worthwhile. Choice **(B)** is the best answer.

41. A

Difficulty: Medium

Category: Inference

Getting to the Answer: Think about the connection the passage makes between laughter and the ability to accomplish challenging tasks. Choice **(A)** is correct. The passage notes that endorphin production is associated with "mental energy and positivity" (lines 27–28).

42. D

Difficulty: Medium

Category: Vocab-in-Context

Getting to the Answer: Notice that all of the answer choices are related to the word "reputable," but the correct answer will reflect the specific context in which the word is used. "Reputable" in this case indicates that the studies are official and are based on empirical data (data based on observation and experiment). This makes **(D)**, "credible," the correct choice.

43. B

Difficulty: Hard

Category: Inference

Getting to the Answer: Eliminate any answer choices that are not suggested in the passage. Choice **(B)** is correct because early results of studies into laughter and health all seem to strengthen the relationship between the two.

44. C

Difficulty: Medium

Category: Command of Evidence

Getting to the Answer: Avoid answer choices like (D) that may not support a general conclusion you could take from the passage. Choice **(C)** is the correct answer. The author expects future research will yield stronger evidence in support of laughter's health benefits.

45. B

Difficulty: Hard

Category: Function

Getting to the Answer: Look at the verbs provided in each of the answer choices. Decide whether the author wanted to "reach," "support," "justify," or "show" by discussing the function of endorphins. After asserting that laughter produces endorphins, the author explains their function in order to help the reader understand why a positive mental state may result. Choice **(B)** is the correct answer.

46. D

Difficulty: Medium

Category: Vocab-in-Context

Getting to the Answer: Look carefully at the paragraph's context to help you decide on the correct answer choice. The phrase "Laughter is the best medicine" (lines 15–16) is an example of an adage, or proverb. Therefore, **(D)** is correct.

47. D

Difficulty: Hard

Category: Inference

Getting to the Answer: Decide whether the phrase "uplifting community" is a reference to a person alone or a group of people. Choice **(D)** is correct. The graph shows that shared humor with others most significantly increased pain tolerance in individuals.

Writing and Language Test

1. B

Difficulty: Medium

Category: Sentence Structure: The Basics

Getting to the Answer: Read the sentence and determine whether it is grammatically complete. To form a grammatically complete sentence, you must have an independent clause prior to a colon. As written, the text that comes before the colon is not grammatically complete because it lacks an independent clause with a subject and predicate. Choice **(B)** correctly adds a verb to the clause before the comma. It also correctly uses the past tense to match with the tense of "hadn't" in the first sentence of the passage.

2. B

Difficulty: Medium

Category: Development: Word Choice

Getting to the Answer: Read the sentences surrounding the word to look for context clues. Watch out for near synonyms that are not quite correct. The word "issues" is not precise and does a poor job of conveying the meaning of the sentence. A better word, such as **(B)**, "adversity," more precisely conveys hardship, difficulties, or painful situations.

3. C

Difficulty: Medium

Category: Sentence Structure: The Basics

Getting to the Answer: Determine whether a clause is independent or dependent to decide between a comma and a semicolon. The clause is dependent, as it contains only a noun ("an idea") and a relative clause to modify it. A semicolon is used to separate two independent clauses, so it cannot be used here. A comma is the appropriate punctuation mark to separate the dependent clause from the independent clause in the sentence. Choice **(C)** is the correct answer.

4. A

Difficulty: Medium

Category: Sentence Structure: Commas, Dashes, and Colons

Getting to the Answer: Figure out the role of the underlined phrase in the sentence to find the correct punctuation. "Like lift and drag on wings" is a parenthetical element provided as an example. The sentence is correctly punctuated as written because it uses dashes to set off the parenthetical element. The answer is **(A)**.

5. B

Difficulty: Hard

Category: Development: Introductions and Conclusions

Getting to the Answer: Read the paragraph and summarize the main idea to predict an answer. Then, look for an answer that matches your prediction. Choice **(B)** correctly establishes that Kranz stood out as a leader in a time of crisis.

6. A

Difficulty: Easy

Category: Agreement: Verbs

Getting to the Answer: Read the paragraph to establish the correct verb tense for the sentence. Other verbs in the paragraph, such as "were" and "fueled," are past tense and indicate that another past tense verb is needed for this sentence. Choice **(A)** is correct because it uses the past tense "was" and logically transitions into the explanation about Kranz's vest making him easy to spot.

7. A

Difficulty: Hard

Category: Development: Introductions and Conclusions

Getting to the Answer: Quickly summarize the main idea of the paragraph. Eliminate choices that may be accurate but do not support this primary focus. Choice **(A)** clearly supports the main focus of the paragraph by drawing attention to Kranz's role as a leader in Mission Control.

8. C

Difficulty: Easy

Category: Agreement: Idioms

Getting to the Answer: Be careful with homophones. Figure out the part of speech and what the target word refers to if it is a pronoun. "Their" is a possessive pronoun indicating ownership. "There" is a pronoun that replaces a place name. "They're" is a contraction that is short for *they are*. Choice **(C)**, "There," is the correct choice.

9. A

Difficulty: Hard

Category: Development: Word Choice

Getting to the Answer: When faced with unfamiliar words, eliminate clearly incorrect answers first. The paragraph indicates that Kranz did not intend for the vest to be stylish. Kranz wore the vest as a military type of symbol, but the correct answer will need to be in contrast to that idea. Choice **(A)** is the correct answer. The word "sartorial" means "having to do with clothing."

10. D

Difficulty: Medium

Category: Organization: Transitions

Getting to the Answer: Think about the commonly confused pair between/among. Consider which preposition is usually used to reference two distinct objects. Choice **(D)** appropriately selects the word "between" because the objects "meetings" and "calculations" are two distinct items. "Among" is used for more than two distinct items.

11. C

Difficulty: Medium

Category: Agreement: Pronouns

Getting to the Answer: Read the target sentence and the sentence before it. Figure out whom or what the pronoun refers to and make sure it matches the antecedent in number. The plural antecedent is found in the previous sentence ("Kranz and the NASA staff") and is clearly plural. Choice **(C)** correctly uses a plural pronoun to refer to a plural antecedent.

12. D

Difficulty: Medium

Category: Development: Word Choice

Getting to the Answer: Read carefully to identify the context of the underlined word. Then, choose the word that best fits the content of the sentence. You're looking for a word that suggests that the organization has developed over time, as is stated in the last part of the sentence. "Built," **(D)**, best fits the context of the sentence.

13. B

Difficulty: Medium

Category: Sentence Structure: Commas, Dashes, and Colons

Getting to the Answer: Read the entire sentence to get a better sense for which punctuation would be correct. A colon will introduce an explanation of the "key feature," allowing the rest of the sentence to elaborate on the preceding clause. Choice **(B)** is correct. In this case, the colon prompts the reader to see that the part of the sentence after the colon defines the phrase "key feature."

14. D

Difficulty: Medium

Category: Organization: Sentence Placement

Getting to the Answer: Watch out for any choices that would make the sentence seem out of place. Choice **(D)** is correct. Sentence 3 offers a transition to a specific discussion of those risks in the next paragraph.

15. B

Difficulty: Medium

Category: Conciseness

Getting to the Answer: Avoid choices that are redundant, or use more words than necessary to communicate an idea. All of the choices communicate the same idea, but one does so with a greater economy of language. Choice **(B)** uses a minimal number of well-chosen words to revise the text.

16. C

Difficulty: Hard

Category: Development: Introductions and Conclusions

Getting to the Answer: Watch out for answer choices that correctly identify supporting points but do not explain the main claim. The paragraph contains evidence, including decreased taxable wealth and decreased control over interest rates, to support the main claim. Choice **(C)** is correct. It expresses the main claim of the paragraph and is supported by the evidence.

17. B

Difficulty: Medium

Category: Sentence Structure: The Basics

Getting to the Answer: Read the text carefully. Notice that the existing structure creates a run-on sentence. Then, consider which answer choice will create two complete sentences. Choice **(B)** revises the run-on sentence to create two grammatically complete sentences.

18. C

Difficulty: Medium

Category: Development: Introductions and Conclusions

Getting to the Answer: Find the main claim in the paragraph and then come back to the question. The statement found in **(C)** best supports the paragraph statements that maintaining the current status may not be an option and moving to the Eurozone may be in the best interest of the UK.

19. A

Difficulty: Easy

Category: Development: Word Choice

Getting to the Answer: Watch out for choices that imply little relationship between the EU and the UK. "Intertwined" most accurately reflects the content of the text, because it implies a complex economic relationship between the UK and the Eurozone. Therefore, **(A)** is correct. No change is necessary.

20. C

Difficulty: Hard

Category: Development: Relevance

Getting to the Answer: Find the central idea of the paragraph and then come back to the question. The central idea in the paragraph is that economic downturns in the Eurozone also affect the UK. Choice **(C)** is correct.

21. D

Difficulty: Easy

Category: Organization: Transitions

Getting to the Answer: Decide which transition word makes the most sense in the context of the sentence by reading each choice in the sentence. The correct choice should connect the two sentences as the text transitions from economic concerns to those of "security, power, and protection." The word "however" is the best transition because it provides a logical contrast between the ideas in the passage. Choice **(D)** is the correct answer.

22. B

Difficulty: Medium

Category: Sentence Structure: Commas, Dashes, and Colons

Getting to the Answer: Consider which punctuation will correctly set off the parenthetical information in this sentence. Dashes are often used to offset parenthetical sentence elements. Choice **(B)** is correct.

23. D

Difficulty: Easy

Category: Development: Word Choice

Getting to the Answer: Review each answer choice and decide which makes the most sense in terms of what the first sentence says. Choice **(D)** is the correct answer. "These days" contrasts with the next sentence's use of "this wasn't always true."

24. C

Difficulty: Medium

Category: Agreement: Verbs

Getting to the Answer: Make sure that verbs agree with the subject. Check back and figure out what the subject is and then see if it agrees. The word "cherries" requires a plural verb. Choice **(C)** is the correct answer.

25. B

Difficulty: Medium

Category: Agreement: Verbs

Getting to the Answer: Read the complete sentence carefully whenever you see a shift in tense or verb form. Decide whether this change is logically correct in the sentence. The verbs in a sentence need to be in parallel form. Choice **(B)** is in parallel form with the first verb "reached," so it is the correct answer.

26. D

Difficulty: Medium

Category: Development: Word Choice

Getting to the Answer: Beware of some answer choices that may have similar meanings but do not fit into the context of this sentence. The word "boasted" is the best fit for the context of the sentence, so **(D)** is the correct answer.

27. D

Difficulty: Medium

Category: Sentence Structure: The Basics

Getting to the Answer: Pay close attention to commas to ensure that they do not create run-on sentences. Notice that this sentence contains two complete thoughts. Choice **(D)** is the correct answer because it combines the two complete thoughts into one sentence in the best way.

28. A

Difficulty: Hard

Category: Development: Introductions and Conclusions

Getting to the Answer: To find the best conclusion, look for the choice that summarizes the main points of the paragraph and best completes the paragraph. The paragraph begins by talking about the lack of record of coffee as cargo on the Mayflower and then introduces when it was first referenced. Choice **(A)** does the best job of retelling what the paragraph is about, therefore providing an effective conclusion.

29. B

Difficulty: Easy

Category: Sentence Structure: Commas, Dashes, and Colons

Getting to the Answer: Study the words in the series and see where commas might need to be placed or eliminated. Choice **(B)** is the correct answer.

30. C

Difficulty: Medium

Category: Development: Word Choice

Getting to the Answer: Replace the word with the other answer choices. See which word works best in the context of the sentence. One answer choice indicates the correct relationship between coffeehouses and counterculture, and that is **(C)**. "Associated" works best within the context of the sentence.

31. C

Difficulty: Medium

Category: Development: Introductions and Conclusions

Getting to the Answer: To find the main topic of a paragraph, identify important details and summarize them in a sentence or two. Then, find the answer choice that is the closest to your summary. Choice **(C)** is the correct answer. The sentence best explains the increasing popularity of coffee in American life, the main topic of the paragraph.

32. D

Difficulty: Medium

Category: Sentence Structure: Commas, Dashes, and Colons

Getting to the Answer: Determine the relationship between the two parts of this sentence, and then consider the purpose of the various forms of punctuation. A colon indicates that the rest of the sentence will be a list or an explanation. Choice **(D)** is the correct answer as it shows the correct relationship between both parts of the sentence.

33. D

Difficulty: Hard

Category: Agreement: Modifiers

Getting to the Answer: Read the complete sentence carefully and look for sections that do not seem to follow logically. The modifiers need to be in the proper order so the sentence's meaning is clear. Choice **(D)** is correct.

34. C

Difficulty: Medium

Category: Agreement: Pronouns

Getting to the Answer: Recall that a pronoun must agree with its antecedent, or the word to which it refers. Begin by identifying the antecedent of the pronoun. Then, check each choice against the antecedent to find the best match. The antecedent for the pronoun "their" is "this phenomenon," which appears in the main clause. The antecedent and its pronoun do not currently agree as "this phenomenon" is singular and "their" is plural. Although the "s" in "Lights" implies many lights, it is still considered a singular phenomenon and so requires a singular pronoun. Choice **(C)** is the correct answer.

35. D

Difficulty: Medium

Category: Agreement: Idioms

Getting to the Answer: Read each answer choice carefully to determine the correct preposition. Choice **(D)** is the correct answer because it correctly uses the preposition "in."

36. C

Difficulty: Medium

Category: Development: Introductions and Conclusions

Getting to the Answer: Choice **(C)** is the correct answer because it provides additional information regarding how people are able to view auroras.

37. B

Difficulty: Hard

Category: Agreement: Verbs

Getting to the Answer: When choosing the correct verb, note how it alters the relationship between the subject, the "sun," and the stated action, in this case "storm activity." Choice **(B)** is correct. The verb "experiences" is the only one that states a direct action upon the subject, the sun, rather than the sun "observing" an action occurring externally, as suggested by the other verbs.

38. B

Difficulty: Easy

Category: Agreement: Modifiers

Getting to the Answer: The placement of the adjective has a great effect upon the intention of the noun. Read the sentence carefully to determine where the adjective makes the most sense. By placing the adjective before the nouns, **(B)** ensures that only those scientists and amateurs interested in the topic at hand use the specific tools mentioned in this passage.

39. C

Difficulty: Hard

Category: Conciseness

Getting to the Answer: Generalized statements with inexact definitions that border on opinion have no place in a scientific essay. The tone and style must exhibit a reliance on verifiable statements. Because "readily available" cannot be quantified and implies the author's opinion, using the word "specific" in **(C)** creates a more exact statement that precedes the information on the precise tools used.

40. A

Difficulty: Medium

Category: Development: Relevance

Getting to the Answer: Reread the paragraph to understand the author's claims. Which answer choice provides a fact that would best support these claims? Make sure the answer choice does not digress from the progression of ideas. The speed of the solar flare is referenced as being three times the speed of normal solar winds, but neither exact speed is given. To make a stronger case for the author's statements, both speeds should be stated. Therefore, **(A)** is the correct answer.

41. B

Difficulty: Medium

Category: Agreement: Verbs

Getting to the Answer: Read closely to find the subject of the verb. Sometimes, the closest noun is not the subject. The subject of the sentence is "strength and direction," not "energy." Choice **(B)** is the correct answer because it matches the subject in number and maintains a consistent tense with the rest of the passage.

42. B

Difficulty: Hard

Category: Conciseness

Getting to the Answer: Eliminate extraneous and redundant information ("the public") and needless prepositions. Then, reorder the verb and nouns to achieve the most efficient language possible. Making adjustments to the passage language as shown in **(B)** results in the most concise phrasing.

43. A

Difficulty: Hard

Category: Organization: Transitions

Getting to the Answer: Consider the meanings of each introductory word carefully. Use the context clues in the rest of the sentence to choose the correct word. The context clues in the rest of the sentence reveal that the Northern Lights can create communication and weather problems and yet are still beautiful. Keeping the word "While" makes the most sense in this context, so **(A)** is the correct answer.

44. D

Difficulty: Hard

Category: Graphs

Getting to the Answer: Reread paragraph 4 for information that will help you understand how to read the graphic. Use that information to calculate the precise start and end time for the solar flare as indicated in the graphic. The passage states that a solar flare is represented by any Kp-Index of 5 or higher. While there is one three-hour period where the Kp-Index reached 6, there is a consistent period where the chart shows readings of level 5 or higher. Choice **(D)** is the correct answer. This choice gives the complete time period showing a reading of level 5 or higher, according to the chart.

Math Test—No-Calculator

1. B

Difficulty: Easy

Category: Heart of Algebra/Linear Equations

Getting to the Answer: The average rate of change for a linear function is the same as the slope of the line. Find the slope of the line by either using the slope formula or by counting the rise and the run from one point to the next. If you start at $(0, -3)$, the line rises 5 units and runs 8 units to get to $(8, 2)$, so the slope, or average rate of change, is $\frac{5}{8}$.

2. D

Difficulty: Easy

Category: Passport to Advanced Math/Quadratics

Getting to the Answer: A root of an equation is an x-value that corresponds to a y-value of 0. The x-intercepts of the graph, and therefore the roots of the equation, are $x = -1$ and $x = 5$. When $x = -1$, the value of $x + 1$ is 0, so one of the factors is $x + 1$. When $x = 5$, the value of $x - 5$ is 0, so the other factor is $x - 5$. The equation in **(D)** is the only one that contains these factors and is therefore correct.

3. C

Difficulty: Easy

Category: Passport to Advanced Math/Exponents

Getting to the Answer: Substitute the values given in the question into the formula. Then, simplify using the rules of exponents. Remember, when raising a power to a power, you multiply the exponents:

$$
\begin{aligned}
KE &= \tfrac{1}{2}\left(2 \times 10^3\right)\left(3 \times 10^3\right)^2 \\
&= \tfrac{1}{2}\left(2 \times 10^3\right)\left(3^2 \times 10^{3 \times 2}\right) \\
&= \tfrac{1}{2} \times 2 \times 10^3 \times 9 \times 10^6 \\
&= 9 \times 10^{3+6} \\
&= 9 \times 10^9
\end{aligned}
$$

Choice **(C)** is correct.

4. B

Difficulty: Medium

Category: Heart of Algebra/Linear Equations

Getting to the Answer: Choose the best strategy to answer the question. You could start by cross-multiplying to get rid of the denominators, but simplifying the numerators first will make the calculations easier:

$$\frac{3(k-1)+5}{2} = \frac{17-(8+k)}{4}$$
$$\frac{3k-3+5}{2} = \frac{17-8-k}{4}$$
$$\frac{3k+2}{2} = \frac{9-k}{4}$$
$$4(3k+2) = 2(9-k)$$
$$12k+8 = 18-2k$$
$$14k = 10$$
$$k = \frac{10}{14} = \frac{5}{7}$$

Choice **(B)** is correct.

5. D

Difficulty: Medium

Category: Passport to Advanced Math/Functions

Getting to the Answer: Whenever a quantity repeatedly increases or decreases by the same percentage (or fraction) over time, an exponential model can be used to represent the situation. Choice (B) is not an exponential equation, so you can eliminate it right away. The amount of garbage is decreasing, so the scenario represents exponential decay and you can use the form $y = a \times (1-r)^t$, where a is the initial amount, r is the rate of decay, and t is time in years. The initial amount is 1,800, the rate is 3%, or 0.03, and t is an unknown quantity, so the correct equation is $y = 1,800 \times (1-0.03)^t$, which is equivalent to the equation $y = 1,800 \times 0.97^t$. **(D)** is correct.

6. C

Difficulty: Medium

Category: Heart of Algebra/Linear Equations

Getting to the Answer: The slope-intercept form of a line is $y = mx + b$. In this question, the graph passes through the origin, so b is 0. Because b is 0, the equation of this line in slope-intercept form is $y = mx$, which can be rewritten as $\frac{y}{x} = m$. Count the rise and

the run from the origin, (0, 0), to the next point, (3, 1), to get a slope of $m = \frac{1}{3}$. This matches **(C)**.

7. D

Difficulty: Medium

Category: Passport to Advanced Math/Polynomials

Getting to the Answer: When multiplying polynomials, carefully multiply each term in the first factor by each term in the second factor. This question doesn't ask for the entire product, so check to make sure you answered the correct question (the coefficient of x). After performing the initial multiplication, look for the x terms and add their coefficients. To save time, you do not need to simplify the other terms in the expression:

$$\left(4x^2 + 7x + 1\right)(3x + 5)$$
$$= 4x^2(3x+5) + 7x(3x+5) + 1(3x+5)$$
$$= 12x^3 + 20x^2 + 21x^2 + \underline{35x + 3x} + 5$$

The coefficient of x is $35 + 3 = 38$, which is **(D)**.

8. C

Difficulty: Medium

Category: Passport to Advanced Math/Functions

Getting to the Answer: A graph is *decreasing* when the slope is negative; it is *increasing* when the slope is positive. Eliminate (A) because there are some segments on the graph that have a positive slope. Eliminate (B) because the slope is negative, not positive, between 2009 and 2010. Choice **(C)** is correct because the slope is negative for each segment between 2004 and 2007 and also between 2009 and 2011.

9. A

Difficulty: Medium

Category: Heart of Algebra/Inequalities

Getting to the Answer: Don't answer this question too quickly. The shading is below the line, but that does not necessarily mean that the symbol in the equation will be the less than symbol ($<$). Start by writing the equation of the dashed line shown in the graph in slope-intercept form. Then, use the shading to determine the correct inequality symbol. The slope of the line shown in the graph is $\frac{1}{4}$ and the y-intercept is -3, so the equation of the dashed line is $y = \frac{1}{4}x - 3$. The graph is shaded below the boundary line, so use the $<$ symbol. When written in slope-intercept form, the inequality is $y < \frac{1}{4}x - 3$. The inequalities in the answer choices are given in standard form ($Ax + By = C$), so rewrite your answer in this form. Don't forget to reverse the inequality symbol if you multiply or divide by a negative number:

$$y < \frac{1}{4}x - 3$$
$$-\frac{1}{4}x + y < -3$$
$$\frac{1}{4}x - y > 3$$

Choice **(A)** is correct.

10. C

Difficulty: Medium

Category: Heart of Algebra/Linear Equations

Getting to the Answer: When you're given only one equation but two variables, chances are that you can't actually solve the equation (unless one variable happens to cancel out), but rather that you are going to need to manipulate it to look like the desired expression (which in this question is $\frac{b}{a}$). This type of question can't be planned out step-by-step—instead, start with basic algebraic manipulations and see where they take you. First, distribute the $\frac{1}{2}$ on the left side of the equation to get $2a + 5b = b$. There are two terms that have a b, so subtract $5b$ from both sides to get $2a = -4b$. You're hoping for plain b in the numerator, so divide both sides by -4 to get $\frac{2a}{-4} = b$. Finally, divide both sides by a to move the a into a denominator position under b. The result is $\frac{2}{-4} = \frac{b}{a}$, which means the ratio $\frac{b}{a}$ is $-\frac{2}{4}$, or $-\frac{1}{2}$, making **(C)** correct.

11. D

Difficulty: Hard

Category: Heart of Algebra/Systems of Linear Equations

Getting to the Answer: Graphically, a system of linear equations that has no solution indicates two parallel lines, or in other words, two lines that have the same slope. So, write each of the equations in slope-intercept form ($y = mx + b$) and set their slopes (m) equal to each

other to solve for a. Before finding the slopes, multiply the top equation by 3 to make it easier to manipulate:

$$3\left(\frac{1}{3}x + \frac{2}{3}y = -8\right) \rightarrow x + 2y = -24 \rightarrow y = -\frac{1}{2}x - 12$$

$$ax + 6y = 15 \rightarrow 6y = -ax + 15 \rightarrow y = -\frac{a}{6}x + \frac{15}{6}$$

The slope of the first line is $-\frac{1}{2}$ and the slope of the second line is $-\frac{a}{6}$. Now, set the slopes equal to each other and solve:

$$-\frac{1}{2} = -\frac{a}{6}$$
$$-6(1) = -a(2)$$
$$-6 = -2a$$
$$3 = a$$

Choice **(D)** is correct.

12. A

Difficulty: Hard

Category: Heart of Algebra/Inequalities

Getting to the Answer: Pay careful attention to units, particularly when a question involves rates. The taxi charges $3.00 for the first $\frac{1}{4}$ mile, which is a flat fee, so write 3. The additional charge is $0.25 per $\frac{1}{8}$ mile, or $0.25 \times 8 = \$2.00$ per mile. The number of miles after the first $\frac{1}{4}$ mile is $m - \frac{1}{4}$, so the cost of the trip, not including the first $\frac{1}{4}$ mile is $2\left(m - \frac{1}{4}\right)$. This means the cost of the whole trip is $3 + 2\left(m - \frac{1}{4}\right)$. The clue "no more than $20" means that much or less, so use the symbol $\leq$. The inequality is $3 + 2\left(m - \frac{1}{4}\right) \leq 20$, which simplifies to $2.5 + 2m \leq 20$, **(A)**.

13. A

Difficulty: Hard

Category: Passport to Advanced Math/Quadratics

Getting to the Answer: The quadratic equation is given in standard form, so use the method of completing the square to rewrite the equation in vertex form. Then, read the value of k to find the maximum height of the projectile:

$$h = -16t^2 + 64t + 8$$
$$= -16\left(t^2 - 4t + \underline{}\right) + 8 - \underline{}$$
$$= -16\left(t^2 - 4t + 4\right) + 8 - (-16 \times 4)$$
$$= -16(t - 2)^2 + 8 - (-64)$$
$$= -16(t - 2)^2 + 72$$

The vertex is (2, 72), so the maximum height is 72 feet, **(A)**.

14. 144

Difficulty: Easy

Category: Heart of Algebra/Linear Equations

Getting to the Answer: There is only one equation given and it has two variables. This means that you don't have enough information to solve for either variable. Instead, look for the relationship between the left side of the equation and the other expression that you are trying to find. Start by clearing the fractions by multiplying both sides of the original equation by 12. This yields the expression that you are looking for, $9x + 10y$, so no further work is required—just read the value on the right-hand side of the equation:

$$\frac{3}{4}x + \frac{5}{6}y = 12$$
$$12\left(\frac{3}{4}x + \frac{5}{6}y\right) = 12(12)$$
$$9x + 10y = 144$$

15. 150

Difficulty: Medium

Category: Additional Topics in Math/Geometry

Getting to the Answer: There are 360 degrees in a circle. You need to figure out how many degrees each minute on the face of a clock represents. There are 60 minutes on the face of an analogue clock. This means that each minute represents $360 \div 60 = 6$ degrees. Between 3:20 and 3:45, 25 minutes go by, so the minute hand rotates $25 \times 6 = \mathbf{150}$ degrees.

16. 8

Difficulty: Hard

Category: Passport to Advanced Math/Exponents

Getting to the Answer: Read the question carefully to determine what part of the expression you need to simplify and what part you don't. Sometimes, you can work a simpler question and still arrive at the correct answer. The question only asks for the exponent on x, so you do not have to simplify the coefficients. Rewrite the expression without the coefficients and simplify using the rules of exponents:

$$\frac{3x^{\frac{3}{2}} \cdot \left(16x^2\right)^3}{8x^{-\frac{1}{2}}} \rightarrow \frac{x^{\frac{3}{2}} \cdot \left(x^2\right)^3}{x^{-\frac{1}{2}}}$$
$$= x^{\frac{3}{2} - \left(-\frac{1}{2}\right)} \cdot x^{2 \times 3}$$
$$= x^{\frac{3}{2} + \frac{1}{2}} \cdot x^6$$
$$= x^2 \cdot x^6$$
$$= x^8$$

The exponent on x is **8**.

17. 3/25 or .12

Difficulty: Hard

Category: Passport to Advanced Math/Functions

Getting to the Answer: When a question involving a function provides one or more ordered pairs, substitute them into the function to see what information you can glean. Start with $x = 0$ because doing so often results in the elimination of a variable:

$$f(x) = a \cdot b^x$$
$$f(0) = a \cdot b^0$$
$$3 = a \cdot b^0$$
$$3 = a \cdot 1$$
$$3 = a$$

Now you know the value of a, so the equation looks like $f(x) = 3 \cdot b^x$. Substitute the second pair of values into the new equation:

$$f(x) = 3 \cdot b^x$$
$$f(1) = 3 \cdot b^1$$
$$15 = 3 \cdot b^1$$
$$15 = 3b$$
$$5 = b$$

The exponential function is $f(x) = 3 \cdot 5x$. The final step is to find the value being asked for, $f(-2)$. Substitute -2 for x and simplify:

$$f(-2) = 3 \cdot 5^{-2} = \frac{3}{5^2} = \frac{3}{25}$$

Grid this in as **3/25 or .12**.

Math Test—Calculator

1. B

Difficulty: Easy

Category: Heart of Algebra/Linear Equations

Getting to the Answer: The total cost consists of a flat installation fee and a price per square foot. The installation fee is a one-time fee that does not depend on the number of feet ordered and therefore should not be multiplied by f. This means that 199 is the installation fee. The other expression in the equation, $3.29f$, represents the cost per square foot (the unit price) times the number of feet, f. Hence, 3.29 must represent the cost of 1 square foot of carpet, **(B)**.

2. B

Difficulty: Easy

Category: Problem Solving and Data Analysis/Statistics and Probability

Getting to the Answer: Quickly read each answer choice. Cross out false statements as you go. Stop when you arrive at a true statement. There is no long "tail" of data on either side, so the shape is not skewed and you can eliminate (A). The shape of the data *is* symmetric because the data is fairly evenly spread out, with about half of the ages above and half below the median. When the shape of a data set is symmetric, the mean is approximately equal to the median, so **(B)** is correct. Don't let (D) fool you—the *median* is 55, not the *mean*.

3. A

Difficulty: Easy

Category: Heart of Algebra/Linear Equations

Getting to the Answer: Think about the best strategy to answer the question. If you distribute the $\frac{1}{3}$, it creates messy numbers. Instead, clear the fraction by multiplying both sides of the equation by 3. Then, use inverse operations to solve for x:

$$\frac{1}{3}(5x - 8) = 3x + 4$$
$$5x - 8 = 3(3x + 4)$$
$$5x - 8 = 9x + 12$$
$$-4x = 20$$
$$x = -5$$

Choice **(A)** is correct.

4. A

Difficulty: Easy

Category: Passport to Advanced Math/Quadratics

Getting to the Answer: The minimum value of a quadratic function is equal to the *y*-value of the vertex of its graph, so vertex form, $y = a(x - h)^2 + k$, reveals the minimum without doing any additional work. Choice **(A)** is the only equation written in this form and therefore must be correct. The minimum value of this function is $-\frac{3}{2}$.

5. C

Difficulty: Medium

Category: Problem Solving and Data Analysis/Rates, Ratios, Proportions, and Percentages

Getting to the Answer: Start with the smallest possible lot size, 3,000 square feet. The next lot must be at least 30% larger, so multiply by 1.3 to get 3,900 square feet. Then, round up to the next thousand (which is not necessarily the nearest thousand) to meet the tax assessment requirement. You must always round up because rounding down would make the subsequent lot size less than 30% larger than the one before it. Continue this process until you reach the maximum square footage allowed, 15,000 square feet:

$$3,000 \times 1.3 = 3,900 \rightarrow 4,000$$

$$4,000 \times 1.3 = 5,200 \rightarrow 6,000$$

$$6,000 \times 1.3 = 7,800 \rightarrow 8,000$$

$$8,000 \times 1.3 = 10,400 \rightarrow 11,000$$

$$11,000 \times 1.3 = 14,300 \rightarrow 15,000$$

Choice **(C)** is correct.

6. D

Difficulty: Medium

Category: Problem Solving and Data Analysis/Functions

Getting to the Answer: Determine whether the change in the amount of pollution is a common difference (linear function) or a common ratio (exponential function), or if it changes direction (quadratic or polynomial function). Each year, the amount of pollution should be $100 - 8 = 92\%$ of the year before. You can write 92% as $\frac{92}{100}$, which represents a common ratio from one year to the next. This means that the best model is an exponential function, **(D)**, of the form $y = a \cdot (0.92)^x$.

7. A

Difficulty: Medium

Category: Passport to Advanced Math/Radicals

Getting to the Answer: Don't spend too much time reading the scientific explanation of the equation. Solve for *r* using inverse operations. First, square both sides of the equation to remove the radical. Then, multiply both sides by *r* to get the *r* out of the denominator. Finally, divide both sides by v^2:

$$v = \sqrt{\frac{2Gm}{r}}$$

$$v^2 = \frac{2Gm}{r}$$

$$v^2 r = 2Gm$$

$$r = \frac{2Gm}{v^2}$$

This matches **(A)**.

8. D

Difficulty: Medium

Category: Heart of Algebra/Systems of Linear Equations

Getting to the Answer: One equation should represent the total *number* of rentals, while the other equation represents the *cost* of the rentals. The number of DVDs plus the number of Blu-rays equals the total number of rentals, 209. Therefore, one equation is $d + b = 209$. This means you can eliminate choices (B) and (C). Now, write the cost equation: cost per DVD times number of DVDs ($2d$) plus cost per Blu-ray times number of Blu-rays ($3.5b$) equals the total amount collected (562). The cost equation is $2d + 3.5b = 562$. Don't let (A) fool you. The question says nothing about the cost *per hour* so there is no reason to divide the cost by 4. Choice **(D)** is correct.

9. B

Difficulty: Medium

Category: Problem Solving and Data Analysis/Rates, Ratios, Proportions, and Percentages

Getting to the Answer: Break the question into short steps. *Step 1*: Find the number of female senators. *Step 2*: Use that number to find the number of female Republican senators. *Step 3*: Find the total number of Republican senators.

Each of the 50 states gets 2 voting members in the Senate, so there are $50 \times 2 = 100$ senators. The ratio of males to females in the 113th Congress was 4:1, so 4 parts male plus 1 part female equals a total of 100 senators. Write this as $4x + x = 100$, where x represents one part and therefore the number of females. Next, simplify and solve the equation to find that $x = 20$ female senators. To find the number of female senators that were Republican, multiply 20% (or 0.20) times 20 to get 4. Finally, add to get 45 male plus 4 female = 49 Republican senators in the 113th Congress, **(B)**.

10. C

Difficulty: Medium

Category: Problem Solving and Data Analysis/Rates, Ratios, Proportions, and Percentages

Getting to the Answer: Find the percent increase by dividing the amount of change by the original amount. Then, apply the same percent increase to the amount for 2012. The amount of increase is $29,400 - 18,750 = 10,650$, so the percent increase is $10,650 \div 18,750 = 0.568 = 56.8\%$ over 8 years. If the total percent increase over the next 8 years is the same, the average student who borrowed money will have loans totaling $29,400 \times 1.568 = 46,099.20$, or about \$46,100. Choice **(C)** is correct.

11. D

Difficulty: Medium

Category: Heart of Algebra/Linear Equations

Getting to the Answer: Write the expression in words first: points per large basket (3) times number of beanbags in large basket (b), plus points per small basket (7) times number of beanbags in small basket. If there are 10 beanbags total and b go into the larger basket, the rest, or $10 - b$, must go into the smaller basket. Now, translate the words to numbers, variables, and operations: $3b + 7(10 - b)$. This is not one of the answer choices, so simplify the expression by distributing the 7 and combining like terms: $3b + 7(10 - b) = 3b + 70 - 7b = 70 - 4b$. This matches **(D)**.

12. D

Difficulty: Easy

Category: Problem Solving and Data Analysis/Statistics and Probability

Getting to the Answer: To calculate the percentage of the voters in each district who had no opinion on fracking, divide the number of voters in *that* district who had no opinion by the total number of voters in *that* district. Choice **(D)** is correct because $3,205 \div 63,539 \approx 0.05 = 5\%$, which is a lower percentage than in the other three districts that were polled (District A = 8%; District B = 7.6%; District C = 6%).

13. A

Difficulty: Medium

Category: Problem Solving and Data Analysis/Statistics and Probability

Getting to the Answer: Scan the answer choices quickly to narrow down the amount of information in the table that you need to analyze. Each choice makes a statement about people from District C who support a ban on fracking that can be expected to vote in the next election. To extrapolate from the follow-up survey sample, multiply the fraction of people from the follow-up survey who plan to vote in the upcoming election $\left(\frac{218}{500}\right)$ by the number of people in District C who support a ban on fracking (43,228) to get 18,847.408, or approximately 19,000 people. Choice **(A)** is correct.

14. B

Difficulty: Medium

Category: Heart of Algebra/Systems of Linear Equations

Getting to the Answer: Solve the system of equations using substitution. Then, check that you answered the right question (find the sum of x and y). First, solve the second equation for x to get $x = 3y - 11$, then substitute this expression into the first equation to find y:

$$2x + 4y = 13$$
$$2(3y - 11) + 4y = 13$$
$$6y - 22 + 4y = 13$$
$$10y - 22 = 13$$
$$10y = 35$$
$$y = \frac{7}{2}$$

Now, substitute the result into $x = 3y - 11$ and simplify to find x:

$$x = 3\left(\frac{7}{2}\right) - 11$$
$$= \frac{21}{2} - 11$$
$$= -\frac{1}{2}$$

The question asks for the sum, so add x and y to get $-\frac{1}{2} + \frac{7}{2} = \frac{6}{2} = 3$, which is **(B)**.

15. C

Difficulty: Medium

Category: Problem Solving and Data Analysis/Statistics and Probability

Getting to the Answer: The keyword in the answer choices is "consistently," which relates to how spread out a player's scores are. Standard deviation, not mean, is a measure of spread so you can eliminate choice (A) right away. A lower standard deviation indicates scores that are less spread out and therefore more consistent. Likewise, a higher standard deviation indicates scores that are more spread out and therefore less consistent. Notice the opposite nature of this relationship: lower standard deviation = more consistent; higher standard deviation = less consistent. Choice **(C)** is correct because the standard deviation of Mae's scores is the lowest, which means she bowled the most consistently.

16. B

Difficulty: Medium

Category: Passport to Advanced Math/Quadratics

Getting to the Answer: Notice the structure of the equation. The expression on the left side of the equation is the square of a quantity, so start by taking the square root of both sides. After taking the square roots, solve the resulting equations. Remember, $4^2 = 16$ and $(-4)^2 = 16$, so there will be *two* equations to solve:

$$(x + 3)^2 = 16$$
$$\sqrt{(x + 3)^2} = \sqrt{16}$$
$$x + 3 = \pm 4$$

$$x + 3 = 4 \rightarrow x = 1$$
$$x + 3 = -4 \rightarrow x = -7$$

Choice **(B)** is correct.

17. C

Difficulty: Medium

Category: Problem Solving and Data Analysis/Rates, Ratios, Proportions, and Percentages

Getting to the Answer: Pay careful attention to the units. You need to convert all of the dimensions to inches, and then set up and solve a proportion. The real statue's height is $305 \times 12 = 3,660 + 6 = 3,666$ inches; the length of the nose on the real statue is $4 \times 12 = 48 + 6 = 54$ inches; the height of the model statue is 26 inches; the length of the nose on the model is unknown. Now set up and solve your equation:

$$\frac{3,666}{54} = \frac{26}{x}$$
$$3,666x = 26(54)$$
$$3,666x = 1,404$$
$$x = \frac{1,404}{3,666} = \frac{18}{47}$$

Choice **(C)** is correct.

18. B

Difficulty: Medium

Category: Passport to Advanced Math/Functions

Getting to the Answer: When evaluating a function, substitute the value inside the parentheses for x in the equation. Evaluate the function at $x = 6$ and at $x = 2$, and then subtract the second output from the first. Note that this is not the same as first subtracting $6 - 2$ and then evaluating the function at $x = 4$:

$$f(6) = 3(6) + 5 = 18 + 5 = 23$$

$$f(2) = 3(2) + 5 = 6 + 5 = 11$$

$$f(6) - f(2) = 23 - 11 = 12$$

Choice **(B)** is correct.

19. A

Difficulty: Medium

Category: Problem Solving and Data Analysis/ Scatterplots

Getting to the Answer: Examine the graph, paying careful attention to units and labels. Here, the years increase by 2 for each grid line and the number of owls by 25. The average change per year is the same as the slope of the line of best fit. Find the slope of the line of best fit using the slope formula, $m = \frac{y_2 - y_1}{x_2 - x_1}$, and any two points that lie on (or very close to) the line. Using the two endpoints of the data, (1994, 1,200) and (2014, 700), the average change per year is $\frac{700 - 1,200}{2014 - 1994} = \frac{-500}{20} = -25$, which is **(A)**. Pay careful attention to the sign of the answer—the number of owls is decreasing, so the rate of change is negative.

20. D

Difficulty: Medium

Category: Passport to Advanced Math/Quadratics

Getting to the Answer: The solution to a system of equations is the point(s) where their graphs intersect. You could solve this question algebraically, one system at a time, but this is not time efficient. Instead, graph each pair of equations in your graphing calculator and look for the graphs that intersect at $x = -4$ and $x = 2$. The graphs of the equations in (A) and (B) don't intersect at all, so you can eliminate them right away. The graphs in (C) intersect, but both points of intersection have a positive x-coordinate. This means **(D)** must be correct. The graph looks like this:

21. C

Difficulty: Medium

Category: Problem Solving and Data Analysis/Statistics and Probability

Getting to the Answer: Read the question, identifying parts of the graphic you need—the question asks about litters of 7 or more pups, so you'll only use the heights of the bars for 7, 8, and 9 pups. Start by finding the percent of the mice in the study that had a litter of 7 or more pups. Of the 200 mice in the sample, $25 + 14 + 5 = 44$ had a litter of 7 or more pups. This is $\frac{44}{200} = \frac{22}{100} = 22\%$ of the mice in the study. Given the same general conditions (such as living in the same geographic region), you would expect approximately the same results, so multiply the number of female mice in the whole population by the percent you found: $35,000 \times 0.22 = 7,700$. Choice **(C)** is correct.

22. C

Difficulty: Medium

Category: Heart of Algebra/Linear Equations

Getting to the Answer: You'll need to interpret the information given in the question to write two ordered pairs. Then you can use the ordered pairs to find the slope and the y-intercept of the linear model. In an ordered pair, the independent variable is always written first. Here, the heart rate depends on the amount of exercise, so the ordered pairs should be written in the form (time, heart rate). They are (8, 90) and (20, 117). Use these points in the slope formula, $m = \frac{y_2 - y_1}{x_2 - x_1}$, to find that $m = \frac{117 - 90}{20 - 8} = \frac{27}{12} = 2.25$. Then, substitute the slope (2.25) and either of the points into slope-intercept form and simplify to find the y-intercept:

$$90 = 2.25(8) + b$$
$$90 = 18 + b$$
$$72 = b$$

Finally, write the equation using the slope and the y-intercept that you found to get $r = 2.25t + 72$. Note that the only choice with a slope of 2.25 is **(C)**, so you could have eliminated the other three choices before finding the y-intercept and saved yourself a bit of time.

23. C

Difficulty: Medium

Category: Heart of Algebra/Linear Equations

Getting to the Answer: Pay careful attention to what the question tells you about the variables. The x-value is the number of payments already made and the y-value is the amount of debt remaining (not how much has been paid). If a solution is (21, 560), the x-value is 21, which means Chantal has made 21 payments already. The y-value is 560, which means $560 is the amount of debt *left to be paid*, making **(C)** correct.

24. D

Difficulty: Hard

Category: Problem Solving and Data Analysis/ Scatterplots

Getting to the Answer: A line that "represents the trend of the data" is another way of saying line of best fit. The trend of the data is clearly linear because the path of the dots does not turn around or curve, so draw a line of best fit on the graph. Remember, about half of the points should be above the line and half below.

Emails per Day by Age

If you draw your line of best fit all the way to the y-axis, you'll save yourself a step by simply looking at the scatterplot to find the y-intercept. For this graph, it's about 35. This means you can eliminate choices (B) and (C). Next, find the approximate slope using two points that lie on (or very close to) the line. You can use the y-intercept, (0, 35), as one of them to save time and estimate the second, such as (72, 4). Use the slope formula to find the slope:

$$m = \frac{y_2 - y_1}{x_2 - x_1} = \frac{4 - 35}{72 - 0} = \frac{-31}{72} \approx -0.43$$

The equation that has the closest slope and y-intercept is **(D)**. (Note that if you choose different points, your line may have a slightly different slope or y-intercept, but the answer choices will be far enough apart that you should be able to determine which is the *best* fit to the data.)

25. B

Difficulty: Hard

Category: Passport to Advanced Math/Functions

Getting to the Answer: Transformations that are grouped with the x in a function shift the graph horizontally and, therefore, affect the x-coordinates of points on the graph. Transformations that are not grouped with the x shift the graph vertically and, therefore, affect the y-coordinates of points on the graph. Remember, horizontal shifts are always backward of what they look like. Start with $(x + 3)$. This shifts the graph left 3, so subtract 3 from the x-coordinate of the given point: $(5, 1) \rightarrow (5 - 3, 1) = (2, 1)$. Next, apply the negative in front of f, which is not grouped with the x, so it makes the y-coordinate negative: $(2, 1) \rightarrow (2, -1)$. Finally, -2 is not grouped with x, so subtract 2 from the y-coordinate: $(2, -1 - 2) \rightarrow (2, -3)$, which is **(B)**.

26. C

Difficulty: Hard

Category: Problem Solving and Data Analysis/Rates, Ratios, Proportions, and Percentages

Getting to the Answer: Draw a chart or diagram detailing the various price reductions for each 30 days.

Date	Percent of Most Recent Price	Resulting Price
Jan 15	$100 - 25\% = 75\%$	$\$1,500 \times 0.75 = \$1,125$
Feb 15	$100 - 10\% = 90\%$	$\$1,125 \times 0.9 = \$1,012.50$
Mar 15	$100 - 10\% = 90\%$	$\$1,012.50 \times 0.9 = \$911.25$

You can stop here because the refrigerator was sold on April 2, which is not 30 days after March 15. The final selling price was $911.25, **(C)**.

27. A

Difficulty: Hard

Category: Additional Topics in Math/Geometry

Getting to the Answer: Organize information as you read the question. Here, you'll definitely want to draw and label a sketch.

The lower level, the vertical distance between levels, and the diagonal elevator track form a 30-60-90 triangle, where the elevator track is the hypotenuse. The vertical distance is opposite the 30° angle so it is the shortest leg. The rules for 30-60-90 triangles state that the shortest leg is half the length of the hypotenuse, so the vertical distance between levels is approximately $170 \div 2 = 85$ feet, **(A)**.

28. 1/6 or .166 or .167

Difficulty: Easy

Category: Problem Solving and Data Analysis/Statistics and Probability

Getting to the Answer: This question requires concentration, but no complicated calculations. First, you need to identify the rows that contain information about the seating on the 777s, which are the bottom two rows. To find the probability that the seat is a Business Class seat, find the total number of seats in that category (in only the bottom two rows), and divide by the total number of seats on the planes (in only the bottom two rows):

$$P(\text{Business Class}) = \frac{37 + 52}{194 + 37 + 16 + 227 + 52 + 8}$$

$$= \frac{89}{534} = \frac{1}{6} = 0.1\overline{6}$$

Grid in your answer as **1/6 or .166 or .167**.

29. 440

Difficulty: Medium

Category: Heart of Algebra/Systems of Linear Equations

Getting to the Answer: Translate from English into math to write a system of equations with t = the cost of the tankless heater in dollars, and c = the cost of the conventional heater in dollars. First, a tankless heater (t) costs $160 more ($+160$) than twice as much ($2c$) as the conventional one, or $t = 2c + 160$. Together, a tankless heater (t) and a conventional heater (c) cost $1,000, or $t + c = 1,000$. The system is:

$$\begin{cases} t = 2c + 160 \\ t + c = 1,000 \end{cases}$$

The top equation is already solved for t, so substitute $2c + 160$ into the second equation for t and solve for c:

$$2c + 160 + c = 1,000$$
$$3c + 160 = 1,000$$
$$3c = 840$$
$$c = 280$$

Be careful—that's not the answer! The conventional hot water heater costs $280, so the tankless heater costs $2(280) + 160 = \$720$. This means the tankless heater costs $\$720 - \$280 = \mathbf{\$440}$ more than the conventional heater.

30. 252

Difficulty: Medium

Category: Problem Solving and Data Analysis/Rates, Ratios, Proportions, and Percentages

Getting to the Answer: Break the question into steps. First, find how long it took Daniel to spray one lawn, and then use that amount to find how long it took him to spray all the lawns. According to the figure, he started the first house at 9:00 and the sixth house at 10:00, so it took him 1 hour, or 60 minutes, to spray 5 houses. This gives a unit rate of $60 \div 5 = 12$ minutes per house. Count the houses in the figure—there are 21. Multiply the unit rate by the number of houses to get $12 \times 21 = \mathbf{252}$ minutes to spray all the lawns.

31. 4

Difficulty: Hard

Category: Problem Solving and Data Analysis/Rates, Ratios, Proportions, and Percentages

Getting to the Answer: This part of the question contains several steps. Think about the units given in the question and what you need to convert so that you can get to the answer. The total acreage of all the lawns in the neighborhood is $21 \times 0.2 = 4.2$ acres. This is equivalent to $4.2 \times 43,560 = 182,952$ square feet. Each gallon of spray covers 2,500 square feet, so divide to find that Daniel needs $182,952 \div 2,500 = 73.1808$ gallons to spray all the lawns. The spray rig holds 20 gallons, so Daniel will need to fill it **4** times. After he fills it the fourth time and finishes all the lawns, there will be some spray left over.